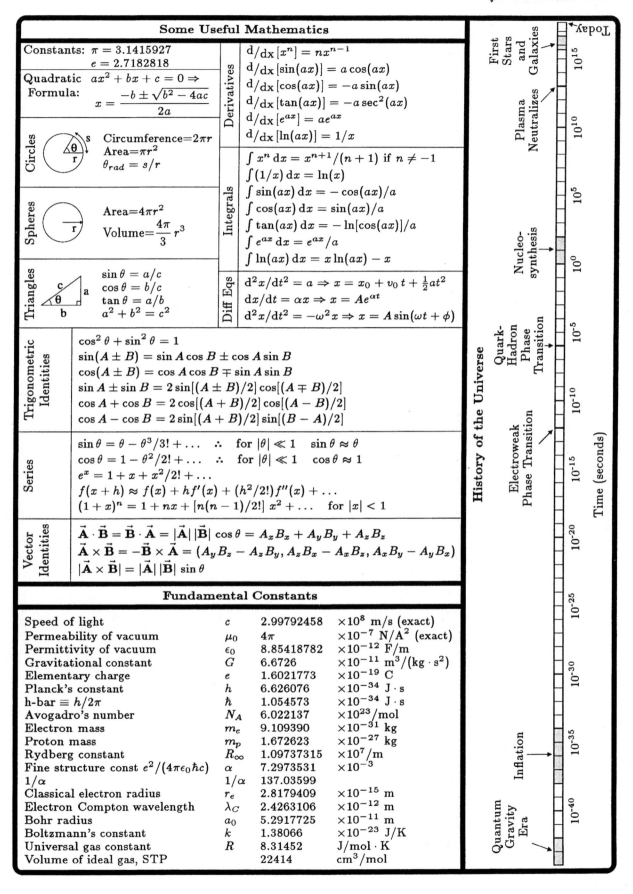

Some Useful Mathematics

Constants: $\pi = 3.1415927$
$e = 2.7182818$

Quadratic $ax^2 + bx + c = 0 \Rightarrow$
Formula: $x = \dfrac{-b \pm \sqrt{b^2 - 4ac}}{2a}$

Circles
Circumference $= 2\pi r$
Area $= \pi r^2$
$\theta_{rad} = s/r$

Spheres
Area $= 4\pi r^2$
Volume $= \dfrac{4\pi}{3} r^3$

Triangles
$\sin\theta = a/c$
$\cos\theta = b/c$
$\tan\theta = a/b$
$a^2 + b^2 = c^2$

Derivatives
$\mathrm{d}/\mathrm{dx}\,[x^n] = nx^{n-1}$
$\mathrm{d}/\mathrm{dx}\,[\sin(ax)] = a\cos(ax)$
$\mathrm{d}/\mathrm{dx}\,[\cos(ax)] = -a\sin(ax)$
$\mathrm{d}/\mathrm{dx}\,[\tan(ax)] = -a\sec^2(ax)$
$\mathrm{d}/\mathrm{dx}\,[e^{ax}] = ae^{ax}$
$\mathrm{d}/\mathrm{dx}\,[\ln(ax)] = 1/x$

Integrals
$\int x^n\,\mathrm{d}x = x^{n+1}/(n+1)$ if $n \neq -1$
$\int (1/x)\,\mathrm{d}x = \ln(x)$
$\int \sin(ax)\,\mathrm{d}x = -\cos(ax)/a$
$\int \cos(ax)\,\mathrm{d}x = \sin(ax)/a$
$\int \tan(ax)\,\mathrm{d}x = -\ln[\cos(ax)]/a$
$\int e^{ax}\,\mathrm{d}x = e^{ax}/a$
$\int \ln(ax)\,\mathrm{d}x = x\ln(ax) - x$

Diff Eqs
$\mathrm{d}^2x/\mathrm{dt}^2 = a \Rightarrow x = x_0 + v_0 t + \tfrac{1}{2}at^2$
$\mathrm{d}x/\mathrm{dt} = \alpha x \Rightarrow x = Ae^{\alpha t}$
$\mathrm{d}^2x/\mathrm{dt}^2 = -\omega^2 x \Rightarrow x = A\sin(\omega t + \phi)$

Trigonometric Identities
$\cos^2\theta + \sin^2\theta = 1$
$\sin(A \pm B) = \sin A \cos B \pm \cos A \sin B$
$\cos(A \pm B) = \cos A \cos B \mp \sin A \sin B$
$\sin A \pm \sin B = 2\sin[(A \pm B)/2]\cos[(A \mp B)/2]$
$\cos A + \cos B = 2\cos[(A+B)/2]\cos[(A-B)/2]$
$\cos A - \cos B = 2\sin[(A+B)/2]\sin[(B-A)/2]$

Series
$\sin\theta = \theta - \theta^3/3! + \ldots \quad \therefore \quad$ for $|\theta| \ll 1 \quad \sin\theta \approx \theta$
$\cos\theta = 1 - \theta^2/2! + \ldots \quad \therefore \quad$ for $|\theta| \ll 1 \quad \cos\theta \approx 1$
$e^x = 1 + x + x^2/2! + \ldots$
$f(x + h) \approx f(x) + hf'(x) + (h^2/2!)f''(x) + \ldots$
$(1 + x)^n = 1 + nx + [n(n-1)/2!]\,x^2 + \ldots \quad$ for $|x| < 1$

Vector Identities
$\vec{A} \cdot \vec{B} = \vec{B} \cdot \vec{A} = |\vec{A}|\,|\vec{B}|\cos\theta = A_x B_x + A_y B_y + A_z B_z$
$\vec{A} \times \vec{B} = -\vec{B} \times \vec{A} = (A_y B_z - A_z B_y, A_z B_x - A_x B_z, A_x B_y - A_y B_x)$
$|\vec{A} \times \vec{B}| = |\vec{A}|\,|\vec{B}|\sin\theta$

Fundamental Constants

Speed of light	c	2.99792458	$\times 10^8$ m/s (exact)
Permeability of vacuum	μ_0	4π	$\times 10^{-7}$ N/A^2 (exact)
Permittivity of vacuum	ϵ_0	8.85418782	$\times 10^{-12}$ F/m
Gravitational constant	G	6.6726	$\times 10^{-11}$ m^3/(kg·s^2)
Elementary charge	e	1.6021773	$\times 10^{-19}$ C
Planck's constant	h	6.626076	$\times 10^{-34}$ J·s
h-bar $\equiv h/2\pi$	$\hbar$	1.054573	$\times 10^{-34}$ J·s
Avogadro's number	N_A	6.022137	$\times 10^{23}$/mol
Electron mass	m_e	9.109390	$\times 10^{-31}$ kg
Proton mass	m_p	1.672623	$\times 10^{-27}$ kg
Rydberg constant	R_∞	1.09737315	$\times 10^7$/m
Fine structure const $e^2/(4\pi\epsilon_0\hbar c)$	α	7.2973531	$\times 10^{-3}$
$1/\alpha$	$1/\alpha$	137.03599	
Classical electron radius	r_e	2.8179409	$\times 10^{-15}$ m
Electron Compton wavelength	λ_C	2.4263106	$\times 10^{-12}$ m
Bohr radius	a_0	5.2917725	$\times 10^{-11}$ m
Boltzmann's constant	k	1.38066	$\times 10^{-23}$ J/K
Universal gas constant	R	8.31452	J/mol·K
Volume of ideal gas, STP		22414	cm^3/mol

History of the Universe

Today
First Stars and Galaxies $\leftarrow 10^{15}$
Plasma Neutralizes $\leftarrow 10^{10}$
10^5
Nucleo-synthesis 10^0
Quark-Hadron Phase Transition $\leftarrow 10^{-5}$
10^{-10}
Electroweak Phase Transition $\leftarrow 10^{-15}$
10^{-20}
10^{-25}
10^{-30}
Inflation $\rightarrow 10^{-35}$
Quantum Gravity Era 10^{-40}

Time (seconds)

Massachusetts Institute of Technology

MIT 8.01 Study Guide

Essentials of

INTRODUCTORY CLASSICAL MECHANICS

Sixth Edition

Wit Busza
Susan Cartwright
Alan H. Guth

Pearson
Custom
Publishing

Printed in the United States of America

10 9 8 7 6 5 4 3 2

This manuscript was supplied camera-ready by the author.

Please visit our web site at www.pearsoncustom.com

ISBN 0–536–72757–0

BA 996262

 PEARSON CUSTOM PUBLISHING
75 Arlington Street, Suite 300, Boston, MA 02116
A Pearson Education Company

Essentials of Introductory Classical Mechanics

A Study Guide to MIT Course 8.01
Sixth Edition

Wit Busza

Francis L. Friedman Professor of Physics
Massachusetts Institute of Technology

Susan Cartwright

Senior Lecturer in Physics
University of Sheffield

Alan H. Guth

Victor F. Weisskopf Professor of Physics
Massachusetts Institute of Technology

INTRODUCTION

WHAT IS CLASSICAL MECHANICS?

This is an introductory book on Classical Mechanics. Mechanics is the branch of science that deals with the motion of objects, how that motion changes with time, the conditions required to induce certain types of motion, etc. *Classical* Mechanics restricts us to circumstances where the speeds we encounter are small compared to the speed of light and the objects we deal with are generally of macroscopic size. Fortunately, almost any situation we are likely to meet in everyday life satisfies these restrictions, so the results of classical mechanics have a wide variety of applications in science and engineering. Furthermore, some of the most important principles of mechanics—such as the conservation laws for energy and momentum—can be fully explored within classical mechanics.

Why is it important to study classical mechanics? We can think of four reasons:

- The modern scientific view of the world, to a large extent, begins with classical mechanics. Newer developments, such as quantum theory and relativity, have all grown from roots in classical mechanics.

- The contents of the subject—the physical laws and principles you will learn, and the methods of applying them to practical problems—are important and relevant in many other fields. A civil engineer designing a bridge, an automobile designer laying out the specifications for the engine or the safety air-bag of a new model, a geologist estimating the likely severity of the next California earthquake: all are using, directly or indirectly, the principles of classical mechanics.

- The structure and development of classical mechanics is a good example of the aims and methods of scientific study. We will see how experimental results and mathematical representations are combined to create testable scientific theories, and how the impossible complexities of most real-life physical situations can be reduced to soluble problems by identifying the essential physical features of the system. This way of working is what distinguishes the scientific approach to situations from the many other ways of looking at them (e.g. artistic, political, business.).

- The study of classical mechanics is an excellent introduction to the art of problem solving. When you finish this book you should be able to extract the essential features of a problem, use them to set up and solve the appropriate mathematical equations, and make quick and easy checks on your answer to catch simple mistakes.

The book will have succeeded in its aims if you come away from it with a grasp of the basic principles governing the motion of objects, a feel for the scientific method, and a strengthened ability to wrestle with difficult problems until they are solved.

HOW IS THE BOOK ORGANIZED?

The book is organized with a fairly rigid structure, to make it as easy as possible for you to locate the information that you want. There are 13 chapters, each of which consists of about one week's work for a student in a freshman physics course. A typical chapter contains:

- a brief *Overview* setting out the main themes of the chapter;

- *the Essentials*, a concise but complete discussion of the topic, explaining what you need to know and giving cross-references to related problems;

- a *Summary* of the material covered to help you review the topic and to provide a handy reference guide for problem solving;

- a set of *Problems and Questions* designed for self-testing and for sharpening problem-solving skills.

Answers are given to all numerical problems. In addition, some problems come with hints to help you get started, while others have fully worked-out solutions to show you how to apply the ideas and equations in the *Essentials* to problem solving. Some of the worked solutions include comments on general problem-solving techniques or on the relevance of the particular problem to other areas of physics.

Furthermore, many chapters include *Supplementary Notes* which discuss some aspects of the material in a wider context, such as how particular points relate to the real world or how they may be developed into more advanced concepts. You don't need to know this material to progress to the next chapter, but it should provide a starting point if you are curious to see how the artificial-seeming problems you may be doing fit into the rest of physics.

About every third chapter (Chapters 3, 7, 10, and 13) consists of review problems rather than new material. The problems in these chapters tend to be slightly more challenging and may use physics from more than one of the preceding chapters. In this sense they are a better representation of "real" applications of classical mechanics than the more specialized problems in normal chapters.

HOW TO USE THIS BOOK

Each chapter (except for the review problem chapters) consists of two different types of material. One type *defines* what you ought to know: this includes the *Overview*, the *Essentials*, and the checklist of new ideas in the *Summary*. The second type *applies* this knowledge to problem solving: in this category are the *Problems and Questions*, *Solutions*, and *Hints*.

The *Essentials*, as the name suggests, are the heart of the book, and your main tool for acquiring the information you will need. They are intended to include everything that you will need to solve the problems and master the material of the chapter. Our goal in writing the *Essentials* was to be as concise as possible, but not more so. We hope that in most cases you will appreciate and benefit from this conciseness, but we recognize that you may sometimes want a more detailed discussion. For such cases we recommend that you consult one of the more standard introductory physics textbooks.

If the *Essentials* are the main tool for *accessing* the necessary information, the main *learning activity* should center on the *Problems and Questions*. You haven't really understood a given topic until you can apply it in solving problems; conversely, the step-by-step process of setting up and solving a problem will often be of more help in grasping a complicated idea than reading an abstract theoretical explanation. For that reason, problems come in three varieties:

- S-type problems, which come with completely worked out solutions;
- H-type problems, which come with hints in the form of questions, and answers to these questions;
- problems with just the answer given.

You will probably find that in many cases the worked solutions will be very useful, but you need not study them in detail if you already know how to solve them. You should nonetheless check them for comments (marked ☺ Learn), which may be of more general relevance.

SOLVING PROBLEMS

Solving problems is a key part of classical mechanics, or indeed any field of science. The theoretical and mathematical frameworks we construct are only of value if they can be applied to understand the behavior of the physical world. Therefore, one of the objectives of this course is to help you to develop your problem-solving abilities. One way to do this is to adopt a general *problem-solving strategy*. This section outlines such a strategy, and the worked solutions you find in this book will normally follow the steps shown here. We believe this is a useful framework for attacking any new problem—but feel free to use any method that works for you! The guidelines are not rigid: for some problems, one or two of the steps shown may be unnecessary, while for more complicated situations you may have to apply some of them more than once.

Some parts of the approach described here may not seem natural at first. Why think through the whole problem conceptually before starting on the math, instead of writing down the equations straightaway? Why calculate everything with symbols first, instead of putting in the numbers immediately? With practice, we think you will agree that working from general physical concepts down to specific numerical values is usually the most effective way to solve problems: it minimizes the risk of making simple numerical errors, and it usually does more to help develop your physical intuition.

Step 1: *Conceptualize*
Read the problem through carefully, noting the information you are given and the information you are asked for. If appropriate, draw a diagram of the situation. Decide which physical concepts are involved and which areas of the theory you have learned will be relevant. Think through your approach to solving the problem.

Step 2: *Formulate*
Express your verbal concepts in mathematical terms. This implies identifying the necessary equations, defining the proper symbols, choosing the appropriate reference frames, etc. We strongly recommend that you introduce symbols to represent any numerical values that you are given. Make sure that you know the physical significance of all the symbols you have introduced. Check that your formulation makes sense: do you have enough equations to calculate all your unknown quantities, for example? Work out a strategy for solving the equations.

3

Step 3: _Solve_

Solve your equations algebraically, i.e. rearrange them so that the quantity you want to evaluate is expressed in terms of other quantities whose values are known. It is usually best to do this symbolically, with algebra, rather than numerically, with arithmetic, for several reasons:

- the algebraic solution is more general: you can substitute in more than one set of numbers, which may be useful later in the problem;

- mistakes are easier to find;

- the physical behavior of the system should be easier to visualize.

Once you have the algebraic solution, substitute numerical values if you have been asked to do so.

(The only common exceptions to this advice are problems with multiple parts which are not closely connected; in such cases it may well be easier to evaluate each answer numerically before going on.)

Step 4: _Scrutinize_

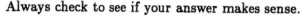

Always check to see if your answer makes sense.

- One of the most powerful tools for doing this is _dimensional analysis_. To find the _dimensions_ of a quantity, we express it in terms of more basic concepts: for example, a velocity, whether measured in m/s, miles per hour, or furlongs per fortnight, is always a length divided by a time: [velocity] = [length]/[time], where square brackets denote "dimensions of". Dimensional analysis involves determining the dimensions of each term in an equation and asking two questions: (i) are they the same (it is meaningless to add quantities with different dimensions—the sum "1 kg + 2 m" is nonsensical), and (ii) are they what we expect (if we are calculating a distance, we expect its dimensions to be [length], not, say, [length]/[mass])? Note, however, that dimensional analysis cannot uncover errors which involve pure numbers, such as a missing minus sign, or a factor of $\frac{1}{2}$ or 2π.

- Missing minus signs or numerical factors can often be caught by considering _special cases_ which are easy to visualize. In a problem involving two masses, for example, we might ask if the solution behaves sensibly when one mass becomes vanishingly small, or extremely large.

- In problems which have numerical solutions, you should also ask yourself if the magnitude of the numerical value seems reasonable: for example, if you were asked to calculate the speed of a car engaged in a collision, an answer of 700 mph would seem unlikely to be correct!

If the authors of this book were given 10 cents every time a student submitted a test answer which he or she could have known was obviously wrong, we would be quite rich.

Step 5: _**Learn**_

Once you are convinced that your solution is correct, take the time to look at how it fits into what you already know. Does it explain phenomena you have noticed in everyday life, but not understood? Is it unexpected or surprising? Does it lead you to make predictions about more complicated systems? Does it illustrate the use of some technique that might be useful for other problems? Have you understood the problem well enough so that now you will be able to quickly solve problems that are closely related? You should find that problem solving gives you much more insight into the physics you are learning than simply reading the theory.

NOTE: This approach to problem-solving was suggested by a similar strategy outlined in *Physics: The Nature of Things*, by Susan M. Lea and John Robert Burke.

ESSENTIALS OF INTRODUCTORY CLASSICAL MECHANICS

CHAPTER 1

SPACE, TIME AND SCIENCE

OVERVIEW

In this chapter we discuss the scientific approach to the study of natural phenomena and introduce the fundamental concepts of space and time. We will see how the Euclidean nature of space and the absolute scale of time allow us to construct mathematical relations between time of observation and position of the observed object in space which can be used to describe and predict the motion of a particle in simple situations.

When you have completed this chapter you should:

- ✔ appreciate the difference between vector and scalar quantities and be able to manipulate vector quantities in equations;

- ✔ understand the concepts of position, distance, time, speed, velocity, and acceleration and their mathematical interrelations;

- ✔ understand what is meant by the dimensions of a physical quantity, and know how to check the dimensional consistency of an equation;

- ✔ understand how to interpret the units of a physical quantity, and know how to convert units when necessary;

- ✔ be able to use what you have learned in describing and predicting the motion of a point particle, including uniform circular motion and the motion of a particle with constant acceleration, such as a projectile.

ESSENTIALS

Physics is an attempt to understand and predict natural phenomena using the scientific method. The scientific method uses the results of observation and/or experiment to construct theories which can be used to predict the results of further experiments.

Supplementary Notes

To formalize the results of observation and experiment we need to introduce simple concepts or quantities which can be expressed numerically and represented by mathematical symbols. Predictive theories consist of relations between these mathematical symbols, i.e. mathematical equations. The most important step in constructing a good theory is choosing the right basic concepts.

Supplementary Notes.

The first two fundamental concepts that are needed for classical mechanics are *time*, and *position in space*. These are necessary to identify a particular event we have observed. It is a basic assumption of classical mechanics that we can in principle specify the position of an object at a given time to arbitrarily high precision.

Supplementary Notes.

Time is said to be *absolute* if the passage of time is unaffected by the position or motion of the observer. Time is found to be absolute to a very good approximation. The basic SI unit of time is the *second*. (SI stands for *Système International*, the standard international system of metric units.) The second was originally defined as 1/86400 of the Earth's rotational period (one day), but this was not precise enough for modern laboratory measurements, so it has been redefined by specifying that the period of the radiation emitted in the transition between the two lowest energy levels of the ^{133}Ce atom is $(1/9,192,631,770)$ s. This is the basis of atomic clocks.

Space is said to be *Euclidean* if it obeys all the axioms of Euclidean geometry, and consequently also obeys the Pythagorean theorem. To a very good approximation space is found to be Euclidean. Space is said to be *three-dimensional*, meaning that three numbers are necessary to identify a point in space unambiguously. The basic SI unit for measuring distances in space is the *meter*, which is defined by specifying that the speed of light in a vacuum is precisely 299,792,458 m/s. (This may seem an odd way to define a standard length, but experimentally it turns out that this definition can be implemented with greater precision than the definition based on a standard platinum-iridium bar, adopted in 1889, or the 1960 definition based on the wavelength of krypton-86 radiation. The current definition was adopted in 1983, but the platinum-iridium bar from 1889 is still preserved by the International Bureau of Weights and Measures.)

Supplementary Notes.

Absolute time and Euclidean space are the basic concepts used to construct classical mechanics. Both of these idealizations are extraordinarily accurate under normal everyday circumstances, and both seem so obvious that it often seems pedantic to discuss them; it is hard to imagine how they could possibly be violated. Nonetheless, since the early part of the twentieth century physicists have become convinced that neither of these idealizations is a completely accurate picture of reality.

The violation of the principle of absolute time was introduced by Albert Einstein in his theory of special relativity (1905). Specifically, the theory proposed, and experiments have confirmed, that all clocks slow down if they travel at high speeds, comparable to that of light $(3.0 \times 10^8$ m/s). Since all clocks slow in exactly the same way, it is fair to say that time itself slows down for high speed observers. While it is difficult to accelerate a wristwatch to near-light speeds, the effect can be seen easily by using unstable subatomic particles as clocks. Particles called muons, for example, decay with a half-life of 1.5×10^{-6} second when they are at rest. Muons produced in the upper atmosphere by cosmic ray collisions, however, typically travel at 99.9% of the speed of light, and are found to have a half-life roughly 20 times longer than the value for stationary muons. Clocks also run slower in very strong gravitational fields, such as those in the vicinity of black holes, and Einstein's theory of general relativity (1916) tells us that in such conditions space is not Euclidean, either. Indeed, on sufficiently large scales the whole universe may be non-Euclidean.

Finally, the assumption that we can in principle specify the position and velocity of an object to arbitrarily high precision breaks down at the atomic scale, where quantum mechanics must be used. Our understanding of the physics of atoms relies on the proposition that the trajectory of an electron in an atom is not only unknown, but cannot even be defined. The mathematical framework of quantum mechanics describes an electron that truly behaves as if it is in many places at once.

Despite these failures in extreme conditions, the assumptions of classical mechanics remain "true" in everyday life—quantum and relativistic effects are unmeasurably small. The laws and techniques we introduce in this book are therefore applicable to a wide range of real-life situations.

The main goal of classical mechanics is to understand motion: why do objects move in the way they do, and how can we predict their motion? Before we can discuss the underlying causes of motion, however, we have to first develop the mathematical machinery needed to simply *describe* how things move. Chapter 1 will be devoted to the description of motion, a subtopic of classical mechanics known as *kinematics*. The study of forces and why things move the way they do, which will be the subject of much of the remainder of the book, is known as *dynamics*.

To specify position in space, relative to a chosen origin, we need both a distance and a direction. The mathematical entities possessing both magnitude (size) and direction are called *vectors*. Positions in space are therefore represented mathematically by vectors.

Problems 1B

To emphasize the difference between a vector and a number, in this book we will denote vectors by boldfaced symbols with an arrow on top, such as $\vec{\mathbf{v}}$. The simplest way to specify a vector $\vec{\mathbf{v}}$ in three dimensions is to choose a coordinate system and then give the components of the vector along the x, y, and z axes, as shown in the diagram:

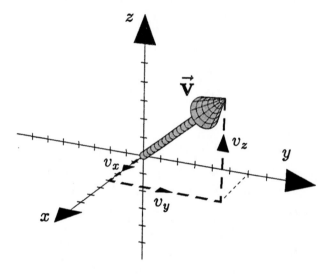

In this book we will express vectors explicitly by writing their three components in brackets:

$$\vec{\mathbf{v}} \equiv \left[v_x, v_y, v_z\right] .$$

The operation of *vector addition* can be defined graphically by placing the tail of the second vector on the head of the first. The sum is then the vector that extends from the tail of the first to the head of the second:

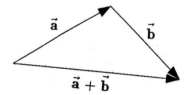

12

In component language, one simply adds the components:

$$\vec{a} + \vec{b} = [a_x, a_y, a_z] + [b_x, b_y, b_z]$$
$$= [a_x + b_x, a_y + b_y, a_z + b_z] \ .$$

The negative of a vector is defined by negating all the components, or equivalently by reversing the direction and leaving the magnitude fixed. One subtracts a vector by adding its negative.

In many textbooks you will find $\vec{v}$ written using vector addition as

$$\vec{v} \equiv v_x \hat{x} + v_y \hat{y} + v_z \hat{z} \ ,$$

where $\hat{x}$ represents the *unit vector* (vector of magnitude 1) in the x-direction, and so on, or as

$$\vec{v} \equiv v_x \hat{i} + v_y \hat{j} + v_z \hat{k} \ ,$$

where $\hat{i}$, $\hat{j}$, and $\hat{k}$ are just a different notation for $\hat{x}$, $\hat{y}$, and $\hat{z}$.

The graphical picture of vector addition makes it clear that *vectors do not have a definite position in space*. The vector $\vec{b}$, moved so that its tail lies on the head of $\vec{a}$, has not become a different vector because it has moved from its original position. A vector is defined by its magnitude and its direction, not its location.

Many physical quantities, such as mass, time, or temperature, have only magnitude and not direction (except perhaps for a plus (+) or minus (−) sign). These quantities are called *scalars*, and each can be represented by a single ordinary number and manipulated according to the familiar rules of algebra and arithmetic. The magnitude of a vector, $v = |\vec{v}| = \sqrt{v_x^2 + v_y^2 + v_z^2}$, is an example of a scalar. Each component of a vector is represented by a single, ordinary number, but technically speaking they are not scalars, since they depend on the direction in which the coordinate system is oriented.

Multiplication of a vector by a positive scalar is defined as the multiplication of the vector's magnitude by the scalar, leaving the direction unchanged. Multiplication of a vector by a negative scalar results in a vector of the opposite direction, with the magnitude given by the product of the original magnitude and the absolute value of the scalar. In terms of components, we multiply a vector $\vec{v}$ by a scalar s by simply multiplying each component by s:

$$s\, [v_x, v_y, v_z] = [s\, v_x, s\, v_y, s\, v_z] \ .$$

13

To divide a vector by a scalar s, one divides each component by s. There are two standard methods of multiplying a vector by a vector, known as the dot product and cross product, which we will introduce when we need them in Chapters 4 and 9, respectively. Please note that other operations are not defined—don't add a scalar to a vector, and don't try to divide by a vector!

Position, velocity, and acceleration are all vectors, while time is a scalar.

The *position vector* of one point in space relative to another is often called the *displacement*. The magnitude of the displacement is the *distance* between the points.

Problems 1B

Velocity is the rate of change of position with time.

Acceleration is the rate of change of velocity with time.

Problems 1A

Rates of change are represented mathematically by *derivatives*. The derivative of a vector with respect to a scalar is a vector, so velocity and acceleration are both vectors. If the displacement vector of an object is given as a function of time by $\vec{r}(t)$, then the velocity of the object is defined by

$$\boxed{\vec{v}(t) \equiv \frac{d\vec{r}}{dt} \equiv \lim_{\Delta t \to 0} \frac{\vec{r}(t + \Delta t) - \vec{r}(t)}{\Delta t}\ .}$$

This is equivalent to differentiating each component of the vector independently. That is, if $\vec{r}(t) \equiv [x(t), y(t), z(t)]$, then

$$\vec{v}(t) = \left[\frac{dx}{dt}, \frac{dy}{dt}, \frac{dz}{dt}\right]\ .$$

(Note that this is different from differentiating the magnitude of $\vec{r}(t)$, which is NOT the right way to find the velocity.) The acceleration of the object is defined by

$$\boxed{\vec{a}(t) \equiv \frac{d\vec{v}(t)}{dt} = \frac{d^2\vec{r}(t)}{dt^2}\ ,}$$

or in component form

$$\vec{a}(t) = \left[\frac{dv_x}{dt}, \frac{dv_y}{dt}, \frac{dv_z}{dt}\right] = \left[\frac{d^2x}{dt^2}, \frac{d^2y}{dt^2}, \frac{d^2z}{dt^2}\right]\ .$$

The magnitude of the velocity is called the *speed*. Note that *distance* and *speed* are both scalars, as they are the magnitudes of the vectors *displacement* and *velocity*, respectively.

Note that the dimensions of velocity are [length]/[time], and of acceleration [length]/[time]^2. In solving problems it is good practice to check that the dimensions of the result are what you expect them to be. The product of an acceleration and a time, for example, will always have dimensions [length]/[time], the dimensions of a velocity. Therefore, if you find that a distance is calculated as the product of an acceleration and a time, then you would know that you made an algebraic error.

Where a numerical value is attached to a physical quantity, we must consider not only its dimensions, but also its *units*: a speed of 1 m/s is not the same as 1 mile per hour. A general method for converting units is demonstrated in the solution to Problem 1A.4.

Problem 1A.4

A change in the velocity of an object does not necessarily require a change in speed. A good example of this is *uniform circular motion*. A particle moving with constant speed v in a circle of radius r does not have constant velocity (because the *direction* of the velocity is changing). In fact the particle has an acceleration of constant magnitude

Problems 1D

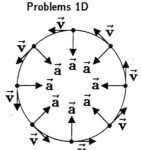

$$|\vec{\mathbf{a}}| = \frac{v^2}{r}$$

directed towards the center of the circle. This is called *centripetal acceleration* (where the word "centripetal" means "pointing towards the center"). The eight dots in the diagram at the right represent the same particle at different times, as it travels around the circle at constant speed.

In the case where the acceleration is *constant*, the velocity $\vec{\mathbf{v}}$ and position $\vec{\mathbf{r}}$ of a body at time t are given by

$$\vec{\mathbf{v}}(t) = \vec{\mathbf{v}}_0 + \vec{\mathbf{a}}\,t$$
$$\vec{\mathbf{r}}(t) = \vec{\mathbf{r}}_0 + \vec{\mathbf{v}}_0\,t + \frac{1}{2}\vec{\mathbf{a}}\,t^2\ ,$$

where $\vec{\mathbf{v}}_0$ and $\vec{\mathbf{r}}_0$ are its velocity and position at time $t = 0$. These equations can be used in *any* case of constant acceleration. They are especially easy to use if a body is confined to one dimension (i.e. can move only back and forth along a given line). In this situation there is no practical difference between vectors and ordinary numbers, as the concept of direction reduces to a plus or minus sign (backwards or forwards along the line). In this context the above equations reduce to

$$v^2 = v_0^2 + 2a(x - x_0)\ .$$

Problems 1A

To solve problems involving more than one dimension, it is often helpful to decompose the vector quantities into their components in a convenient coordinate system. In the simplest cases each component equation forms a *separate* one-dimensional problem.

Problems 1C

An important example in which the component equations can be treated separately is the motion of freely falling bodies. If we neglect air resistance (as we will until Chapter 6), then near the Earth's surface a freely falling body has a constant acceleration $\vec{g}$ directed downwards. The magnitude g of $\vec{g}$, to two significant figures, is 9.8 m/s². If the falling body initially has no horizontal velocity component, then the motion is purely vertical and hence one-dimensional. If the object is not simply dropped, but instead is launched with velocity $\vec{v}$ at some angle to $\vec{g}$, then we call it a *projectile*, and we decompose the motion into horizontal and vertical components. The horizontal acceleration is zero, and therefore the horizontal velocity is constant. The vertical component of the motion behaves exactly as in the previous case, when there was no horizontal velocity. Projectile motion is two-dimensional.

Problems 1C.2, 1C.3, and 1C.4

In many cases it is useful to consider the position or velocity of an object as seen by an observer who is not located at the origin of the coordinate system, and/or is not stationary. If an object is at position $\vec{r}$, then its position vector $\vec{r}'$ *relative* to an observer O at position $\vec{r}_0$ is

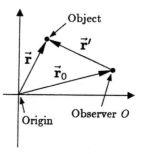

$$\vec{r}' = \vec{r} - \vec{r}_0 \ .$$

Similarly, if the velocity of an object is $\vec{v}$, then its velocity *relative* to an observer O whose velocity is $\vec{v}_0$ is

$$\vec{v}' = \vec{v} - \vec{v}_0 \ .$$

Problems 1E

One can also introduce a new coordinate system—also called a new *frame of reference*—with the observer O as the origin. The position and velocity of the object in this new frame of reference are $\vec{r}'$ and $\vec{v}'$, respectively, as calculated from the formulas above.

Vectors (or scalars) measured with respect to a particular observer, stationary or moving, are said to be measured in a particular *frame of reference*. Changing frames of reference—i.e., changing the point of view from which you observe the motion—can often be a useful tool in solving problems.

Since velocity is the *derivative* of position with respect to time, it follows that the position at a given time t_1 relative to the position at time $t = 0$ can be calculated by *integrating* the velocity:

$$\vec{r}(t_1) = \vec{r}_0 + \int_0^{t_1} \vec{v} \, dt \ ,$$

where $\vec{r}_0$ is the position at time $t = 0$. The velocity $\vec{v}(t_1)$ can similarly be obtained by integrating the acceleration $\vec{a}$:

$$\vec{v}(t_1) = \vec{v}_0 + \int_0^{t_1} \vec{a}\, dt \;.$$

The x-component of the velocity v_x is the derivative of x with respect to t, which can be displayed graphically on a plot of x versus t, as shown below on the left. For any time t, v_x is the slope of the line tangent to the curve at the specified value of t. The change Δx in the x-component of the displacement during the time interval between t_1 and t_2 is the area under the graph of v_x versus t, as shown on the graph below on the right. Analogous relations hold for the y- and z-components.

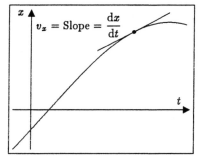 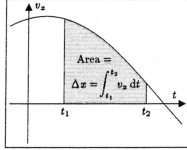

Problem 1A.6

The phrase *average velocity* requires definition, since the method of averaging must be specified. You will usually find a different answer if you average over distance than if you average over time. Most physics books, including this one, define average velocity to mean the average over *time*:

Problem 1A.3

$$v_{x,\text{average}} \equiv \frac{1}{t_2 - t_1} \int_{t_1}^{t_2} v_x(t)\, dt \;.$$

Since the integral of the derivative $v_x(t) \equiv dx/dt$ is the original function $x(t)$, the average velocity can be written simply as

$$v_{x,\text{average}} = \frac{x(t_2) - x(t_1)}{t_2 - t_1} = \frac{\Delta x}{\Delta t} \;,$$

Problem 1A.4

as illustrated on the following graph:

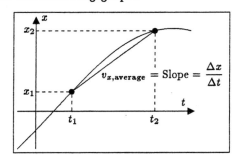

Since Δx is equal to both $v_{x,\text{average}}\,\Delta t$ and also $\int_{t_1}^{t_2} v_x \, dt$, it follows that the area under the average velocity graph is equal to the area under the graph of v_x versus t:

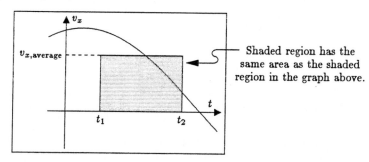

Shaded region has the same area as the shaded region in the graph above.

The relations in this paragraph apply to the y- and z-components as well, so they can be written as vector equations:

$$\vec{\mathbf{v}}_{\text{average}} \equiv \frac{1}{t_2 - t_1} \int_{t_1}^{t_2} \vec{\mathbf{v}}(t)\, dt = \frac{\Delta \vec{\mathbf{r}}}{\Delta t} \; .$$

Similarly, the *average acceleration* is defined to be the average over *time*, so

$$a_{x,\text{average}} \equiv \frac{1}{t_2 - t_1} \int_{t_1}^{t_2} a_x(t)\, dt \; .$$

Integrating the derivative $a_x(t) = dv_x/dt$, one finds

$$a_{x,\text{average}} = \frac{v_x(t_2) - v_x(t_1)}{t_2 - t_1} = \frac{\Delta v_x}{\Delta t} \; .$$

Problem 1A.7

The full vector equation can then be written as

$$\vec{\mathbf{a}}_{\text{average}} \equiv \frac{1}{t_2 - t_1} \int_{t_1}^{t_2} \vec{\mathbf{a}}(t)\, dt = \frac{\Delta \vec{\mathbf{v}}}{\Delta t} \; .$$

SUMMARY

* Natural phenomena can be described in terms of basic quantifiable concepts.

* Mathematical equations relating these basic concepts can be used to predict the outcome of experiments.

* Physical concepts introduced in this chapter: space, time, velocity, acceleration, speed.

* Near the Earth's surface a freely falling body accelerates downwards with uniform acceleration $\vec{g}$ (magnitude g). To two significant figures the value of g is 9.8 m/s^2.

* Mathematical concepts introduced in this chapter: vector, scalar, derivative, integral.

  A vector $\vec{v}$ is represented in component form as $\vec{v} = [v_x, v_y, v_z]$.

  Vector addition: $\vec{a} + \vec{b} = [a_x + b_x, a_y + b_y, a_z + b_z]$.

  Multiplication by scalar s: $s\vec{v} = [s\,v_x, s\,v_y, s\,v_z]$.

  Differentiation with respect to scalar s: $\dfrac{d\vec{v}}{ds} = \left[\dfrac{dv_x}{ds}, \dfrac{dv_y}{ds}, \dfrac{dv_z}{ds}\right]$.

  Position in space $\vec{r}$, velocity $\vec{v}$, and acceleration $\vec{a}$ are vectors; time t, distance r and speed v are scalars.

* Equations introduced in this chapter:

$$\vec{v} = \frac{d\vec{r}}{dt}\,; \qquad \vec{a} = \frac{d\vec{v}}{dt} = \frac{d^2\vec{r}}{dt^2}\,; \qquad \vec{r}(t_1) = \vec{r}_0 + \int_0^{t_1} \vec{v}\,dt\,; \qquad \vec{v}(t_1) = \vec{v}_0 + \int_0^{t_1} \vec{a}\,dt\,.$$

  For *constant* acceleration $\vec{a}$, if $\vec{r} = \vec{r}_0$ and $\vec{v} = \vec{v}_0$ at time $t = 0$, then

$$\vec{v}(t) = \vec{v}_0 + \vec{a}t$$

$$\vec{r}(t) = \vec{r}_0 + \vec{v}_0 t + \frac{1}{2}\vec{a}t^2\,.$$

  For one-dimensional motion with constant acceleration a:

$$v^2 = v_0^2 + 2a(x - x_0)\,.$$

  For circular motion at constant speed v:

$$a = \frac{v^2}{r}\,,$$

  where r is the radius of the circle, and the acceleration is directed towards the center of the circle.

  If an object has position $\vec{r}$ and velocity $\vec{v}$, its position and velocity relative to an observer with position $\vec{r}_0$ and velocity $\vec{v}_0$ are given respectively by

$$\vec{r}' = \vec{r} - \vec{r}_0\,, \qquad \vec{v}' = \vec{v} - \vec{v}_0\,.$$

  Average velocity and acceleration are given by

$$\vec{v}_{\text{average}} = \frac{\Delta\vec{r}}{\Delta t}\,, \qquad \vec{a}_{\text{average}} = \frac{\Delta\vec{v}}{\Delta t}\,.$$

19

PROBLEMS AND QUESTIONS

By the end of this chapter you should be able to answer or solve the types of questions or problems stated below.

Note: throughout the book, in multiple-choice problems, the answers have been rounded off to 2 significant figures, unless otherwise stated.

At the end of the chapter there are answers to all the problems. In addition, for problems with an (H) or (S) after the number, there are respectively hints on how to solve the problems or completely worked-out solutions.

1A   VELOCITY AND ACCELERATION IN ONE DIMENSION

1A.1   An athlete runs at a uniform speed of 9.5 m/s. How long does it take him to run a distance of 200 m?

(a) 19 s; (b) 21 s; (c) 22 s; (d) none of these

1A.2   An auto accelerates uniformly from rest to 100 km/h in 8.0 s. What is its acceleration?

(a) 12.5 m/s^2; (b) 12.5 km/h; (c) 3.5 m/s; (d) 3.5 m/s^2

1A.3   An athlete runs 50 m along a straight track at a constant speed of 10 m/s. She then slows to 8 m/s for another 50 m.

(a) How long does it take her to run each segment?

(b) Plot (i) her position as a function of time; (ii) her velocity as a function of time; and (iii) her velocity as a function of distance.

(c) Over the complete 100 meters, what is her average velocity, averaged over time? What is her average velocity, averaged over distance?

1A.4 (S) (a) You have arranged to meet a friend at his home, which is five miles from yours. You drive there, averaging about 20 miles per hour as both of you live in the city. How long does it take you to reach your friend's home? How long would it take if you lived in a rural district where it was possible to average 45 mph?

(b) If you were driving in Europe and saw a sign saying 'Paris 120 km', how long would it take you to reach there if you were traveling on a French autoroute at 75 miles per hour?

(c) A good sprinter takes about ten seconds for the 100 meter sprint. What is his average speed in miles per hour? If he could maintain this speed indefinitely, how long would it take him to run a marathon (26 miles 385 yards)?

1A.5 (H) An object moves along the x-axis with constant acceleration a. Its position and velocity at time $t = 0$ are $x = x_0$ and $v = v_0$ respectively; at some later time t it has position x and velocity v. Use the definitions of velocity and acceleration to prove that

$$x = x_0 + v_0 t + \frac{1}{2} a t^2$$

and

$$v^2 = v_0^2 + 2a(x - x_0) .$$

[It is very easy to prove this with calculus, but for constant acceleration you don't actually *need* calculus to derive these equations.]

1A.6 The graph shows the velocity of a particle (along the x-axis) as a function of time.

(a) When is the acceleration of the particle (i) positive, (ii) negative, (iii) zero?

(b) What is the particle's displacement after 3.5 s? After 7 s?

(c) Describe in words the motion of the particle.

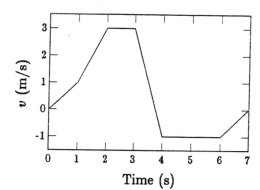

1A.7 (S) Two cars race along a straight track for 1 km, starting from rest. The first accelerates at 4 m/s² for 10 s, then continues at constant velocity. The second accelerates at 5 m/s² for 5 s, then at 1.5 m/s² for 10 s, then at 0.5 m/s² for the rest of the race.

(a) How long does each car take to complete the race?

(b) Overall, what is the average acceleration and average velocity of each car?

(c) What is the average acceleration of each car after 15 s of the race?

(d) What distance has each car covered after 15 s of the race?

(e) Draw a graph of velocity and distance covered against time for each car.

1A.8 (H) A bus is moving along a straight road 1 km long. Between stops it travels at the local speed limit, which is 40 km/h. Approaching a stop it decelerates at 1 m/s², stops for 30 s to let passengers on and off, and then accelerates at 1.5 m/s². There are two stops on this stretch of road, one at 200 m from the start and one at 650 m.

(a) How far before a stop does the bus start to decelerate?

(b) How long does it take the bus to complete this section of its route? What is its average velocity? Draw a graph of the bus's velocity against time.

(c) A cyclist doing 20 km/h entered the stretch of road at the same time as the bus. Draw a graph of position against time for both the cyclist and the bus. How often does the cyclist overtake the bus, and vice versa?

21

1A.9 (S)   A crewman on the starship Enter-
prise is on shore leave on a distant
planet. He drops a rock from the top
of a cliff and observes that it takes
3.00 s to reach the bottom. He now
throws another rock vertically upwards so that it reaches a height of
2.0 m before dropping down the cliff
face. The second rock takes 4.12 s
to reach the bottom of the cliff. The
planet has a very thin atmosphere
which offers negligible air resistance.
How high is the cliff, and what is the
value of g on this planet?

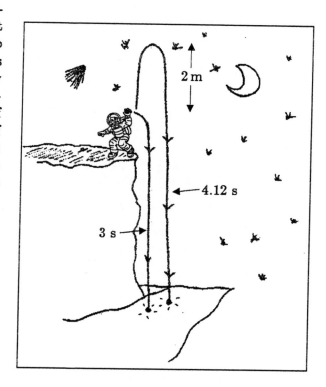

1B   USING VECTORS

1B.1   You are standing 10 m south of a tree. A squirrel runs 6 m up the tree and then climbs
out 4 m on an eastward-pointing branch. In a coordinate system where x is east, y
north and z up, what are the coordinates of the squirrel *relative to you*?

(a) [10, 6, 4] m; (b) [4, −10, 6] m; (c) [4, 10, 6] m; (d) [−10, 4, 6] m.

What is the distance between you and the squirrel, to the nearest meter?

(a) 20 m; (b) 14 m; (c) 12 m; (d) none of these

1B.2 (H)   Albert, Betty, Carol, and Dave are playing frisbee in a square field whose sides happen
to run due east and due north. Albert's position vector relative to one corner of the
field is [10, 7, 0] m, where x is east and y north (z is up, but you can assume that the
field is level).

(a) Betty is 14 m northeast of Albert, Carol is 10 m east of Betty, and Dave is 8 m south of
Carol. What are the position vectors of Betty, Carol, and Dave? (Take the same corner
of the field as origin for all position vectors.)

(b) How far is Albert from Carol?

(c) Dave's dog Ernie runs from Dave to Betty at 3 m/s. What is his velocity vector? How
long does it take him to reach Betty? What is his position vector 4 s after leaving Dave?

(d) Make a scale drawing of the field, showing the positions of Albert, Betty, Carol, Dave,
and Ernie 4 s after Ernie leaves Dave.

22

1C   VELOCITY AND ACCELERATION AS VECTORS

1C.1   At a certain time, a particle has velocity $[3, 1, -2]$ m/s. Its acceleration, which is constant, is $[0, -0.6, 0]$ m/s^2. What is its speed after 10 s?

(a) 10 m/s; (b) 12 m/s; (c) 2 m/s; (d) none of these

What is the distance between its position at the start of the 10 s and at the end?

(a) 41 m; (b) 60 m; (c) 7 m; (d) 30 m

1C.2 (S)   A cannonball emerges from a cannon with speed v, independent of the angle at which the barrel of the cannon is inclined. If the cannon is set on level ground, at what angle should the gunner set the cannon to maximize the range? What will the range be at this angle (in terms of v and g) and what height will the ball reach? Neglect any effects of air resistance.

1C.3 (H)   A child is kicking a soccer ball in her backyard. If the ball leaves her foot with speed v_0 directed at an angle θ to the horizontal, derive expressions for the distance x that the ball travels and the height h that it reaches (assuming that it starts from $h = 0$, that the yard is level, and that air resistance is negligible).

   (a) She kicks the ball with a speed of 8 m/s at an angle of 70° to the horizontal. How far from her does it hit the ground, and what maximum height does it reach? Take $g = 9.8$ m/s^2.

   (b) She kicks the ball straight up and it reaches a height of 5 m. How far would it have gone horizontally if she had kicked it with the same speed, but at an angle of 45°? At what angle would she need to kick (again assuming the same speed) if she wants it to land a distance $x = 8$ m away? Draw the ball's trajectory for both possible answers. Can you do this problem if you do *not* know the value of g?

1C.4 (S)   In a shooting contest, a clay pigeon is launched from the ground at a speed of 50 m/s at 60° to the horizontal, directed eastwards. The contestant is standing 100 m south of the clay's line of flight and 40 m east of the launch point. His gun has a muzzle velocity of 200 m/s and he hits the clay when it is directly ahead of him as he faces north. When did he fire, and at what elevation? (Neglect air resistance; take $g = 9.8$ m/s^2 and assume the shot is fired from a height of 1.6 m above ground level.)

1D   CIRCULAR MOTION

1D.1   A car traveling at a steady 40 km/h negotiates a 60° left bend. The bend is an arc of a circle of radius 100 m. What is the magnitude of the acceleration of the car at any point in the bend?

(a) 1.2 m/s^2; (b) 0 m/s^2; (c) 1.6 m/s^2; (d) 1.4 m/s^2.

1D.2 (S)   A motorcycle negotiates a 40° right-hand bend at 60 km/h. The bend consists of a 40° arc of a circle of radius 75 m. What is the centripetal acceleration of the bike at any point in the bend, and what is the total velocity change between entering the bend and leaving it?

1D.3   (a) A geosynchronous or geostationary satellite is so called because it takes 24 hours to complete one orbit. Such satellites orbit at a height of 35,800 km above the Earth's surface. What is the centripetal acceleration of geosynchronous satellites? [The radius of the Earth is 6,400 km.]

(b) What is the centripetal acceleration of a point on the Earth's equator, at sea level?

Compare your answers to both parts of the question with the value of g at sea level (9.8 m/s^2).

1E   REFERENCE FRAMES

1E.1 (S) (a) A ferryboat crosses a river of width d. The speed of the boat (relative to the water) is v and the speed of the river current is V. Assuming that the landing point of the ferry is directly opposite its starting point, how long does it take for a round trip?

(b) In the Ferryman of the Year competition the ferryman is required to complete a course of the same distance $2d$ by rowing a distance d directly upstream and then back downstream to his starting point. (The distance is defined by posts on the river bank.) How long does it take him to complete the course, and is this longer or shorter than the round trip across the river?

(c) An invading army is approaching the river. The ferryman is anxious to get across to the other side as quickly as possible, without caring where he lands. How long does it take him, and where does he land?

1E.2 (S) The pilot of a light plane wishes to fly from Bristol to Edinburgh (625 km due north). Her cruising speed, measured relative to the air, is 150 km/h. There is a 20 km/h west wind blowing (where "west wind" refers to a wind blowing *from* the west).

(a) In what direction should she point her plane, and how long will her journey take? (Ignore the time spent in take-off and landing and assume that she flies at a constant altitude.)

(b) When she starts her return trip the wind has shifted to southwest and increased to 50 km/h. What heading should she take, and how long is the return journey?

1E.3 (H) You are in an airplane flying due west at 150 m/s. The plane has a glass window in the floor, through which you see a second airplane directly below you. It is flying northwest at 100 m/s. Both craft are maintaining a constant altitude.

What is the velocity (magnitude and direction) of the second plane relative to yours? Draw a sketch of the second airplane showing the direction of this relative velocity vector. Describe in words the apparent motion of the plane as you see it from your window.

COMPLETE SOLUTIONS TO PROBLEMS WITH AN (S)

1A.4   (a) *You have arranged to meet a friend at his home, which is five miles from yours. You drive there, averaging about 20 miles per hour as both of you live in the city. How long does it take you to reach your friend's home? How long would it take if you lived in a rural district where it was possible to average 45 mph?*

Conceptualize

In this problem we are given the distance that we need to travel, and the speed at which we are moving. We are asked to find the time that the trip will take.

What does the word "distance" mean in this context? To solve the problem, we have to assume that the distance of five miles quoted in the problem refers to the actual road distance that you travel. The road distance is usually longer than the value given by our formal definition of distance ("the magnitude of the displacement vector"), which would give the straight-line distance ("as the crow flies"). However, as long as one recognizes that the motion discussed in this problem is along a specified route, and that all distances are to be measured along that route, then the solution to this problem is essentially identical to the case of motion along a line. We can label each point along the route by a coordinate s, defined to be the road distance from the start. In this context the speed v is defined by $v = \mathrm{d}s/\mathrm{d}t$, and the average speed is just the total road distance divided by the time.

Formulate

In mathematical form our relationship is $t = s/v$, where s is the total road distance.

Solve

time in city $=$ (5 miles)/(20 mi/h) $= 0.25$ h $= 15$ minutes;

time in rural district $=$ (5 miles)/(45 mi/h) $= 0.11$ h $= 6$ minutes 40 seconds.

Scrutinize

The dimensions of the answer are correct: [length]/([length]/[time]) gives a time. One must also make sure that the *units* are correct—0.25 *hours*, not seconds or years! In this case there was no problem, but see the next part.

  (b) *If you were driving in Europe and saw a sign saying 'Paris 120 km', how long would it take you to reach there if you were traveling on a French autoroute at 75 miles per hour?*

Conceptualize

We are using the same concepts as in the previous problem, but this time we have the added complication that our units of *distance* are not consistent with our units of *speed*. We will have to express the distance in miles, or alternatively the speed in km/h, before doing the calculation. Consulting reference books, we find that to two significant figures 1 mile = 1.6 km.

Formulate and Solve

Our conversion factor 1 mile = 1.6 km is equivalent to saying that 1 = (1 mile)/(1.6 km). Multiplying any quantity by 1 does not change it, so we can multiply 120 km by (1 mile)/(1.6 km) to obtain

$$120\,\mathrm{km} = 120\,\cancel{\mathrm{km}} \times \frac{1\,\mathrm{mile}}{1.6\,\cancel{\mathrm{km}}} = \frac{120}{1.6}\,\mathrm{miles} = 75\,\mathrm{miles}.$$

25

1A.4, continued:

We then apply $t = s/v$ to obtain

$$t = (75\,\text{miles})/(75\,\text{miles/hour}) = 1\,\text{hour}.$$

Alternatively, it is often convenient to leave the unit conversions for the final step, as numerical values are inserted. Again, the idea is to look for ways to insert expressions for 1 that cause the units to cancel and give the answer in the desired units. For this problem, one would write:

$$t = \frac{s}{v} = \frac{120\,\text{km}}{75\,\text{mile} \cdot \text{hour}^{-1}} \times \frac{1\,\text{mile}}{1.6\,\text{km}} = 1\,\text{hour}.$$

Even when no unit conversion is needed, cancellation of units like this is a good way to check for dimensional consistency.

Scrutinize
We can check the arithmetic by converting the speed to km/h instead of converting the distance to miles: multiplying by $1 = (1.6\,\text{km})/(1\,\text{mile})$ we have

$$75\,\text{miles/hour} = 75\,\frac{\text{miles}}{\text{hour}} \times \frac{1.6\,\text{km}}{1\,\text{mile}} = 120\,\text{km/hour},$$

and it is clear that this gives $t = 1$ hour as before.

Learn
In numerical problems like this we always need to extend our checking of the *dimensions* of an equation to a check of the actual *units*. Inches, meters and miles all have dimensions of length, but 1 inch is not the same as 1 mile!

The method of unit conversion used here may seem a little labored for this simple problem, but it is a general method which can be used successfully in much more complicated equations.

(c) *A good sprinter takes about ten seconds for the 100 meter sprint. What is his average speed in miles per hour? If he could maintain this speed indefinitely, how long would it take him to run a marathon (26 miles 385 yards)?*

Conceptualize
This problem uses the same concepts as the previous two, except that here we are given time and asked to calculate speed rather than vice versa. Once again we will have to take care to convert all our numerical values into consistent units.

Formulate
The only equation we need is $x = vt$.

Solve
The sprinter is traveling at 10 m/s. There are 3,600 s in 1 hour, so this is 36,000 meters per hour, or 36 km/h.

1A.4, continued:

Since 1 mile = 1.6 km, 36 km/h = 22.5 mph.

There are 1,760 yards in one mile, so 26 miles 385 yards is $26\frac{385}{1760} = 26.22$ miles. The time it would take to run the marathon is then $(26.22 \text{ miles})/(22.5 \text{ mi/h}) = 1.165$ hours or 1 hour 10 minutes.

Scrutinize

The time calculated for the marathon is much shorter than we would expect in real life, but this is no surprise—we know that human beings cannot keep up sprinting speeds for longer than a few tens of seconds. The sprinter's speed seems reasonable: for comparison, a four-minute mile implies an average speed of 15 mph, and we would expect a sprinter to be running considerably faster than a miler.

Learn

Why don't we give our final answer more precisely, as 1 h 9 min 55 s? The reason is that it would be meaningless to do so. The original data in the question gave the sprinter's time for the 100 m as "about 10 s"—we could interpret this as "between 9.5 s and 10.5 s", or perhaps "between 9.8 s and 10.2 s", but surely not as "between 9.99 s and 10.01 s". If we take the time as 9.8 s, the average speed comes out to 23.0 mph, and the time for a marathon as 1 h 8 m 31 s. Thus quoting the time to the nearest second is unjustified—we simply do not have that accuracy in the data supplied to us. This is an important point in experimental science, where we often want to know if two measurements of a quantity are consistent or inconsistent. Much of the work of experimental physicists involves not so much determining a value as determining the *precision* with which that value is known.

1A.7 *Two cars race along a straight track for 1 km, starting from rest. The first accelerates at 4 m/s² for 10 s, then continues at constant velocity. The second accelerates at 5 m/s² for 5 s, then at 1.5 m/s² for 10 s, then at 0.5 m/s² for the rest of the race.*

(a) *How long does each car take to complete the race?*

(b) *Overall, what is the average acceleration and average velocity of each car?*

(c) *What is the average acceleration of each car after 15 s of the race?*

(d) *What distance has each car covered after 15 s of the race?*

(e) *Draw a graph of velocity and distance covered against time for each car.*

Conceptualize

In this problem the acceleration of the cars is not constant. However, we can divide each car's trip into time segments during which the acceleration is constant—for the first car, $0 \le t \le 10$ s, with $a = 4$ m/s², and the rest of the race, with $a = 0$. The way to solve the problem is to take each individual time segment as a separate constant-acceleration problem. This is a case where it is likely to be easiest to work out the numerical results as we go along, since otherwise the equations are going to get very messy!

Formulate

We apply our standard formulas for constant acceleration a:

$$v = v_0 + at$$

1A.7, continued:

$$x = x_0 + v_0 t + \frac{1}{2} a t^2$$

(note that this is a one-dimensional problem, so we can regard all quantities as numbers—only the x-components of vectors will be nonzero). We treat each time segment as a separate problem, resetting the clock at the end of each one. For the first segments, where we have the end time, solving the equations is simple: we have a and t, and the answer to the previous time segment will give us v_0 and x_0. The final time segment of each car's race is different, though: in this case we have x, because we know the distance over which the race is run, but not t. If the velocity is constant, we can use $t = x/v$, but if $a \neq 0$ we must solve a quadratic equation for t:

$$t = \frac{1}{a} \left(-v_0 \pm \sqrt{v_0^2 + 2a(x - x_0)} \right) .$$

In general, quadratic equations have two roots. How do we know which one we want? In this case there is no problem—one root is negative, and thus relates to a time before the start of this time segment, i.e. to a time for which this equation does not apply. If the acceleration were negative, however, we would have two positive roots. This corresponds to a situation in which the car passes the finish line, continues to decelerate and eventually goes into reverse, crossing the finish line again in the opposite direction! It is clear that in such a case we want the smaller value of t, trusting the time-keeper to stop the watch the *first* time the car hits the finish line.

Solve

We can display our information in tabular form as shown below. Starting from the top line of the table, we then use our equations $v = v_0 + at$ and $x = x_0 + v_0 t + \frac{1}{2} a t^2$ to fill in most of the blanks, as in the second copy of the table.

Car	Time Segment	t_i (s)	$t_f - t_i$ (s)	a (m/s^2)	v_i (m/s)	x_f (m)
1	1	0	10	4	0	?
	2	10	?	0	?	1000
2	1	0	5	5	0	?
	2	5	10	1.5	?	?
	3	15	?	0.5	?	1000

1A.7, continued:

Car	Time Segment	t_i (s)	$t_f - t_i$ (s)	a (m/s^2)	v_i (m/s)	x_f (m)
1	1	0	10	4	0	200
	2	10	20	0	40	1000
2	1	0	5	5	0	62.5
	2	5	10	1.5	25	387.5
	3	15	14	0.5	40	1000

Finally we use the quadratic equation for t to fill in the last blank, shown shaded in the table. This was not necessary for car 1, because its acceleration is zero in stage 2, and so the time taken is simply the distance divided by the (constant) speed.

Now we are in a position to answer the questions posed in the problem.

(a) Calculating t_f from the last line for each car, we see that car 1 takes 30 s to complete the race and car 2 takes 29 s. The race is won by car 2.

(b) The average acceleration is the total change in velocity divided by the total time for the race, and the average velocity is the total displacement over the total time. To calculate these we need one further piece of information, the final speed of car 2. From $v = v_0 + at$ this comes out to 47 m/s. The average velocities and accelerations for the two cars are then:

$$\text{Car 1}: \quad v_{\text{average}} = \frac{1000 \text{ m}}{30 \text{ s}} = 33 \text{ m/s} ; \qquad a_{\text{average}} = \frac{40 \text{ m/s}}{30 \text{ s}} = 1.3 \text{ m/s}^2$$

$$\text{Car 2}: \quad v_{\text{average}} = \frac{1000 \text{ m}}{29 \text{ s}} = 34 \text{ m/s} ; \qquad a_{\text{average}} = \frac{47 \text{ m/s}}{29 \text{ s}} = 1.6 \text{ m/s}^2$$

(c) After 15 s the speed of car 1 is 40 m/s, and that of car 2 is, as it happens, also 40 m/s: their average accelerations are therefore both the same, namely (40 m/s)/(15 s) = 2.7 m/s^2.

(d) The distance covered by car 2 after 15 s is in the table: rounded to 2 significant figures, it is 390 m. For car 1 we calculate the distance traveled in 5 s at a constant speed of 40 m/s, (40 m/s) $\times$ (5 s) = 200 m, and add this to the distance of 200 m covered in the first 10 s, giving a distance of 400 m after 15 s. At this point in the race, therefore, car 1 was in the lead.

(e) The graphs of velocity and distance are shown on the next page.

29

1A.7, continued:

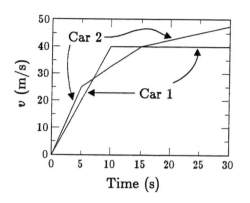 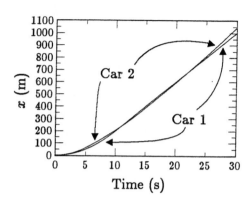

The graph of position is difficult to interpret, because the cars are close together. So let's also draw a graph of the *difference* in position $\Delta x = x_1 - x_2$. We can then see the progress of the race more clearly.

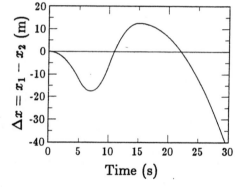

Scrutinize

The numbers appear to make sense—the car which wins the race has a higher average speed and a higher average acceleration, for example, and the average acceleration of each car lies between its minimum acceleration and its maximum acceleration (0 and 4 m/s² for car 1, 0.5 and 5 m/s² for car 2), as we expect of an average.

Learn

Notice that the formula $x = x_0 + v_0 t + \frac{1}{2}at^2$ definitely does not work for non-constant acceleration. We can see this clearly in the answers to parts (c) and (d), where the two cars have the same average acceleration, yet have covered different distances (and neither distance is that given by the formula, which comes out to 300 m).

This problem is one of the rare cases where working symbolically until the last moment does not pay. If you try it, you will find that the equations become steadily more complicated as you go on: the initial velocity for stage 2 is $v_2 = v_1 + a_1 t_1$, giving an initial velocity for stage 3 of $v_3 = v_1 + a_1 t_1 + a_2 t_2$, for example. Since a_1 is not related to a_2, nor t_1 to t_2, this is not increasing our understanding of the problem—it's just increasing the chances of getting confused. This is in fact the exception discussed in "Solving Problems": a problem consisting of multiple disconnected parts. If the parts were more closely related—if the acceleration halved after a fixed time interval, for instance, instead of having arbitrary values maintained for arbitrary times—it *would* pay to work algebraically.

1A.9   *A crewman on the starship Enter-prise is on shore leave on a distant planet. He drops a rock from the top of a cliff and observes that it takes 3.00 s to reach the bottom. He now throws another rock vertically upwards so that it reaches a height of 2 m before dropping down the cliff face. The second rock takes 4.12 s to reach the bottom of the cliff. The planet has a very thin atmosphere which offers negligible air resistance. How high is the cliff, and what is the value of g on this planet?*

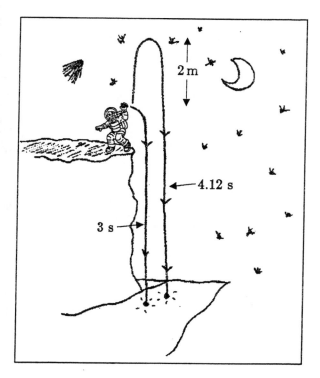

Conceptualize

This problem involves projectile motion in one dimension. We have two unknowns, the height H of the cliff and the acceleration g of the falling stones, so in formulating the problem we need to construct at least two equations.

$\Sigma\!\int$ Formulate

The situation is shown in the diagrams (where the arrows representing the motion of the stones have been shifted sideways slightly for clarity). Taking a coordinate system such that z points vertically upwards and $z = 0$ at the bottom of the cliff, we have the following information:

for stone 1:
    initial velocity $v_i = 0$;
    initial position $z_i = H$ (unknown);
    total time $\quad = t_1$;

for stone 2:
    initial velocity $v_i = v_0$ (unknown);
    initial position $z_i = H$ (unknown);
    total time $\quad = t_2$.

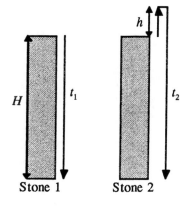

We can construct the equations

$$z_f(1) = 0 = H - \tfrac{1}{2}gt_1^2 \; ;$$
$$z_f(2) = 0 = H + v_0 t_2 - \tfrac{1}{2}gt_2^2 \; .$$

This won't do at all: we have two equations, but three unknowns: H, g and v_0. We need at least one more equation.

Fortunately there is information about stone 2 that we have not used: we know its

31

1A.9, continued:

maximum height h above the cliff ($z = h + H$). At this point $v = 0$ (since immediately beforehand the stone is moving **up**, and immediately after it's going **down**). We can apply $v^2 = v_0^2 + 2a(z - z_0)$ to this point to get

$$0 = v_0^2 - 2gh.$$

This gives us a third equation, so we can now solve for three unknowns. Our new equation gives us v_0 in terms of g, and by eliminating H from the first two equations we can solve for g.

Solve
We first solve the third equation for v_0: $v_0 = \sqrt{2gh}$.

Our first two equations then become

$$H = \frac{1}{2}gt_1^2 \; ;$$

$$H = \frac{1}{2}gt_2^2 - t_2\sqrt{2gh}$$

and we can equate the right-hand sides of these to get

$$\frac{1}{2}g(t_2^2 - t_1^2) = t_2\sqrt{2gh} \; .$$

Squaring this and rearranging gives

$$\frac{1}{4}g^2(t_2^2 - t_1^2)^2 = 2ght_2^2$$

so

$$g = \frac{8ht_2^2}{(t_2^2 - t_1^2)^2} \; .$$

We can substitute this back into our original equation for stone 1 to discover that

$$H = \frac{1}{2}gt_1^2 = \frac{4ht_1^2t_2^2}{(t_2^2 - t_1^2)^2} \; .$$

Numerically, $g = 4.27 \text{ m/s}^2$ and $H = 19.2 \text{ m}$.

Scrutinize
Our final expression for g has dimensions $[\text{length}] \times [\text{time}]^2 / [\text{time}]^4$, which gives $[\text{length}]/[\text{time}]^2$ as we expect for an acceleration. We can cross-check the consistency of our calculations by seeing if the results from **both** our original equations for H agree:

$$H = \frac{1}{2}gt_1^2 = \frac{1}{2}(4.27 \text{ m/s}^2)(3.00 \text{ s})^2 = 19.2 \text{ m};$$

$$H = \frac{1}{2}gt_2^2 - v_0t_2$$

$$= \frac{1}{2}(4.27 \text{ m/s}^2)(4.12 \text{ s})^2 - \left(\sqrt{2 \times 4.27 \text{ m/s}^2 \times 2 \text{ m}}\right)(4.12 \text{ s}) = 19.2 \text{ m}.$$

1A.9, continued:

This sort of check can find errors such as lost numerical factors which will not show up in considering the dimensions of an equation.

Learn

The most important step in this problem is the formulation. We had to develop a strategy for solving the problem which gave us enough equations to account for all our unknowns. The difficulty of this depends very much on the information that you have been given: this problem would be much easier to formulate if we had been given v_0 instead of h (or instead of t_2 or t_1, for that matter).

1C.2   _A cannonball emerges from a cannon with speed v, independent of the angle at which the barrel of the cannon is inclined. If the cannon is set on level ground, at what angle should the gunner set the cannon to maximize the range? What will the range be at this angle (in terms of v and g) and what height will the ball reach? Neglect any effects of air resistance._

Conceptualize

This is a case of projectile motion in two dimensions. The initial velocity of the cannonball is shown in the diagram. Since we are told to neglect air resistance, the cannonball is freely falling and therefore has a constant downward acceleration g. Its vertical velocity, which is initially $v_y(0) = v \sin \theta$, will therefore decrease to zero and become negative (downwards), thus returning the cannonball to Earth. The horizontal distance it has traveled in the interim is its range. Our task is to find the value of θ which maximizes the range. Those of you who are already familiar with calculus will

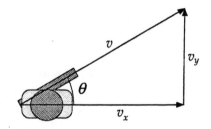

know that one standard method for doing this is to obtain an equation for the range x in terms of the angle θ and then differentiate. Minima and maxima of x correspond to zero values of $dx/d\theta$.

It is not always necessary to use calculus to identify the maximum (for example, the maximum value of $A \cos \theta$ is obviously A), but in any case the path to the solution clearly lies in finding an equation for x in terms of θ.

Formulate

We define a coordinate system with x horizontal along the cannon's direction of fire and y vertical, and the origin $x = y = 0$ at the location of the cannon. (We assume that the height of the cannon's barrel above the ground is negligible compared with the length of the ball's flight, i.e. the ball is launched from, and lands at, $y = 0$.) For uniform acceleration, the general equations for the velocity and position are

$$\vec{v}(t) = \vec{v}_0 + \vec{a}t$$

$$\vec{r}(t) = \vec{r}_0 + \vec{v}_0 t + \frac{1}{2}\vec{a}t^2 \ .$$

1C.2, continued:

In this case $\vec{a} = [0, -g, 0]$, and $\vec{v}_0 = [v\cos\theta, v\sin\theta, 0]$. (If you are having difficulty distinguishing the sine from the cosine, a practical technique is to always draw your angles noticeably smaller than 45°, as was done here. Then the short side of the triangle is always proportional to the sine, and the long side is proportional to the cosine.) Writing the equations in components, one has

$$v_x = v\cos\theta$$

$$v_y = v\sin\theta - gt \ .$$

Similarly the position $\vec{r} = [x, y, z]$ is given in components as

$$x = vt\cos\theta \tag{1}$$

$$y = vt\sin\theta - \frac{1}{2}gt^2 = t\left(v\sin\theta - \frac{1}{2}gt\right) \ . \tag{2}$$

The cannonball is at $y = 0$ at two times: $t = 0$, the launch, and

$$t = \frac{2v}{g}\sin\theta \ , \tag{3}$$

which must be the landing. To solve the problem we will calculate the range using this value for t, and then find the maximum value of the resulting formula for x. The maximum height can be found by finding the time at which $v_y = 0$ for this value of θ, or alternatively we can recognize that the trajectory is symmetrical, and therefore the maximum height is reached halfway between launch and landing. The first method is safer, because it will still work if our cannon is not on level ground.

Solve

Substituting the value for t in Eq. (3) into the expression for x in Eq. (1), the range of the cannon is found to be

$$x = \frac{2v^2 \sin\theta \cos\theta}{g}$$

for any angle θ. We want the angle that gives the largest possible x. To work this out without calculus we use the trigonometric identity

$$\sin 2\theta = 2\sin\theta\cos\theta \ .$$

Using this formula we can rewrite the equation for x as

$$x = \frac{v^2 \sin 2\theta}{g} \ ,$$

from which it is clear that the maximum value occurs when $2\theta = 90°$, i.e. when $\theta = 45°$. The value of x at this maximum is

$$x_{max} = \frac{v^2}{g} \ .$$

1C.2, continued:

The time for which $v_y = 0$ is $t = \dfrac{v}{g}\sin\theta$. This gives

$$y = \frac{v^2}{g}\sin^2\theta - \frac{1}{2}g\frac{v^2\sin^2\theta}{g^2} = \frac{v^2\sin^2\theta}{2g} \;,$$

which for $\theta = 45°$ yields

$$y_{\max} = \frac{v^2}{4g} \;.$$

Scrutinize

The dimensions of v^2/g are $([\text{length}]^2/[\text{time}]^2)/([\text{length}]/[\text{time}]^2)$, i.e. length, which is correct. Note that dimensional analysis cannot give us the factor of 4 in the expression for y, nor can it confirm that our sines and cosines are in the right places.

The calculus approach to finding the maximum would be

$$\frac{\mathrm{d}x}{\mathrm{d}\theta} = \frac{\mathrm{d}}{\mathrm{d}\theta}\left(\frac{2v^2\sin\theta\cos\theta}{g}\right)$$

$$= \frac{2v^2}{g}(\cos^2\theta - \sin^2\theta)$$

$$= 0 \text{ when } \cos\theta = \pm\sin\theta \;.$$

This gives $\theta = 45°$ or $135°$ (the other two quadrants, $-45°$ and $-135°$, are clearly unphysical). The second solution just corresponds to the cannon facing in the opposite direction.

Learn

This solution seems at first to contradict common sense—one might argue that to maximize the horizontal distance we should maximize the horizontal component of velocity, which is clearly not what we have done. The reason for this is that we also have to consider flight time: a ball with zero vertical velocity launched from zero height instantly plows into the ground. Flight time is maximized by maximizing the vertical component of velocity—but a ball launched vertically upwards comes back down on our heads. The trade-off between longer flight times and larger horizontal velocities is what gives us our 45° angle.

Golfers and field sports enthusiasts may feel that this calculation does not accord with their experience of reality. This is quite true: air resistance is rarely negligible in real situations, and other factors such as spin may come into play as well. We will consider some of these complications in later chapters.

1C.4   *In a shooting contest, a clay pigeon is launched from the ground at a speed of 50 m/s at 60° to the horizontal, directed eastwards. The contestant is standing 100 m south of the clay's line of flight and 40 m east of the launch point. His gun has a muzzle velocity of 200 m/s and he hits the clay when it is directly ahead of him as he faces north. When did he fire, and at what elevation? (Neglect air resistance; take $g = 9.8$ m/s² and assume the shot is fired from a height of 1.6 m above ground level.)*

Conceptualize

Here we have two projectile problems combined, making a three-dimensional problem (an individual projectile's motion is two-dimensional). Fortunately we can in fact deal with each projectile separately, making two two-dimensional problems. Our strategy will be:

- First find the time at which the clay pigeon is directly ahead of the contestant, and calculate the clay's height at that time.

- This gives us the position at which the shot hit the clay. We then use this information to determine the flight time and initial direction of the shot.

Formulate

The general equations for uniform acceleration are

$$\vec{v}(t) = \vec{v}_0 + \vec{a}t$$

$$\vec{r}(t) = \vec{r}_0 + \vec{v}_0 t + \frac{1}{2}\vec{a}t^2 \ .$$

For this problem, let us call east the x direction, north y and up z, so $\vec{a} = [0, 0, -g]$, for both the clay and the shot. The velocity vector of the clay is $\vec{v} \equiv [v_x, 0, v_z]$, and that of the shot is $\vec{w} \equiv [0, w_y, w_z]$. If the clay is fired at $t = 0$, the component equations for its velocity and position at time t are

$$v_x = v\cos\theta \qquad v_y = 0 \qquad v_z = v\sin\theta - gt \qquad (1)$$

$$x_c = vt\cos\theta \qquad y_c = 0 \qquad z_c = vt\sin\theta - \frac{1}{2}gt^2 \ , \qquad (2)$$

where we know $v = 50$ m/s and $\theta = 60°$. We are measuring all position vectors relative to the launch point of the clay.

The contestant fired his shot sometime later, at $t = t_0$, at an angle α to the horizontal. Its component equations are:

$$w_x = 0 \qquad w_y = w\cos\alpha \qquad w_z = w\sin\alpha - g(t - t_0) \qquad (3)$$

$$x_s = x_0 \qquad y_s = y_0 + w(t - t_0)\cos\alpha \qquad z_s = z_0 + w(t - t_0)\sin\alpha - \frac{1}{2}g(t - t_0)^2 \ , \quad (4)$$

where $y_0 = -100$ m, $z_0 = 1.6$ m is the height from which the shot was fired, and $x_0 = 40$ m, since we are told that the contestant is 40 m east of the launch point. We also know

36

1C.4, continued:

$w = 200$ m/s. Note that $w_x = 0$, since we are told that the shot hits the clay directly in front of the contestant, and w_x is a sideways component of the shot's velocity.

We know that the shot hits the clay (i.e. they are in the same place at the same time!). With this information we can solve the clay's equations for t and z_c. This gives us z_s for the shot at impact, and we already know $y_s = 0$ since the clay has no y-component of velocity. We then have the information needed to solve the shot's equations for t_0 and α.

Solve

The impact occurs at $x_c = x_s = x_0$, so from the 1st of Eqs. (2) one has

$$t = \frac{x_0}{v \cos \theta} = \frac{40 \text{ m}}{50 \text{ m/s} \times \cos 60°} = 1.6 \text{ s}.$$

Therefore at the point of impact $z_c = z_s = vt \sin \theta - \frac{1}{2} g t^2 = 56.7$ m.

To solve the shot's equations we first note that at impact $y_s = y_c = 0$, so from the 2nd of Eqs. (4) one has

$$t - t_0 = -\frac{y_0}{w \cos \alpha}.$$

We can use this to eliminate $t - t_0$ from the 3rd of Eqs. (4):

$$z_s - z_0 = -y_0 \tan \alpha - \frac{g y_0^2}{2w^2} \sec^2 \alpha$$

$$= -y_0 \tan \alpha - \frac{g y_0^2}{2w^2} (1 + \tan^2 \alpha)$$

using a standard trigonometric identity (which you can easily prove if you remember that $\cos^2 \alpha + \sin^2 \alpha = 1$ for any angle α). This is a quadratic equation for $\tan \alpha$. Its solution is

$$\tan \alpha = \frac{w^2}{g y_0^2} \left[-y_0 \pm \sqrt{y_0^2 - \frac{2g y_0^2}{w^2} \left(\frac{g y_0^2}{2w^2} + z_s - z_0 \right)} \right].$$

Numerically this gives $\tan \alpha = 0.567$ or 81.1, corresponding to $\alpha = 29.6°$ or $89.3°$ respectively. The first of these is clearly the one we want; the second is possible in principle, but not in practice (the flight time would be extremely long, requiring the contestant to shoot well before the clay was launched!).

Finally we use our value of α to find

$$t - t_0 = (100\text{m})/(200\text{m/s} \times \cos 29.6°) = 0.58 \text{ s}.$$

Since $t = 1.6$ s, $t_0 = 1.0$ s to 2 significant figures. The contestant fired 1.0 s after the clay was launched, at 30° to the horizontal.

1C.4, continued:

Scrutinize

The units of gy^2/w^2 are $(m/s^2)(m^2)/(m/s)^2$, i.e. meters, and using this it is straightforward to check that $\tan\alpha$ is dimensionless, as it should be.

Are the values sensible? We can check the solution of the shot's equations by recognizing that the effect of gravity is quite small (if the flight time is 0.6 s, the change in velocity is only about 6 m/s, which is small compared to the initial value of 200 m/s). Setting $g = 0$ in the shot's equations gives $z_s - z_0 = -y_0\tan\alpha$, so $\tan\alpha = 0.551$ and $\alpha = 28.9°$. This is reassuringly close to our exact value, the difference being about 3% (it is *not* a coincidence that this is equal to the percentage change in the velocity, $6/200 = 3\%$).

Learn

"Back-of-the-envelope" approximate calculations like this are very useful, especially if trying to decide whether something is likely to be possible or not (e.g. can a massive black hole supply enough power to account for the observed brightness of quasars?). If the approximate calculation suggests that it is possible, then we can go on to the more difficult exact calculation. If not, we have not expended large amounts of time and effort on a proposal that will not work.

Note that when the contestant fired, the x coordinate of the clay was only $(50 \text{ m/s}) \times (1 \text{ s}) \times (\cos 60°) = 25$ m. To hit the clay, the contestant had to aim *ahead* of the clay's position at the time he fired. Did he in fact aim at the actual point of impact, $[40, 0, 56.7]$ m? If not, why not?

1D.2   *A motorcycle negotiates a 40° right-hand bend at 60 km/h. The bend consists of a 40° arc of a circle of radius 75 m. What is the centripetal acceleration of the bike at any point in the bend, and what is the total velocity change between entering the bend and leaving it?*

Conceptualize

We can treat the motorcycle negotiating the bend as a point mass in circular motion. The velocity change is not zero, because its direction has changed (although its magnitude has not). The acceleration will be directed towards the center of the circle defined by extrapolating the arc of the bend, and its magnitude can be found by using the formula for circular motion.

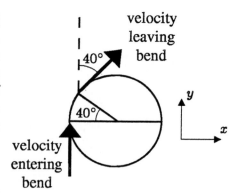

Formulate

The acceleration of a particle traveling with speed v in a circle of radius r has magnitude v^2/r and is directed towards the center of the circle.

If we take the initial direction of the motorcycle to be the y-direction, its velocity entering the bend is $\vec{v}_i = [0, v, 0]$, where $v = 60$ km/h, and its velocity leaving the bend is $\vec{v}_f = [v\sin\theta, v\cos\theta, 0]$, where $\theta = 40°$ (as can be seen from the diagram with the aid of a little geometry).

1D.2, continued:

 Solve

To get the acceleration in sensible units we need to convert 60 km/h into m/s: 60 km/h = (60,000 m/h)/(3,600 s/h) = 16.67 m/s. The magnitude of the acceleration is $v^2/r = (16.67 \text{ m/s})^2/(75 \text{ m}) = 3.7 \text{ m/s}^2$; as we have said, it is directed towards the center of curvature of the bend.

The change in velocity is

$$\Delta \vec{\mathbf{v}} = \vec{\mathbf{v}}_f - \vec{\mathbf{v}}_i = [v \sin \theta, v(\cos \theta - 1), 0] = [39, -14, 0] \text{ km/h}.$$

Its magnitude is 41 km/h. If we write its vector in the form

$$[w \cos \alpha, w \sin \alpha, 0] ,$$

where $w = 41$ km/h, we have $\cos \alpha = 0.940$ and $\sin \alpha = -0.342$, giving $\alpha = -20°$.

 Scrutinize

We can make a geometrical check on the direction of our velocity change vector by redrawing the "before" and "after" velocities with their tails touching, as shown. The two vectors form an isosceles triangle with apex angle 40°, so each of the other two angles is 70° and $|\alpha| = 20°$.

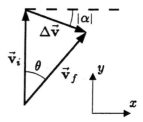

 Learn

Notice that the centripetal acceleration required to negotiate the bend increases rapidly with the speed of the vehicle. This is why it is necessary to slow down when taking a sharp curve. We will see in the next chapter how banking the curve can make it easier to negotiate (without changing the acceleration required).

1E.1 (a) *A ferryboat crosses a river of width d. The speed of the boat (relative to the water) is v and the speed of the river current is V. Assuming that the landing point of the ferry is directly opposite its starting point, how long does it take for a round trip?*

 Conceptualize

There are two reference frames important to this problem, the *bank* frame which is stationary relative to an observer on the river bank, and the *river* frame which is stationary relative to an observer drifting with the current. The ferry's speed v is specified in the river frame, which has speed V downstream relative to the bank frame.

1E.1, continued:

Formulate

We will define a coordinate system in which the x-axis points downstream for both frames. If the ferry is moving at an angle θ to the downstream direction, its velocity in component form, in the river frame of reference, is

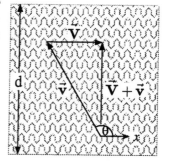

$$\vec{\mathbf{v}} = [v \cos \theta, v \sin \theta, 0] . \qquad (1)$$

In the bank frame we must add on the velocity $\vec{\mathbf{V}} = [V, 0, 0]$ of the current: thus in this frame the boat's velocity is

$$\vec{\mathbf{v}}' = [V + v \cos \theta, v \sin \theta, 0] . \qquad (2)$$

To solve the problem we note that the ferry's starting and finishing points are specified in the bank frame. We must use the second form of the ferry's velocity vector. The only unknown is θ.

Solve

Relative to its starting point, the ferry's position vector in the bank frame is just t times its velocity vector, assuming constant velocity. We want to reach a point on the bank opposite the starting point, i.e. with $x = 0$, so we must have

$$V + v \cos \theta = 0 ,$$

$$\text{i.e. } \cos \theta = -\frac{V}{v} .$$

An observer on the bank will then see the ferry traveling straight across the river with speed $v \sin \theta = v\sqrt{1 - \frac{V^2}{v^2}} = \sqrt{v^2 - V^2}$. A one-way trip will thus take a time $t = d/\sqrt{v^2 - V^2}$, where d is the width of the river, and the round trip will be twice this.

Scrutinize and Learn

The ratio $-V/v$ is dimensionless, as it should be, and the negative sign implies that $\theta > 90°$— the ferryman has to steer upstream, against the current. This is clearly correct.

Notice that for $v < V$ the equation for t involves the square root of a negative number. This is not a problem: if you think about the situation, you will see that in this case the boat cannot possibly make a landing directly opposite its starting point, because even if the ferryman steers directly upstream he is still being washed downstream at a speed $V - v$. In many cases physically impossible situations are signaled in the mathematical representation of the problem by mathematically illegal operations such as this. Another example might be a value of cosine or sine outside the range -1 to 1, and indeed in this example $v < V$ implies that $\cos \theta < -1$.

(b) *In the Ferryman of the Year competition the ferryman is required to complete a course of the same distance 2d by rowing a distance d directly upstream and then back downstream*

1E.1, continued:

to his starting point. (The distance is defined by posts on the river bank.) How long does it take him to complete the course, and is this longer or shorter than the round trip across the river?

Conceptualize
The situation is much the same as before, with the distance again being defined in the bank frame, and the same techniques can be used to solve this problem.

Formulate
The boat's velocity vectors in the two frames are still given by equations (1) and (2), with $\theta = 180°$ for the upstream leg of the course and $0°$ for the downstream leg. The velocity of the boat relative to the bank is therefore $[V - v, 0, 0]$ for the first leg (displacement $[-d, 0, 0]$) and $[V + v, 0, 0]$ for the second leg (displacement $[+d, 0, 0]$).

Solve
The total time for the course is

$$t = \frac{-d}{V - v} + \frac{d}{V + v} = \frac{2dv}{v^2 - V^2} \ .$$

The difference between this time and the return journey across the river is

$$\frac{2dv}{v^2 - V^2} - \frac{2d}{\sqrt{v^2 - V^2}} = \frac{2dv}{v^2 - V^2}\left(1 - \sqrt{1 - \frac{V^2}{v^2}}\right) \ .$$

This is always positive for $v > V$, so the up- and downstream course takes longer than rowing across the current.

Scrutinize
A good check of this answer is to consider the case where $V = 0$ (a lake rather than a river). River frame and bank frame are then identical, and so are the two round trips. The journey time is the distance divided by the speed, $2d/v$. It is easy to see that both our expressions for t do indeed reduce to this when $V = 0$, and the time difference becomes 0.

(c) *An invading army is approaching the river. The ferryman is anxious to get across to the other side as quickly as possible, without caring where he lands. How long does it take him, and where does he land?*

Conceptualize
The ferryman wants to minimize the journey time across the river. The distance across the river is d in the y-direction, so to minimize the journey time he should steer so as to maximize the y-component of his velocity.

Formulate and Solve
Equations (1) and (2) still apply, so to maximize the y-component he needs $\sin \theta = 1$, regardless of whether we work in the bank frame or the river frame. His velocity is $[0, v, 0]$ *in the river frame of reference*, and he reaches the other side in a time $t = d/v$.

41

1E.1, continued:

In the bank frame his velocity is $[V, v, 0]$, so he lands a distance Vd/v downstream of his starting point.

Scrutinize

The total distance covered in the bank frame of reference is

$$d\sqrt{1 + \frac{V^2}{v^2}} \ .$$

This is slightly surprising at first sight—surely the minimum journey time should correspond to the minimum distance traveled? However, the answer seems sensible if we remember that the maximum speed is specified in the *river* frame, not the bank frame. The distance traveled in the river frame is indeed d, the minimum required to cross the river.

Note that in this case the expression under the square root is never negative. As long as we don't care how far downstream we end up, it is always possible to get across the river.

Learn

It is never **necessary** to change reference frames to solve a problem. In some cases, however, it is certainly easier to visualize the situation by choosing a particular reference frame, and sometimes it can greatly simplify the mathematics.

The actual physical phenomena we are describing are of course independent of the choice of reference frame—the results of an experiment are unaffected by the motion of the observer. However, as we see in the next chapter, one must be careful if one frame of reference is accelerating relative to another frame.

1E.2   *The pilot of a light plane wishes to fly from Bristol to Edinburgh (625 km due north). Her cruising speed, measured relative to the air, is 150 km/h. There is a 20 km/h west wind blowing (where "west wind" refers to a wind blowing from the west).*

   (a)   *In what direction should she point her plane, and how long will her journey take? (Ignore the time spent in take-off and landing and assume that she flies at a constant altitude.)*

Conceptualize

The subtlety of this problem is that the speed of the plane is specified *relative to the air around it* (air speed). The velocity of the plane relative to the air will be called its air velocity. The velocity of the plane relative to the *ground* (ground velocity) is made up of the vector sum of the plane's air velocity and the wind velocity. We want this resultant ground velocity to point due north. We can therefore draw a vector diagram of the velocity as shown below. To solve the problem we simply choose a suitable coordinate system and construct this vector sum.

1E.2, continued:

$\Sigma\int$

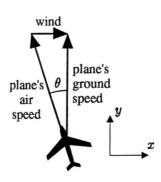

Formulate

We choose a coordinate system in which x points east and y points north. If we call the plane's air velocity $\vec{v}$, the wind velocity $\vec{w}$, and the plane's ground velocity $\vec{V}$, then the velocity relation can be written

$$\vec{V} = \vec{v} + \vec{w} .$$

In component form this becomes

$$[V_x, V_y, 0] = [v_x, v_y, 0] + [w_x, 0, 0] .$$

We know the wind velocity ($w_x = 20$ km/h), the magnitude of the plane's air velocity ($v = \sqrt{v_x^2 + v_y^2} = 150$ km/h), and the fact that we want $V_x = 0$. Hence we have two unknowns, V_y and the angle θ between the plane's air velocity and north. Since each component of a vector equation is an equation in its own right, we have two equations (the z component gives $0 + 0 = 0$, which doesn't count!). Writing $v_x = -v\sin\theta$ and $v_y = v\cos\theta$, we have two equations in two unknowns, and can solve for θ and V. The time required for the journey is simply the distance divided by the speed, as usual.

Solve

Our two equations are

$$0 = -v\sin\theta + w_x , \tag{1}$$

$$V_y = v\cos\theta . \tag{2}$$

Eq. (1) gives

$$\sin\theta = w_x/v = 0.133 ,$$

from which $\theta = 7.7°$, and substituting this into Eq. (2) yields

$$V_y = (150 \text{ km/h})\cos 7.7° = 149 \text{ km/h}.$$

The journey will take $(625 \text{ km})/(149 \text{ km/h}) = 4.2$ h, or 4 h 12 min.

Scrutinize

From the diagram, we can see that the vectors form a right-angled triangle with the plane's airspeed as hypotenuse. So we can check our result with the Pythagorean theorem: the ground speed of the plane is $\sqrt{150^2 - 20^2} = 149$ km/h, in agreement with the component method.

(b) *When she starts her return trip the wind has shifted to southwest and increased to* 50 *km/h. What heading should she take, and how long is the return journey?*

Conceptualize

The setup is the same as in part (a), and we solve it in the same way. The only difference is that our two equations will be slightly more complicated, because the wind's vector now has two nonzero components.

43

1E.2, continued:

Formulate

The wind vector is now $\vec{\mathbf{w}} = [w\cos\alpha, w\sin\alpha, 0]$, where $w = 50$ km/h and $\alpha = 45°$ as shown in the diagram, and the plane's air velocity is $\vec{\mathbf{v}} = [-v\sin\theta, -v\cos\theta, 0]$, where $v = 150$ km/h and θ is defined in the diagram. Since we want to fly south, $V_x = 0$, and we can define $V \equiv -V_y$, with $V > 0$. The unknowns are V and θ.

The velocity relation $\vec{\mathbf{V}} = \vec{\mathbf{v}} + \vec{\mathbf{w}}$ can be written in components as

$$0 = -v\sin\theta + w\cos\alpha \, ,$$

$$-V = -v\cos\theta + w\sin\alpha \, .$$

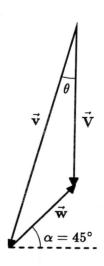

Solve

The first equation gives

$$\sin\theta = \frac{w}{v}\cos\alpha = 0.236 \, ,$$

which yields $\theta = 13.6°$, and hence

$$-V = -v\cos\theta + w\sin\alpha = -110 \text{ km/h} \, .$$

The plane's air velocity must be directed 13.6° west of south, and its ground speed is 110 km/h. The journey will take $(625 \text{ km})/(110 \text{ km/h}) = 5.7$ h, or 5 h 40 min.

Scrutinize

The ground speed is less on the return journey, because the plane is now flying into a headwind. Our sketch of the vector diagram is too rough to provide an exact check, but certainly indicates that our answers are in the right ballpark. Note that angles are dimensionless, as are trigonometric functions: all our equations for sines or cosines are in terms of the ratio of two speeds.

Learn

It would also be possible to check this result geometrically, as we did in part (a), but as the triangle is not right-angled we would have to use more complicated trigonometry, such as the cosine rule. Such a "check" would not be very useful, as the chances of making an error in the trigonometry are probably higher than in the original calculation! The power of the component approach is that it avoids the need for such tedious geometrical exercises and lets us set up the problem in a standard way (in contrast, for the geometric methods each vector addition is a different triangle). However, it is always worth drawing the vector triangle, roughly to scale and with vectors pointing in about the right directions, to provide a visual check on the results.

HINTS FOR PROBLEMS WITH AN (H)
The number of the hint refers to the number of the problem

1A.5 To do this without calculus, sketch the graph of v against t. Convince yourself that the distance traveled between times 0 and t is the area under this graph. What rectangular area (i.e. what constant velocity) would give the same value for the distance traveled?

1A.8 (a) How long does it take the bus to decelerate to zero velocity?

(b) What is the total time taken to negotiate a bus stop, from the start of deceleration to the end of acceleration? (Remember to include the time the bus is stationary!) What distance is covered during this time?

You may also find it helpful to review the solution to 1A.7.

1B.2 (a) If you are confused, it will help to start with a scale drawing. Put in what you already know and add additional information as you go along.

(b) What is the position vector of Carol relative to Albert?

(c) What is the position vector of Betty relative to Dave? What is its magnitude?

What is the *direction* of Ernie's velocity vector? What is its *magnitude*?

1C.3 Think of the horizontal and vertical motions separately. What is the acceleration in each direction? What is the vertical velocity at maximum height? How long does it take the ball to reach maximum height?

1E.3 (a) Draw the velocity vectors of the two airplanes in two reference frames: (i) the frame in which the air is stationary; (ii) the frame in which your plane is stationary.

(b) Which frame is best suited to this problem?

ANSWERS TO HINTS

1A.5 To get the same area for a constant speed, we need a speed of $v_0 + \frac{1}{2}at$.

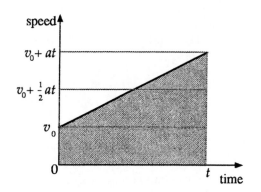

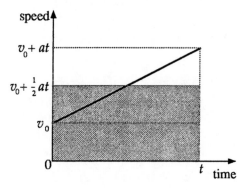

1A.8 (a) 11.1 s.

  (b) 48.5 s; 103 m.

1B.2 (b) $[20, 10, 0]$ m.

  (c) $[-10, 8, 0]$ m; 12.8 m.

  Same direction as $[-10, 8, 0]$;

  3 m/s.

1C.3 0 in horizontal direction, $-g$ vertically; zero; $\frac{v_0}{g}\sin\theta$ (initial vertical velocity is $v_0\sin\theta$).

1E.3 (a)

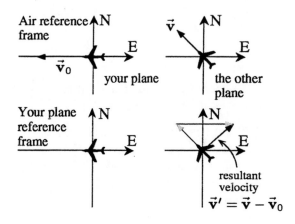

  (b) The second frame.

ANSWERS TO ALL PROBLEMS

1A.1 b.

1A.2 d.

1A.3 (a) 5 s; 6.25 s.

(b)

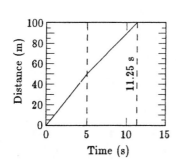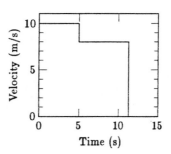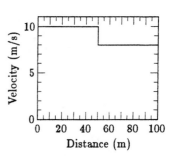

(c) 8.89 m/s; 9.00 m/s.

1A.4 15 min.; 6 min. 40 sec; 1 hour; 1 hour 10 min.

1A.5 Calculus:

As $a = \dfrac{dv}{dt}$, $v(t) = v_0 + \displaystyle\int_0^t a\,dt'$, so $v(t) = v_0 + at$, where v_0 is the velocity at time $t = 0$. Similarly,

$$ v = \frac{dx}{dt} \implies x(t) = x_0 + \int_0^t \left(v_0 + at'\right) dt', \qquad \text{so } x(t) = x_0 + v_0 t + \tfrac{1}{2}at^2, $$

where x_0 is the position at $t = 0$.

(Non-calculus: see hints.)

For the second equation, use the expression for the velocity to solve for t:

$$ t = \frac{(v - v_0)}{a} \, . $$

Then substitute this into the equation for x.

1A.6 (a) Acceleration is positive from 0 to 2 s and from 6 to 7 s, negative from 3 to 4 s, and zero from 2 to 3 s and from 4 to 6 s.

(b) After 3.5 s $x = 6.5$ m; after 7 s $x = 4$ m (taking $x = 0$ at $t = 0$).

(c) The particle starts from rest and accelerates uniformly for 1 s, reaching a speed of 1 m/s. It then accelerates at a higher rate for 1 s, reaching a speed of 3 m/s which it maintains for a further 1 s. It then decelerates rapidly, coming to a halt 3.75 s after $t = 0$ and reversing direction, so that 4 s after $t = 0$ it is moving back towards its starting point at 1 m/s. It maintains this velocity for a further 2 s before decelerating uniformly to come to rest 7 s after $t = 0$.

47

1A.7 See complete solution.

1A.8 (a) 62 m.

(b) 170 s; 5.9 m/s.

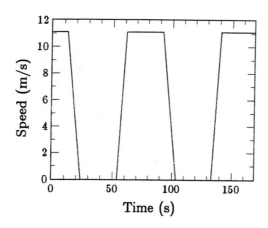

(c) Twice each.

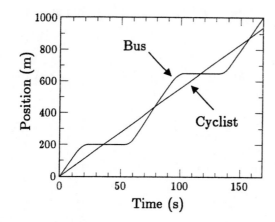

1A.9 See complete solution.

1B.1 c; c.

1B.2 (a) Betty: [20, 17, 0] m; Carol: [30,17, 0] m; Dave: [30, 9, 0] m.

(b) 22 m.

(c) [−2.3, 1.9, 0] m/s; 4.3 s; [21, 16, 0] m, to 2 significant figures. (The y-component of Ernie's position vector is almost exactly 16.5 m: depending on how and when you round off, you may get 17 m instead of 16.)

(d)

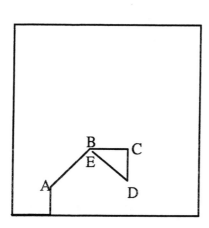

1C.1 d; a.

1C.2 See complete solution.

1C.3 (a) 4.2 m; 2.9 m.

   (b) 10 m; 26.6° or 63.4°. See graph on right.
   Yes.

1C.4 See complete solution.

1D.1 a.

1D.2 See complete solution.

1D.3 0.22 m/s^2; 0.034 m/s^2.

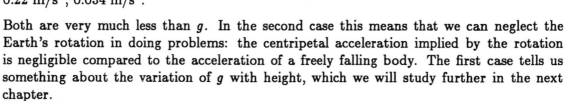

Both are very much less than g. In the second case this means that we can neglect the Earth's rotation in doing problems: the centripetal acceleration implied by the rotation is negligible compared to the acceleration of a freely falling body. The first case tells us something about the variation of g with height, which we will study further in the next chapter.

1E.1 See complete solution.

1E.2 See complete solution.

1E.3 106 m/s, at 138° clockwise to the direction of your plane (i.e. 138° northwards from west).

The airplane is apparently moving sideways to its right (see diagram).

49

SUPPLEMENTARY NOTES

PHYSICS AS AN EXPERIMENTAL SCIENCE

What is physics, and why are we studying it?

Physics is our attempt to *understand* and *predict* natural phenomena. Studying physics is valuable both philosophically—most of the world's civilizations have a long history of seeking to understand the world around us—and practically, in dealing with such everyday questions as the design of bridges, energy generation and conservation, atmospheric circulation, etc.

Natural phenomena appear complex and infinitely varied. If I drop a glass on the floor, many things happen: there is a loud noise, the glass breaks into several pieces, the floor covering may be marked or damaged. Empirically we know that some things about this incident can be predicted— the glass *will* fall when I let go of it, and it *will* (under normal circumstances) break when it hits the ground. Other aspects appear to be unpredictable, at least with the information we have—I don't know how many pieces the glass will break into or where the fracture lines will be. Our predictions in this are based on our past experience with similar objects: if I came from a culture which used only wooden or basketwork utensils, I would not expect the glass to break.

The scientific study of natural phenomena is based on this empirical approach.

- We make *observations* (if I let go of a glass, it falls to the floor and breaks).

- If possible, we make *controlled observations* or *experiments* (I take several glasses, as near to identical as I can find, and drop them from different heights, or onto different types of floor covering).

In an ideal controlled experiment, we make all the conditions of the experiment identical except one: for example, we take identical glasses and drop them onto identical floor coverings, but change the height from which they are dropped. If we in fact want to study the effect of varying several of the experimental conditions (for example height, nature of floor covering, and type of glass), this means that we have to repeat the experiment a large number of times, which is tedious and time-consuming. Nevertheless it is still the best method (why?).

- From these observations, we try to define basic features of the phenomenon which can be represented by mathematical symbols (the height at which I hold the glass, for example). Relations between these basic *variables* derived from our experimental results can then be expressed as mathematical equations (I would find that the speed at which the glass is moving when it hits the floor is determined by the height from which I dropped it, and I could deduce an equation relating these two variables).

- The equations we deduce can be used to *predict* what will happen in a new series of experiments (if I have measured the velocity of the glass for heights between one meter and two meters from the floor, I can predict what it will be if I drop the glass from a height of three meters, and then test this prediction by actually doing so).

50

In some sciences, particularly astronomy (but also, for example, palaeontology and geology), it is not possible to do controlled experiments in this way, because the necessary conditions cannot be duplicated in the lab or because the scale of the phenomena (in space or in time) is too large. In such cases one must use the theory to predict the results of observations yet to be made. For example, if we have a theory that birds are descended from dinosaurs, we may predict that well-preserved fossils of small dinosaurs will have feathers, or structures clearly ancestral to feathers. This is less satisfactory, because the crucial observations may be very difficult to make (fossils well enough preserved to show feathers are extremely rare), but the principle is the same.

- If the prediction succeeds, we can try other tests (does our prediction of the velocity of the falling glass work for heights of 300, rather than 3, meters? Does it depend on the type of glass?). If it fails, we must return to the original experimental measurements, with the new information gained from our second set, and make another attempt to deduce the correct relation between our variables.

This is the *scientific method*. Its most fundamental feature is that *it works*—it is indeed possible to deduce mathematical relations between observed quantities which allow us to predict the behavior of these quantities in different conditions. We can use our understanding of gravity as derived from observations of the planets and experiments on Earth to direct the Voyager spacecraft on their grand tour of the outer planets, and we can be confident that this will work even though no planet has an orbit remotely similar to the trajectory we want for our probe. This is a remarkable finding; it is not at all obvious philosophically that the universe is required to behave in this predictable manner.

Another important feature of the scientific method is that its findings are intimately related to the results of observation and experiment. A scientific theory must always be abandoned or modified if its predictions turn out to be in disagreement with a secure experimental result, no matter how many previous predictions have been successful. Newton's theory of gravity was extremely successful for some 250 years, but it was nonetheless necessary to replace it with General Relativity when it failed to predict the results of observations on the orbit of Mercury and the bending of starlight in the gravitational field of the Sun. New experimental results may force us to abandon a theory completely (the Ptolemaic system in which the Sun and the other planets revolve around the Earth is simply wrong) or just to modify it (the laws of gravity as derived from General Relativity are indistinguishable from those of Newton except under very extreme conditions—Newton's laws were used to guide the Voyager spacecraft and we will use them in this book).

ABSOLUTE TIME AND EUCLIDEAN SPACE

To describe the results of our observations of natural phenomena we need some quantitative concepts. The most basic of these is some way of identifying the particular event we have observed. The only unambiguous way of doing this is to state *where* and *when* it happened, i.e. its position in space and time, as accurately as possible. (Limitations on accuracy may be imposed by the precision of our measuring equipment or by the quantum mechanical properties of the phenomenon we are observing.)

Everyday observation indicates that *the flow of time is absolute*, that is, it does not depend on the location or motion of the observer. If I leave my home at 6 a.m., drive to the airport, fly to another city and return home to meet a friend at 9 p.m., we will arrive at the rendezvous together, provided that both our wristwatches keep accurate time. My measurement of the difference between 6 a.m. and 9 p.m. has not been affected by the traveling I have done in the interim.

This property of time is fundamental to the way we measure and predict the motion of objects, but it is *only approximately true*. If I were carrying a state-of-the-art atomic clock capable of measuring with a precision of 10^{-12} s, I would in fact observe that my clock ran more slowly while I was on board the airplane. However, the difference is so tiny that when we are dealing with normal, everyday situations it is impossible to detect. The results that we get by assuming that time is absolute are thus approximate, but practically speaking indistinguishable from what we would have obtained using more sophisticated theories.

Measurement of *position* requires us to state the location of the object relative to some agreed reference point. To specify the position unambiguously we need three numbers, or *coordinates* (this is what we mean by saying that space is three-dimensional). For example, to get from the bus stop to my apartment I might need to walk 100 meters north, turn left at an intersection and walk 50 meters west, then climb two floors (about six meters). The position of my apartment relative to the bus stop could be expressed in these coordinates as [100, 50, 6] m. This could be specified in different ways—if a spy standing at the bus stop were trying to bug my apartment he would probably think in terms of polar coordinates: a range of 112 meters, bearing 26.5 degrees west of north, elevation 3 degrees—but we always need three coordinates.

In calculating the distance between the bus stop and my apartment I used the Pythagorean theorem: the length of the hypotenuse h of a right-angled triangle of sides x and y is given by $h^2 = x^2 + y^2$. If this is true space is said to be *Euclidean*, i.e. its geometry is that described in the treatises by the famous Ancient Greek mathematician Euclid. If we are considering distances on the Earth's surface the Pythagorean theorem is *not* true for large distances, and large triangles do not have angles that sum to 180° (for example, consider the triangle joining the North Pole, the point on the equator with longitude 0°, and the point on the equator with longitude 90°E. *Each* of the angles of this triangle is a right angle!). This is because the Earth is (approximately) spherical, not flat. For short distances this effect is negligibly small, but for large distances it is very important. Let's look at how this affects an attempt to describe distances on the Earth's surface in terms of vectors. Consider moving from Boston (longitude 71°W, latitude 42°N) to London (longitude 0°, latitude 51°N). If we first travel east to longitude 0°, latitude 42°N, we have gone a distance $(r \cos \theta)\phi$, where r is the radius of the Earth (6400 km), θ is the latitude, and ϕ is the difference in longitudes expressed in radians. This comes to 5900 km.

To reach London we must now travel north a distance $r\Delta\theta$ km, where $\Delta\theta$ is the difference in latitudes expressed in radians. This comes to 1000 km. In Euclidean space we would therefore argue that the (two-dimensional) position vector of London relative to Boston is [5900, 1000] km, and the distance from London to Boston should be the magnitude of this vector, or 6000 km.

Now let's do it by first moving to the point with longitude 71°W and latitude 51°N. This is a distance of 1000 km, as before. However, to get to London we now need to travel east only 5000 km, giving a 'vector' of [5000, 1000] km and a 'distance' of 5100 km. *It matters which way round we do things.* This is completely unlike genuine vector algebra and shows we are not dealing with a flat two-dimensional surface. It is also the reason that flat maps of large portions of the Earth's surface are distorted: it is impossible to represent this non-Euclidean two-dimensional space on the

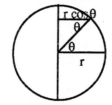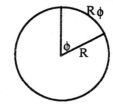

Euclidean two-dimensional space of a flat map without distorting the relationships between points.

Try this calculation for longitude and latitude differences of 10°, 1°, 0.1°. What happens to the discrepancy as you go to smaller angles? Can you explain why? [Notice that the non-Euclidean properties of distances on the Earth occur because we confine ourselves to moving on the Earth's surface. If we traveled from Boston to London through the Earth's interior rather than staying on the surface, we would have no problems, as the three-dimensional space in the vicinity of the Earth is very accurately Euclidean.]

If we leave the Earth's surface and consider interplanetary or interstellar space, is it Euclidean? For the purposes of this book, *yes*, space is Euclidean. The distance between the Earth and Voyager 2, which recently left the solar system, can be calculated in the same way as the distance between the bus stop and my apartment, if we know the relevant coordinates.* However, as in the case of time, the Newtonian description is not the complete truth, but a very good approximation which breaks down when we consider extreme conditions. Our best theory of gravity, General Relativity, holds that gravitational effects are due to local distortions of space and time caused by the mass of the gravitating bodies. In the Solar System, therefore, space is not *perfectly* Euclidean, because it is distorted by the masses of the Sun and planets. The difference between this picture and the Newtonian theory of gravity which we will study in this book is detectable only very close to a very massive object, and only by making very precise measurements. In the solar system, the orbit of Mercury, the innermost planet, is perturbed by 43 seconds of arc per century, and light rays passing very close to the Sun are bent by 1.75 seconds of arc. These were two early tests of General Relativity (the latter requires a total solar eclipse [at least if we use visible light], so that we can *see* stars so close to the Sun). Although the effects of general relativity are small, they are nonetheless needed for very high precision projects. The clocks used in the satellites of the Global Positioning System have to be corrected to account for relativistic effects. Relativistic time dilation associated with by the motion of the satellites causes the clocks to run slowly by 7.11 microseconds per day, but gravitational effects cause then to run faster by 45.7 microseconds per day, leading to a net error of 38.59 microseconds per day.

If we ignore these local distortions caused by concentrations of mass, could space 'as a whole' be Euclidean? This turns out to be related to a deep question in modern cosmology, which is not yet definitively resolved. Nonetheless, very significant progress has been made in just the past few years, and it now appears that the space of the universe is extraordinarily close to being Euclidean.

Cosmologists usually assume that if the local distortions are ignored, the universe can be described as being *homogeneous* (i.e., it looks the same at all locations) and *isotropic* (i.e., it looks the same in all directions). Given these assumptions, the geometry of the universe is described by one number: its curvature. If the curvature is positive, then the universe is called *closed*. In this case the space wraps back on itself in a manner very similar to the surface of a sphere. A closed universe has a finite volume, but no boundaries—if a spaceship traveled very far in what appears to be a straight line, it would eventually return to its starting point. In a closed universe, the sum of the angles in a triangle is more than 180°, and the ratio of the circumference of a circle to its diameter is less than π. If the curvature is negative then the universe is called *open*. In such a universe the sum of the angles in a triangle is less than 180°, and the ratio of the circumference

---

* In the summer of 2002, Voyager 2 is still returning data, 25 years after its launch! See http://web.mit.edu/space/www/voyager/voyager.html.

of a circle to its diameter is more than π. The ideal mathematical version of an open universe is infinitely large, but we can only speculate about the nature of the real universe at distances larger than what we can observe. The third possibility is that the curvature is zero, in which case the axioms of Euclidean geometry are valid and the universe would therefore be called *flat*. An ideal Euclidean space is also infinitely large.

According to general relativity, the geometry of the universe is determined by the relation between its (average) mass density and its expansion rate. The expansion of the universe is described by *Hubble's law*, discovered in 1929 by Edwin Hubble, which states that, on average, any two galaxies separated by distance r are moving apart from each other with a relative speed $v = Hr$, where H is called the *Hubble constant* (or sometimes the Hubble parameter, in recognition of the fact that it changes with time over the life of the universe). The present value of the Hubble constant is not known precisely, but was measured in 2001 by the Hubble Space Telescope Key Project to be 72 ± 8 km·sec^{-1}·Mpc^{-1}, where 1 Mpc $= 3.26 \times 10^6$ light-year $= 3.09 \times 10^{22}$ m. The mass density that gives a precisely flat universe is called the *critical density*, and is given by

$$\rho_c = \frac{3H^2}{8\pi G} ,$$

where G is Newton's gravitational constant (see Chapter 2). Using the Hubble Key Project value for H, the critical density is given by $\rho_c = (9.7 \pm 2.2) \times 10^{-30}$ g/cm$^3 \approx 10^{-29}$ g/cm^3. Note that this is a phenomenally small density, far lower than the density of the best vacuum that can be produced with current technology on Earth. Using ρ to denote the actual average mass density of the universe, cosmologists use the symbol Ω (upper-case Greek Omega) to denote the ratio ρ/ρ_c.

The simplest versions of inflationary theories of cosmology predict that $\Omega = 1$, so the curvature should be zero and the universe should be flat. Until 1998 most of the evidence pointed to $\Omega \approx 0.3$. *Baryonic matter*, matter made of protons, neutrons, and electrons like the atoms of which we are composed, is known to make up only about 5% of the critical density. The rest of the 0.3 is attributed to *dark matter*, matter which is not seen, but which is believed to exist because we see its gravitational effect on visible matter. The composition of the dark matter remains a mystery, but it is believed to be composed of something different from protons, neutrons, or electrons. Starting in 1998, however, astronomers have been accumulating evidence for yet another contribution to the cosmic inventory, now often called the *dark energy*. The evidence for dark energy began with the observation that the expansion of the universe is apparently not being slowed by the force of gravity, but instead the relative velocity between galaxies has been speeding up over the last 5 billion years or so. If this observation is correct, it means that the universe is being influenced by an exotic form of gravity, which acts repulsively instead of attractively. Such a gravitational repulsion is consistent with general relativity, but only if the universe is permeated with a peculiar kind of material that would need to have a negative pressure. General relativity allows us to calculate what the mass density of this material would have to be in order to cause the observed acceleration, and it turns out to be just the right value to contribute 0.7 to Ω, bringing it up to one.

In addition, astronomers studying the cosmic microwave background radiation have also uncovered strong evidence for $\Omega = 1$. This radiation is interpreted as the afterglow of the heat of the big bang, and is found to have the same intensity in all directions (after correcting for the motion of the Earth) to an accuracy of one part in 100,000. Nonetheless, there are subtle ripples in the intensity of the radiation at the level of one part in 100,000, and these ripples can now be measured so accurately that their study has essentially become a new subfield of astronomy. The ripples reflect the oscillations of gases in the early universe, and their motions are believed to be so well understood that the observation of these ripples can be used to measure Ω (and a number of other cosmological parameters as well). For example, a 2002 study by the Cosmic Background Imager team combined the measurements of the cosmic background radiation with measurements of H and some information about large scale structure, concluding that $\Omega = 1.03 \pm 0.04$. When they included the data about the cosmic acceleration as well, they found $\Omega = 1.00 \pm 0.03$.

How Euclidean, then, is the geometry of the universe? Suppose we assume, as the data suggests, that Ω is equal to one to within 5%. In that case, for a circle the size of the solar system, the cosmological curvature causes the circumference to differ from π times the diameter by only about 1 part in 10^{29}, approximately the diameter of a single proton! (If the Sun were at the center of the circle, its gravitational field would cause a much larger difference, but still only about 2 parts per billion.) The possible deviations from Euclidean geometry become more significant at larger distances, but they are still very small. For a circle of radius 10 billion light-years, roughly the size of the visible universe, Euclid's relation between the circumference and diameter would still be accurate to one half of one percent.

ESSENTIALS OF INTRODUCTORY CLASSICAL MECHANICS

CHAPTER 2

MASS, FORCE, AND NEWTON'S LAWS

OVERVIEW

In this chapter we introduce the new basic concepts of *mass* and *force*. If we consider an accelerating particle, the force on it is the external influence which is causing it to accelerate, and its mass determines the magnitude of the acceleration produced by a given force. A body which is not being acted on by any net external force has zero acceleration (but *not* necessarily zero velocity). The mathematical relationship between mass, force, and acceleration, $\vec{F} = m\vec{a}$, is Newton's second law. Although experimentally measured forces may be produced in many ways leading to widely varying apparent properties, there appear to be only four basically different *fundamental forces* in nature, and even these are very likely related to each other.

As Newton's laws depend upon our assumptions that space is Euclidean and time is absolute, they cease to be good descriptions of nature when these approximations are no longer valid, i.e. when we are considering relative motions close to the speed of light. We will assume for the rest of this book that we are dealing with objects moving at speeds much less than the speed of light, which is, of course, the case for almost all practical applications. We also assume that the systems are large enough so that we do not have to invoke the principles of quantum mechanics.

When you have completed this chapter you should:

> ✔ recognize the principle of inertia: a particle undisturbed by external influences will either be at rest or will maintain a constant velocity;
>
> ✔ understand the experimental definition of mass;
>
> ✔ be able to distinguish between mass and weight;
>
> ✔ understand the experimental definition of force, including the fact that force is a vector quantity;
>
> ✔ know the mathematical relationship between force, mass and acceleration, Newton's second law, and be able to use it to solve problems;
>
> ✔ understand the concept of inertial reference frames;
>
> ✔ qualitatively understand the relationship between the forces measured in the laboratory and the four underlying fundamental forces of nature.

ESSENTIALS

Observation shows that a body set in motion with a constant velocity will slow down and stop if left alone. However, it is clear from experiment that this is the result of an interaction between the body and its environment (e.g. friction with the ground, air resistance). In the absence of such effects, the body would continue to move: for example, the orbital speed of a satellite does not decrease appreciably with time if it is high enough so that atmospheric drag can be ignored. We conclude that

a body left undisturbed maintains a constant velocity.   Problem 2A.1

This is *Newton's first law*, also called the *law of inertia*. (Note that the constant velocity could be zero.)

Acceleration is produced when the body is subjected to an exter-   Problems 2A.3 and
nal influence. The same external influence (e.g. a compressed spring)   2A.4
will produce *different* accelerations in different objects, but the *ratio* of accelerations of the two bodies is the same regardless of the nature of the external influence (except in the case of gravity—see below). Hence the factor which produces the difference is a property of the object: we call it the object's *mass* and define the masses of bodies 1 and 2 such that

$$\frac{m_1}{m_2} = \frac{a_2}{a_1} .$$

Mass is a measure of a body's inertia—its resistance to acceleration.   Problem 2A.2
The SI unit of mass is the kilogram and is defined relative to a standard reference mass (a platinum-iridium alloy cylinder in Paris).

It follows from the above definition that the product $m_i a_i$ is   Problem 2C.1
constant for a given "external influence". It can be regarded as a quantitative measure of the experimental factors affecting the motion of the body. This quantitative concept is called the *force* exerted on the body. The direction of the acceleration gives the direction of the force, so force is a vector. In vector form we have

$$\boxed{\vec{\mathbf{F}} = m\vec{\mathbf{a}} .}$$

This is *Newton's second law*. The unit of force is the *newton*. Unlike the other units we have met so far, the newton can be expressed in terms of more basic units: $1\ \text{N} = 1\ \text{kg·m/s}^2$. In words, one newton is the force necessary to accelerate a 1 kg mass at $1\ \text{m/s}^2$.

Newton's third law, which completes Newton's laws of motion, will be discussed in Chapter 5.

Since in practice the velocity of an object must be defined relative to some reference frame, the meaning of the word "velocity" in

Newton's first law requires clarification. Stated precisely, we are assuming that there exists a reference frame in which the law of inertia holds. That is, we assume that there exists a reference frame with respect to which any undisturbed body maintains a constant velocity. Such a reference frame is called *inertial*. The inertial reference frame is not unique, however: any frame of reference that is moving at a constant velocity relative to an inertial reference frame is also an inertial reference frame. The measured value of an acceleration or force is unchanged when viewed by a second observer moving at a constant velocity relative to the first observer, so an acceleration or force has the same value in all inertial reference frames. Newton's laws of motion hold in all inertial reference frames, and sometimes a problem can be simplified by working it in a frame of reference that is different from the one in which it was posed.

Often two or more forces will be acting on the same body simultaneously. The *net force* (also called the *total force*), which produces the observed acceleration, is the vector sum of all the forces acting on the body. For example, a light fixture hanging from the ceiling has zero acceleration relative to the room, but there are two forces acting: the gravitational force due to the mass of the fixture, and an upward force exerted by the wire by which it is suspended. Taking the ground to be an inertial reference frame (an approximation, as the Earth rotates, but we normally neglect the effects of this), these two forces are equal in magnitude and opposite in direction, so there is no net force and no acceleration.

Problems 2C

Experimentally observed forces seem to arise from many sources (gravity, compression of a spring, contact with a hard surface, friction, etc.). Physicists believe, however, that all the forces of nature can be explained in terms of four *fundamental forces*.

Supplementary Notes.

The most familiar fundamental force in our everyday lives is gravity. We are accustomed to feeling the gravitational attraction of the Earth, but in fact any two objects exert a gravitational attraction on each other. The force of gravity on an object of mass m caused by an object of mass M is given by

Problem 2B.1.

$$\vec{\mathbf{F}} = -\frac{GMm}{r^2}\hat{r},$$

where G is a constant, r is the distance between the objects, and $\hat{r}$ is a unit vector pointing from M to m. The force on M caused by m is given by the same formula, and therefore has the same magnitude. In this case, however, $\hat{r}$ points from m to M, so the force on M is in the opposite direction from the force on m—each object is attracted towards the other. We usually consider cases in which $M \gg m$ (e.g.,

M is the Earth, and m is a block of cement): in these cases the acceleration of M can be ignored, as it is too small to be measured.

The constant G, called the *gravitational constant* or sometimes *Newton's constant*, has the value 6.67×10^{-11} N·m²/kg².

As a fundamental law, the equation for the gravitational force above applies when M and m are point masses. Larger objects are viewed as being composed of point masses, each of which experiences a gravitational force given by this formula. It can be shown, however, that the formula holds for any two spherically symmetric objects (e.g., solid spheres, spherical shells), where r is the distance between their centers. While the proof of this statement is beyond the scope of this book, we will use the result.

The fact that the 'masses' entering this formula (the *gravitational mass*) are the same as the 'masses' found from $\vec{F} = m\vec{a}$ (the *inertial mass*) is called the Principle of Equivalence, and is the starting point for the development of General Relativity. The fact that the gravitational mass is proportional to the inertial mass, which is not logically necessary, has been confirmed experimentally to an accuracy of one part in 10^{11}.

Closely related to gravity is the concept of *weight*. As long as one deals with inertial frames of reference only, the weight of an object is simply the magnitude of the gravitational force acting on it. We learned in the last chapter that a freely falling object near the Earth's surface has an acceleration $\vec{g}$. Therefore, if we work in the approximation that the Earth's surface can be taken as an inertial frame, the gravitational force on such an object is $m\vec{g}$, and the weight is mg, where $g = |\vec{g}|$. Since the value of g on the moon is less than it is on Earth, your weight would be lower if you were on the moon, but your mass would be the same as it is on Earth. Since the mass of an object is independent of its location, it tends to be a more useful physical concept than weight. Note that mass and weight have different dimensions and are measured in different units: mass is measured in kilograms, whereas weight, being the magnitude of a force, is measured in newtons.

Problem 2B.7

The definition of weight becomes more complicated if one considers non-inertial frames of reference. In this book we will rarely mention non-inertial frames, but the concept of weight in a non-inertial frame is important enough to make an exception. The surface of the Earth, for example, is not truly an inertial frame, since the Earth is rotating about its axis and revolving around the Sun. One might also want to talk about the weight of an astronaut in a space capsule, which is a highly non-inertial frame of reference. For such non-inertial frames, the vector $\vec{g}$ is defined to be the acceleration

Problem 2B.4

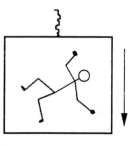

of a freely falling object relative to the frame. The weight, according to the official SI (Système International) definition, is given by $W \equiv m|\vec{g}|$. For example, suppose all cables attached to an elevator are cut, so the elevator falls freely downward. The occupants would fall at the same rate, so they could float inside the elevator with no contact with the walls. They would feel weightless (until they hit the ground). In the non-inertial frame of the elevator these occupants would be freely falling with zero acceleration, so their weight would be zero. (Note that the weight of an object is affected by the acceleration of the frame of reference (or, equivalently, the acceleration of the observer), but it is not affected by the acceleration of the object: to a stationary observer, a book on a desk is not accelerating, but it has the same weight as a similar book falling off the desk!)

A force similar in form to gravity is the *electrostatic* force between two electrically charged particles, which has the form

Problems 2B.5 and 2B.6

$$\vec{\mathbf{F}} = \frac{1}{4\pi\epsilon_0}\frac{Qq}{r^2}\hat{r} \, ,$$

where Q and q are the charges and $1/(4\pi\epsilon_0)$ is a constant. In this case the charge of the particle is different from its mass, and there is no 'equivalence principle'. Charges are measured in a unit called the coulomb, abbreviated as C, with

$$\frac{1}{4\pi\epsilon_0} = 8.99 \times 10^9 \text{ N·m}^2/\text{C}^2 \, .$$

It seems peculiar to denote the constant by $1/4\pi\epsilon_0$, rather than by a single symbol, but you will see when you study electromagnetism that other equations are simplified by this choice.

The electrostatic force is an aspect of the fundamental force of electromagnetism. The electromagnetic force encompasses the effects of both electric forces—such as the force that holds electrons in orbit about the atomic nucleus—and magnetic forces. Electric and magnetic fields can interact with each other to form electromagnetic waves, which include microwaves, radio waves, visible light, and X-rays.

Gravity and electromagnetism are two of the four fundamental forces. The other two are both short-range, acting over distances comparable to the diameter of an atomic nucleus. The *weak force* is responsible for the radioactivity of some types of atomic nuclei. The *strong force* is responsible for the structure of protons and neutrons, each of which are believed to be composed of three particles called *quarks*, bound together by the strong force. The strong force also holds protons and neutrons together inside the atomic nucleus. Gravity is by far the weakest of the four forces, and the strong force is the strongest. It is hard to believe that gravity is the weakest of the forces, since it exerts such a strong influence on our everyday world. Gravity gives the illusion of being strong, however, because it is long-range and always attractive, so we feel the combined attraction of all 10^{52} particles that make up the Earth; in contrast, although the electromagnetic force is much stronger, the Earth contains almost exactly equal numbers of positively and negatively charged particles, so the total electrostatic force at long range is practically zero.

It is now believed that the weak and electromagnetic forces are different aspects of a single force, called the *electroweak force*, and it is possible that all four fundamental forces can be explained in terms of a single, unified force.

Many commonly encountered forces are not fundamental, but rather are the large-scale observable effects of the electromagnetic force acting on a microscopic scale between atoms and molecules. For example, contact forces between surfaces are caused by temporary electromagnetic bonds being formed between neighboring atoms on the two surfaces. We describe here several of the most commonly encountered *macroscopic* forces: the *normal force* between surfaces in contact, the *tension* in a string, and the force associated with the compression or stretching of a spring.

The *normal force* is that part of the contact force that one object exerts on another which is in the direction perpendicular to the surface between the two objects. (The part of the contact force tangential to the surface is called friction, and will be ignored in this book until Chapter 6.) When a book rests on a table, the force of gravity acts downward on the book. The book does not fall through the table, however, because the table exerts a normal force upward, of equal strength. (Of course the book could be so heavy that the table breaks apart, but for now we will assume that all our tables, inclined planes, road surfaces, roller coaster tracks, etc., are completely rigid and indestructible.) The situation is slightly more complicated if the table is tilted, and the book is sliding along its surface. Again we know that the book will not fall through the table, and that the book will not fly upward. The general rule is that any two objects that touch each other exert normal forces on each other. The force is by definition normal (i.e., perpendicular) to the surface joining them, directed so as to push the objects apart. Its magnitude is just large enough to prevent the objects from penetrating each other. The force can vanish if no force is needed to prevent penetration, but it can never pull the objects together.

Another frequently encountered force is the *tension* in a string, rope, or wire. Just as we are assuming for simplicity that table surfaces cannot bend or break, we will also assume for now that

Supplementary Notes

Problems 2C.1 and 2C.5

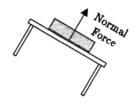

Problems 2C.3 and 2C.5

all ropes can be approximated as massless and inextensible (i.e, they cannot be stretched). When such a rope is pulled taut, it exerts forces on the objects at both ends, in each case pulling the object towards the rope. The forces at the two ends have the same magnitude, called the tension of the rope. The magnitude of the tension is whatever is necessary to prevent the rope from stretching. The tension of a rope can be positive or zero, but never negative.

$|\vec{\mathbf{F}}_1| = |\vec{\mathbf{F}}_2| = T$

T = tension

If a body is at rest with no net force acting on it, it will clearly remain in the same position: it is then said to be in *equilibrium*. [Note that we are presently assuming that the body we are dealing with is a point mass, with negligible size, and we can therefore assume that all the forces acting on it act at the same point. Later in the book we will see what happens when this is not the case.]

Equilibrium will be further discussed in Chapter 4.

An equilibrium position is *stable* if a particle slightly displaced from the position of equilibrium is subject to a force which tends to restore equilibrium. An example of this is a mass suspended from a string: in equilibrium the mass hangs directly below the suspension point of the string, and if it is displaced slightly from this position in any direction it will move back towards it when released—i.e. there is a restoring force. In this and many other cases, the magnitude of the restoring force is proportional to the displacement from equilibrium, so it can be written (in one dimension) as

Problems 2D

$$F_x = -kx \qquad (k \text{ a suitably dimensioned constant}).$$

Using $F_x = ma_x$, one finds the *differential equation*

$$m\frac{\mathrm{d}^2 x}{\mathrm{d}t^2} = -kx \ .$$

It is useful to rewrite this formula in the standard form

$$\boxed{\frac{\mathrm{d}^2 x}{\mathrm{d}t^2} = -\omega^2 x \ ,}$$

where in this case $\omega^2 = k/m$. This equation recurs frequently in physics, and the motion it describes is called *simple harmonic motion*. Note that x and ω might have different meanings for different problems, but the mathematical solution is always the same. It is easy to check that the differential equation is satisfied if

$$\boxed{x(t) = A\sin\omega t \ ,}$$

where A is any constant. It can be shown that any function which satisfies the differential equation can be written this way, provided that one chooses to start one's clock so that $t = 0$ when $x = 0$. The quantity ω is called the **angular frequency**; its units are radians per second, so that ωt is an angle in radians*. Since one cycle of the sine function is 2π radians,

$$\omega = 2\pi f \, ,$$

where f is the frequency measured in cycles per second. 1 cycle per second is also called a **hertz**, abbreviated Hz. The **period** of oscillation is the time for one cycle,

$$T = \frac{1}{f} = \frac{2\pi}{\omega} \, .$$

An example of simple harmonic motion is a mass attached to a stretched or compressed spring. To a good approximation, springs are found to exert a restoring force proportional to the amount of stretching or compression:

Problems 2B.2 and 2B.3

$$F_x = -kx \, .$$

In this case x is the difference between the spring's natural length and its length when compressed or stretched, and the constant k is called the **spring constant**. The units of k are N/m. (This is called 'Hooke's law', although in this case the word 'law' is ill-chosen— Hooke's law is a simple experimental relation valid for a restricted class of objects, not a widely applicable fact of nature like Newton's laws.)

---

* The radian is the SI unit of angle. It is defined as the angle between two radii of a circle that cut off on the circumference an arc equal in length to the radius: i.e., as the circumference of a circle of radius r is $2\pi r$, there are 2π radians in a complete circle (360°). Angles are dimensionless, so the dimensions of ω are 1/[time].

SUMMARY

* A body subject to no disturbance from outside will either be and remain at rest or maintain a state of uniform unaccelerated motion (Newton's first law).

* If external forces are applied to a body, it will accelerate with an acceleration equal to the total applied force, divided by the mass of the accelerated body (Newton's second law). Two observers in uniform relative motion will observe the same acceleration and the same force, provided that their relative speed is small compared to that of light.

* The gravitational force between two objectsis attractive, with a magnitude proportional to the product of their masses and inversely proportional to the square of the distance between them. The fact that the mass as defined in this way is proportional to the mass defined by the ratio of accelerations produced by a given force is known as the Principle of Equivalence, a fundamental property of nature and one of the cornerstones of the theory of General Relativity.

* The magnitude of the electrostatic or *Coulomb* force between two objects is proportional to the product of their charges and inversely proportional to the square of the distance between them: it is therefore analogous in form to the gravitational force. The force is repulsive if the two charges have the same sign, and otherwise it is attractive.

* Physical concepts introduced in this chapter: mass, force, inertial reference frame, electrical charge.

* Mathematical concepts introduced in this chapter: differential equation.

* Equations introduced in this chapter:

$$\vec{\mathbf{F}} = m\vec{\mathbf{a}} \qquad \text{(Newton's second law);}$$

$$\vec{\mathbf{F}} = -\frac{GMm}{r^2}\hat{r} \qquad \text{(the gravitational force between two particles);}$$

$$\vec{\mathbf{F}} = \frac{1}{4\pi\epsilon_0}\frac{Qq}{r^2}\hat{r} \qquad \text{(the electrostatic force between two particles);}$$

$$\frac{\mathrm{d}^2 x}{\mathrm{d}t^2} = -\omega^2 x \qquad \text{(for a particle near a point of stable equilibrium; equation leads to simple harmonic motion);}$$

$$x = A\sin\omega t \qquad \text{(a solution to the above equation; any solution can be written this way if we choose } t = 0 \text{ when } x = 0\text{);}$$

$$\omega = 2\pi f \qquad \text{(relation between angular frequency and frequency);}$$

$$T = \frac{1}{f} = \frac{2\pi}{\omega} \qquad \text{(period of an oscillator).}$$

* The *weight* of an object measured in an inertial reference frame is the magnitude of the gravitational force on the object. In a non-inertial frame the weight of an object is mg, where m is its mass and g is the magnitude of the acceleration that it would have if allowed to fall freely in that reference frame. (An astronaut thus has zero weight in the non-inertial reference frame of her orbiting spacecraft, although the magnitude of the gravitational force acting on her is not greatly decreased from its value at the surface

of the Earth.) The Earth's surface is not strictly an inertial reference frame, although we usually treat it as such when doing calculations.

* A position at which there is no net force on a body is called a position of *equilibrium*. If a body is displaced from a position of equilibrium, in many cases the force acting on the body is (to a good approximation) proportional to the distance from the equilibrium point and directed towards it. In this case the body will undergo *simple harmonic motion*, which means qualitatively that it will *oscillate* back and forth about the point of equilibrium.

* Any two objects that touch each other can exert *normal forces* on each other, perpendicular to the surface joining them and directed so as to push the objects apart. The magnitude is just large enough to prevent the objects from penetrating each other. The force can vanish if no force is needed to prevent penetration, but it can never pull the objects together.

* Strings, ropes, and wires can be approximated as being massless and inextensible. Such a rope pulls the objects at each end toward the rope with a force whose magnitude is equal to the *tension* of the rope. The value of the tension is whatever is necessary to prevent the rope from stretching. The tension is never negative.

PROBLEMS AND QUESTIONS

By the end of this chapter you should be able to answer or solve the types of questions or problems stated below.

Note: throughout the book, in multiple-choice problems, the answers have been rounded off to 2 significant figures, unless otherwise stated.

At the end of the chapter there are answers to all the problems. In addition, for problems with an (H) or (S) after the number, there are respectively hints on how to solve the problems or completely worked-out solutions.

2A   FUNDAMENTAL CONCEPTS (FORCE, MASS, AND NEWTON'S SECOND LAW)

2A.1   An airplane is flying due west (relative to the ground) at a constant speed of 600 km/h. The mass of the plane is 8500 kg, and the engines are supplying a constant forward thrust of 5000 N. To the nearest 10 N, what is the magnitude of the net force acting on the plane?

(a) 83300 N; (b) 5000 N; (c) 83450 N; (d) none of these

2A.2   In the context of the physics of this chapter, why is it easier to catch and hold a tennis ball than it is to catch and hold a lead ball of the same size, moving with the same velocity?

2A.3   A man pushing a cart with a mass of 180 kg can accelerate it from rest to 3 m/s in 4s. Approximately how long would you expect it to take him to accelerate the same cart to 3 m/s if a 120 kg mass is placed on the cart?

(a) 5.2; (b) 5.2 s; (c) 6.7 s; (d) none of these

2A.4 (H)   A spring gun is used to accelerate small pucks horizontally across a frictionless surface. A puck with a mass of 100 g is found to accelerate at 3 m/s². When the experiment is repeated with two other pucks of unknown mass, one accelerates at 1.7 m/s² and the other at 4.1 m/s². Calculate their masses. If the three pucks were glued together so as to form one larger mass, what would its acceleration be in this experiment?

2B   FUNDAMENTAL AND MACROSCOPIC FORCES

2B.1   An astronaut of mass 80 kg is a member of the crew of a space shuttle orbiting the Earth at an altitude of 220 km. What is the magnitude of the gravitational force on the astronaut? Assume that the radius of the Earth is 6400 km, and take g at the surface of the Earth as 9.8 m/s².

(a) 730 N; (b) 780 N; (c) 0 N; (d) none of these

2B.2   A spring balance is constructed using a spring with $k = 150$ N/m. How far will the spring extend when a mass of 1.8 kg is suspended from it?

(a) 12 mm; (b) 8.5 cm; (c) 8.5 mm; (d) 12 cm

2B.3 (H)   A body-building accessory consists of two handgrips joined by four identical springs. If each individual spring obeys Hooke's law with constant k, what is the spring constant of the whole device? What if the four springs had different constants?

2B.4 (H)   An astronaut aboard an orbiting spacecraft observes that he and other objects within the spacecraft are weightless. Is it true that no net force acts on them? If not, how is the presence of a force reconciled with the weightlessness of the contents of the spacecraft?

2B.5 (S)   Protons have a mass of 1.67×10^{-27} kg and a charge of 1.60×10^{-19} coulomb. The protons in an atomic nucleus are separated by distances of around 10^{-15} m. Calculate the electrostatic force between neighboring protons. Estimate the acceleration with which protons would depart from the nucleus if this were the only force operating, and comment on your result.

2B.6 (H)   Calculate the electrostatic force exerted on an electron by a proton at a distance of 10^{-10} m. Compare this with the gravitational force between the two. In the light of your comparison, discuss why gravity, and not electromagnetism, is the fundamental force most apparent to us on a macroscopic scale. (The mass of the proton is 1.67×10^{-27} kg, that of the electron is 9.11×10^{-31} kg, and their charges are $\pm 1.60 \times 10^{-19}$ coulomb respectively. The numerical values (in SI units) of the relevant constants are $1/4\pi\epsilon_0 = 8.99 \times 10^9 \, \text{N} \cdot \text{m}^2/\text{C}^2$ for the electrostatic force and $G = 6.67 \times 10^{-11} \, \text{N} \cdot \text{m}^2/\text{kg}^2$ for the gravitational force.)

2B.7   Explain, in 100 words or less, the difference between *mass* and *weight*. Would an object have the same mass on the Moon as it does on the Earth? Would it have the same weight?

2C   NEWTON'S SECOND LAW: FORCE, MASS, AND ACCELERATION

2C.1   A block of mass 1.5 kg slides down a frictionless slope inclined at 40° to the horizontal. What is the magnitude of its acceleration down the slope?

(a) 9.8 m/s²; (b) 6.3 m/s²; (c) 7.5 m/s²; (d) none of these

What is the magnitude of the force exerted on it by the slope?

(a) 6.3 N; (b) 7.5 N; (c) 11.3 N; (d) 9.4 N

2C.2 (S)   In the toy known as a Newton's cradle, steel balls are suspended by fine threads from a wooden frame. In a particular specimen, each ball has a mass of 50 g and the threads each make an angle of 20° to the vertical. Assuming that the ball is not moving, what forces are acting on it?

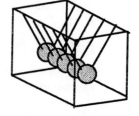

2C.3 (H)   A tight-rope walker stands midway along a high wire of length ℓ. If her mass is m, what must the tension T in the wire be if it sags by an amount y? Would it be possible to arrange the wire so that it did not sag at all ($y = 0$)? If the length of the wire is 25 m and the acrobat's mass is 55 kg, calculate the tension in the wire if it sags by 5 cm.

2C.4 (H) Two tugboats are towing a liner out of harbor. Their lines are arranged as in the diagram. If tug A exerts a force of magnitude F_A, derive an expression (in terms of F_A and the angles A and B) for the magnitude F_B of the force that tug B must exert if the net acceleration of the liner is to be straight ahead. Calculate F_B if $F_A = 3.1 \times 10^5$ N, with angle $A = 15°$ and angle $B = 18°$.

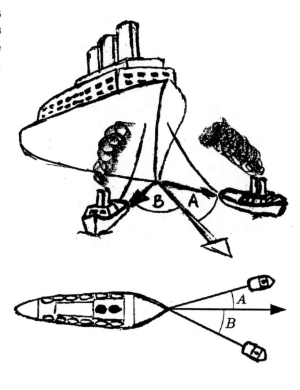

2C.5 (S) A mother tows her daughter on a sled on level ice. The friction between the sled and the ice is negligible, and the tow rope makes an angle of 40° to the horizontal. The combined mass of the sled and the child is 25 kg. If the sled accelerates at 1 m/s², calculate the tension in the rope. What is the normal force exerted by the ice? (As will be justified in Chapter 5, the child and sled can be treated in this problem as if they comprised a single particle.)

2D   VARIABLE FORCES

2D.1 (S) (a) A spring compressed by some amount is found to give a 1.3 kg mass an acceleration of 1.1 m/s². The experiment is repeated with a second object which accelerates at 2.4 m/s². Calculate the mass of the second object.

(b) The amount of compression was 1.0 cm. Calculate the force constant of the spring, assuming it behaves according to Hooke's law. By how much would you have had to compress the spring to give the second mass the same acceleration as the first?

(c) The first mass is now hung vertically from the same spring. By how much does the spring extend?

(d) If you hold the hanging mass slightly below its equilibrium position, extending the spring an additional amount Δx, what forces are now acting on the mass? What happens if you let go?

2D.2 (S) (a) A pendulum consists of a 250 g bob suspended by a string of negligible mass. If I hold the bob so that the string is taut and makes an angle θ with the vertical, and then release it, what forces are acting at the moment of release?

(b) If I agree to displace the bob by no more than 5° from the vertical, find a differential equation that describes (to a good approximation) the subsequent motion of the bob. Show that this equation is satisfied if the motion of the bob takes the form

$$\theta = A\sin(\omega t + \phi)$$

2D.2, continued:

where A and ϕ are arbitrary constants, and derive an expression for ω. Describe in words the motion of the bob.

(c) I wish to use the pendulum to drive a clock. What length of string should I use to get a period of 1.00 s, and how fast will the bob then move at the bottom of its sweep if the maximum angle is $\pm 2°$?

2D.3 (H) A small object of mass m is held by two springs with spring constant k_1 and k_2 as shown. The mass rests on a smooth surface so that the effects of friction are negligible. Left undisturbed, the mass sits at position $x = 0$.

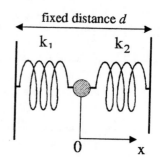

(a) If it is now displaced to position $x = -A$ and released, what forces are acting on it at the instant of release?

(b) Obtain a differential equation describing the motion of the mass after its release, and use this to derive an expression for its period of oscillation.

(c) If I turn the device on end, so that the springs hang vertical, what is the effect on the position of the stable configuration and on the motion of the mass when displaced? Assume the springs themselves have negligible mass.

COMPLETE SOLUTIONS TO PROBLEMS WITH AN (S)

2B.5 *Protons have a mass of 1.67×10^{-27} kg and a charge of 1.60×10^{-19} coulomb. The protons in an atomic nucleus are separated by distances of around 10^{-15} m. Calculate the electrostatic force between neighboring protons. Estimate the acceleration with which protons would depart from the nucleus if this were the only force operating, and comment on your result.*

Conceptualize
This is an application of $\vec{\mathbf{F}} = m\vec{\mathbf{a}}$. We know the form of the electrostatic force, which depends on the charges of the interacting bodies and the distance between them. To calculate the acceleration we also need to know the mass of the accelerating body. All this information is provided in the question.

Formulate
The electrostatic force exerted by a proton on another is

$$\frac{1}{4\pi\epsilon_0}\frac{q^2}{r^2} \, ,$$

where q is the charge on each proton and r is the separation of the two. The numerical value of the constant $1/4\pi\epsilon_0$ is 8.99×10^9 N $\cdot$ m^2/C^2.

Solve
The force is $(8.99 \times 10^9 \text{N} \cdot \text{m}^2/\text{C}^2) \times (1.60 \times 10^{-19}\text{C})^2/(10^{-15}\text{m})^2 = 230$ N. This would yield an acceleration of $(230 \text{ N})/(1.67 \times 10^{-27} \text{ kg}) = 1.4 \times 10^{29}$ m/s^2!

Obviously, we must conclude (since nuclei containing 80 or so protons are perfectly stable) that the electrostatic force is not the only one acting. Of course one additional force is gravity, but you can check for yourself (see problem 2B.6) that this is far too weak to counteract the electrostatic repulsion.

Scrutinize
The dimensions of the electrostatic force are correct once we take into account the dimensions of the constant $1/4\pi\epsilon_0$. The numerical values do not appear reasonable, but this is the point of the question (signaled in the wording of the question by the phrase "comment on your result").

Learn
We are of course neglecting all sorts of quantum mechanical and relativity complications here, but the conclusion is certainly sound. Protons are bound in the nucleus by the effects of one of the two short-range fundamental forces: this one is called the 'strong force', for reasons which should now be apparent.

73

2C.2   *In the toy known as a Newton's cradle, steel balls are suspended by fine threads from a wooden frame. In a particular specimen, each ball has a mass of 50 g and the threads each make an angle of 20° to the vertical. Assuming that the ball is not moving, what forces are acting on it?*

Conceptualize

We start by drawing a force diagram for the ball. One force acting on the ball is obviously gravity, so there is a force $m\vec{g}$ directed downwards. The threads holding the ball must also be exerting a force and it is apparent from everyday experience that this force is directed along the line of the thread (think of towing a car, hanging a picture, etc.). This very common type of force is called the **tension** in the thread.

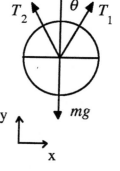

We also know that the ball is not accelerating. Therefore the **net** force on the ball is zero. We solve this problem by constructing and solving the component equations for the net force.

Formulate

We define a coordinate system with x and y axes as shown. The z-axis is directed out of the page; all z-components in this problem are zero. The component equations for the net force are:

$$F_x = T_1 \sin\theta - T_2 \sin\theta = 0;$$
$$F_y = T_1 \cos\theta + T_2 \cos\theta - mg = 0.$$

Solve

The first equation tells us that both string tensions are equal in magnitude. Since the arrangement is symmetrical, this is what we would expect. Defining $T \equiv T_1 = T_2$, the second equation gives us

$$T = \frac{mg}{2\cos\theta}.$$

Substituting the numerical values, with $g = 9.8$ m/s^2, the forces acting on the ball are

$(0.05 \text{ kg}) \times (9.8 \text{ m/s}^2) = 0.49$ N downwards;

$(0.49 \text{ N})/(2 \times \cos 20°) = 0.26$ N at 20° left of vertically upwards;

$(0.49 \text{ N})/(2 \times \cos 20°) = 0.26$ N at 20° right of vertically upwards.

Scrutinize

Sine and cosine functions arise trigonometrically from the ratio of two lengths (two sides of a triangle) and are therefore dimensionless, so a force divided by a cosine is another force. As mentioned above, the system is clearly symmetrical about a line drawn vertically through the center of the ball, so the two string tensions should be equal in magnitude, as indeed they are.

Learn

Notice that θ can have any value from 0 up to a maximum of 90°, which corresponds to the strings having no sag at all. It can be seen from our result, however, that the

2C.2, continued:

> tension approaches infinity as θ approaches 90°. Since the tension can never really be infinite, it is impossible for θ ever to be exactly 90°.

2C.5   *A mother tows her daughter on a sled on level ice. The friction between the sled and the ice is negligible, and the tow rope makes an angle of 40° to the horizontal. The combined mass of the sled and the child is 25 kg. If the sled accelerates at 1 m/s², calculate the tension in the rope. What is the normal force exerted by the ice? (As will be justified in Chapter 5, the child and sled can be treated in this problem as if they comprised a single particle.)*

Conceptualize

We treat the system of child and sled as a point particle, assuming that all the forces act at the same point. The forces acting on this "particle" are gravity, a normal force from the ice, and the tension in the tow-rope. The net force must be in the horizontal direction, since the sled is not rising into the air or sinking into the ice.

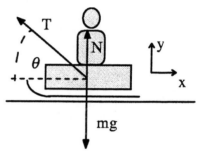

The force diagram is shown on the right. We know the acceleration of the sled, and can therefore calculate the components of the total force. Our strategy will be to construct and solve the equations giving this total force in terms of the three individual forces acting.

Formulate

$\Sigma\!\int$

The component equations for the net force are

$$\begin{aligned} F_x &= -T\cos\theta &= ma_x\,; \\ F_y &= T\sin\theta + N - mg &= ma_y\,. \end{aligned}$$

Our unknowns are T and N; we are given $a_x = -1$ m/s², $a_y = 0$, $m = 25$ kg, and $\theta = 40°$.

Solve

The x-component of the force on the sled is $ma_x = -25$ N. This is $-T\cos 40°$, so the tension in the rope must be 33 N.

The y-component of the force is zero, so $N = mg - T\sin 40° = 220$ N to two significant figures, taking $g = 9.8$ m/s².

Scrutinize

This is a straightforward problem presenting no difficulties. The units of our answer are obviously consistent and the numerical values seem reasonable.

2D.1   (a) *A spring compressed by some amount is found to give a 1.3 kg mass an acceleration of 1.1 m/s². The experiment is repeated with a second object which accelerates at 2.4 m/s². Calculate the mass of the second object.*

2D.1, continued:

Conceptualize
We defined the ratio of the masses of two bodies in terms of the ratio of their accelerations when subjected to the same force. This is exactly the situation we have here, so we can use that defining equation to calculate the mass ratio.

Formulate
The relevant equation is

$$\frac{m_2}{m_1} = \frac{a_1}{a_2} \, ,$$

where the subscript 1 refers to the first object and 2 to the second.

Solve
The second mass must be $(1.3 \text{ kg}) \times (1.1 \text{ m/s}^2)/(2.4 \text{ m/s}^2) = 0.60$ kg.

Scrutinize
The dimensions are correct, since the ratio of two accelerations is dimensionless. The smaller mass has the greater acceleration, which conforms to our expectations—pushing a wheelbarrow is easier than pushing a truck.

Learn
Note that we don't need to know the magnitude of the force, or its source (we have nowhere used the fact that a spring is involved). All we need is the information that the same experimental conditions (and thus the same net force) applied in both cases. The only exception is gravity, where the force is proportional to the mass, and thus applying the same experimental conditions to different masses does *not* produce the same net force.

(b) *The amount of compression was 1.0 cm. Calculate the force constant of the spring, assuming it behaves according to Hooke's law. By how much would you have had to compress the spring to give the second mass the same acceleration as the first?*

Conceptualize
We know the mass and acceleration of each of the two bodies, and can therefore use $\vec{F} = m\vec{a}$ to calculate the force. We can also obtain an expression for the force, in terms of the unknown spring constant, from Hooke's law. We should therefore be able to equate these two expressions to calculate the spring constant. Since this is a one-dimensional problem, we have only one component equation.

Formulate and Solve
Hooke's law says that $F_x = -kx$, where $x = \ell - \ell_0$ is the difference between the present length ℓ of the spring and its unstretched length ℓ_0 ($x < 0$ if the spring is compressed and $x > 0$ if it is stretched). Applying Newton's second law, $F = ma$, gives us

$$k = -\frac{ma}{x} \, .$$

With $x = -0.01$ m, $a = 1.1$ m/s^2, and $m = 1.3$ kg, we obtain $k = 140$ N/m to

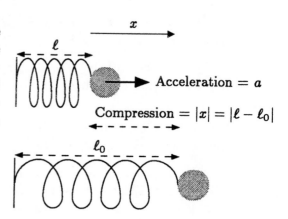

2D.1, continued:

two significant figures. Note the sign of x compared to a: the mass accelerates in the positive direction ($F_x > 0$) if the spring is compressed ($x < 0$).

Using the same equation with $m = 0.60$ kg, $a = 1.1$ m/s^2, and $k = 140$ N/m gives $x = -0.0046$ m $= -4.6$ mm for the compression required to give the second mass the same acceleration as the first.

Scrutinize

Note that the constant k must have units N/m (dimensions [force]/[length], or in terms of more basic quantities [mass]/[time]^2), in order for $-kx$ to be a force. This agrees with the dimensions of ma/x.

In the second part a and k are the same for both masses: if $ma = -kx$ it follows that the x values must have the same ratio as the masses. We can use this to check our answer: $0.6/1.3 = 0.46$, so $x = -0.46$ cm.

(c) *The first mass is now hung vertically from the same spring. By how much does the spring extend?*

Conceptualize

If the mass is stationary, the total force on it must be zero. We can therefore calculate the extension of the spring by equating the magnitudes of the spring force and the weight of the mass.

Formulate and Solve

The net force acting on the mass in the x-direction (downwards) is

$$F_x = mg - kx \ .$$

When the mass is stationary the net force must vanish, so

$$x = \frac{mg}{k} \ , \qquad \text{where } x = \ell - \ell_0 \ .$$

Numerically $x = (1.3 \text{ kg}) \times (9.8 \text{ m/s}^2)/(140 \text{ N/m}) = 0.089$ m.

Scrutinize

This is the same equation we used in part (b), so for the same mass and k the ratio of compression lengths must be the same as the ratio g/a. So our spring extension should be $(9.8 \text{ m/s}^2)/(1.1 \text{ m/s}^2)$ times 1 cm, i.e. 8.9 cm, in agreement with the above calculation.

Learn

We could apply this equation in reverse, i.e. measure the extension of a spring of known k when a mass is suspended from it, and use this to determine the mass. This is the operating principle of a **spring balance**. In contrast to a **beam balance**, where we measure the mass m relative to a known mass M (essentially by balancing mg against Mg), the reading of a spring balance is sensitive to the value of g. Spring balances measure weight, so they should really be calibrated in newtons rather than kilograms.

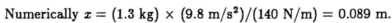

ℓ_0

x

Extension
$\ell - \ell_0$

kx

mg

2D.1, continued:

(d) *If you hold the hanging mass slightly below its equilibrium position, extending the spring an additional amount Δx, what forces are now acting on the mass? What happens if you let go?*

Conceptualize

The situation is the same as in part (c), but the magnitude of the spring force is increased by the larger extension. Therefore we expect that the total force on the mass from gravity and the spring is nonzero and is directed upwards. While you are holding the mass stationary, this upward force is balanced by a downward force exerted by you, and the total force on the mass is zero (as it must be, since the mass is not accelerating). If you let go, the mass will accelerate upwards. It will continue to accelerate upwards until it reaches the equilibrium position, where the force will go through zero and then become downwards. The mass will cross the equilibrium position with some nonzero speed, but then the downward force will cause it to slow down, stop, and start to move downwards. Once again it will be moving when it passes the equilibrium position, and the cycle will repeat. We therefore expect that the mass will *oscillate* above and below its position of equilibrium.

Formulate

The forces acting are mg downwards from gravity and kx upwards from the spring, plus the force you exert while holding the mass. We already know that $mg = kx_0$, where x_0 is the extension of the spring when the mass hangs in the equilibrium position (i.e. 8.9 cm, as we calculated in part (c)), so the spring force and gravity contribute a total of $k(x - x_0)$ upwards. While you are holding the mass, the total force is zero, so you must exert a force $k(x - x_0)$ downwards.

When you let go, the total force on the mass is $F_x = -k(x - x_0) = -kx'$, where $x' \equiv x - x_0$. The equation of motion of the mass is then

$$F_x = -kx' = m\frac{\mathrm{d}^2 x}{\mathrm{d}t^2} = m\frac{\mathrm{d}^2 x'}{\mathrm{d}t^2} \; ,$$

so

$$\frac{\mathrm{d}^2 x'}{\mathrm{d}t^2} = -\frac{k}{m}\, x' \; .$$

Solve

Our equation is of the form $\mathrm{d}^2 x'/\mathrm{d}t^2 = -\omega^2 x'$, where in this case $\omega^2 = k/m$. We saw in the *Essentials,* and will see again in Problem 2D.2, that a solution to this equation is

$$x' = A\sin\omega t \; ,$$

where A is a constant. If we have no preference for how the clock that defines t was

2D.1, continued:

started, then any solution to the differential equation can be written this way. Replacing x' by $x - x_0$ and ω by $\sqrt{k/m}$, the solution can be rewritten as

$$x = x_0 + A \sin\left(\sqrt{\frac{k}{m}}\, t\right).$$

Thus the mass will oscillate sinusoidally about the equilibrium position x_0, with angular frequency $\omega = \sqrt{k/m}$.

Scrutinize

The form of the differential equation agrees with our expectation: larger extensions produce greater acceleration, and the acceleration is always directed towards the equilibrium point. The acceleration is increased if the spring constant k is increased, but decreased if the mass m is increased.

The solution is oscillatory, as we predicted when conceptualizing the problem. The period of the oscillations is $2\pi/\omega$, i.e. $2\pi\sqrt{m/k}$, which has the dimensions of time as we expect (recall that the dimensions of k are $[\text{mass}]/[\text{time}]^2$). The period increases if the mass increases, but decreases if we use a larger k (i.e., a "springier" spring).

Learn

An essential part of this solution was the changing of variables necessary to cast the differential equation into a simple form: we introduced $x' \equiv x - x_0$, and $\omega \equiv \sqrt{k/m}$. This is the standard technique for solving problems involving simple harmonic motion, and more generally one finds that differential equations can often be simplified by a judicious change of variables.

Above we wrote down a general solution to the differential equation: neither the constant A nor the starting value of t was specified. With more thought, however, we can determine the precise solution that applies to this problem. If we choose to use a time variable t that starts at $t = 0$ at the moment the mass is released, then we know that at $t = 0$ the value of x' was Δx and the value of dx'/dt was 0. The differential equation can be solved by a sine or cosine function (or a sum of the two), but only the cosine has zero derivative when its argument vanishes. The initial value of the time derivative can therefore be satisfied by writing

$$x' = A \cos\left(\sqrt{\frac{k}{m}}\, t\right).$$

The initial value of x' can then be matched by choosing $A = \Delta x$, completely determining the solution. Thus, the amplitude of the oscillation is equal to the initial displacement.

Earlier we said that the most general solution can be written as $x' = A \sin \omega t$, so you might be wondering how this can be consistent with the cosine solution above. Remember, however, that $\cos \omega t = \sin(\omega t + \pi/2) = \sin \omega t'$, where $t' = t + (\pi/2\omega)$, so the two forms are related by a redefinition of the origin of time.

2D.2 (a) *A pendulum consists of a 250 g bob suspended by a string of negligible mass. If I hold the bob so that the string is taut and makes an angle θ with the vertical, and then release it, what forces are acting at the moment of release?*

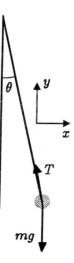

Conceptualize

One force acting on the bob is obviously gravity. If this were the only one, the bob would accelerate straight downward on being released, which it clearly does not do. It is prevented from doing so by the string, which must therefore be exerting a tension force. We saw in Problem 2C.2 that tension forces act along the line of the string, so we can draw a force diagram for the bob as shown. It is apparent that there is a net force in the x-direction, which will accelerate the bob back towards its equilibrium position (hanging directly under the point of suspension); there must also be a net force along the line of the string, providing the centripetal acceleration to maintain the bob on its circular arc.

Formulate

We define a coordinate system with y vertical and x horizontal as shown. Then the component equations for the total force are

$$F_x = ma_x = -T\sin\theta;$$
$$F_y = ma_y = T\cos\theta - mg.$$

Solve

In this context, 'solving' the equations means using them to determine the subsequent motion of the bob. It would be very difficult to do this for the equations in the form we have them at present. Instead we consider, in part (b), the special case of small θ, where the equations are simplified considerably.

(b) *If I agree to displace the bob by no more than 5° from the vertical, find a differential equation that describes (to a good approximation) the subsequent motion of the bob. Show that this equation is satisfied if the motion of the bob takes the form*

$$\theta = A\sin(\omega t + \phi),$$

where A and φ are arbitrary constants, and derive an expression for ω. Describe in words the motion of the bob.

Conceptualize

The conceptual picture here is the same as before. Only the formulation will differ, because we can use small angle approximations.

Formulate

It can be shown that for small angles

$$\cos\theta \approx 1 - \tfrac{1}{2}\theta^2 \approx 1;$$
$$\sin\theta \approx \theta \text{ (in radians)}.$$

2D.2, continued:

Is 5° a small angle? Converting to radians (2π radians $= 360°$) gives 0.0873 radians, which is certainly a small number compared with 1 or π. In fact $\sin(0.0873$ radians$) = 0.0872$, a difference of 0.13%. As a general rule, angles up to about 10° can be regarded as 'small'.

If $\cos\theta \approx 1$, the vertical motion of our bob is negligible, since its distance below the suspension point is $\ell\cos\theta \approx \ell$. Therefore, the vertical force must also be negligible, so we can write

$$F_y = T\cos\theta - mg \approx T - mg \approx 0.$$

This tells us that $T = mg$. From the diagram, $\sin\theta = x/\ell$, so the x-component of the force becomes

$$ma_x = m\frac{\mathrm{d}^2x}{\mathrm{d}t^2} = -\frac{mg}{\ell}x,$$

which is a differential equation for x. As $x = \ell\sin\theta \approx \ell\theta$, a differential equation for x is equivalent to a differential equation for θ, so solving this equation would give us an expression for θ.

Solve

Solving differential equations from scratch is beyond the mathematical level of this book, but in this case we have already been given a possible solution to try. We simply differentiate it twice and see what we get:

$$x \approx \ell\theta = \ell A\sin(\omega t + \phi)$$

$$\frac{\mathrm{d}x}{\mathrm{d}t} = \omega\ell A\cos(\omega t + \phi)$$

$$\frac{\mathrm{d}^2x}{\mathrm{d}t^2} = -\omega^2\ell A\sin(\omega t + \phi) = -\omega^2 x \ .$$

This has the required form, and is a solution if $\omega = \sqrt{g/\ell}$. A and ϕ are arbitrary, in the sense that any value of A or ϕ yields a valid solution, but they do have well-defined interpretations in terms of the physical motion of the bob: A gives the maximum deviation from equilibrium (the *amplitude*) and ϕ gives the starting point.

The sine function has maximum and minimum values ± 1 and repeats every 2π radians. Therefore the mass will oscillate between the positions $\theta = -A$ and $\theta = +A$, where A is the original displacement from vertical, and it will complete one full cycle during each time interval of length $2\pi/\omega$. Since sine has its maximum value where cosine is zero, and vice versa, the bob will reach its maximum speed as it passes through equilibrium, at $\theta = 0$. Its maximum acceleration occurs at the same time as its maximum displacement, when it reverses direction at the end of each sweep.

Scrutinize

The dimensions of ω^2 are $([\text{length}]/[\text{time}]^2)/[\text{length}]$, so ωt is dimensionless, as it must be since it is the argument of a sine function. Note that our final equations have no dependence on the mass of the bob; this is typical of systems where the force acting is

2D.2, continued:

gravity, because we tend to end up with equations of the form $F = ma = Kmg$, where K is some dimensionless coefficient such as a sine or cosine, and the mass then cancels out. However, the bob must be massive enough to allow us to neglect the mass of the string by comparison, and also compact enough that we can treat it as a point mass.

Learn
Why does the mathematical solution to our differential equation leave A and ϕ undetermined? This is typical of differential equations; it arises because in solving the differential equation we are effectively doing an integration, and therefore introducing an unknown integration constant. The number of undetermined quantities we get comes from the number of integrations we have to do—two, in this case, because $d^2\theta/dt^2$ is a second derivative. Physically, we can understand the two undetermined constants by thinking about the role of the initial conditions. As in the simple case of uniform acceleration along a line, $d^2x/dt^2 = a_x$, the differential equation contains no information about how the motion was started. The differential equations of classical mechanics generally tell us the rate of change of the velocity, but we need to know the initial velocity before the velocity at any given time can be determined. Similarly, the velocity tells us the rate of change of the position, but we need to know the initial value of the position to determine its value at later times. Thus, the solution to the uniform acceleration equation is written as $x = x_0 + v_0 t + \frac{1}{2}a_x t^2$, where x_0 and v_0 are the initial position and velocity. Similarly, for the pendulum we could determine the actual values of A and ϕ if we are told the initial position and velocity of the pendulum.

(c) *I wish to use the pendulum to drive a clock. What length of string should I use to get a period of* 1.00 s, *and how fast will the bob then move at the bottom of its sweep if the maximum angle is* $\pm 2°$?

Solve
(This is simply a numerical application of part (b), so we have already carried through the conceptualization and formulation.)

The period of oscillation T is $2\pi/\omega$, i.e.

$$T^2 = 4\pi^2 \ell/g \text{ , or } \ell = gT^2/4\pi^2 \text{ .}$$

For $T = 1$ s, the length is $(9.8 \text{ m/s}^2) \times (1 \text{ s})^2/4\pi^2 = 0.25$ m.

The speed of the bob is

$$\frac{dx}{dt} = \ell\frac{d\theta}{dt} = \ell\omega A\cos(\omega t + \phi) \text{ .}$$

At the bottom of the swing the speed is maximized, so the cosine is 1 and the speed is $\ell\omega A = A\sqrt{g\ell}$, where A is the swing amplitude *in radians* ($2° = 0.035$ radians). This comes to 0.054 m/s.

Scrutinize
Since the dimensions of ω are 1/[time], it follows that $1/\omega$ represents a time. The factor of 2π is dimensionless and cannot be detected by dimensional analysis; in this problem the same is true of A (thus $\ell\omega A$ and $\ell\omega$ both have dimensions of [length]/[time]). There is

2D.2, continued:

no easy way to detect errors involving dimensionless factors, though checks of particular numerical values can help.

The numerical value of the length seems plausible when we consider the size of real pendulum clocks (which admittedly might have pendulum periods of 0.5 s or 2 s rather than 1 s).

Learn

From the point of view of a clock designer, the important feature of a pendulum is that the swing period is independent of the swing amplitude, provided that the amplitude is small. The typical clock pendulum is not simply a heavy bob on a light string, so the analysis is slightly different, but the motion still turns out to be simple harmonic.

What happens if the swing amplitude is not small? Clearly the motion is still oscillatory, because the force on the bob is always directed towards the equilibrium position. Analyzing the exact equation mathematically is beyond the scope of this book, but just by looking at the form of the force we can get a qualitative idea of what would happen. For angles which are not small, $\sin \theta < \theta$, so the acceleration will be smaller than you would calculate from the small angle approximation. Therefore the velocity will also be smaller, and so we conclude that the period of a pendulum increases when the amplitude is increased beyond the limits of the small angle approximation.

To summarize, we have made three approximations in this analysis compared to a real experiment: we have assumed that we can treat a pendulum as a point mass suspended on a massless string; we have assumed small swing amplitudes and therefore used the approximation that $\sin \theta \simeq \theta$; and we have neglected frictional effects in assuming that the only forces acting are the string tension and gravity. If we had not made these approximations, there would have been differences in the details of the motion—the "effective length" of a real pendulum is different from its physical measured length; the period of a pendulum depends on its amplitude if the amplitude is not small; friction causes the pendulum to "run down" instead of swinging with the same amplitude forever—but the essential physics would be unaltered. On the other hand, the equations we would have had to solve would have been very much more complicated, and quite beyond the sort of simple math we have been using here. This use of idealization to simplify complex problems without changing their essential features is one of the most important features of the scientific approach to problem solving.

HINTS FOR PROBLEMS WITH AN (H)
The number of the hint refers to the number of the problem

2A.4 What is the meaning of the word "mass"? How could you tell that one mass was three times another mass?

2B.3 If the device is extended by an amount Δx, what is the force exerted on the handgrip by one spring? What is the total force exerted on the handgrip? If you replaced the four springs by one single spring, what would its spring constant be?

2B.4 What is the motion of the spacecraft and its contents? Is this motion unaccelerated? What is the acceleration of the astronaut in the (non-inertial) rest frame of the spacecraft? What is the sensation of weight?

2B.6 What is the total charge Q of a body consisting of a large number of protons and an exactly equal number of electrons? What is the net electrostatic force on such a body due to a distant charged object?

2C.3 Draw a force diagram for the tight-rope walker. What is the net horizontal component of force? The net vertical component? If the wire were absolutely straight, could the net vertical component of the force be exactly zero?

A review of the solution of 2C.2 might be useful if you are having difficulty with 2C.3 or 2C.4.

2C.4 What is the liner's acceleration perpendicular to its direction of motion? What must the net force be in that direction? What's the net force in that direction written in terms of F_A and F_B?

2D.3 (a) A tricky aspect of this problem is that we are not told the unstretched lengths of the springs. So consider three possibilities:

(i) Suppose the springs are initially unstretched at $x = 0$. If the object is moved to the left a distance A, is the spring on the left compressed or stretched? What force $F_{x,1}$ will it exert on the object? Will the spring on the right be compressed or stretched, and what force $F_{x,2}$ will it exert?

(ii) Now suppose both springs are initially compressed; for simplicity, assume that they are compressed by a distance greater than A. What is the net force on the object at $x = 0$? When the object is moved to $x = -A$, is the spring on the left compressed more or less? By what amount $\Delta F_{x,1}$ does the force it exerts on the object change? Answer these same questions for the spring on the right.

(iii) If the springs are initially stretched, by a distance greater than A, what are the answers to the questions in the previous part?

(iv) Draw a force diagram for the mass at position $x = -A$.

(b) What is the net force on the object at an arbitrary position x?

(c) In the vertical orientation, where is the mass in equilibrium? If we call this position $y = 0$, what vertical forces act on the mass at some arbitrary position y? Define the positive y-direction to be downward.

ANSWERS TO HINTS

2A.4 Ratio of two masses is defined through $m_1/m_2 = a_2/a_1$ for the same applied force. The absolute value is defined by reference to an arbitrary standard mass.

2B.3 $k\Delta x$; $4k\Delta x$; $4k$.

2B.4 Orbiting the Earth in uniform circular motion with the same velocity and therefore the same acceleration; no. Zero. You feel pushed against the floor—if the floor were not there, you would accelerate downwards.

2B.6 Zero; almost zero—it would be exactly zero if the protons and electrons in the body were at exactly equal distances from the charged object.

2C.3 Zero $(T\cos\theta - T\cos\theta)$;

$2T\sin\theta - mg$ (= 0, as she is not moving).

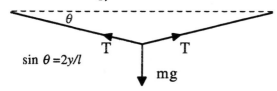

$\sin\theta = 2y/l$

No, because θ would be 0.

2C.4 Zero; zero; $F_A\sin A - F_B\sin B$.

2D.3 (a) (i) Spring on left compressed, $F_{x,1} = k_1 A$. Other spring stretched, $F_{x,2} = k_2 A$ (same direction).

(ii) Net force at $x = 0$ is zero. Spring on left compressed more, $\Delta F_{x,1} = k_1 A$. Other spring compressed less, $\Delta F_{x,2} = k_2 A$ (same direction again).

(iii) Net force at $x = 0$ is again zero. Spring on left stretched less, $\Delta F_{x,1} = k_1 A$. Other spring stretched more, $\Delta F_{x,2} = k_2 A$. In all cases, $\Delta F_{x,1} = k_1 A$ and $\Delta F_{x,2} = k_2 A$.

(iv)

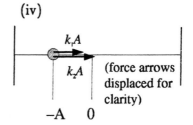

(b) $F_x = -(k_1 + k_2)x$.

(c) When vertical, equilibrium is lower than original equilibrium position $x = 0$ by a displacement d, where $mg = (k_1 + k_2)d$. At arbitrary position y,

$$F_y = mg - (k_1 + k_2)(d + y)$$
$$= -(k_1 + k_2)y .$$

ANSWERS TO ALL PROBLEMS

2A.1 d (The net force is zero.)

2A.2 Since the lead ball is more massive, more force is required to decelerate it to zero velocity, if one tries to stop it in the same distance.

2A.3 c

2A.4 180 g; 73 g; 0.86 m/s^2.

2B.1 a

2B.2 d

2B.3 4k; $\sum k_i$, where k_i is the constant of spring i ($i = 1$ through 4).

2B.4 No: the force of gravity is not much less than its surface value. However, the spacecraft and its contents are all undergoing circular motion around the Earth, with a centripetal acceleration equal to the acceleration due to gravity at this distance from Earth. The astronaut therefore has no acceleration *relative to the spacecraft*, and thus has no tendency to 'fall' within the craft. He would experience the same feeling if unfortunate enough to be trapped inside an elevator with a broken cable. (Hence the more physically motivated term for this situation—'free fall'.)

2B.5 1.4×10^{29} m/s^2.

2B.6 Electrostatic force: 2.3×10^{-8} N;

gravitational force: 1.0×10^{-47} N;

both directed towards the proton.

Electric charge comes with both positive and negative sign, and matter on a large scale is generally neutral, so a large object exerts no net electrostatic force on a charged particle, if the particle is sufficiently far away that the different positions of individual charges within the large body are not significant. Mass, on the other hand, is always positive, so the gravitational force exerted by a large amount of matter is cumulative.

2B.7 There is, of course, no single "correct" answer to the first part of this problem. An acceptable answer would be:

"*Mass* is an intrinsic property of a given object which will have the same value regardless of the object's environment and of the frame in which the measurement is made. *Weight*, on the other hand, is the magnitude of the local force of gravity on the object as measured in the relevant reference frame, which may not be inertial. It therefore depends on the environment (the mass and distance of the body exerting the gravitational force) and the choice of reference frame."

An object would have the same mass on the Moon, but different weight.

2C.1 b; c.

2C.2 See complete solution.

2C.3 $T = \ell mg/4y$, for small θ; 6.7 kN; no.

2C.4 2.6×10^5 N.

2C.5 33 N; 220N perpendicular to the ice.

2D.1 (a) 0.60 kg.

(b) 140 N/m

(c) 8.9 cm.

(d) See complete solution.

2D.2 See complete solution.

2D.3 (a) In equilibrium, the forces from spring 1 and spring 2 acting on the object cancel each other. When the object is displaced, the force $F_{1,x}$ from the first spring increases by $k_1 A$; i.e. there is now an additional force $k_1 A$ acting toward positive x. The force $F_{2,x}$ from the second increases by $k_2 A$, which also corresponds to an additional force toward positive x. Hence the net force is $F_x = (k_1 + k_2)A$ towards positive x.

(b)

$$m\frac{\mathrm{d}^2 x}{\mathrm{d}t^2} = -(k_1 + k_2)x \ .$$

The mass will oscillate around $x = 0$ in simple harmonic motion, i.e. with $x = -A \cos \omega t$, where ω is given by $\sqrt{(k_1 + k_2)/m}$. The limits of the oscillation are $\pm A$ and the period is $2\,\pi/\omega$.

(c) The stable position will be displaced downwards by an amount $d = mg/(k_1 + k_2)$; the motion will be unaffected, except for the shift in the equilibrium point.

CHAPTER 2

SUPPLEMENTARY NOTES

SIMPLE EXAMPLES VS THE REAL WORLD

The examples and problems we have considered to date have introduced the well-known arti-facts of Physics-Problem Land: frictionless slopes, projectiles immune to air resistance, superdense objects with masses of 1 kg but negligible size, massless strings, and so on. These objects are not common in everyday experience—friction and air resistance *matter* in calculating, for example, the acceleration and top speed of a newly designed automobile. Yet we have claimed that physics, like all other sciences, is a structure of mathematical laws derived from and based upon experimental results. Are we, therefore, cheating by ignoring these important practical effects in formulating our problems? Can we really gain insight by considering such artificial examples? In some sense, of course, we are indeed cheating. If we were doing a calculation with a view to applying the results to a particular experimental situation, we would have to consider *all* the circumstances pertaining to the experiment and decide if any of them has an effect (e.g. friction in the suspension bearing of a pendulum, or calibration errors in the clock we are using to measure its period). We might conclude that there is no effect (it doesn't matter what color I paint the bob of the pendulum), that an effect is present in principle but too small to measure (we have already seen that the dif-ferences between the properties of space and time in Newtonian theory and General Relativity are completely negligible in everyday experience), that an effect is present and must be considered in the analysis (if we wanted to use the pendulum to calculate the mass of the Earth to three or more significant figures by measuring g, we would have to consider the effect of the Earth's rotation), or that the effect is present and so large that we must redesign the experiment to avoid it (we are unlikely to get an accurate measurement of g by dropping a feather, unless we conduct the experiment in a vacuum tube).

The sources and sizes of effects making significant contributions to the result of the exper-iment will depend on the details of the experimental setup. In a well-designed experiment, the phenomenon you want to study will be the dominant effect, and other contributions will be small. For example, the effect of friction on the motion of objects can be reduced to very near zero by conducting experiments on a linear air track, and air resistance can be minimized by using a small dense projectile moving at a comparatively low speed, or eliminated altogether by conducting the experiment in a vacuum.

Physics-Problem Land is an idealized version of these well-designed experiments in which the additional effects have been reduced to zero. In many cases the degree of idealization is quite small: it is not too difficult to construct a pendulum in which the mass of the string is very small compared to the mass of the bob, and where frictional effects are unimportant. In other examples the difference between the idealized version and the real thing is significant: the effect of air resistance on the flight of an arrow is certainly not negligible. However, if we included the effect of air resistance, we would not change the *principles* of the problem—we would just make it very much more difficult to solve. In practice, problems of this sort often do not have neat algebraic solutions; they are actually 'solved' by calculating the trajectory by computer, in a series of tiny steps (this is called 'numerical integration'). Doing this is a useful exercise in programming skills for a computer science student, and a vital part of the design process for an aeronautical engineer, but it does not provide further illumination of the underlying physics. The principles governing the motion of freely falling bodies were worked out by Galileo in a series of carefully controlled experiments with balls rolling down inclined planes which allowed him to distinguish between the fundamental physics (the action of gravity) and the environmental effects such as friction and air resistance. (Contrary to popular belief, he did *not* drop cannonballs off the Leaning Tower of Pisa: if he had, air resistance effects might have led him to the wrong conclusions!)

Do the idealized, soluble problems of Physics-Problem Land have any practical application? Certainly they do. A well-chosen idealization can allow us to extract the basic physics of a system without the need to set up complex and expensive computer simulations or engineering models. Theoretical physicists often set up "toy models"—highly idealized systems—to see if a new theory has any prospect of describing real phenomena, before proceeding with more realistic calculations. Likewise, an engineer may use approximate, idealized calculations to check whether the basic principles of a new design are sound, before proceeding to fill in the details for computer simulations and wind-tunnel test models. The art of choosing good idealizations, which retain the essential physical properties of the real system while simplifying its mathematical description, is a vital part of scientific work.

The apparent complexity of the behavior of objects in the real world stems largely from the fact that we are not dealing with single particles, but with assemblies of 10^{25} or so atoms and molecules. The forces acting between the individual atoms are quite simple and readily calculable, although because of the small sizes involved we have to add the ideas of quantum mechanics to the tools we are developing in this book. If it were possible to keep track of the motion of each individual atom, we would not have to worry about concepts such as friction and air resistance, and we could do everything in terms of the fundamental forces, which all behave very simply. However, it is clearly not possible to do this—we can neither make the observations (what is the 45 millionth iron atom in my desk doing at this precise moment?) nor do the calculations (imagine drawing 10^{25} individual force diagrams!). The complicated behavior of macroscopic forces like friction is not a fundamental property of nature, but a consequence of our insistence on working with macroscopic objects instead of basic building blocks. We will see later in the book how physical phenomena not obviously related to Newton's laws, such as heat and the pressure of a gas, are also consequences of the unobserved motion of atoms and molecules.

FUNDAMENTAL FORCES

Physicists distinguish between *macroscopic* forces, such as the force produced by a compressed spring, and *fundamental* forces such as gravity. This distinction is of very little value in terms of calculating the acceleration of an object—we draw the same force diagrams and use the same equations regardless of the source and nature of the force. Conceptually, however, it is a vital step in understanding the laws governing the structure of the universe, rather as the construction of the Periodic Table was a vital step towards the modern understanding of chemistry. If we had to try to understand every experimentally observed type of force individually (e.g. spring forces, friction, normal forces, muscular forces, etc., etc.), there would be little hope of learning more about the underlying structure of natural phenomena. (Newton was in this position, and hence the only force for which he could formulate a general law was gravity, which happened to be a fundamental force accessible to him; Newton's first and second laws, on the other hand, relate measured forces to measured accelerations, but tell us nothing about what the force in a given situation will actually be.) Once we know that measured forces are derived from only a few truly different fundamental forces, we are in a much better position to develop a real understanding. In fact, as this understanding progresses, we are learning that three of the four forces we now recognize (all but gravity) act in very similar ways at the elementary particle level, so that there is a possibility of including all of them in a single theoretical framework (a so-called *grand unified theory*). Many theoretical physicists are even exploring the possibility that all four forces can be described by a single interaction in the context of what is called *superstring* theory. Either of these unifications would be a further advance along the road which started in the nineteenth century when electricity and magnetism, previously believed to be different things, were recognized as different aspects of the electromagnetic force, and continued in the 1960's and 70's with the uncovering of the close relationship of electromagnetism and the weak nuclear force.

ESSENTIALS OF INTRODUCTORY CLASSICAL MECHANICS

CHAPTER 3

THE MOTION OF A POINT PARTICLE

OVERVIEW

This chapter contains no new ideas. Instead, we take the material covered in Chapters 1 and 2 and use it to solve more complicated problems. Notice that in this chapter we will not divide the problems up into sections dealing with specific topics; instead you will have to decide for yourself which of the physical principles you have learned are relevant to a given problem. This is a very important aspect of the technique of problem solving—real-life problems, such as designing a bridge support or an artificial hip joint, do not come with neat subtitles directing you to the right equations!

When you have completed this chapter you should:

> ✔ be able to extract the essential features of a problem and express them in mathematical equations;
>
> ✔ be capable of manipulating the equations relevant to a problem to obtain an expression for the required quantity, either symbolically or numerically;
>
> ✔ be able to analyze a hypothetical situation in terms of the physics presented in previous chapters, and explain that analysis clearly in non-mathematical terms.

PROBLEMS AND QUESTIONS

By the end of this chapter you should be able to answer or solve the types of questions or problems stated below.

Note: throughout the book, in multiple-choice problems, the answers have been rounded off to 2 significant figures, unless otherwise stated.

At the end of the chapter there are answers to all the problems. In addition, for problems with an (H) or (S) after the number, there are respectively hints on how to solve the problems or completely worked-out solutions.

3.1 (S) (a) A particle moves along the x-axis. Its position at any time is given by

$$x = x_0 + bt + ct^2 \ ,$$

where $x_0 = 1$ m, $b = 2$ m/s and $c = -3$ m/s^2.

   (i) What are the particle's velocity and acceleration at any time t?

   (ii) Calculate its velocity and acceleration for each time it passes through the point $x = 0$.

   (iii) Is its velocity ever zero? If so, what are its position and acceleration at that time?

   (iv) Plot its position and velocity as functions of time for the time interval -10 s to $+10$ s.

   (b) Now consider a particle moving in three dimensions with position vector

$$\vec{r} = [a_1 + a_2 t, b_1 + b_2 t^3, c_1 + c_2 t^2] \ ,$$

where $a_1 = 1$ m, $a_2 = 6$ m/s, $b_1 = 4$ m, $b_2 = -1$ m/s^3, $c_1 = 2$ m and $c_2 = -1$ m/s^2. What are its velocity and acceleration vectors at time t? What is its speed and the magnitude of its acceleration at time $t = -3$ s?

3.2   An astronaut on the Moon throws a stone with velocity $\vec{v}$. It is in flight for a time Δt, reaches a height h and travels a horizontal distance x. He now throws a second stone with velocity $2\vec{v}$. Which of the following statements (A) through (L) are true? (List *all* that apply.)

(A) Its flight lasts four times as long.   (B) Its flight lasts twice as long.
(C) It reaches a height $2h$.   (D) It travels four times as far.
(E) It travels twice as far.   (F) It goes four times as high.
(G) It travels half as far.   (H) It goes half as high.
(I) It travels the same distance, but goes higher.
(J) It goes higher, but travels less far.
(K) It reaches the same height, but travels further.
(L) The maximum height is less, but the horizontal distance is greater.

He throws a third stone with the same speed v as the first. Its flight lasts twice as long as that of the first stone. Which of the statements (C) through (L) above *must* be true? (List *all* that apply.)

3.3   A toy train moves at constant speed on a level circular track of radius r, taking a time T to complete one circuit. Obtain expressions for the speed v of the train, the magnitude a of its centripetal acceleration, and the x- and y-components of its velocity at time t. What is the source of the force producing the acceleration? If $r = 1.2$ m and $T = 30$ s, calculate v and a, and plot the x- and y-components of the position, velocity and centripetal acceleration of the train over one complete circle, assuming that it is traveling counterclockwise and that its position at $t = 0$ is $x = r$, $y = 0$.

3.4 (S)   A local agricultural show features a display of archery. An archer is practicing at the target as the celebrity who is to open the show is arriving by helicopter. If the archer directs his arrow at 45° with a speed of 60 m/s and the helicopter is descending vertically with a constant speed of 10 m/s, plot the trajectory of the arrow as seen by (a) an observer on the ground and (b) an observer in the helicopter. What are the velocity and acceleration vectors at time t in each frame of reference? Take $g = 10$ m/s^2, ignore air resistance, and choose coordinates so that the launch point of the arrow is at the origin in both frames of reference.

3.5 (H)   A certain unorthodox archeologist is trapped on top of a truck traveling at 40 km/h. His friends, pursuing in a jeep, finally overtake the truck at a speed of 45 km/h. With a perfectly timed leap our hero throws himself from the top of the truck to land in the back of the jeep. The top of the truck is 3 m above the jeep and there is 2 m between the vehicles as they pass.

     (a) Assuming our man launches himself horizontally and directly outward from the truck, at what speed does he need to jump to land safely in the jeep—say 0.5 m from the side of the jeep, i.e. 2.5 m from the side of the truck?

     (b) He was standing 4 m from the front of the truck and lands 2 m from the front of the jeep. If he jumped straight outward from the truck, what were the relative positions of truck and jeep at the moment of takeoff?

     (c) Plot his trajectory, in terms of height relative to initial vertical position against horizontal distance traveled, as seen (i) from the truck, (ii) from the jeep, (ii) by a baffled Bedouin standing by the side of the road.

     Take $g = 10$ m/s^2 and neglect air resistance throughout.

3.6 (H)   Household scales, although (when metric) always calibrated in kilograms, actually balance the *weight* of the object against some other force—either the force of gravity on a reference mass (a beam balance) or the compression or extension of a spring (a spring balance). If I accurately calibrate a beam balance and a spring balance in Boston and then take them to the top of Mount Everest, will they give the same reading when I use them to weigh a rock? Explain your reasoning.

3.7   The acceleration of freely falling bodies, g, and the radius of the Earth, R, are far easier to measure than the gravitational constant G. Derive an expression for the orbital period of a satellite in a circular orbit with radius r (that is, its height above the Earth's surface is $h = r - R$) which involves *only* g, R and r (i.e. does not require a measurement of G or of the mass of the Earth).

     In the light of this result, discuss why it is that G is so difficult to determine experimentally (it is one of the least well known of the fundamental constants).

3.8 (S)   A bobsled run includes a bend in the form of a circular arc of radius 25 m. A sled approaches the bend at a constant speed of 90 km/h. At what angle must the sled bank in order to take the curve successfully? Assume that this part of the course is level, and that there is no friction between the sled runners and the ice.

3.9 (H)   In a conical pendulum, the bob describes a horizontal circle while the string (which is of negligible mass) makes a fixed angle with the vertical. By what fraction does (i) the speed of the bob and (ii) the period of the conical pendulum change if I change the angle the string makes with the vertical from 5° to 10°? In the small angle approximation, how does the period of a pendulum working in this way compare with the period of the same pendulum swinging in the conventional fashion (i.e. back and forth with small amplitude in a line passing under the point of suspension)?

3.10 (S) Calculate the final velocity of a mass m (a) falling freely from rest through a distance h; (b) sliding a distance ℓ down a frictionless slope making an angle ϕ to the horizontal, where $\sin\phi = h/\ell$; (c) forming the bob of a simple pendulum of length ℓ which makes a maximum angle with the vertical of $\theta = \sqrt{2h/\ell}$ (in this case calculate the velocity at $\theta = 0$). Give an expression for the net force acting in each case. Assume $h \ll \ell$.

3.11   A child has a toy rocket of mass m attached to a string of negligible mass. She whirls the toy at speed v in a horizontal circle of radius ℓ, at height h above the (level) ground.

Draw a force diagram for the rocket and use it to find:

(a) the angle θ that the string makes with the horizontal;

(b) the tension T in the string.

Assume the motion of the child's hand is negligible compared to ℓ.

(c) At a certain point the string breaks. How far from the child's feet does the rocket hit the ground?

3.12 (H) It's raining, and you forgot your umbrella. You have 2 km to walk back to your apartment. There is no wind and the rain is coming down vertically. What are you going to do: walk slowly, on the grounds that then only your head and shoulders are exposed to the rain, or run, arguing that the less time you are out the less wet you will get? This problem is a mathematical analysis of your situation, albeit with several simplifying approximations.

Assume for simplicity that a person is basically cuboidal, with dimensions $h \times w \times d$ (height, width, depth), and walks at a speed v. The rain is coming down with constant speed V, and the amount of rain per cubic meter is ρ kg/m^3.

(a) If you walk erect, how much rain will fall on you if you walk a distance ℓ? Your answer will be a function of h, w, d, v, V, ρ and ℓ.

(b) How does your formula behave as v becomes very small or very large? What do you conclude about the best strategy for minimizing the amount of rain you catch?

(c) In practice, you are not compelled to walk erect. If the rain is coming down at 20 km/h, and the fastest speed at which you can run 2 km is 12 km/h, what is your best plan?

3.13 (S)　The distance between the Earth and the Moon is 384 thousand kilometers, and the mass of the Moon is 7.4×10^{22} kg. Calculate the acceleration of the Earth due to the Moon's gravitational attraction. If a point mass were describing a circular orbit with this centripetal acceleration and a period of 27.3 days, what would be the radius of the orbit? Take $G = 6.67 \times 10^{-11}$ N·m²/kg².

3.14　The mass of the Sun is 2.0×10^{30} kg and the mass of the Earth is 6.0×10^{24} kg. The Moon (which has a mass of 7.4×10^{22} kg) orbits the Earth at a distance of 384 thousand kilometers, and the Earth and Moon together orbit the Sun at a distance of 150 million kilometers. Find the gravitational pull on the Moon from the Sun and from the Earth. Hence calculate the acceleration of the Moon (a) when it is directly between the Sun and the Earth; (b) when the Earth is directly between it and the Sun; (c) when Sun, Earth and Moon form a right-angled triangle. Which of the forces acting is more important? Why do we nonetheless see the Moon as simply orbiting the Earth?

3.15　A mass M is held stationary by many light springs as shown. If the spring on the right breaks, what is the acceleration of the mass immediately afterwards? Explain your reasoning clearly. Assume that the spring in question obeys Hooke's law with a force constant k, and that before breaking it was extended by an amount x; also assume that the total mass of all the springs is negligible compared to M.

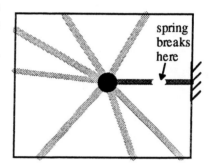

spring breaks here

COMPLETE SOLUTIONS TO PROBLEMS WITH AN (S)

3.1   (a) *A particle moves along the x-axis. Its position at any time is given by*

$$x = x_0 + bt + ct^2 \ ,$$

where $x_0 = 1$ m, $b = 2$ m/s and $c = -3$ m/s^2.

(i) *What are the particle's velocity and acceleration at any time t?*

(ii) *Calculate its velocity and acceleration for each time it passes through the point $x = 0$.*

(iii) *Is its velocity ever zero? If so, what are its position and acceleration at that time?*

(iv) *Plot its position and velocity as functions of time for the time interval -10 s to $+10$ s.*

Conceptualize

We are given the position x, and asked to find the velocity and the acceleration. This is a one-dimensional problem, so we have only one component equation—instead of $\vec{r}$, $\vec{v}$ and $\vec{a}$ we have to consider only x, v_x and a_x. To solve it we use the definitions of velocity and acceleration from Chapter 1: velocity is the rate of change of position with time, and acceleration is the rate of change of velocity with time.

Formulate

The definitions of velocity and acceleration are:

$$\vec{v} = \frac{d\vec{r}}{dt} \ ; \qquad \vec{a} = \frac{d\vec{v}}{dt} = \frac{d^2\vec{r}}{dt^2} \ .$$

In this one-dimensional problem these reduce to

$$v_x = \frac{dx}{dt} \ ; \qquad a_x = \frac{dv_x}{dt} = \frac{d^2x}{dt^2} \ .$$

Solve

To answer (i), we differentiate the expression for $x(t)$ to find

$$v_x = b + 2ct \ ;$$

$$a_x = 2c = -6 \text{ m/s}^2 \ .$$

Note that the acceleration is constant—no factors of t remain.

For part (ii) we first solve the quadratic equation $x(t) = 0$ to find the times t at which $x = 0$:

$$t = \frac{1}{2c}(-b \pm \sqrt{b^2 - 4cx_0}) \ .$$

98

3.1, continued:

Numerically this yields $t = -\frac{1}{3}$ s and $t = 1$ s. The corresponding values of the velocity $v_x = b + 2ct$ are

$$(2 \text{ m/s}) + \left[2 \times \left(-3 \text{ m/s}^2\right) \times \left(-\tfrac{1}{3} \text{ s}\right)\right] = 4 \text{ m/s} \text{ for } t = -\tfrac{1}{3} \text{ s} , \text{ and}$$

$$(2 \text{ m/s}) + \left[2 \times \left(-3 \text{ m/s}^2\right) \times (1 \text{ s})\right] = -4 \text{ m/s} \text{ for } t = 1 \text{ s} .$$

The acceleration, being constant, is of course -6 m/s^2 in both cases.

For part (iii) we solve the velocity equation for $v = 0$, which gives

$$t = -\frac{b}{2c} = \frac{1}{3} \text{ s.}$$

The position at this time is

$$x = (1 \text{ m}) + \left[(2 \text{ m/s}) \times \left(\tfrac{1}{3} \text{ s}\right)\right]$$
$$+ \left[\left(-3 \text{ m/s}^2\right) \times \left(\tfrac{1}{3} \text{ s}\right)^2\right]$$
$$= \tfrac{4}{3} \text{ m} ,$$

and the acceleration is still -6 m/s^2.

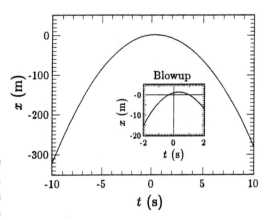

The graphs of position and velocity are shown at right. Note that the position graph is quadratic (proportional to t^2) whereas the velocity graph is linear (proportional to t). What would the acceleration graph look like?

Scrutinize
The units of $b + ct$ are m/s, and c is in m/s^2, so the dimensions of our equations for velocity and acceleration are correct. Note that, dimensionally, differentiating with respect to a variable is like dividing by it: the dimensions of dx/dt are the same as those of x/t.

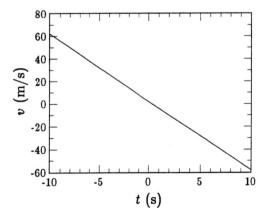

We can check our answer to part (ii) by substituting our values of t back into the original

99

3.1, continued:

equation:

$$x(t = -\tfrac{1}{3}\,\mathrm{s}) = (1\,\mathrm{m}) + \left[(2\,\mathrm{m/s}) \times (-\tfrac{1}{3}\,\mathrm{s})\right] + \left[\left(-3\,\mathrm{m/s}^2\right) \times \left(-\tfrac{1}{3}\,\mathrm{s}\right)^2\right]$$

$$= \left(1 - \tfrac{2}{3} - (3 \times \tfrac{1}{9})\right)\,\mathrm{m} = 0;$$

$$x(t = 1\,\mathrm{s}) = (1\,\mathrm{m}) + \left[(2\,\mathrm{m/s}) \times (1\,\mathrm{s})\right] + \left[\left(-3\,\mathrm{m/s}^2\right) \times (1\,\mathrm{s})^2\right]$$

$$= (1 + 2 - 3)\,\mathrm{m} = 0.$$

Learn
If the derivative of a function is zero at some point, the value of the function there is a local maximum, a local minimum, or occasionally a saddle point. In this case the position graph shows clearly that the zero of velocity corresponds to a global maximum value of x—the particle never reaches $x > \tfrac{4}{3}$ m.

(b) *Now consider a particle moving in three dimensions with position vector*

$$\vec{r} = [a_1 + a_2 t, b_1 + b_2 t^3, c_1 + c_2 t^2]\ ,$$

where $a_1 = 1$ m, $a_2 = 6$ m/s, $b_1 = 4$ m, $b_2 = -1$ m/s^3, $c_1 = 2$ m and $c_2 = -1$ m/s^2. What are its velocity and acceleration vectors at time t? What is its speed and the magnitude of its acceleration at time $t = -3$ s?

Conceptualize
This is the same type of problem, but in three dimensions. We can solve it in the same way, treating each component as a separate one-dimensional problem.

Formulate
The equations for the x-component are

$$v_x = \frac{\mathrm{d}x}{\mathrm{d}t}\ ; \qquad a_x = \frac{\mathrm{d}v_x}{\mathrm{d}t} = \frac{\mathrm{d}^2 x}{\mathrm{d}t^2}\ ,$$

and likewise for the y- and z-components.

Solve
The velocity and acceleration vectors are

$$\vec{v} = [a_2, 3b_2 t^2, 2c_2 t]\ ;$$

$$\vec{a} = [0, 6b_2 t, 2c_2]\ .$$

The acceleration this time is not constant. At $t = -3$ s, the velocity and acceleration are

$$\vec{v} = [6, -27, 6]\ \mathrm{m/s}\ ;$$

$$\vec{a} = [0, 18, -2]\ \mathrm{m/s}^2\ .$$

3.1, continued:

We want the magnitudes of these vectors, namely

$$v = \sqrt{6^2 + (-27)^2 + 6^2} = \sqrt{801} = 28 \text{ m/s (to 2 sig. fig.) and}$$
$$a = \sqrt{0^2 + 18^2 + (-2)^2} = \sqrt{328} = 18 \text{ m/s}^2 \ .$$

Scrutinize

Checking units for the expression for $\vec{\mathbf{v}}$, we see that they are correct: the units of $b_2 t^2$ are $(\text{m/s}^3)(\text{s}^2)$, or m/s, and likewise $c_2 t$ has units of $(\text{m/s}^2)(\text{s})$. The differentiation to find the expression for $\vec{\mathbf{a}}(t)$ eliminates one factor of t, resulting in units of m/s^2 for both nonzero components. Our equations are therefore dimensionally correct. Note that in this case the velocity is never zero overall, although both v_y and v_z are zero at $t = 0$ (a saddle point in y, a global maximum in z).

Learn

Working with symbols instead of substituting in the numbers allows us to maintain a check on the consistency of our units through the calculation. It also results in a more general solution: if we were told that b_2 was $+1$ m/s^3 instead of -1 m/s^3, we would not have to redo the whole calculation. If you do choose to put in the numbers earlier, you ***must*** remember that they are not ***really*** numbers (in the sense that the 3 in $3b_2 t$ is really a number) but represent quantities with dimensions and units.

3.4   *A local agricultural show features a display of archery. An archer is practicing at the target as the celebrity who is to open the show is arriving by helicopter. If the archer directs his arrow at 45° with a speed of 60 m/s and the helicopter is descending vertically with a constant speed of 10 m/s, plot the trajectory of the arrow as seen by (a) an observer on the ground and (b) an observer in the helicopter. What are the velocity and acceleration vectors at time t in each frame of reference? Take $g = 10$ m/s^2, ignore air resistance, and choose coordinates so that the launch point of the arrow is at the origin in both frames of reference.*

Conceptualize

This problem involves projectile motion and the concept of reference frames. We have two natural reference frames: the archer frame, which is fixed relative to the ground, and the helicopter frame, which is fixed relative to the helicopter. (The third possible frame, fixed relative to the arrow, is a non-inertial frame, with a nonzero acceleration relative to the inertial frames. We will postpone discussion of non-inertial frames until Chapter 6.) The archer frame is the simplest to work in, since the velocities specified in this problem are all given in this frame.

Formulate

We define a coordinate system in which y points vertically upwards and x is the horizontal direction of the arrow. In the archer's frame of reference, the component equations of the arrow's velocity $\vec{\mathbf{v}}(t)$ are

$$v_x(t) = v_0 \cos\theta \ ;$$
$$v_y(t) = v_0 \sin\theta - gt \ ,$$

3.4, continued:

where $t = 0$ at the moment the arrow is launched, $v_0 = 60$ m/s is the initial speed of the arrow, and $\theta = 45°$ is the angle its initial velocity makes with the horizontal.

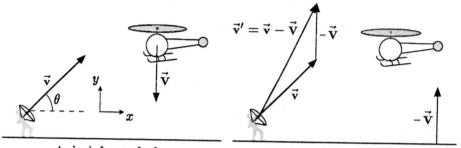

Archer's frame of reference   Helicopter's frame of reference

In the helicopter's frame of reference, the arrow's velocity is

$$\vec{v}'(t) = \vec{v}(t) - \vec{V} ,$$

where $\vec{V} = [0, -10, 0]$ m/s is the velocity of the helicopter. (Note that $-\vec{V}$, the velocity of the ground relative to the helicopter, is a vector pointing upward of magnitude 10 m/s.) In components,

$$v'_x(t) = v_0 \cos \theta ;$$

$$v'_y(t) = V + v_0 \sin \theta - gt ,$$

where $V = |\vec{V}| = 10$ m/s.

To plot the trajectory we will need the equations for x and y in both frames: in the archer frame, the trajectory of the arrow is

$$x(t) = v_0 t \cos \theta ;$$

$$y(t) = v_0 t \sin \theta - \frac{1}{2}gt^2 .$$

In the helicopter frame we know the velocity $\vec{v}'(t)$ of the arrow, so we can determine the position either by integrating the velocity, or by using its initial value and the fact that the acceleration is uniform with value $[0, -g, 0]$. With either method, we need to specify the initial position as $x'_0 = 0$, $y'_0 = 0$, since the problem tells us to choose the coordinate system with the launch point of the arrow at the origin. The flight of the arrow in the helicopter frame is therefore described by

$$x'(t) = x(t) = v_0 t \cos \theta ;$$

$$y'(t) = (V + v_0 \sin \theta)t - \frac{1}{2}gt^2 .$$

Solve

The trajectory that we are asked to plot is a graph of y against x, but so far we have calculated each as a function of time. However, the equation for $x(t)$ (or equivalently $x'(t)$) can easily be solved to give $t = x/(v_0 \cos \theta) = x'/(v_0 \cos \theta)$, which can then be

3.4, continued:

used to eliminate t from the equations for $y(t)$ and $y'(t)$. One finds that

$$y = x \tan \theta - \frac{g x^2}{2 v_0^2 \cos^2 \theta}$$

and

$$y' = x' \tan \theta + \frac{V x'}{v_0 \cos \theta} - \frac{g x'^2}{2 v_0^2 \cos^2 \theta} .$$

These equations are graphed at the right.

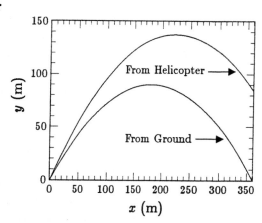

We have already written algebraic expressions for the velocity of the arrow in each
frame, so all that remains is to insert numbers. The components of the arrow's velocity
in the archer frame are

$$v_x = (60 \text{ m/s}) \cos 45° = 42 \text{ m/s} ;$$

$$v_y = (60 \text{ m/s}) \sin 45° - (10 \text{ m/s}^2) t = [42 - (10 \text{ s}^{-1}) t] \text{ m/s} .$$

In the helicopter frame $v'_x = v_x = 42$ m/s, and

$$v'_y = 10 \text{ m/s} + (60 \text{ m/s}) \sin 45° - (10 \text{ m/s}^2) t = [52 - (10 \text{ s}^{-1}) t] \text{ m/s} .$$

In the archer frame, the acceleration is clearly $\vec{\mathbf{g}} = [0, -g, 0]$, and this is unchanged by
adding a constant (i.e., unaccelerated) velocity to transform into the helicopter frame.
Summarizing:

$$\vec{\mathbf{v}} = [42, 42 - (10 \text{ s}^{-1}) t, 0] \text{ m/s} , \qquad \vec{\mathbf{a}} = [0, -10, 0] \text{ m/s}^2$$

in the archer frame, and

$$\vec{\mathbf{v}}' = [42, 52 - (10 \text{ s}^{-1}) t, 0] \text{ m/s} , \qquad \vec{\mathbf{a}}' = [0, -10, 0] \text{ m/s}^2$$

in the helicopter frame.

Learn

Notice that the ground is moving upwards at 10 m/s as seen from the helicopter, so
the arrow in the helicopter frame does not return to the same y-coordinate value. Also,
it reaches its maximum y-coordinate value later in the helicopter frame. However, the
acceleration in both frames is the same: an observer in the helicopter using the flight
of the arrow to measure g would get the same result as an observer on the ground.

In the *Essentials* of Chapter 1 we learned that if an object has position $\vec{\mathbf{r}}$ and velocity
$\vec{\mathbf{v}}$ in some reference frame, then its position and velocity in the frame of an observer O
are given by

$$\vec{\mathbf{r}}' = \vec{\mathbf{r}} - \vec{\mathbf{r}}_0$$

$$\vec{\mathbf{v}}' = \vec{\mathbf{v}} - \vec{\mathbf{v}}_0 ,$$

3.4, continued:

where $\vec{r}_0$ and $\vec{v}_0$ are the position and velocity of the observer O in the original frame. In the solution above we used the second of these equations, but you might wonder why we did not also use the first. Our choice was just a matter of convenience: we were given the velocity of the helicopter, but not its position. Furthermore, the first equation leads to a coordinate system with the observer O at the origin, while we were asked to describe the arrow in a reference frame with the velocity of the helicopter, but with the launch point at the origin.

An unusual feature of this problem is the peculiar mix of variables with numerical constants in the final answer for the velocities. One tricky point is the handling of units. The answer for v_y, for example, was correctly written as $[42 - (10 \text{ s}^{-1})t]$ m/s. It would **not** be correct, however, to write it as $(42 - 10t)$ m/s, even though this expression has the right units at the end. The problem with the latter expression is that 42 is a pure number, while $10t$ is a time, with units of seconds, hours, fortnights, or something else. There is no well-defined way to add a time to a pure number.

3.8   *A bobsled run includes a bend in the form of a circular arc of radius 25 m. A sled approaches the bend at a constant speed of 90 km/h. At what angle must the sled bank in order to take the curve successfully? Assume that this part of the course is level, and that there is no friction between the sled runners and the ice.*

Conceptualize

The bobsled needs to move in a horizontal circle. It must therefore have an acceleration v^2/r directed towards the center of the circle, i.e. horizontally. The forces acting are gravity, which is vertical and therefore cannot possibly produce a horizontal acceleration, and the normal force from the surface of the ice. If the sled is to negotiate the bend successfully, the normal force must have a vertical component which cancels the weight of the sled—there is no vertical acceleration—and a horizontal component producing the required centripetal acceleration. The ratio of these two components gives $\tan A$, the angle the normal force makes with the vertical, and since the normal force is always directed perpendicular to the surface this is necessarily the angle that the surface of the ice makes with the horizontal, which is what we are asked to calculate.

Formulate

Defining a coordinate system with y up and x horizontally along the direction of motion, the components of the total force are

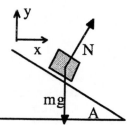

$$F_x = N \sin A \; ;$$
$$F_y = N \cos A - mg \; .$$

The orientation of $\vec{N}$ is defined by the fact that (as its name implies) it is perpendicular to the surface of the slope. The horizontal component of $\vec{N}$ is the only horizontal force acting, so it must produce the necessary centripetal acceleration:

$$N \sin A = \frac{mv^2}{r} \; ,$$

3.8, continued:

while, since the sled has no vertical acceleration, $F_y = 0$, implying

$$N \cos A = mg \ .$$

Solve
Dividing the first equation by the second gives

$$\tan A = \frac{v^2}{gr} \ , \quad \text{or } A = 69° \ .$$

Scrutinize
The dimensions of gr are $([\text{length}]/[\text{time}]^2) \times [\text{length}] = ([\text{length}]/[\text{time}])^2$, so v^2/gr is dimensionless. If the velocity goes to zero, there is no centripetal acceleration, so no banking is required, and indeed in this case $\tan A = 0$; conversely, a very large velocity will produce a very large $\tan A$, and hence require a nearly vertical bank (as in circus "Wall of Death" motorcycle rides).

Learn
The same principle explains why sharp bends on roads are banked, and why if you take the bend too fast you end up running off the outer edge of the bend. You have *not* been 'thrown outwards'—rather, you are still being acted on by a force $N \sin A = mv^2/r$, but because your v is greater than the road engineers expected it to be, r is larger (N and A are fixed by the mass of your car and the angle of bank), and you do not turn sharply enough to make the bend. In the case of automobiles frictional forces also act (unless the road is very icy), which is why you don't have to take the curve at *exactly* its design speed.

3.10   *Calculate the final velocity of a mass m (a) falling freely from rest through a distance h; (b) sliding a distance ℓ down a frictionless slope making an angle ϕ to the horizontal, where $\sin \phi = h/\ell$; (c) forming the bob of a simple pendulum of length ℓ which makes a maximum angle with the vertical of $\theta = \sqrt{2h/\ell}$ (in this case calculate the velocity at $\theta = 0$). Give an expression for the net force acting in each case. Assume $h \ll \ell$.*

Conceptualize
By now we have developed a standard approach to dealing with problems involving forces, accelerations and velocities:

- draw a force diagram;

- choose a suitable coordinate system;

- write down the component equations for $\vec{\mathbf{F}}$, $\vec{\mathbf{v}}$ and (if necessary) $\vec{\mathbf{r}}$;

- solve for the requested quantities.

The choice of coordinate system depends on the individual problem. In the case of part (c), we will also want to assume that the angle θ is small—we saw in Problem 2D.2 that without this assumption the pendulum's equations of motion are too difficult to solve.

3.10, continued:

Formulate and Solve (a)

This is a one-dimensional constant-acceleration problem. Taking down to be positive, we have $v = gt$ and $h = \frac{1}{2}gt^2$. If we substitute $t = v/g$ in the equation for h we can solve for v to obtain $v = \sqrt{2gh}$, directed downwards. The net force is obviously $m\vec{g}$, also directed downwards.

Formulate (b)

The force diagram is as shown. Choosing a coordinate system with the x direction directed down the slope, the components of the forces acting are

$$F_x = mg\sin\phi$$

$$F_y = N - mg\cos\phi$$

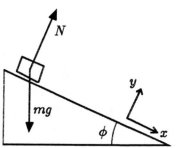

There is no acceleration, and thus no net force, in the y direction. In the x direction,

$$v = gt\sin\phi$$

$$\ell = \frac{1}{2}gt^2\sin\phi \ .$$

Solve (b)

We can solve these equations for v as we did for case (a) to get

$$v = \sqrt{2g\ell\sin\phi} \ .$$

Putting in $\sin\phi = h/\ell$ gives

$$v = \sqrt{2gh}$$

in the x-direction, i.e. down the slope.

The net force, as we have already determined, is $mg\sin\phi$ directed down the slope.

Formulate (c)

As in Problem 2D.2(b), we assume θ is small and choose a coordinate system with y along the string (i.e., for small θ, vertical) and x perpendicular to the string.

$$F_y = T - mg\cos\theta \approx T - mg$$

$$F_x = -mg\sin\theta \approx -mg\theta \ .$$

The y-component provides the centripetal force which maintains the bob's circular motion (i.e. it produces an acceleration v^2/r). The x-component gives us the equation of motion for the bob

$$\frac{d^2\theta}{dt^2} = -\frac{g}{\ell}\theta \ .$$

3.10, continued:

Solve (c)

We saw in Chapter 2 that the solution of this equation is $\theta = A\cos\omega t$, where in this case $A = \sqrt{2h/\ell}$ and $\omega = \sqrt{g/\ell}$, and the choice of cosine rather than sine defines $t = 0$ at maximum amplitude. The tangential speed of the bob is given by

$$v = \ell\frac{\mathrm{d}\theta}{\mathrm{d}t} = -\sqrt{2gh}\sin\omega t \,,$$

so at $\theta = 0$ we once again have $v = \sqrt{2gh}$, directed horizontally (with or without a minus sign, depending on the direction in which the bob is swinging when it passes through $\theta = 0$). The net forces are given above.

Scrutinize

The dimensions of $\sqrt{2gh}$ are $\sqrt{[\text{length}]/[\text{time}]^2 \times [\text{length}]} = [\text{length}]/[\text{time}]$, which is appropriate for v. We can also see that $v \to 0$ if $g \to 0$ or $h \to 0$, as we would expect—in zero gravity the objects would not fall, and falling through zero height is equivalent to not falling at all.

Learn

All three cases were set up so that the mass starts from rest and falls through a vertical distance h (see diagram at right if you are unconvinced about this for part (c)). Notice that in each case the mass ends up with exactly the same speed that it would have had if it had simply fallen freely from rest through a height h. The _velocities_ are not the same, because the directions are different.

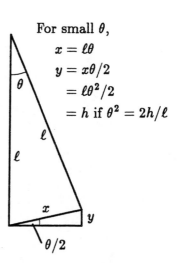

For small θ,
$$x = \ell\theta$$
$$y = x\theta/2$$
$$= \ell\theta^2/2$$
$$= h \text{ if } \theta^2 = 2h/\ell$$

This result is not a coincidence. In any experimental situation we could contrive where a mass starts from rest and moves under the influence of gravity through a vertical distance h, it will end up with the same speed $\sqrt{2gh}$. To understand why this is so, we need to introduce the new physical concept of _energy_, which is the subject of the next chapter.

3.13   _The distance between the Earth and the Moon is 384 thousand kilometers, and the mass of the Moon is 7.4×10^{22} kg. Calculate the acceleration of the Earth due to the Moon's gravitational attraction. If a point mass were describing a circular orbit with this centripetal acceleration and a period of 27.3 days, what would be the radius of the orbit? Take $G = 6.67 \times 10^{-11}$ N · m^2/kg^2._

Conceptualize

The diameters of the Earth and the Moon are small compared to the distance between them, so we can treat them as point particles. The force acting is gravity, but because we are considering distance large compared to the sizes of the gravitating objects we must use Newton's inverse square law, not simply $m\vec{g}$! Recognizing this supports our

13.13, continued:

decision to treat Earth and Moon as point masses, because, as mentioned in Chapter 2, the gravitational force exerted by any spherically symmetric body is the same as that of a point particle of the same mass.

Formulate
Newton's laws for the Earth-Moon system give

$$\frac{GM_{earth}M_{moon}}{r^2} = M_{earth}a \ .$$

A particle in uniform circular motion has acceleration v^2/r, where v is its speed and r the radius of the circle. To express v in terms of the period P, we note that

$$v = \frac{\text{circumference of circle}}{\text{period}} = \frac{2\pi r}{P} \ .$$

Solve
The Earth's acceleration is

$$a = \frac{(6.67 \times 10^{-11} \ \text{N} \cdot \text{m}^2/\text{kg}^2) \times (7.4 \times 10^{22} \ \text{kg})}{(384 \times 10^6 \ \text{m})^2} = 3.3 \times 10^{-5} \ \text{m/s}^2 \ .$$

A circular orbit has

$$a = \frac{v^2}{r} = \frac{4\pi^2 r}{P^2} \ ,$$

so for this acceleration and a period of 27.3 days

$$r = \frac{(3.3 \times 10^{-5} \ \text{m/s}^2) \times (27.3 \times 24 \times 60 \times 60 \ \text{s})^2}{4\pi^2} = 4.7 \times 10^6 \ \text{m} \ .$$

Scrutinize
1 N = 1 kg $\cdot$ m/s^2, so the units of G can be expressed as m^3/kg $\cdot$ s^2. In this form it is clear that the units of GM/r^2 are m/s^2, as expected. In this problem it is certainly necessary to check *units*, rather than simply *dimensions*, since forgetting to convert 27.3 days into seconds would not affect the dimensions of your answer, but would definitely change its numerical value!

For a given period, the radius of the orbit is proportional to the centripetal acceleration, which in turn is proportional to the mass exerting the gravitational force. The Moon's mass is about 1% of the Earth's (more exactly, 1/81), so we expect the radius we calculate to be about 1% of the Earth-Moon distance. This is in good agreement with the value that we get.

Learn
The fact that 4700 km is so small compared to the distance between the Earth and the Moon (in fact it is smaller than the radius of the Earth) explains why we can treat the Earth-Moon system as if only the Moon moved. Astronomers have studied many *binary stars*, in which two stars form a gravitationally bound system. In this case the masses of the two stars may be quite similar, and the motion of both partners has to be taken into account.

108

HINTS FOR PROBLEMS WITH AN (H)
The number of the hint refers to the number of the problem

3.5 Visualize the man's motion in the truck's frame of reference. What is his horizontal motion in this frame? His vertical motion? How long does he take to cover the vertical distance from truck roof to jeep? In the truck's frame of reference, how far does the jeep move in this time? In the Bedouin's frame, in which the road is stationary, how far does the truck move?

If you're still stuck, try reviewing the solution to problem 3.4.

3.6 What is the general form of the gravitational force? What does this tell you about the value of g on Everest? What other forces are involved in weighing the rock?

3.9 What is the acceleration required to keep an object moving in a horizontal circle? Draw a force diagram for the bob. What net force acts to produce this acceleration?

You may also find it helpful to review the solution to problem 2D.2.

3.12 (a) If you move with speed v, at what angle to the vertical is the rain in your reference frame? How much rain will cross a plane area A in 1 s if the velocity of the rain makes an angle θ with the normal (i.e. perpendicular) to the surface? A diagram will probably help.

(c) How can you minimize the effective area you present to the rain?

ANSWERS TO HINTS

3.5 None; $v = -gt$, where t is the time since he jumped.

0.77 s; 1.1 m; 8.6 m.

3.6 $-GMm/r^2$; on Everest g will be less, because r is increased. For beam balance, no other force; for spring balance, $-kx$.

3.9 v^2/r, directed horizontally inwards towards the axis of rotation.

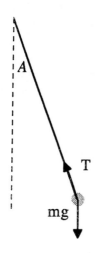

$T \sin A$.

3.12 (a) At an angle θ such that $\tan \theta = v/V$; $\rho A v \cos \theta$, i.e. ρA times the component of the rain's velocity normal to the plane area.

(c) By leaning forward at the angle θ to the vertical (so the rain strikes only your head and shoulders).

ANSWERS TO ALL PROBLEMS

3.1 See complete solution.

3.2 B,D,F; F.

3.3 $v = 0.25$ m/s, $a = 0.053$ m/s^2. The normal force from the rails.

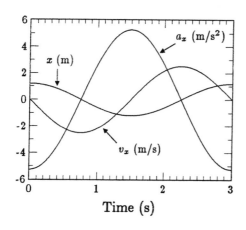 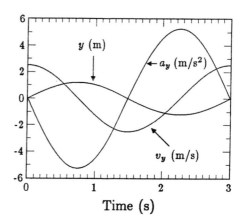

3.4 See complete solution.

3.5 (a) 3.2 m/s

(b) Front of jeep 3.1 m behind front of truck.

(c)

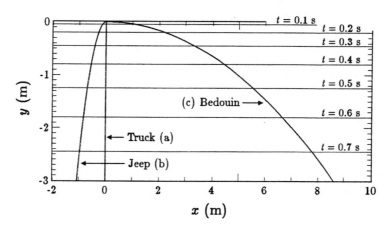

3.6 No: the beam balance will give a larger reading than the spring balance.

3.7 $T = 2\pi \sqrt{\dfrac{r^3}{gR^2}}$

The difficulty in measuring G arises from the fact that the only way to accurately determine the mass of a celestial body such as the Earth is to use $|\vec{\mathbf{F}}| = GMm/r^2$. We know m, the mass of our test object, accurately, and we can measure r accurately also. But we can only determine M if we already know G, and vice versa. Hence we must determine G by measuring the gravitational force between two *known* masses M and m, and this inevitably means that M is much smaller than the mass of a planet. As gravity is so weak (see Problem 2B.6), the gravitational force between two relatively small masses is tiny, and very difficult to measure accurately, so the resulting value of G is not very precise.

3.8 See complete solution.

3.9 Speed: twice as large for $10°$; period: 0.6% shorter for $10°$. Periods of conventional and conical pendulum are equal in the small angle approximation.

3.10 See complete solution.

3.11

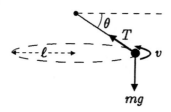

(a) $\tan \theta = g\ell/v^2$;

(b) $T = \dfrac{m}{\ell}\sqrt{v^4 + g^2\ell^2}$.

(c) $x = \sqrt{\dfrac{2h}{g}\, v^2 + \ell^2}$.

3.12 (a) $\rho\ell w \left(d\dfrac{V}{v} + h \right)$.

(b) Very small v: becomes very large. Very large v: becomes $\rho\ell wh$. Best strategy will involve large v.

(c) Bend forward at $31°$ to vertical and run at 12 km/h.

3.13 See complete solution.

3.14 4.2×10^{20} N; 1.9×10^{20} N.

3.2×10^{-3} m/s^2 towards Sun;

8.6×10^{-3} m/s^2 towards Sun;

6.5×10^{-3} m/s^2 at $25°$ Earthwards of the line joining Sun and Moon.

That due to the Sun; because Earth and Moon share effectively the same orbit, and thus the same centripetal acceleration, relative to the Sun, so we see only the Moon's motion relative to us.

3.15 kx/M, directed to the left.

ESSENTIALS OF INTRODUCTORY CLASSICAL MECHANICS

113

ENERGY

OVERVIEW

In this chapter we introduce the concept of *energy*. Unlike the concepts we have previously encountered (position, velocity, force, etc.), energy can take a number of different forms. It can be stored and transferred from one object to another or from one form to another, but the overall energy of a closed system remains constant—we say that energy is *conserved*. This is of great practical value in solving problems, but it is also a fundamental property of nature, which remains true even under conditions when Newton's laws must be modified by relativity or quantum mechanics.

When you have completed this chapter you should:

- ✔ understand what is meant by conservation of energy;

- ✔ be able to calculate the kinetic energy of a body and use it in problems;

- ✔ be able to calculate the work done by a given force and relate this to a transfer of energy;

- ✔ understand the concept of potential energy and be able to calculate and use the potential energy associated with gravity, spring forces, and electrostatic forces;

- ✔ recognize the existence and importance of other forms of energy;

- ✔ understand how conservative forces can be derived from a potential energy function, and relate this to the condition of equilibrium.

ESSENTIALS

We found in Chapter 1 that for a body moving in one dimension with a constant acceleration, the equations for $v(t)$ and $x(t)$ can be combined to give the useful formula

$$v^2 = v_0^2 + 2ax ,$$

where v_0 is the velocity at the beginning of some time interval, v is the velocity at the end of the interval, x the distance the body travels during the time interval, and a is the acceleration. If m is the body's mass, we can rewrite this as

$$\frac{1}{2}mv^2 = \frac{1}{2}mv_0^2 + Fx ,$$

where $F = ma$ is the (constant) force acting. If F is the uniform force of gravity near the surface of the earth, then it is common practice to measure x as positive upwards, and to call it h, for height. Since $F = -mg$, the equation can be written as

$$\boxed{\frac{1}{2}mv^2 + mgh = \frac{1}{2}mv_0^2 \, .}$$

The equation states that the quantity on the left-hand side maintains a constant value throughout the motion. Furthermore, the equation can be shown to hold regardless of whether the body is falling vertically, sliding down an inclined plane, moving as a projectile with horizontal and vertical velocity, etc., provided no air resistance or frictional forces are involved.

Problem 3.10

This equation is extremely useful for solving problems where the detailed time dependence of the motion is not important. More importantly, the quantity on the left-hand side, $\frac{1}{2}mv^2 + mgh$, is an example of a quantity that has important implications in all fields of physics. This quantity is a new basic concept: the *energy* of the body. Energy is a scalar quantity, measured in joules: 1 J = 1 N·m = 1 kg·m^2/s^2.

Supplementary Notes.

As can be seen from the equations above, energy occurs in several different forms. The quantity $\frac{1}{2}mv^2$ is the *kinetic energy* of the body, while mgh is the (gravitational) *potential energy* that it has by virtue of being a vertical distance h above some reference level, such as the floor or the ground. Potential energy can be regarded as energy which is temporarily stored and which is capable of being released. For example, energy which is stored by lifting a book above the ground can be released by dropping the book, which will then accelerate and gain kinetic energy. The potential energy is really a property of a particular configuration of the whole system (e.g., a compressed spring, or two separated objects exerting a gravitational or electrostatic force on each other). Note that the reference level from which h is measured can be chosen arbitrarily—only the difference in potential energy between two configurations is meaningful.

Problems 4A and 4B.1

Energy can be transformed from potential energy to kinetic energy and vice versa (e.g., the motion of a projectile or pendulum), but it cannot be created or destroyed. We call a system *closed* if it is not communicating in any way with the rest of the universe; i.e., if no objects or forces are entering or influencing the system from the outside. Experiments show that the *total* energy of a closed system never changes. We say that *energy is conserved*. Conservation of energy has played an extremely important role in the development of physics, because it appears to be an exact principle that applies in all known circumstances.

If a net force acts on a particle, it accelerates, so its kinetic energy must change. To quantify this, consider a force $\vec{F}$ acting on a particle of mass m and initial velocity $\vec{v}_0$. For simplicity, let us restrict ourselves to the case of one-dimensional motion. Suppose the force acts for a short time Δt and produces an acceleration a, so that the final speed is $v = v_0 + a\Delta t$. Then the final kinetic energy is

$$\begin{aligned}
\tfrac{1}{2}mv^2 &= \tfrac{1}{2}m\left(v_0 + a\Delta t\right)^2 \\
&= \tfrac{1}{2}mv_0^2 + ma\left(v_0\Delta t + \tfrac{1}{2}a\Delta t^2\right) \\
&= \tfrac{1}{2}mv_0^2 + F\Delta x,
\end{aligned}$$

where $\Delta x = v_0\Delta t + \tfrac{1}{2}a\Delta t^2$ is the distance the particle has moved in time Δt. The change in kinetic energy is given by the applied force times the displacement of the particle. We call this the *work* done by the force on the particle: thus

$$\boxed{W \equiv F\Delta x.}$$

Problem 4B.2

From the derivation above it is clear that in the absence of other forces *the work done by a force on an object is equal to the amount of kinetic energy transferred to the object*. If more than one force acts, we can repeat the calculation using the net acceleration produced by all the forces, $a_{\text{net}} = \sum F_i/m$, and we find that the same relation holds: the total work done ($\sum F\Delta x$) is equal to the net change in kinetic energy. This is the *work-energy theorem*:

$$\boxed{W = K_f - K_i,}$$

where K_i is the initial kinetic energy, K_f the final kinetic energy, and W the total work done by all the forces acting on the body.

Supplementary Notes.

In situations involving a continuous transfer of energy, it is often useful to think in terms of the work done per unit time. This is called the *power*, and is measured in watts: $1 \text{ W} = 1 \text{ J/s}$.

Problem 4C.2

Since work is a scalar while force and displacement are vectors, the definition of work in more than one dimension requires a modification of the $W \equiv F \Delta x$ definition given above. We have already seen, however, that the kinetic energy of a projectile varies with its height, but is not affected by the horizontal motion which is perpendicular to the gravitational force. To generalize this principle to arbitrary forces, we introduce the *dot product*, or scalar product, between two vectors, which can be defined by

$$\vec{a} \cdot \vec{b} \equiv |\vec{a}||\vec{b}| \cos \theta \, ,$$

where $\vec{a}$ and $\vec{b}$ are arbitrary vectors, $|\vec{a}|$ and $|\vec{b}|$ denote their magnitudes, and θ is the angle between them. Equivalently, one can write

$$\vec{a} \cdot \vec{b} = |\vec{a}| \times \text{component of } \vec{b} \text{ in direction of } \vec{a}.$$

$$= |\vec{b}| \times \text{component of } \vec{a} \text{ in direction of } \vec{b}.$$

It can also be shown that in terms of the components of the vectors, $\vec{a} = [a_x, a_y, a_z]$ and $\vec{b} = [b_x, b_y, b_z]$, the dot product is given by

$$\vec{a} \cdot \vec{b} = a_x b_x + a_y b_y + a_z b_z \, .$$

In three dimensions it is only the component of the force in the direction of the displacement $\vec{\Delta r}$ that contributes to the work done, so for a constant force

Problems 4C

$$W \equiv \vec{F} \cdot \vec{\Delta r} \, .$$

If the force acts at right angles to the displacement, the dot product is zero, so no work is done and no energy is transferred.

If the force is not constant, we must integrate over the displacement to find the work done. In one dimension this gives

$$W \equiv \int F(x) \, dx \, ,$$

while in three dimensions

$$W \equiv \int_{\vec{\mathbf{r}}_1}^{\vec{\mathbf{r}}_2} \vec{\mathbf{F}} \cdot \vec{\mathbf{dr}} \ .$$

It can be shown that the work-energy theorem holds for non-constant forces, and for three-dimensional motion, with W defined by the above equation.

Does it matter *how* we get from $\vec{r}_1$ to $\vec{r}_2$? Even in one dimension there are clearly an infinite number of ways to get from x_1 to x_2: we can go directly there and stop, or we can overshoot and come back; we can travel slowly or rapidly, at constant speed or with varying speed. Does this make a difference to the work done?

Supplementary Notes.

The answer depends on the nature of the force. In the one-dimensional case, if the force exerted on a body depends only on the body's position, and not on its velocity or the history of its past motion, then there can be no dependence on the precise route from x_1 to x_2: if the force does not depend on velocity, clearly the velocity does not affect the work done, and if we overshoot, the work $F(x)\Delta x$ that we do in going from x to $x+\Delta x$ is cancelled by the work $F\cdot(-\Delta x)$ that we do coming back from $x+\Delta x$ to x. So in this case the body at position x_2 has a well-defined *potential energy* compared to the body at x_1: if we move from x_1 to x_2, no matter how we do it, we will do a certain well-defined amount of work. A force which behaves in this way is called a *conservative force*. Gravity, the electrostatic force and the spring force are all conservative forces. Friction, which we will discuss in Chapter 6, is an example of a non-conservative force: as we know from everyday experience, friction acts to resist the relative motion of two surfaces, and therefore the frictional force exerted on a body at position x depends on whether its velocity is positive or negative. Hence it is no longer true that the work done in moving from x to $x+\Delta x$ cancels the work done moving from $x+\Delta x$ to x, and the route we take from x_1 to x_2 does matter. For non-conservative forces, therefore, we cannot calculate the work done just from the initial and final positions of the particle.

In two or three dimensions, the situation seems more complicated, because the body can take an infinite number of routes from $\vec{r}_1$ to $\vec{r}_2$ without retracing its path. It is therefore not sufficient to conclude that retracing our steps from $\vec{r} + \overrightarrow{\Delta r}$ back to $\vec{r}$ will cancel the work done in moving from $\vec{r}$ to $\vec{r} + \overrightarrow{\Delta r}$. Note, however, that any two routes P_1 and P_2 can be combined to form a closed loop P_{12}, consisting of P_1 followed by the reverse of P_2:

119

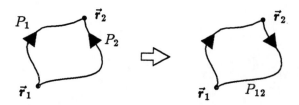

Since the work done along the path P_2 changes sign if the path is traversed in the opposite direction, the statement that the work along P_1 and P_2 are equal is equivalent to the statement that the work done along the closed path is zero. Thus, a force is conservative if the work done on an object when it travels around a closed loop is exactly zero. In this chapter, we consider only conservative forces.

The definition of the potential energy, specified above to be equal to mgh for a uniform gravitational field, can be generalized to describe any conservative force. The potential energy of an object at a point $\vec{r}_p$ is defined to be the work that must be done to bring the object to that point. Since only potential energy differences are meaningful, one arbitrarily chooses a reference point $\vec{r}_0$, defining the potential energy at $\vec{r}_0$ to be an arbitrarily chosen number U_0. The potential energy at any other point $\vec{r}_p$ is then the potential energy at $\vec{r}_0$, plus the work that is required to bring the object from $\vec{r}_0$ to $\vec{r}_p$:

$$U(\vec{r}_p) \equiv U_0 - \int_{\vec{r}_0}^{\vec{r}_p} \vec{F} \cdot \vec{dr} \ .$$

The minus sign appears in front of the force term because we need to calculate the work that would have to be done by a force from outside the system to **oppose** the force $\vec{F}$ exerted by the objects in the system. In one dimension, this relation reduces to

$$U(x_p) \equiv U_0 - \int_{x_0}^{x_p} F \, dx \ .$$

In this chapter we will be concerned mainly with the following four cases:

Problems 4B.3, 4B.4, and 4B.5

Force	Force Law	Potential Energy
Uniform gravity	$\vec{\mathbf{F}} = -mg\hat{y}$	$U = mgy$
Gravity of sphere	$\vec{\mathbf{F}} = -\dfrac{GMm}{r^2}\hat{r}$	$U = -\dfrac{GMm}{r}$
Electrostatics	$\vec{\mathbf{F}} = \dfrac{Qq}{4\pi\epsilon_0 r^2}\hat{r}$	$U = \dfrac{Qq}{4\pi\epsilon_0 r}$
Spring	$F = -kx$	$U = \frac{1}{2}kx^2$

Using the path-independence of the integral, one can show that for any two points,

$$U(\vec{\mathbf{r}}_2) - U(\vec{\mathbf{r}}_1) = -\int_{\vec{\mathbf{r}}_1}^{\vec{\mathbf{r}}_2} \vec{\mathbf{F}} \cdot \vec{\mathbf{dr}} \ .$$

Since the work-energy theorem guarantees that the integral on the right (without the minus sign) is the amount by which the kinetic energy of the object increases as it moves from $\vec{\mathbf{r}}_1$ to $\vec{\mathbf{r}}_2$, it follows that

$$\boxed{K_2 + U(\vec{\mathbf{r}}_2) = K_1 + U(\vec{\mathbf{r}}_1) = \text{constant} \ ,}$$

Problems 4D

where K_1 and K_2 denote the kinetic energy at $\vec{\mathbf{r}}_1$ and $\vec{\mathbf{r}}_2$, respectively. So, for conservative forces, the total *mechanical energy*, the sum of the kinetic and potential energies, does not change with time. (In this chapter we will not consider nonconservative forces (e.g., friction), but it is worth mentioning that such forces can convert energy into other forms (e.g., heat, or electromagnetic waves).)

The above discussion has assumed that only one particle in our system is moving, and the potential energy of the system is then a function of the position of that one object—we can reasonably, if loosely, say that it is a property of the object. This is a good approximation in many real situations: for example, in projectile problems the Earth can be regarded as stationary, so the potential energy of the Earth-projectile system is determined by the position of the projectile and we say that "the projectile has gravitational potential energy mgh." However, this is not always true: if we consider, say, the electrostatic forces between two charged particles of equal mass,

Problem 4D.6

121

in general both of them will move. In such cases the potential energy difference between two configurations of the system is the work required to move all the particles from one configuration to the other.

For motion in one dimension, the change in potential energy as an object moves from x to $x + \Delta x$, for infinitesimal Δx, is given by $\Delta U = -F\,\Delta x$. It follows that

$$F = -\frac{dU}{dx}.$$

In three dimensions the analogous relation is

$$\vec{\mathbf{F}} = \left[-\frac{\partial U}{\partial x}, -\frac{\partial U}{\partial y}, -\frac{\partial U}{\partial z} \right].$$

The symbol $\partial U/\partial x$, the **partial derivative of U with respect to x**, is used to describe a derivative of a function of more than one variable: it means to differentiate U with respect to x, treating the other variables (in this case y and z) as constants.

Since the force can be determined from the potential energy, and vice versa, a physical situation can be specified equally well by specifying the force law or the potential energy function. In many situations it is more convenient to specify the potential energy.

From $F = -dU/dx$ it is apparent that positions of equilibrium **Problem 4E.1** for a force correspond to places where the derivative of U is zero, i.e. (local) minima or maxima, or occasionally saddle points, of the potential. Stable equilibria correspond to local minima.

Any smooth function $y(x)$ can be expressed in the form of a **Problems 4E.2, 4E.3,** power series **4E.4, and 4E.5**

$$y(x) = y(0) + k_1 x + k_2 x^2 + k_3 x^3 + \ldots,$$

where k_1, k_2, etc., are constants. If we do this for a potential energy function, then

$$U(x) = U(0) + k_1 x + k_2 x^2 + k_3 x^3 + \ldots.$$

Since only potential differences are defined, we are free to choose $U(0) = 0$, which shifts the function by an overall constant. Furthermore, we can define the x coordinate so that $x = 0$ is a local minimum of $U(x)$. Differentiating with respect to x gives

$$F(x) = -dU/dx = -k_1 - 2k_2 x - 3k_3 x^2 - \ldots,$$

but the statement that $x = 0$ is a local minimum implies that $k_1 = 0$ (the derivative vanishes at a local minimum) and that $k_2 \geq 0$ (because if it were negative $x = 0$ would be a local maximum). Hence if x is very small, so that the terms in x^2 and higher powers of x are negligible compared to the term in x, we have

$$F(x) \approx -2k_2 x \,,$$

which (as we saw in Chapter 2) is the type of force that leads to simple harmonic motion. Thus, in nearly all cases, a sufficiently small displacement from any local minimum of the potential energy function will lead to simple harmonic motion. The rare exceptions are cases where $k_2 = 0$ at a local minimum, so that the force is proportional to $-x^3$—this will still cause oscillations, but not simple harmonic oscillations—and certain types of functions which cannot be expressed as power series. Such functions are not found to arise physically, although sometimes they do appear in idealized physics problems.

SUMMARY

* The quantities $\frac{1}{2}mv^2$ and mgh which arise in some formulations of projectile and related problems are not just calculational conveniences, but different forms of a new physical concept, the *energy* of the body.

* Unlike force, velocity, etc., energy can occur in different guises: $\frac{1}{2}mv^2$ is the *kinetic energy* of a moving object, and mgh is the *gravitational potential energy* of a body near the Earth's surface, at a height h relative to some reference level.

* Forces can do work on an object. The work done by a constant force on an object is defined as the dot product of the force $\vec{F}$ and the displacement vector $\overrightarrow{\Delta r}$ through which the object has moved, i.e., $\Delta W = \vec{F} \cdot \overrightarrow{\Delta r}$. The *work-energy theorem* states that kinetic energy of the object increases by the total amount of work done on it by all the forces acting on it. (If the total work done is negative, then the kinetic energy of the object decreases.) The amount of work done per unit time is called the *power*.

* In the case of a non-constant force, the above definition of work still holds for an *infinitesimally small* displacement $\overrightarrow{\Delta r}$. The total work over a large displacement is obtained by integrating $\vec{F} \cdot \overrightarrow{\Delta r}$ along the path taken by the object, so $W = \int_{\text{Path}} \vec{F} \cdot \overrightarrow{dr}$.

* The total amount of energy present in any closed system is unchanged by these transformations: energy is *conserved*. As far as we can tell the principle of energy conservation is an exact truth, which remains valid even under circumstances that require Newtonian mechanics to be replaced by relativity and/or quantum theory.

* Energy can be stored in the configuration of a system, e.g. the compression of a spring, or the separation of two gravitationally interacting bodies (the Sun and the Earth, or the Earth and a projectile, for instance). If the work done by a force depends only on the initial and final configurations, but not on the path between them, then the force is called *conservative*. For such forces, which include gravitational, electrostatic, and ideal spring forces, one can define a *potential energy* function to describe the energy stored in the configuration. For the gravitational force between two spheres, or between a sphere and a point mass, the potential energy is $U = -GMm/r$, where G is Newton's constant, M and m are the masses, and r is the distance between their centers. The potential energy of a spring is $\frac{1}{2}kx^2$, where k is the spring constant and x is the displacement from the natural length.

* For conservative forces, the total *mechanical energy* (kinetic energy plus potential energy) is conserved. For non-conservative forces, such as friction, other forms of energy, such as heat, have to be included in the conservation law.

* For conservative forces, the force can be expressed as the derivative of the position-dependent potential energy, and the positions of equilibrium correspond to local maxima or minima of the potential energy. A stable equilibrium corresponds to a local minimum of the potential energy.

* Physical concepts introduced in this chapter: energy, kinetic energy, potential energy, conservation of energy, work, power.

* Mathematical concepts introduced in this chapter: dot (or scalar) product, partial derivative.

* Many of the equations introduced in this chapter are summarized in the following table:

1 Dimension	3 Dimensions	Description
$W \equiv F\Delta x$	$W \equiv \vec{\mathbf{F}} \cdot \overrightarrow{\mathbf{\Delta r}}$	Work done by a constant force $\vec{\mathbf{F}}$
$W \equiv \displaystyle\int F(x)\,\mathrm{d}x$	$W \equiv \displaystyle\int_{\vec{\mathbf{r}}_1}^{\vec{\mathbf{r}}_2} \vec{\mathbf{F}} \cdot \overrightarrow{\mathbf{dr}}$	Work done by a varying force $\vec{\mathbf{F}}$
$U(x_p) \equiv U_0 - \displaystyle\int_{x_0}^{x_p} F\,\mathrm{d}x$	$U(\vec{\mathbf{r}}_p) \equiv U_0 - \displaystyle\int_{\vec{\mathbf{r}}_0}^{\vec{\mathbf{r}}_p} \vec{\mathbf{F}} \cdot \overrightarrow{\mathbf{dr}}$	Potential energy derived from force $\vec{\mathbf{F}}$
$F = -\dfrac{\mathrm{d}U}{\mathrm{d}x}$	$\vec{\mathbf{F}} = \left[-\dfrac{\partial U}{\partial x}, -\dfrac{\partial U}{\partial y}, -\dfrac{\partial U}{\partial z} \right]$	Force derived from potential energy

* Other equations introduced in this chapter:

$$\vec{\mathbf{a}} \cdot \vec{\mathbf{b}} = |\vec{\mathbf{a}}||\vec{\mathbf{b}}| \cos\theta \qquad \text{(scalar (or dot) product of two vectors)}$$

$$= a_x b_x + a_y b_y + a_z b_z$$

$$\frac{1}{2}mv^2 + mgh = \frac{1}{2}mv_0^2 \qquad \text{(kinetic \& potential energy for projectile)}$$

$$\frac{1}{2}mv^2 + U(x) = \text{constant} \qquad \text{(energy conservation)}$$

$$W = K_f - K_i \qquad \text{(work-energy theorem)}$$

$$U = \frac{1}{2}kx^2 \qquad \text{(potential energy for spring force)}$$

$$U = mgh \qquad \text{(gravitational potential energy, near Earth)}$$

$$U = -\frac{GMm}{r} \qquad \text{(gravitational potential energy, spherical bodies)}$$

PROBLEMS AND QUESTIONS

By the end of this chapter you should be able to answer or solve the types of questions or problems stated below.

Note: throughout the book, in multiple-choice problems, the answers have been rounded off to 2 significant figures, unless otherwise stated.

At the end of the chapter there are answers to all the problems. In addition, for problems with an (H) or (S) after the number, there are respectively hints on how to solve the problems or completely worked-out solutions.

4A   KINETIC ENERGY

4A.1   A particle of mass 0.3 kg moves with velocity [0.6, 1.2, - 0.5] m/s. What is its kinetic energy?

(a) 0.25 J; (b) 0.79 J; (c) 0.31 J; (d) 0.52 J.

4A.2   A projectile of mass m is launched over level ground with an initial speed of v_0 at an angle θ to the horizontal. Neglecting air resistance, what is its kinetic energy (a) just after launch, (b) at the top of its flight, (c) when it lands?

4B   WORK AND POTENTIAL ENERGY IN ONE DIMENSION

4B.1   A book of mass 0.5 kg is lifted at constant speed from the floor to the top of a filing cabinet 1.5 m high. By how much has its potential energy changed?

(a) 0.75 J; (b) 7.4 J; (c) 0 J; (d) none of these.

4B.2 (S)   You lift a box of mass m from the floor and place it on a shelf a height h above floor level.

(a) How much work have you done on the box? What is the total work done on the box? What happens to the energy of the box? Do the details of the motion of the box during the lift make a difference to your answers?

(b) At the instant when the box has reached height $\frac{1}{2}h$, is the work you have done on it so far more or less than half of the total work you will do during the lift? Explain your reasoning.

4B.3   Suppose that a spring obeys Hooke's law with spring constant k. Show that the potential energy stored in it when it is compressed (or extended) by an amount x is given by $\frac{1}{2}kx^2$, taking the potential energy of the unstretched spring to be zero.

4B.4 (S)   The gravitational potential energy of a mass m outside a spherical body of mass M is given by $U(r) = -GMm/r$, where r is the distance of the mass m from the center of the body M. Show that this expression can be reduced to the form $U = mgh$ for a mass m near the Earth's surface.

4B.5 (H)   Derive expressions for, and plot, the potential energy

(a) of a space probe of mass m as a function of distance from the Sun, which has mass M (neglect the effect of the planets);

(b) of a positive charge q as a function of distance from a positive charge Q;

126

4B.5, continued:

(c) of a negative charge $-q$ as a function of distance from a positive charge Q.

It is convenient to be able to draw the plots in a way that is independent of the specific values of M, m, Q, and q. To do this, introduce an arbitrary reference distance r_0. In case (a) the scale on your y-axis should be in terms of GMm/r_0, while in cases (b) and (c) the scale is in terms of $Qq/(4\pi\epsilon_0 r_0)$. In all cases the horizontal axis can be taken as r/r_0, and U_0 should be defined so that U is zero when the distance is infinitely large. For simplicity you may treat this as a one-dimensional problem, considering motion only along a line joining the two objects. (The correct answer to the one-dimensional problem is also valid in three dimensions, but you are not asked to show this.)

4B.6   In 100 words or less explain what is meant by the term "potential energy".

4C   WORK IN THREE DIMENSIONS

4C.1   A skier of mass 70 kg skis 40 m down a frictionless ski-slope inclined at 30° to the horizontal. How much work has been done by gravity on the skier?

(a) 2.8 kJ; (b) 27 kJ; (c) 14 kJ; (d) 24 kJ.

4C.2 (S)   A horse tows a barge along a canal. The horse exerts a constant force of 750 N and the tow-rope makes an angle of 30° with the direction of motion of the barge. How much work is done by the horse on the barge, via the tow-rope, over a distance of 1 km? If the horse is traveling at 1 m/s, what power does it supply to the barge? Assume that this stretch of the canal is straight.

4C.3 (H)   A particle moves with constant velocity [4, −2, 1] m/s. If its mass is 3 kg, what is its kinetic energy? One of the forces acting on it is given by $\vec{F} = [-1, 2, 2]$ N. Find the work done by this force on the particle as it moves a distance of 3 m. What is the total work done on the particle, and why?

4C.4 (S)   A boy swings a pail of water on the end of a rope in a vertical circle. If the rope is 90 cm long, the mass of the pail plus water is 1.5 kg, and the rope is just taut at the top of the swing, what is the speed of the pail at the bottom of the swing, what work is done as the pail moves, and what force is responsible for the work? Assume that the boy's hand does not move during the period considered in this problem.

4D   CONSERVATION OF ENERGY

4D.1 (S)   **Energy Conservation Riddles**

(a) John is holding a 17 inch computer monitor, with a mass of 25 kg, at a constant height. He complains that it is hard work, and he is becoming exhausted. Jim, who is taking physics, tells him that since there is no displacement in the direction of the applied force, he is not doing any work, and therefore should not be tired. Who is right, and why?

(b) Mary is riding an elevator from the 4th to the 7th floor, wearing a backpack of mass M. Between the 5th and 6th floors the elevator is moving at constant speed, through a distance ℓ. Joan, another physics student, argues that since the velocity of Mary's

127

4D.1, continued:

backpack is constant, the total force must be zero, and therefore Mary is applying an upward force just enough to cancel that of gravity, Mg. Since the displacement is upward by a distance ℓ, the work that Mary has done on the backpack is $W = Mg\ell$. Mary, on the other hand, points out that the weight she feels is just the same as it would be if she were stationary on the sidewalk, in which case there would be no displacement and therefore no work. Since she is burning no more calories than she would if she were on the sidewalk, and since energy cannot be created from nothing, there is no energy available for her to do work on the backpack. Who is right, and why?

(c) A skater on a frictionless ice rink is initially stationary. Holding onto a rope attached to the wall, he gives a yank and starts himself moving toward the wall. Jean, a physics student who is watching, tells her friend Joe that since the kinetic energy of the skater has increased, work must have been done. It was the rope that applied the force, Jean explains, so it was the rope that did the work on the skater. "Nonsense," Joe replied, "ropes can't do work! Ropes don't have any source of energy, so the principle of energy conservation implies that they can't do work. Obviously it was the skater who did the work." "But the skater can't possibly exert a net force on himself," retorted Jean, "so he can't have done the work." Who is right here, and why?

4D.2 A construction worker uses a hoist to lift a 50 kg bag of cement at constant speed from the ground to the top of a scaffold 10 m high.

(a) What is the *total* work done on the cement?

(b) What is the work done on the cement by the hoist?

(c) What is the change in the potential energy of the cement?

(d) Discuss your answers in terms of the principle of energy conservation.

(e) Would your answers be different if the speed were not constant?

4D.3 (S) A cannon is capable of firing cannonballs with a fixed speed v_0 but at a range of elevation angles. What will be the speed of the ball at a height h?

4D.4 (H) A simple pendulum consisting of a mass m attached to a string of length ℓ is released from rest at an angle θ_0. A pin is located at a distance L below the pivot point. When the pendulum swings down, the string hits the pin as shown.

(a) What is the maximum angle α that the string makes with the vertical after hitting the pin?

(b) If the bob had been released with an initial velocity v_0 as shown, what would be the maximum value of α? How would this be affected if v_0 were in the opposite direction?

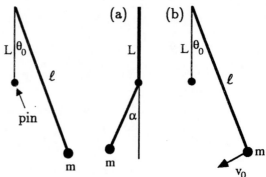

4D.5 (S) A spring with spring constant k is used to power a spring gun which launches a ball of mass m vertically upwards. If the spring is compressed by an amount x beyond its equilibrium position to launch the ball, derive an expression for the maximum height reached by the ball, measured from its position when the spring is compressed. If k is 200 N/m, $m = 50$ g, and the spring is initially compressed by 4 cm, how high will the ball go?

4D.6 (S) Two objects of equal mass m are connected by a spring of negligible mass, unstretched length ℓ_0, and spring constant k. They are initially at rest on a frictionless air table. An experimenter pulls the objects apart until they are separated by a distance $\ell > \ell_0$. What is the potential energy of the system of masses and spring? If the experimenter now lets go, at what speed is each mass moving when the spring has contracted back to its unstretched length? Compare this with the situation where one end of the spring is attached to a body of mass m and the other to a fixed point on the air table.

4E   EQUILIBRIUM AND OSCILLATIONS

4E.1 The potential energy of a particle is given in terms of its position x by $U = -x + 2x^2$, where U is measured in joules and x in meters. At what value of x is the particle in equilibrium?

(a) 0.25 m; (b) 0 m; (c) 0.5 m; (d) none of these.

4E.2 (S) (a) The interior of an ornamental bowl forms a hemisphere of radius 10 cm. The surface is smooth and highly polished. If I place a small object at a distance s from the bottom of the bowl (where s is measured along the inner surface of the bowl, so that s varies from 0 to $\pi R/2$, $R = 10$ cm), how fast will it be moving when it reaches the bottom of the bowl?

(b) What is the form of the potential energy of the object if s is small? Deduce the force acting on the object if it is displaced slightly from the bottom of the bowl and then released, and describe the resulting motion.

4E.3 (S) A small charge of mass 10 g moves in one dimension in a complicated linear distribution of fixed charges. Over a certain range of distances, the potential energy of the charge is found to be described to a good approximation by

$$U(r) = U_0 + ar + br^2 + cr^3 ,$$

where $U_0 = 10$ J, $a = -1$ J/m, $b = 2$ J/m^2, and $c = -1$ J/m^3. At what values of r would the particle be in equilibrium, and what would the period of small oscillations (if any) around these equilibrium positions be?

4E.4 (H) A slider of mass 50 g moves on a frictionless linear air track built in the form of a sine wave, so that the height of the track at any point x is given by $y = A \sin kx$, where $A = 0.3$ m and $k = 2$ m^{-1} (i.e. the track describes a complete cycle of the sine function over a distance of π meters in x, reaching a maximum height of 30 cm and a minimum height of -30 cm). The length of the track is 4 m, so $0 \leq x \leq 4$ m.

(a) If the potential energy of the slider is defined to be zero where the track reaches its minimum height what is its value at an arbitrary point x?

129

(b) At what values of x would a stationary slider be in equilibrium? Are small oscillations possible about any of these points, and if so what is the period of these oscillations?

(You may find it useful to recall that for small angles $\cos\theta = 1 - \frac{1}{2}\theta^2$.)

4E.5 (H) A 1 kg mass is suspended from a spring of spring constant 120 N/m. The coordinate system is defined so that y is directed vertically upwards and $y = 0$ when the spring is at its natural length. The mass is first positioned at $y = 0$, and then lowered gently until it is hanging freely from the spring.

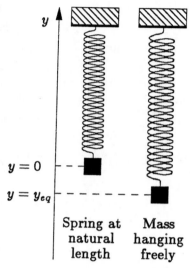

Where does the mass come to rest? What then is its gravitational potential energy, and what is the potential energy stored in the spring, compared to their values when the mass is at $y = 0$? Explain why these two quantities are not equal. What work was done (i) by gravity, (ii) by the spring force, as the mass was lowered from $y = 0$ to its equilibrium position? If instead of being lowered gently the mass had simply been released at $y = 0$ and allowed to fall under the combined effects of gravity and the spring force, at what speed would it be moving when it crosses the equilibrium value of y, and what would be its subsequent motion (be quantitative as far as possible)?

COMPLETE SOLUTIONS TO PROBLEMS WITH AN (S)

4B.2 (a) *You lift a box of mass m from the floor and place it on a shelf a height h above floor level. How much work have you done on the box? What is the total work done on the box? What happens to the energy of the box? Do the details of the motion of the box during the lift make a difference to your answers?*

Conceptualize
There are two basic ways to deal with energy problems, the work approach and the conservation of energy approach. In the work approach, we focus on a **single object**, the forces acting on it, and its displacement. Since potential energy is a **system** property, it plays no role in the work approach to energy problems. In contrast, the conservation of energy approach focuses on the **total** energy of a **system**: in this case the potential energy of the system must be included, but we do not need to consider forces acting and work done internally within the system (although if the system is not closed we may need to consider the work done by an external force to calculate the transfer of energy into or out of the system).

In this case most of the question is phrased in terms of work, so we should use the work approach. The object in question is clearly the box, its displacement is h, vertically upwards, and the forces acting on it are gravity and the force supplied by you. Both of these are acting vertically, i.e. parallel to the displacement of the box, and therefore both can do work on the box.

Formulate
The work-energy theorem states that the total work done on the box is

$$W_{fi} = K_f - K_i .$$

This is clearly zero, as initial and final kinetic energy are both zero.

At first sight it is not obvious how to calculate the work you do on the box, because we are not told what force you exerted. However, we do know the gravitational force on the box, mg directed downwards, and can therefore calculate the work done by gravity on the box,

$$\vec{\mathbf{F}} \cdot \overrightarrow{\mathbf{\Delta y}} = -mgh$$

(the minus sign comes from the fact that the force is directed downwards, whereas the displacement is directed upwards). Since we know that the total work done is zero, we can easily determine the work done by the only other force acting, namely your muscular effort.

To calculate the energy of the box, or more exactly of the box-Earth system, we need to include the gravitational potential energy. Since the box's height above the Earth's surface has increased by h, the system potential energy has increased by mgh.

Solve
The work you do on the box is $0 - (-mgh) = mgh$. As stated above, the total work done on the box is zero, independent of the details of the motion (the only stipulation is that the box starts from rest and finishes at rest). As we will see in part (b), however,

131

4B.2, continued:

the work done at an arbitrary point during the lift *does* depend to some extent on the details of the motion, specifically on the speed at which the box is lifted.

The total energy of the box-Earth system has increased by mgh, the increase in its gravitational potential energy. This is equal to the work done by you, which represents an energy transfer into the system from outside (in contrast, the work done by gravity is internal to the box-Earth system, and does not change the total energy of the system).

Scrutinize and Learn

Our solution appears to be self-consistent, since the work you do accounts for the increase in the gravitational potential energy of the box. But where has this energy come from? Your kinetic energy has not decreased, and nor has your gravitational potential energy. What has happened is that exothermic chemical reactions in your muscles release chemical potential energy, some of which goes into supplying energy to the box. (Much of it unfortunately goes into raising your body temperature—muscle effort is not a very efficient form of energy transfer.) Chemical potential energy and heat are two more forms that the energy of a body can take. We consider heat as a form of energy later in the book, in Chapter 11.

4B.2 (b) *At the instant when the box has reached a height $\frac{1}{2}h$, is the work you have done on it so far more or less than half of the total work you will do during the lift? Explain your reasoning.*

Conceptualize

Most of the conceptualization carries over from part (a). We are still considering work done on the box, and the forces doing work are gravity and the force exerted by you. This time the displacement is $\frac{1}{2}h$. At first sight it looks as though this problem is trivial, but there is another factor we must consider: the lift is still in progress at this point, and therefore the box is *moving* when it passes the point $\frac{1}{2}h$. Hence there is some kinetic energy involved, and this must be included when we apply the work-energy theorem.

Formulate and Solve

The conceptualization has essentially solved the problem. At height $\frac{1}{2}h$, gravity has done work $-\frac{1}{2}mgh$ on the box. The total work done on the box is equal to the kinetic energy it has gained, $\frac{1}{2}mv^2$, where v is its speed at the moment we are considering. Therefore the work you have done is $\frac{1}{2}mgh + \frac{1}{2}mv^2$, which is more than half of the total work you will do.

Scrutinize and Learn

If we assume that you lift the box at constant speed, it's clear that the "extra" work $\frac{1}{2}mv^2$ is done in the first instant of the lift. Right at the end of the lift you exert an upward force of magnitude less than mg, allowing the box to come to rest on the shelf: during this period there is a net downward force which does work $-\frac{1}{2}mv^2$, giving zero total work as we calculated in part (a). This does accord with our experience that the hardest part of the lift is getting the box off the ground in the first place. Other aspects of our formal definition of work, however, are not so consistent with everyday experience: see, for example, the energy conservation riddle 4D.1(a).

4B.4   *The gravitational potential energy of a mass m outside a spherical body of mass M is given by $U(r) = -GMm/r$, where r is the distance of the mass m from the center of the body M. Show that this expression can be reduced to the form $U = mgh$ for a mass m near the Earth's surface.*

Conceptualize

The gravitational potential energy mgh is the difference between the potential energy at height h and the potential energy at a reference point, which we take as the surface of the Earth, $h = 0$. We can calculate this by considering the difference between the potential energy at radius $r_E + h$ and the potential energy at radius r_E, where r_E denotes the radius of the Earth. Since we are dealing with a mass "near the Earth's surface" the value of h will be small compared to the radius of the Earth, or $h \ll r_E$.

Formulate

We can use the form of $U(r)$ given in the question, namely $U(r) = -GMm/r$, where M is the mass of the Earth and r the distance from its center. This gives

$$\Delta U(h) = -\frac{GMm}{r_E + h} - \left(-\frac{GMm}{r_E} \right) \ .$$

This equation alone cannot be enough, because we have G and M here and g in the expression we are trying to justify. So we also need an equation for g, which we can obtain by applying $F = ma$ to a freely falling body near the Earth's surface:

$$\frac{GMm}{r_E^2} = mg \ .$$

With these two equations we can solve the problem: we will use the second equation to eliminate GM from our expression for $\Delta U(h)$. It is not immediately obvious that we will also be able to eliminate r_E.

Solve

Simplifying the expression for $\Delta U(h)$,

$$\Delta U(h) = -GMm \left(\frac{1}{r_E + h} - \frac{1}{r_E} \right) = -GMm \left(\frac{-h}{r_E(r_E + h)} \right) \ .$$

Since $h \ll r_E$ (i.e., we are near the Earth's surface), $r_E(r_E + h)$ is not significantly different from r_E^2. We can therefore write:

$$\Delta U(h) = \frac{GMm}{r_E^2} h \ ,$$

which becomes, on using our expression for mg,

$$\Delta U(h) = mgh \ ,$$

and this is exactly what we were asked to show.

4B.4, continued:

Scrutinize

Since we were given the final expression in the question, the dimensions are "obviously" correct, but we can check anyway: mgh represents mass × acceleration × length, i.e. force × distance, which is what we expect for work or energy.

The crucial step in our argument is that $r_E(r_E + h) \approx r_E^2$; this is what allows us to eliminate r_E from our final equation. Is this reasonable? If we recall that the radius of the Earth is about 6400 km, and consider the largest values of h we are likely to use, for example a commercial airliner flying at $h = 11$ km, the difference between $r_E(r_E + h)$ and r_E^2 is 0.17%. It does seem reasonable to argue that this difference is negligible.

Learn

We seem to have achieved the impossible here: we have taken an initial equation with four parameters, i.e. G, M, r_E and h, used only one additional equation, and ended up with an expression with only two parameters, g and h! Where did the other variables go? The answer is that in this case G, M and r_E are not behaving like separate variables—they occur in the same combination in both equations, so they can all be eliminated as if they were a single variable.

The technique we applied here, namely neglecting a small quantity in combination with a much larger one (setting $r_E + h \approx r_E$) is very widely used in physics and engineering. If you use it, however, you must be sure that the large quantity is not going to cancel out at some later stage in the calculation—for example, in this problem it would *not* be helpful to set $r_E + h \approx r_E$ in $1/(r_E + h) - 1/r_E$!

There are realistic problems where h is not much smaller than r_E, such as the calculation of the gravitational potential energy of a communications satellite ($h \approx 36000$ km). For such calculations we must use $U = -GMm/r$ rather than $U = mgh$.

4C.2   *A horse tows a barge along a canal. The horse exerts a constant force of 750 N and the tow-rope makes an angle of 30° with the direction of motion of the barge. How much work is done by the horse on the barge, via the tow-rope, over a distance of 1 km? If the horse is traveling at 1 m/s, what power does it supply to the barge? Assume that this stretch of the canal is straight.*

Conceptualize

It seems natural to accept that the force applied by the horse does work on the barge, but, as we will see in Problem 4D.1, "common sense" is not always a good guide when dealing with the physicist's definition of work. We had better start by analyzing this problem using the conservation-of-energy approach.

The horse pulls on the rope, applying a force to it. The rope moves, and therefore work has been done on it ($\vec{F} \cdot \vec{\Delta r} \neq 0$). However, the rope's kinetic energy does not increase, nor does it stretch, so the energy of the rope has not increased. Hence the energy supplied to the rope system by the horse must be balanced by the energy supplied by the rope to something else, namely the barge: the rope does work on the barge equal to the work done on the rope by the horse.

4C.2, continued:

It is, therefore, correct to equate the work done by the horse to the work done on the barge. Since the force that the horse is applying to the barge is not parallel to the direction of motion of the barge, we will need the dot product $\vec{F} \cdot \vec{r}$, which corresponds to taking the projection of the force along the barge direction.

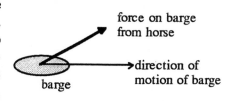

force on barge from horse

direction of motion of barge

barge

The power supplied to the barge is simply the work done per unit time.

Formulate

The projection of the force along the direction of motion is $F \cos\theta$, where F is the magnitude of the force and θ is the angle between the force and the direction of motion. The work done is therefore

$$W = Fr \cos\theta \, ,$$

where r is the displacement of the barge.

The work done per unit time is

$$\frac{dW}{dt} = F \cos\theta \cdot \frac{dr}{dt} = Fv \cos\theta \, ,$$

where v is the speed of the barge (both F and θ are constant, remember).

Solve

Our formulation has already produced the algebraic solutions. All that remains is to put in the numbers:

Work done over 1 km = 750 N × 1000 m × cos 30° = 650 kJ.
Power supplied = 750 N × 1 m/s × cos 30° = 650 W.

Scrutinize

The common British and American unit for the power supplied by an engine, the *horsepower*, does indeed derive from estimates of the power of one (strong) horse. In SI units 1 hp = 746 W. Our value for the power is therefore reasonable. The dimensions are clearly correct, as can be seen in the numerical calculations above.

Learn

In this example we did not need to use the integral formula for the work done, because we were working with a constant force and a constant velocity. If the angle of the towrope had been varying during the period covered by the problem, we would have had to calculate $\int \vec{F} \cdot \vec{dr}$ explicitly, instead of simply multiplying the total displacement by the projection of the force.

Note that the barge continues to move at constant velocity, so the *total* work done on it must be zero. The positive work done by the horse is balanced by negative work

4C.2, continued:

done by the water of the canal, which exerts a drag force on the barge in the direction opposite to its direction of motion.

4C.4   *A boy swings a pail of water on the end of a rope in a vertical circle. If the rope is 90 cm long, the mass of the pail plus water is 1.5 kg, and the rope is just taut at the top of the swing, what is the speed of the pail at the bottom of the swing, what work is done as the pail moves, and what force is responsible for the work? Assume that the boy's hand is stationary.*

Conceptualize

We are asked for the speed of the pail at the bottom of its swing, but we have more information about the forces acting at the top of the swing, since we are told that the rope is only just taut, i.e. the tension in it is zero, at that point. We can therefore break this problem into three parts:

- Calculate the speed of the pail at the top of its swing. This we can do using Newton's laws, since we know the force and the acceleration.

- Calculate the final kinetic energy. We can do this by applying conservation of energy to the Earth-pail system. This gives us the speed of the pail at the bottom of its swing.

- Find the work done on the pail considered as a single object. Since we now know the change in its kinetic energy, we can do this by using the work-energy theorem.

What force is doing the work? It cannot be the tension in the rope, because the pail is moving in a circle, and therefore its velocity is always at right angles to the direction of the rope. A force acting at right angles to the direction of motion cannot do work ($\cos\theta = 0$). Therefore the only force doing work on the pail is gravity.

Formulate

At the top of the swing, the only force acting is gravity, $m\vec{g}$, where m is the mass of the pail. Since the pail is engaged in circular motion, its acceleration is v_0^2/r, where v_0 is the speed at the top of the swing and r is the length of the rope. So we have

$$mg = m\frac{v_0^2}{r} \ . \tag{1}$$

When the pail reaches the bottom of its swing, it has traveled through a vertical distance $2r$ and has therefore lost potential energy $2mgr$, so its kinetic energy must have increased by this amount. Calling the speed at the bottom v, conservation of energy gives us

$$\frac{1}{2}mv^2 = \frac{1}{2}mv_0^2 + 2mgr \ . \tag{2}$$

Solve

From Eq. (1), the speed of the pail at the top of its swing is $v_0^2 = rg$. Putting this into the conservation of energy equation (2) and dividing through by $\frac{1}{2}m$ gives

$$v^2 = rg + 4rg = 5rg$$

136

4C.4, continued:

for the speed of the pail at the bottom of the swing. For the numerical values in the question

$$v = 6.6 \text{ m/s}.$$

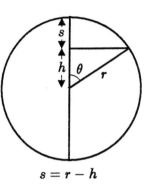

We have already concluded that the only force that can do work on the pail is gravity. We know gravity is a conservative force, and therefore the work done depends only on the vertical distance through which the pail moves (see problem 3.10 for some demonstrations of this). Starting, for example, when the pail is at the top of its motion, the work done on the pail by the time it makes an angle θ with respect to the vertical is mgs, where $s = r(1 - \cos\theta)$ is the amount by which the height has decreased from its maximum, as shown in the diagram.

$$s = r - h$$

The total work done increases (positive work is being done; kinetic energy is increasing) as the pail descends and decreases (negative work being done; kinetic energy decreasing) as it ascends again. Over a full circle no net work is done; the work done over a half circle is $2mgr = 26.5$ J.

Scrutinize
The dimensions of the result are certainly correct, as it involves equations we have checked in earlier problems. We can check the value of v^2 by recognizing that the speed of the pail would be the same if it had simply fallen freely through a distance $2r$, so we can use the equation $v^2 = v_0^2 + 2as$ from Chapter 1:

$$v^2 = v_0^2 - 2g(-2r)$$
$$= rg + 4gr = 5rg.$$

Learn
This is an example of a problem which is easy to solve using energy conservation but very difficult using $\vec{F} = m\vec{a}$. To use $\vec{F} = m\vec{a}$ directly, we would have had to decompose the forces acting into components parallel and perpendicular to the rope and then integrate the perpendicular component over the path of the pail. This is a non-trivial integration, because the tension force is changing in both magnitude and direction as the pail moves.

4D.1 (a) *John is holding a 17 inch computer monitor, with a mass of* 25 kg, *at a constant height. He complains that it is hard work, and he is becoming exhausted. Jim, who is taking physics, tells him that since there is no displacement in the direction of the applied force, he is not doing any work, and therefore should not be tired. Who is right, and why?*

Conceptualize
John is of course telling the truth when he says that he is becoming exhausted, but he is wrong in saying that he is doing work. Jim has correctly applied the physicist's definition of work—the dot product of the force and the displacement—which clearly

4D.1, continued:

vanishes if there is no displacement. It is hard to believe that John is doing no work, since he is getting so tired, but keep in mind that the same job of holding the monitor can be done by a desk, which can hold the monitor for many years without getting tired. Apparently John becomes tired because human muscles are very inefficient in applying a static force. Even though the static force requires no energy, in fact John's muscles cannot exert this force unless they are metabolizing chemical energy and converting it into heat. All of this energy is "wasted," in that all of it goes into heat, not work.

Solve

(This is really a conceptual problem, so we can now just state the solution.) Neither John nor Jim was entirely right. Jim was correct in saying that John had done no work, but wrong when he concluded that John should not expect to become tired. The human body can convert chemical energy to heat even when it is not doing work.

Learn

In this problem we were asked to choose between Jim's formal logic based on the definition of "work," and John's application of "common sense." Once one finds the right answer, it is usually apparent that it is consistent with both. If either is lacking, it is always a good idea to think again.

4D.1 (b) *Mary is riding an elevator from the 4th to the 7th floor, wearing a backpack of mass M. Between the 5th and 6th floors the elevator is moving at constant speed, through a distance ℓ. Joan, another physics student, argues that since the velocity of Mary's backpack is constant, the total force must be zero, and therefore Mary is applying an upward force just enough to cancel that of gravity, Mg. Since the displacement is upward by a distance ℓ, the work that Mary has done on the backpack is $W = Mg\ell$. Mary, on the other hand, points out that the weight she feels is just the same as it would be if she were stationary on the sidewalk, in which case there would be no displacement and therefore no work. Since she is burning no more calories than she would if she were on the sidewalk, and since energy cannot be created from nothing, there is no energy available for her to do work on the backpack. Who is right, and why?*

Conceptualize

We can't find anything wrong with Joan's logic. The force that Mary is applying to the backpack is certainly Mg upward, and the displacement of the backpack during the time interval under discussion is certainly ℓ, also upward. The work done, the dot product of the force and the displacement, is unavoidably $W = Mg\ell$. Looking more carefully at Mary's argument, however, we can find a flaw: while she argues correctly that she is burning no more calories than if she were on the sidewalk, she has not considered the possibility of other sources of energy. What about the force of the elevator floor on her feet? That force is larger than it would be if she were not carrying the backpack, by an amount Mg. Since her displacement during this time period is also ℓ, the extra work that the floor does on her, because she is carrying the backpack, is precisely $Mg\ell$. The source of the energy has been found.

Solve

Joan was correct. Mary was wrong because she failed to realize that the floor was doing more work on her than it would have if she were not carrying the backpack.

4D.1, continued:

Learn
When one needs to find all the forces acting on an object, one should never forget to do the simple exercise of looking around the boundary to see what the object is touching. Within the context of this book, the only forces that are not transmitted by direct contact are gravity and the electrostatic force.

This problem also illustrates another important principle, an elaboration of the principle of energy conservation: Energy is not merely conserved, but it is "locally" conserved. This means that it is not only impossible for the total energy of a closed system to change, it is also impossible for energy to disappear in one place and reappear somewhere else. Energy has to be transmitted. It can be transmitted through contact forces, and also by long range effects such as gravity or electromagnetic fields. The Earth obtains energy from the Sun, for example, mainly by electromagnetic waves. In this problem the energy comes from the motor that drives the elevator, and it is transmitted to Mary by the force of the elevator on her feet, and then to the backpack through the force that Mary's shoulders exert on it.

4D.1 (c) *A skater on a frictionless ice rink is initially stationary. Holding onto a rope attached to the wall, he gives a yank and starts himself moving toward the wall. Jean, a physics student who is watching, tells her friend Joe that since the kinetic energy of the skater has increased, work must have been done. It was the rope that applied the force, Jean explains, so it was the rope that did the work on the skater. "Nonsense," Joe replied, "ropes can't do work! Ropes don't have any source of energy, so the principle of energy conservation implies that they can't do work. Obviously it was the skater who did the work." "But the skater can't possibly exert a net force on himself," retorted Jean, "so he can't have done the work." Who is right here, and why?*

Conceptualize
This problem is very subtle, so we will try to puzzle it through one step at a time. Let's begin by examining the statements made by the characters in the problem. Was Jean right when she said that work must have been done on the skater? Of course she was, because the kinetic energy of the skater clearly increased, and the work-energy theorem guarantees that the work done on an object is equal to the change in kinetic energy. Was Jean also right when she claimed that it was the rope that applied the force that started the skater moving? Yes, again she is on target. In the absence of friction from the ice, there is no way that a skater could start himself moving without some external agent applying a force. (This issue will be discussed in more detail in the next chapter, but in a nutshell we can say that it is possible for the skater's shoulder, for example, to apply a force to his arm, but his arm will always apply an equal and opposite force to his shoulder. The net force that the skater exerts on himself is always zero. The net force that any object exerts on itself is always zero.) Finally, was Joe right when he said that the rope has no source of energy, and therefore could not possibly be the agent which did the work on the skater? Yes, Joe was right, too. It would be different if someone were at the other end of the rope pulling, but in this case the rope was tied to the motionless wall. There was no input of energy to the rope, so the principle of energy conservation implies that the rope could not transfer energy to the skater. So,

4D.1, continued:

we have concluded that the skater exerted no net force on himself, but that work was done on the skater by something other than the rope. Where do we go next?

Solve

In this case conceptualization did not get us as far as usual, as we still seem to be missing something crucial. When the solution to a problem seems out of sight, the clever puzzle-solver will try to warm up with a simpler problem that has most of the same ingredients. A skater is complicated, so let's imagine replacing him by a massless pointlike hand attached to a massless arm, which is in turn attached to a pointlike body, which contains all the mass. Muscles are complicated, too, so let's replace the massless arm by a spring. We will assume that the spring starts in a stretched state, so it exerts a force of contraction, much like the muscle it is replacing. The problem then looks like the following:

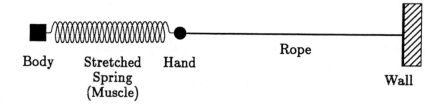

When the spring contracts it exerts a force on the hand, toward the left, and a force of equal magnitude on the body, toward the right. The net force of the spring on the "skater" is zero, as we expected. Now focus on the hand. The spring is pulling it to the left, but it clasps rigidly to the rope so that it cannot move to the left. As long as the hand holds tightly to the rope, the rope will develop a tension equal to the force of the spring on the hand, so that the net force on the hand will be zero. The rope is therefore exerting a force on the skater, but is it doing work? No, because the displacement is zero! Even as the body starts to slide to the right, the hand that is holding the rope does not move. Since the rope is in contact with the hand, not the body, the work done by the rope is calculated from the displacement of the hand—so it vanishes.

In response to the force applied by the spring, the body will start to move to the right. As it undergoes a displacement to the right, the spring will be doing work on it. Since the spring is part of the skater, the skater is doing work on himself. The net *force* that the skater exerts on himself is zero, since the spring pulls the hand to the left with the same force that it pulls the body to the right. But the hand is stationary and the body moves, so the net *work* done by the skater on himself is positive. It is crucial here that the skater is not rigid, so that his body can move while his hand is standing still. If the skater were rigid, he would not be able to pull on the rope.

Since the question is qualitative rather than quantitative, the answer to the simplified problem carries over to the real problem. Although the skater can exert no net force on himself, he can nonetheless do net work on himself. As long as he is not rigid, so that different parts of his body can have different displacements, then the net work that he

4D.1, continued:

does on himself can be nonzero, even though the net force he exerts on himself is always zero.

Learn
The secret of solving a hard problem is to isolate the relevant features, stripping away the complexity that can confuse the issue. The spring and point mass model of the skater shown above is a classic example of how oversimplifications can sometimes be very helpful in analyzing a complicated situation. There is an often-told joke that when a theoretical physicist was asked to examine the problem of how dairy farmers could increase milk production, she began her analysis with "Consider a spherical cow." If you want to think more about this, we suggest that you start by considering a spherical joke.

4D.3 *A cannon is capable of firing cannonballs with a fixed speed v_0 but at a range of elevation angles. What will be the speed of the ball at a height h?*

Conceptualize
This problem is clearly a candidate for the energy conservation approach. We consider the Earth-cannonball system, which is a closed system at any time during the cannonball's flight. The total energy is therefore conserved, and the gain in system potential energy produced when the cannonball's height above the ground increases by h must be balanced by a loss in kinetic energy. We work in the reference frame where the Earth is stationary, and so the change in kinetic energy must come from a change in the speed of the cannonball.

Formulate
The initial kinetic energy is $\frac{1}{2}mv_0^2$, and the kinetic energy at height h is $\frac{1}{2}mv_h^2$, where v_h is the speed at height h. The potential energy at height h is mgh. We do not know the mass m of the ball, but note that it occurs linearly in all three expressions and will therefore cancel out.

Solve
We simply write $\frac{1}{2}mv_h^2 = \frac{1}{2}mv_0^2 - mgh$

and thus $v_h = \sqrt{v_0^2 - 2gh}$.

Scrutinize
An acceleration multiplied by a length has dimensions of $[\text{length}]^2/[\text{time}]^2$, which is the same as $[\text{velocity}]^2$, so the dimensions of the answer are correct.

We can verify the exact form (and demonstrate the comparative simplicity of the energy approach!) by using the techniques for analyzing projectile motion that we learned in Chapter 1. The velocity of the cannonball at time t is given by

$$v_y = v_0 \sin\theta - gt \qquad\qquad v_x = v_0 \cos\theta \ ,$$

where θ is the angle the initial velocity makes with the horizontal. The height h is

$$h = v_0 t \sin\theta - \tfrac{1}{2}gt^2 \ .$$

141

4D.3, continued:

This is a quadratic equation for t which we can solve to find

$$t = \frac{v_0 \sin \theta}{g} \left(1 \pm \sqrt{1 - \frac{2gh}{v_0^2 \sin^2 \theta}} \right) \; .$$

The minus sign represents the time when the ball reaches this height on its way up, and the plus sign when it's on the way down. If the expression under the square root is negative, the ball never reaches this height (notice that this is extra information that we didn't get from the energy solution). Now substitute this value for t into v_x and v_y and combine them to get

$$v_h^2 = v_x^2 + v_y^2 = v_0^2 \sin^2 \theta - 2 v_0 g t \sin \theta + g^2 t^2 + v_0^2 \cos^2 \theta$$

$$= v_0^2 + g^2 t^2 - 2 v_0 g t \sin \theta$$

$$= v_0^2 + v_0^2 \sin^2 \theta \left(1 \pm \sqrt{1 - \frac{2gh}{v_0^2 \sin^2 \theta}} \right)^2 - 2 v_0^2 \sin^2 \theta \left(1 \pm \sqrt{1 - \frac{2gh}{v_0^2 \sin^2 \theta}} \right) \; .$$

Expanding this truly horrible-looking expression gives us

$$v_h^2 = v_0^2 + v_0^2 \sin^2 \theta + v_0^2 \sin^2 \theta - 2gh \pm 2 v_0^2 \sin^2 \theta \sqrt{1 - \frac{2gh}{v_0^2 \sin^2 \theta}}$$

$$- 2 v_0^2 \sin^2 \theta \mp 2 v_0^2 \sin^2 \theta \sqrt{1 - \frac{2gh}{v_0^2 \sin^2 \theta}}$$

and all the terms in $v_0^2 \sin^2 \theta$ cancel out to leave $v_h^2 = v_0^2 - 2gh$ as before.

Learn
It is clear that the energy approach provides a much simpler path to the solution! To find whether the cannonball could actually reach the specified height for a given angle, we could have combined the two techniques by using Newton's laws to analyze the horizontal motion of the ball—which, in the absence of air resistance, is very simple—and energy conservation to deal with the vertical motion. Our solution to the horizontal motion would assure us that the kinetic energy associated with this is constant, and so we can ignore it in applying energy conservation to the vertical motion.

The fact that the force approach confirms the speed to be independent of the angle at which the cannonball was launched is another demonstration that gravity is a conservative force: the kinetic energy gained by the ball (and the potential energy lost) in reaching height h is independent of the path by which it reached that height.

4D.5   _A spring with spring constant 200 N/m is used to power a spring gun which launches a 50 g ball vertically upwards. If the spring is compressed by 4 cm beyond its equilibrium position to launch the ball, how high will the ball go?_

4D.5, continued:

Conceptualize
Working in terms of energy conservation, we consider the closed system of Earth, spring and ball. The total energy of this system is made up of three parts: the potential energy stored in the configuration of the spring, the gravitational potential energy of the ball-Earth system, and the ball's kinetic energy. We could choose various reference points from which to define the gravitational potential energy: the most obvious is the starting point, at which the spring is compressed (and hence has some potential energy) and the ball is stationary. The total energy of the system is then equal to the initial potential energy of the spring. [Note that we could also conceptualize this problem in terms of forces, as we did in Chapter 2, but as we saw in Problem 4D.4 the energy approach is often very much simpler than the force approach.]

Formulate
First we must find the potential energy associated with the compression x_c of a spring. We did this in problem 4B.3; the result was

$$U(x_c) = \int_0^{x_c} kx \, dx = \frac{1}{2}kx_c^2 \ .$$

The kinetic energy is given by $\frac{1}{2}mv^2$, and the gravitational potential energy by mgh, where h is the height reached above the starting point. Thus the total energy of the system of spring plus ball at the start of the problem is

$$E_i = \frac{1}{2}kx_c^2 \ .$$

At maximum height, since the spring is no longer compressed and the ball's velocity is zero, the total energy is

$$E_f = mgh \ .$$

Energy conservation tells us that the initial and final energies must be equal, so combining these two equations will solve the problem.

Solve
Combining our two equations,

$$mgh = \frac{1}{2}kx_c^2 \ .$$

The maximum height that the ball reaches above its starting point is

$$h = \frac{kx_c^2}{2mg} = \frac{200 \text{ N/m} \times (.04 \text{ m})^2}{2 \times 0.05 \text{ kg} \times 9.8 \text{ m/s}^2} = 0.33 \text{ m} = 33 \text{ cm} \ .$$

Scrutinize
The dimensions of k are [force]/[length], since the spring force is $-kx$, and we know that mg is a force. So $kx^2/2mg$ is a length, as it should be. The ball reaches greater heights for larger spring forces or greater spring compression, which is sensible, and if

4D.5, continued:

you increase the mass of the ball (or imagine increasing g) it will not go so high, which is also sensible.

Note that this problem is simplified by the fact that the spring gun is directed vertically. If it had instead been directed at some angle to the vertical, we would have had to include the ball's horizontal kinetic energy when calculating E_f. We could determine this by solving the equations of motion for the horizontal component only, as discussed in the previous solution.

Learn

Like Problem 4D.4, this is an example of a problem which can be solved by $\vec{F} = m\vec{a}$, but whose solution is very much simpler using energy methods. This is generally true: if a problem can be solved either way, the solution using conservation laws is almost always easier than that using the full differential equation. On the other hand, the energy solution generally gives less information than the force solution, because it is insensitive to details of the motion. For example, the energy approach does not tell us that the velocity in this case is directed vertically, in contrast to the horizontal motion in problem 4C.4.

4D.6   *Two objects of equal mass m are connected by a spring of negligible mass, unstretched length ℓ_0, and spring constant k. They are initially at rest on a frictionless air table. An experimenter pulls the objects apart until they are separated by a distance $\ell > \ell_0$. What is the potential energy of the system of masses and spring? If the experimenter now lets go, at what speed is each mass moving when the spring has contracted back to its unstretched length? Compare this with the situation where one end of the spring is attached to a body of mass m and the other to a fixed point on the air table.*

Conceptualize

Our system consists of the two equal masses and the spring. Since all the motion takes place on a level table, we do not need to consider gravitational potential energy, so the total energy of the system is the potential energy of the spring and the kinetic energy of the two masses. This is initially zero: the string is at its unstretched length and the masses are stationary. When the experimenter separates the two masses, she does work on at least one of them, and it in turn does work on the spring. The stretched system, held still, has zero kinetic energy, but positive potential energy stored in the configuration of the spring. When the experimenter lets go, the masses-and-spring system is closed—no net external force is acting—and so its total energy must remain constant. As the spring contracts back to its unstretched length, both masses will gain kinetic energy. Since the system is symmetrical, the kinetic energy gain is split equally between the two masses. In contrast, if one end of the spring is fixed, all the kinetic energy must go to the mass on the free end.

Formulate

As we saw in 4B.4, the potential energy of a spring stretched by an amount x is $\frac{1}{2}kx^2$, so the total energy of the system is $\frac{1}{2}k(\ell - \ell_0)^2$. When the spring has contracted back to its unstretched length, the system's potential energy is zero, so its kinetic energy $2 \times \left(\frac{1}{2}mv^2\right)$ must be equal to the total energy.

4D.6, continued:

Solve

The kinetic energy of each mass when the spring is back to its unstretched length is

$$\tfrac{1}{2}mv^2 = \tfrac{1}{4}k(\ell - \ell_0)^2,$$

so the speed of each mass at this point is

$$v = \sqrt{\frac{k}{2m}}(\ell - \ell_0).$$

If one end of the spring is held fixed and the other attached to a mass m, the kinetic energy of that mass is

$$\tfrac{1}{2}mv_1^2 = \tfrac{1}{2}k(\ell - \ell_0)^2,$$

so its speed is

$$v_1 = \sqrt{\frac{k}{m}}(\ell - \ell_0).$$

Scrutinize

Recalling that the dimensions of k are $[\text{mass}]/[\text{time}]^2$, we see that the two expressions for v are dimensionally correct. They also behave sensibly if we change the input parameters: if the spring is not stretched initially ($\ell = \ell_0$), the velocity is zero; if the spring has no resistance to stretching and therefore stores no potential energy ($k = 0$, so $\tfrac{1}{2}kx^2 = 0$), the velocity is again zero.

Learn

We might have expected that the two-mass system would look the same as the one-mass system in the reference frame where one of the masses is stationary. However, that is not so: in such a frame the speed of the second mass is

$$v_2 = 2v = \sqrt{\frac{2k}{m}}(\ell - \ell_0),$$

and this is not equal to v_1. In a system where more than one mass moves, we must keep track of all the moving bodies, not just the one we might be interested in. In the next chapter we will develop the concepts needed to do this in a systematic way.

4E.2 (a) *The interior of an ornamental bowl forms a hemisphere of radius 10 cm. The surface is smooth and highly polished. If I place a small object at a distance s from the bottom of the bowl (where s is measured along the inner surface of the bowl, so that s varies from 0 to $\pi R/2$, $R = 10$ cm), how fast will it be moving when it reaches the bottom of the bowl?*

Conceptualize

This is another problem in which energy conservation implies that a loss of gravitational potential energy mgh is balanced by a gain in kinetic energy $\tfrac{1}{2}mv^2$.

4E.2, continued:

Formulate and Solve

We need to find an expression for h in terms of s; from the diagram this is

$$h = R \left(1 - \cos \frac{s}{R} \right) \ .$$

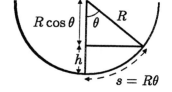

Hence the speed of the object at the bottom of the bowl is

$$v = \sqrt{2gh} = \sqrt{2gR \left(1 - \cos \frac{s}{R} \right)} \ .$$

Scrutinize and Learn

Note that angles are dimensionless, so anything we take a cosine or sine of must have no dimensions—one can't take cos(1 meter) or sin(0.3 kg). In our expression s/R is a ratio of two lengths, which is OK. We have checked in earlier problems that the dimensions of an acceleration times a length are the same as velocity squared.

Is our expression for v ever going to involve the square root of a negative number? (This usually corresponds to a situation which cannot physically occur.) In this case the answer is no, because the cosine function has a maximum value of 1.

(b) *What is the form of the potential energy of the object if s is small? Deduce the force acting on the object if it is displaced slightly from the bottom of the bowl and then released, and describe the resulting motion.*

Conceptualize

The form of the gravitational potential energy of the object for any s can be easily calculated by taking the standard form mgh and using our expression for h. The effect of taking a *small* s is to make the angle θ small, and so we can use the standard approximate forms of the trigonometric functions for small angles. We can then use the potential energy to find the net force acting on the object.

If we visualize the situation described in the problem, we can see that the object should slide partway up the opposite side of the bowl and then slide down again. Energy conservation implies that (in the absence of friction) it will reach the same height above the bottom of the bowl as its starting point (since it should have the same potential energy). Therefore we can see that the ball should repeat the same motions indefinitely—it will oscillate about the bottom of the bowl.

Formulate

Taking $U = mgh$ and using our expression for h gives, in terms of s,

$$U(s) = mgR \left(1 - \cos \frac{s}{R} \right) \ .$$

This defines U such that it is zero at the bottom of the bowl.

4E.2, continued:

For small angles θ, as we noted in Chapter 2,

$$\sin\theta \approx \theta ,$$

so we can use the standard trigonometric relation

$$\cos 2\alpha = \cos^2\alpha - \sin^2\alpha = 1 - 2\sin^2\alpha$$

to deduce that for small θ

$$\cos\theta \approx 1 - \frac{1}{2}\theta^2 .$$

The force can be found by differentiating the potential energy, using

$$F(s) = -\frac{dU}{ds} .$$

Our strategy for solving the problem is now clear: we will use the small-angle approximation to obtain an approximate form for $U(s)$ in the case where s is small, and then differentiate this to find the force. We expect to find that the form of the force implies oscillatory motion.

Solve

Substituting $\cos\theta \approx 1 - \frac{1}{2}\theta^2$ into our potential energy expression gives

$$U(s) = \frac{mg}{2R}s^2 \qquad \text{(for } s \ll R\text{).}$$

Then

$$F(s) = -\frac{dU}{ds} = -\frac{mg}{R}s .$$

This has the standard form that we associate with simple harmonic motion: the force is proportional to the distance from a position of equilibrium (the bottom of the bowl) and directed towards it. The equation of motion can be cast in the standard form

$$m\frac{d^2 s}{dt^2} = -\frac{mg}{R}s \quad \Longrightarrow \quad \frac{d^2 s}{dt^2} = -\omega^2 s , \quad \text{with} \quad \omega = \sqrt{g/R} .$$

We conclude that the object will perform simple harmonic oscillations about the bottom of the bowl, with $\omega = \sqrt{g/R}$ and period $T = 2\pi/\omega = 2\pi\sqrt{R/g} = 0.63$ s.

Learn

You should observe a similarity to our analyses of the simple pendulum. This is just what we should expect, as the motion of the object is *exactly* equivalent to pendulum motion—we are just using the surface of the bowl to force it to remain a fixed distance R from the bowl's center, instead of using a string to force it to remain a distance ℓ from the suspension point.

4E.2, continued:

Note that energy conservation implies that the object will oscillate around the bottom of the bowl for any initial value of s, since the argument about returning to the same level of potential energy does not depend on small angles. However, for larger angles the form of the force is more complicated, and the motion is not exactly simple harmonic. This is, of course, also true for the simple pendulum.

4E.3 *A small charge of mass 10 g moves in one dimension in a complicated linear distribution of fixed charges. Over a certain range of distances, the potential energy of the charge is found to be described to a good approximation by*

$$U(r) = U_0 + ar + br^2 + cr^3 ,$$

where $U_0 = 10$ J, $a = -1$ J/m, $b = 2$ J/m^2 and $c = -1$ J/m^3. At what values of r would the particle be in equilibrium, and what would the period of small oscillations (if any) around these equilibrium positions be?

Conceptualize

An equilibrium position is one at which the charge feels no net force. Therefore, to find the equilibria we must find the force (by differentiating the potential energy) and locate the positions r at which the force is zero.

To determine whether the charge will oscillate, we can consider the force on it if it is moved a small distance from the equilibrium point. If this force points back towards the equilibrium, there will be oscillations; if not, there won't be. For sufficiently small displacements, the oscillations will have the standard simple harmonic form and we will be able to determine the period.

Formulate

The force acting on the charge is:

$$F(r) = -\frac{dU}{dr} = -a - 2br - 3cr^2 .$$

This is a case where it is simpler to insert the numerical coefficients, giving

$$F(r) = 1 - 4r + 3r^2 = (1 - r)(1 - 3r) ,$$

where r is measured in meters and F in newtons.

Solve

There are clearly two equilibrium points, at $r = 1$ m and $r = \frac{1}{3}$ m. We consider these in turn.

Case $r = 1$ m:

Formulate

We need to re-express the potential energy in terms of displacements from the equilibrium position. Defining x to be this displacement, so that in this case $x = r - 1$. The potential energy becomes

$$U(x) = U_0 - (x + 1) + 2(x + 1)^2 - (x + 1)^3$$
$$= U_0 - x^2 - x^3 \approx U_0 - x^2 \text{ for small } x .$$

4E.3, continued:

Solve
Differentiating $U(x)$, the force $F(x) = +2x$ for small x. This is **not** the form that we expect for simple harmonic motion: the direction of the force is such that if the charge is displaced slightly from equilibrium it will tend to move further away from $x = 0$. This is a position of **unstable** equilibrium, and no oscillations are possible. Examination of $U(r)$ shows that $r = 1$ m is a local maximum of the potential.

Case $r = \frac{1}{3}m$:

Formulate and Solve
Following the same procedure, but defining $x = r - \frac{1}{3}$, we obtain

$$U(x) = U_0 - \left(x + \tfrac{1}{3}\right) + 2\left(x + \tfrac{1}{3}\right)^2 - \left(x + \tfrac{1}{3}\right)^3$$
$$= 9\tfrac{23}{27} + x^2 - x^3 \approx 9\tfrac{23}{27} + x^2 \text{ for small } x.$$

The force $F(x) = -2x$ for small x. This time we do have the appropriate conditions for oscillation. The equation of motion of the small charge is

$$-2x = m\frac{\mathrm{d}^2 x}{\mathrm{d}t^2} \ ,$$

so the solution will be of the form $x = A\sin\omega t$ with $\omega = \sqrt{2/m}$ and period $2\pi/\omega$, or 0.44 s.

Learn
It is easy to see that in the first case the potential energy **decreases** as x moves away from zero, whereas in the second case it **increases**. These are the conditions for unstable and stable equilibrium respectively. (There are equilibria which are neutral, i.e. neither stable nor unstable, such as a puck resting on a level frictionless surface. What happens to the potential energy when the puck is displaced in such a situation? What is the subsequent motion of the puck?) Notice that in neither case considered here has U reached its absolute or global minimum (or maximum) value: for this particular function U tends to $-\infty$ as r tends to $+\infty$ and vice versa. For oscillations to be possible it is only necessary that the potential energy increase locally in all accessible directions—it can decrease again further away.

HINTS FOR PROBLEMS WITH AN (H)
The number of the hint refers to the number of the problem

4B.5 (a) By how much does the potential energy of the mass change when it is moved radially away from the sun by an infinitesimal distance Δr?

(b) & (c) What is the force between two charges? How does it compare to that between two masses?

4C.3 What is the displacement Δr of this particle in a time Δt? How long does it take to travel 3 m?

What is the net force acting on a particle moving at constant velocity?

4D.4 What is the potential energy of the pendulum as a function of angle before and after the string hits the pin? What can you say about the total energy of the pendulum? [Take the potential energy to be zero at the bottom of the pendulum's swing.]

4E.4 What is the potential energy function for a small displacement s from each of the equilibrium positions?

If you are having trouble with this problem, study the solution to problem 4E.3.

4E.5 Draw a force diagram for the mass. What condition must hold for the mass to be at rest?

What does the word 'gently' imply in the phrasing of this question?

When the mass is dropped, what is the change in its potential energy between its starting position and the equilibrium position? What does this tell you about the change in its kinetic energy?

ANSWERS TO HINTS

4B.5 (a) $\Delta U = -\vec{\mathbf{F}} \cdot \overrightarrow{\Delta \mathbf{r}} = \dfrac{GMm}{r^2} \Delta r$

[Note that the outward movement corresponds to a gain in potential energy.]

(b) & (c) See Chapter 2, *Summary*.

4B.6 An acceptable answer would be

"The potential energy of a particle at position $\vec{\mathbf{r}}$ relative to an arbitrary reference position $\vec{\mathbf{r}}_0$ is the work done by a conservative force in moving the particle from $\vec{\mathbf{r}}_0$ to $\vec{\mathbf{r}}$. Because the force is conservative, this energy is 'stored' in the new configuration and would be released if the particle were to move back from $\vec{\mathbf{r}}$ to $\vec{\mathbf{r}}_0$."

4C.3 $\Delta \vec{\mathbf{r}} = \vec{\mathbf{v}} \Delta t$
    $= ([4, -2, 1]\,\mathrm{m}) \times (\Delta t/\mathrm{s})$;
    $3/\sqrt{21}$ s.

Zero net force.

4D.4 Before: $mg\ell(1 - \cos\theta)$;

After: $mg(\ell - L)(1 - \cos\alpha)$.

The total energy is conserved, so it is equal to the potential energy at the ends of the swing (when the kinetic energy is zero).

4E.4 $0.294(1 - s^2)$ J (for $x = \pi/4$ m, s in m);

$+0.294 s^2$ J (for $x = 3\pi/4$ m, s in m).

4E.5

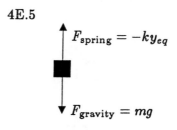

$mg = -ky$

At negligible velocity, so acceleration and kinetic energy are effectively zero.

-0.40 J; its kinetic energy must increase by 0.40 J.

151

ANSWERS TO ALL PROBLEMS

4A.1 c

4A.2 $\frac{1}{2}mv_0^2$; $\frac{1}{2}mv_0^2\cos^2\theta$; $\frac{1}{2}mv_0^2$

4B.1 b

4B.2 See complete solution.

4B.3 If the spring is compressed (or extended) by an amount s, the force it exerts is $F(s) = -ks$. The potential energy $U(x)$ corresponding to a compression (or extension) x is, by definition,

$$U(x) = U_0 - \int_0^x F(s)\,ds = -\int_0^x (-ks)\,ds,$$

where we have set $U_0 = 0$ (i.e. the potential energy is zero when the spring is at its natural length). Evaluating this integral gives

$$U(x) = \frac{1}{2}kx^2$$

as required.

4B.4 See complete solution.

4B.5 Derivations:

(a) $U(r_p) = U_0 - \int_\infty^{r_p} F\,dr = -\int_\infty^{r_p} \left[-\frac{GMm}{r^2} \right] dr = -\frac{GMm}{r}\bigg|_\infty^{r_p} = -\frac{GMm}{r_p}$.

(b) $U(r_p) = U_0 - \int_\infty^{r_p} F\,dr = -\int_\infty^{r_p} \left[\frac{1}{4\pi\epsilon_0}\frac{Qq}{r^2} \right] dr = \frac{1}{4\pi\epsilon_0}\frac{Qq}{r}\bigg|_\infty^{r_p} = \frac{1}{4\pi\epsilon_0}\frac{Qq}{r_p}$.

(c) Same as (b), but with opposite sign, so $U(r_p) = -\frac{1}{4\pi\epsilon_0}\frac{Qq}{r_p}$.

Graphs:

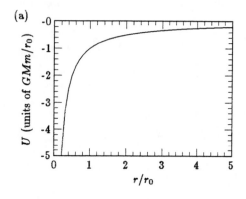

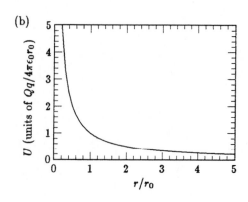

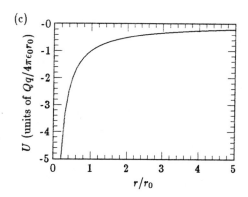

(c)

4C.1 c

4C.2 See complete solution.

4C.3 31.5 J; −3.9 J; 0 J (constant velocity implies no net force, so no net work).

4C.4 See complete solution.

4D.1 See complete solution.

4D.2 0 J; 4.9 kJ; 4.9 kJ.

Since the cement moves at constant speed, there is no change in kinetic energy, and hence no work is done. Gravity does negative work on the cement, since the force of gravity is opposite the direction of motion. The hoist, therefore, must do an equal magnitude of positive work to compensate. The potential energy of the cement is increased, and that energy must be balanced by a loss of chemical potential energy in the body of the worker.

A changing speed would have no effect on the overall work done, provided that the final kinetic energy was the same as the initial kinetic energy. During periods of acceleration upwards, the hoist is exerting a greater force (doing more work) than gravity; when the cement is slowing down (acceleration directed downwards) the reverse is true.

4D.3 See complete solution.

4D.4(a) $\cos \alpha = \dfrac{\ell \cos \theta_0 - L}{\ell - L}$;

(b) $\cos \alpha = \dfrac{\ell \cos \theta_0 - L - v_0^2/2g}{\ell - L}$;

Not changed.

4D.5 See complete solution.

4D.6 See complete solution.

4E.1 a

4E.2 See complete solution.

4E.3 See complete solution.

153

4E.4(i) $0.147(1 + \sin 2x)$ J, where x is in meters.

(ii) At $x = \pi/4$, $3\pi/4$; oscillations possible about the second of these, with period 1.8 s.

4E.5 $y = -8.2$ cm; -0.80 J; 0.40 J; not equal because the spring force decreases as $|y|$ decreases, so in the region $0 \le |y| \le 8.2$ cm the spring force is smaller in magnitude than the gravitational force, and hence is doing less work, so the 'stored' potential energy must also be less. No work is done overall (the mass's kinetic energy does not change) because the person lowering the mass "gently" to its equilibrium point exerts an additional upward force to prevent it from falling freely.

(i) 0.80 J;   (ii) -0.40 J.

0.89 m/s; simple harmonic motion with $\omega = \sqrt{k/m} = 11$ rad/s and period 0.57 s.

SUPPLEMENTARY NOTES

CONSERVATION LAWS

The law of conservation of energy is different in character from Newton's laws. Newton's laws provide precise descriptions of the motion of an object, provided that we can completely specify the situation (i.e. the mass and current motion of the object and the size, direction and behavior of all forces acting on it). Often we cannot do this—for example, it may be very difficult in practice to specify the action of air resistance on an object of complicated shape—and in this case we must make approximations which may seriously affect the accuracy of our calculations. In other cases the situation may be relatively simple to specify, but the resulting differential equations may have no easy solution. An example of this is gravitational interactions involving more than two bodies. We already know how to set up the equations (we just use $Gm_i m\hat{r}_i/r_i^2$ for the force on mass m due to each of the other masses m_i and then add the resulting forces vectorially), but the system of equations we get can't be solved generally for even the simplest case of three objects. Astronomers studying, for instance, the question of whether Jupiter's moons may be captured asteroids must use large computers to tackle the problem by numerical methods.

Energy conservation is different. Except for simple problems involving motion in one dimension, energy conservation does not give us enough information to predict how a system will behave. For the problem of three particles interacting gravitationally with each other, for example, energy conservation will allow us to determine the speed of any one particle, if somebody tells us the positions of all the particles and the speeds of the other two particles. On the other hand, the partial information provided by energy conservation can sometimes be very useful in understanding important properties of a system. For example, if a chemical reaction occurs inside an insulated container, conservation of energy will allow us to calculate how much the temperature will rise, even though it would be unimaginable to calculate the trajectories of the colossal number of molecules involved in the reaction. Furthermore, physicists have developed so much confidence in the principle of energy conservation that they are likely to rely on it even in situations when the underlying physics is unknown. One example is the story of the neutrino, which began in 1914 when the British physicist, James Chadwick, discovered that energy appeared to be lost in a process known as beta decay. In this process an electron (which at that time was called a beta particle) is emitted by the decay of a radioactive nucleus, which then increases in atomic number by one unit. Chadwick found that the electron could be emitted with a range of energies, extending up to the value that would be expected by energy conservation. For a decade and half physicists searched for some way that the energy could have escaped, but none could be found. Finally, in 1931 the Austrian-born physicist Wolfgang Pauli proposed what he called a "desperate solution." Perhaps, he suggested, a new type of particle is given off in the reaction—a particle that interacts so weakly that it could not be detected. Two years later the particle was named a neutrino by the Italian physicist Enrico Fermi , but the particle remained undetected for another 23 years! Finally, in 1956 Pauli received a telegram from Clyde L. Cowan, Jr. and Frederick Reines, informing him that the elusive neutrino had finally been detected, at the Savannah River reactor in South Carolina.

155

The application of energy conservation is easy on the microscopic scale, because on this scale all forms of energy can be well identified. The only forms in which energy occurs are kinetic energy, potential energy associated with the forces, and mass (which is a form of energy described by probably the most famous equation in all of science, Einstein's $E = mc^2$). On the macroscopic scale we face difficulties associated with the fact that when we are dealing with real objects made up of atoms a great deal of the energy of a system can be 'hidden' in the kinetic and potential energy of these atoms, which we do not measure directly. This leads to the apparent 'loss' of energy associated with forces such as friction. Even though the energy is not really lost, just hidden, in practical calculations we have to recognize that the energy which makes the hood and tires of your car feel hot after a long drive has not gone into providing kinetic energy for the car, and is thus lost from the point of view of an automobile engine designer. We will look at situations like this in more detail in Chapter 6.

Energy conservation is not the only conservation law. In the next chapter we will meet another, the conservation of *momentum*. Many problems can be solved completely or almost completely using only momentum and energy conservation, without ever referring directly to the forces acting on the system.

One of the subtle ideas to arise from the study of physics is a deep connection between conservation laws and symmetries. This connection is not obvious; it was not seen by Newton, and indeed the connection is not even logically necessary when the laws of motion are expressed in Newtonian language, as $\vec{F} = m\vec{a}$. The science of mechanics, however, was rewritten in the eighteenth century. Many mathematicians and physicists contributed to this development, including Johann Bernoulli (1667-1748), Leonhard Euler (1707-1783), and Jean Le Rond d'Alembert (1717-1783). The work culminated in the publication in 1788 of *Mécanique analytique*, by Comte Joseph Louis Lagrange (1736-1813).* The key idea was to reformulate the equations of classical mechanics in a way that makes no direct reference to forces, but instead uses a "principle of least action." The action S is defined as the integral over time of the *Lagrangian L*:

$$ S = \int_{t_1}^{t_2} L \, dt \, , $$

where L is the kinetic energy *minus* the potential energy. For a specified value of the initial position (at time t_1) and final position (at time t_2) of a particle (or particles), Lagrange invented a way to find the trajectory that minimizes S. This trajectory is called the path of least action, and Lagrange found that it was identical to the trajectory implied by Newton's $\vec{F} = m\vec{a}$ equations. The method is less general than Newton's, because it works only when the forces can be described by a potential energy function, so nonconservative forces are excluded from the beginning. The Lagrangian method turns out, however, to be a very powerful technique for treating difficult problems, and it also provides a formulation of classical mechanics that leads to a natural bridge to quantum theory.

Since the motion of any system is determined by the principle of least action, everything that one needs to know about a system is contained in its Lagrangian. This idea transcends classical

---

* Contrary to the style of this book, Lagrange boasted in his introduction that "No diagrams will be found in this book. The methods that I explain in it require neither constructions nor geometrical or mechanical arguments, but only the algebraic operations inherent to a regular and uniform process."

mechanics, so today particle theorists describe relativistic quantum field theories by writing an expression for the Lagrangian. It seems plausible that if we knew the right Lagrangian, we would know all of the laws of physics.

Finally—and this was our purpose in introducing Lagrangians here—the principle of least action leads to a fundamental connection between symmetries and conservation laws. If the laws of physics do not change with time—and as far as we can tell they do not—then the Lagrangian does not depend on time, and the principle of least action can be used to show that energy is necessarily conserved. If the Lagrangian does not depend on position in space—and as far as we can tell it does not, as long as all parts of an experiment are moved together, so that their relative positions do not change—then the principle of least action implies that momentum is conserved. Not surprisingly, the conservation of both energy and momentum still hold even when we consider extreme situations, such as speeds close to that of light, when Newton's laws are no longer valid. In the context of Lagrangians, any transformation of the positions and velocities of particles that leaves the Lagrangian unchanged is called a symmetry. For any symmetry, the principle of least action guarantees that there will be a corresponding conservation law.

Another conservation law that we will meet later in the book is the analog of momentum conservation for *rotational* motion, as opposed to motion in a straight line. This relates to the fact that the Lagrangian is unchanged by a rotation of the entire system, since the results of an experiment do not depend on the orientation of the laboratory in space. When you study electromagnetism you will discover that electric charge is conserved, and if you take a course in nuclear or particle physics you will be introduced to exotic conserved quantities like baryon number and lepton flavor. Conservation laws pervade physics, each of them pointing to some underlying symmetry or invariance of the structure of the universe. The existence, or sometimes the failure, of established conservation laws strongly constrains the form of theories put forward to describe natural phenomena. For example, oddly enough, the results of experiments involving neutrinos *may* depend on whether the experiment is described using a left-handed or a right-handed coordinate system. This is reflected in the *non*-conservation of a quantity called parity. The non-conservation of parity is an experimental fact of nature, and has been incorporated into the structure of modern theories of particle physics.

FORCES AND FIELDS

We have defined the gravitational force between two bodies in terms of the mass of each body and their separation. We do not have a definition for the gravitational force exerted by a single object—we insist on another body for the force to act on. However, our intuitive feeling is that the gravity of an object is somehow 'there' even if the object exists in isolation: a single proton floating in intergalactic space would still have the potential to exert gravitational and electrostatic forces even though in fact there may be no other particle close enough for us to measure such a force. We might picture the space surrounding the proton as being affected by the presence of the proton in such a way that any other stray proton or electron wandering into the vicinity would automatically feel the appropriate gravitational and electrostatic forces.

This is a case where the mathematical development of physics coincides with our common sense. The physical concept which corresponds to our 'effect of the particle on its surrounding space' is called a *field*. We say that the proton creates a gravitational field described at any point by $-GM\hat{r}/r^2$, where $\hat{r}$ is the position vector of the point relative to the proton. The force on a particle of mass m due to the gravity of the proton is then given by the value of the field times the mass of the particle. We can treat the electrostatic force in the same way, defining an electrostatic field $\vec{\mathbf{E}}$ with which the particle interacts according to its charge: $\vec{\mathbf{F}} = q\vec{\mathbf{E}}$, where q is the charge of the particle.

Just as the gravitational force can also be specified in terms of the gravitational potential energy, so the gravitational field can be specified in terms of a gravitational *potential*. The potential is the integral of the field with respect to displacement, just as the potential energy is the integral of the force. Field and potential are different ways of describing the same thing: we use whichever is more convenient for a given situation. We meet the electric potential in everyday life whenever we check the voltage supplied by a battery: this is simply the difference in electrical potential between the two terminals of the battery.

The field picture is enormously useful because it lets us separate the problem into two parts: the creation of the field by object A, and the action of the field on object B. For example, in dealing with the motion of an electron in a TV set we can first calculate the electric (and magnetic) fields set up by the components of the set, and then worry about the effect of those fields on the motion of the electron. If we later modify the set so that the electrons enter our area of interest with a different velocity, we don't have to redo the first part of the calculation. However, fields are more than a calculational convenience. They carry energy: we have described potential energy as 'stored energy'—now we can interpret this as energy stored in the field. In the study of electromagnetism we find that fields can also carry momentum, leading to cases where momentum conservation seems not to hold if we consider the interaction of particle A directly with particle B, but does hold if we consider the separate interactions of A with the local electromagnetic field and B with *its* local electromagnetic field.

Finally, the field picture can be viewed as the classical, macroscopic description of the modern microscopic view of the fundamental forces. For all the forces that we think we understand at a quantum mechanical level, the action of the force is transmitted by a physical particle emitted by object A and absorbed by object B (or vice versa), with momentum and energy conserved in both emission and absorption. The particles, however, are really quantum mechanical objects called "virtual particles," which do not necessarily have the same relation between energy and momentum or between velocity and momentum that classical particles have. (The only fundamental force we don't understand at this level is gravity, since general relativity is not formulated in terms of quantum mechanics.) In the absence of any object B, object A still emits force particles, so the field is still there, but it subsequently re-absorbs them itself, thus maintaining constant energy and momentum. This reinforces the reality of fields as physical entities rather than mathematical conveniences.

The field concept is a subtle one, and in this book we will never meet a situation where it is *essential* to think in terms of fields. Fields are, however, essential to understanding many phenomena associated with electromagnetism, including such important effects as the transmission of energy from the Sun to the Earth in the form of light, which is a traveling wave of electric and magnetic fields. It was only when the field concept was invented in the nineteenth century that the modern theory of electromagnetism could be developed.

ENERGY CONSERVATION AND THE ORIGIN OF THE UNIVERSE

Energy conservation, and particularly the concept of gravitational potential energy, has interesting consequences when applied to the largest known system, the entire universe. We know that the visible part of the universe contains about 100 billion galaxies, each consisting of typically 100 billion stars with masses roughly similar to the mass of the Sun. According to the theory of relativity, any object of mass M has an equivalent "rest" energy Mc^2, where c is the speed of light. Since c is a large velocity, these rest energies tend to be huge. Further, all of these galaxies are moving apart as the universe expands, and thus they all have associated kinetic energy. We may be tempted to conclude that the energy of the whole universe is incalculably huge, and that its theoretical origin in a big bang represents a gigantic violation of our wonderful new law of energy conservation.

This would not necessarily be a disaster. The conditions prevailing at the origin of the universe are so extraordinary in both physical and mathematical terms that it is conceivable that our presently known laws of physics do not apply. However, in fact we are not forced to resort to this rather drastic remedy. It is perfectly possible to argue that *the total energy of the entire universe is zero!*

The justification for this apparently nonsensical suggestion is that we have not yet included the gravitational potential energy of the universe in our calculations. Clearly, the mass in the universe must produce a gravitational potential, and energy is stored in this potential. The point to recognize is that the stored energy has a *negative* sign (we saw the effects of this when we looked at planetary orbits). The total energy of the universe, taking into account the positive contributions from the matter and its kinetic energy and the negative contribution of the gravitational potential energy, could be positive, negative or (if they just cancel) zero.

While many features of cosmology can be described well by Newtonian physics, the best understanding that we currently have is based on Einstein's theory of general relativity. To discuss a concept as global as the total energy of the universe, one needs to use the general relativistic description. General relativity is really a theory of gravity—one which was designed to be consistent with Einstein's theory of special relativity. General relativity describes gravity not as a force, but instead as a distortion of space and time. As discussed in the Supplementary Notes at the end of Chapter 1, the assumption that the universe is homogeneous and isotropic (i.e., the same in all places and in all directions) leads to three possible geometries for the universe: open, closed, and flat. For a closed universe the total energy is always exactly zero, with the positive energy of matter exactly canceled by a negative contribution from the gravitational potential energy. For an open universe, the total energy is infinite. The total energy of a flat universe is less well-defined, since it sits right on the borderline between an open universe of infinite energy and a closed universe of zero energy. However, a flat universe is always observationally indistinguishable from a very large closed universe, and therefore a universe that appears to be flat is always consistent with the possibility of zero total energy. Consequently, the evidence for a flat universe discussed in Chapter 1 can be interpreted as evidence that the total energy of the universe could be zero. Thus, the creation of the universe—however it happened—need not have constituted a violation of the principle of energy conservation.

ESSENTIALS OF INTRODUCTORY CLASSICAL MECHANICS

CHAPTER 5

SYSTEMS OF PARTICLES

OVERVIEW

So far we have considered the motion of a single particle acted on by an external force. In many situations this is an oversimplified view, since we are actually dealing with several objects which exert forces *on each other*, such as one pool ball hitting another. Each pool ball, in turn, is composed of perhaps 10^{24} atoms, all exerting forces on each other. In this chapter we will see how to extend our analyses to such cases, starting with the simplest system of two bodies. We will use the word *system* to refer to *any* specified set of objects, such as a set of two pool balls, the set of all the atoms in one pool ball, or the set of all atoms in two pool balls.

When you have completed this chapter you should:

✔ understand what is meant by the concept of momentum;

✔ know that momentum, like energy, is a conserved quantity, and be able to relate this to Newton's third law;

✔ understand how to relate forces to the rate of transfer of momentum;

✔ be able to use the conservation of momentum and energy to solve problems involving the interaction of two bodies;

✔ understand the concept of center of mass; be able to relate the total momentum of a system to the velocity of the center of mass, and the total applied force to the acceleration of the center of mass;

✔ distinguish between internal and external forces and their effects on the motion of the center of mass;

✔ understand the concept of impulse and the relation between impulse and momentum.

163

ESSENTIALS

The forms of the force laws of gravitation and electrostatics are symmetrical—the force exerted on body A by body B is the same magnitude as the force exerted on B by A, but opposite in direction. An attractive force (e.g., gravity or the electrostatic force between opposite charges) causes A to accelerate towards B, and B to accelerate towards A. A repulsive force (e.g., the electrostatic force between charges of the same sign) causes A to accelerate away from B, and B away from A. Thus we can write

Supplementary Notes. Problems 5A.1 and 5A.3

Attractive:

Repulsive:

$$\vec{F}_{AB} = -\vec{F}_{BA} \ ,$$

where $\vec{F}_{AB}$ is the force exerted on A by B and vice versa. *Newton's third law* states that this is *always* true, for any force (though one must be careful in formulating the law in some cases, particularly those involving moving electric charges; you will find out about this when you study electromagnetism). Thus the third law states that *the force exerted on body A by body B is equal in magnitude and opposite in direction to that exerted on B by A.*

(This is often expressed as "action equals reaction", but in fact the law is completely symmetrical between the two forces. There is no motivation to call one the 'action' and the other the 'reaction'.)

Consider a system of particles that has no forces acting on it from the outside, and let $\vec{f}_i$ denote the total force exerted on the ith particle by all the other particles in the system. It follows from the third law that

$$\sum_i \vec{f}_i = 0 \ ,$$

since all the internal forces between pairs of particles cancel. Using the *second* law we can rewrite this as

$$\sum_i m_i \frac{d\vec{v}_i}{dt} = 0 \ .$$

Since individual masses do not change with time, we can further manipulate the relation to give

$$\sum_i \frac{d(m_i \vec{v}_i)}{dt} = 0 \ .$$

By the mathematical identity $\frac{d}{dt}(a + b) = \frac{da}{dt} + \frac{db}{dt}$, this is the same as

$$\frac{d}{dt}\left(\sum_i m_i \vec{v}_i \right) = 0 \ .$$

The equation above has the form of a conservation law, since it says that the quantity in parentheses is independent of time. To express this conservation law in a simple way, we define the *momentum* $\vec{p}$ of a particle by

$$\vec{p} \equiv m\vec{v} \, ,$$

where m is its mass and $\vec{v}$ is its velocity. The SI unit of momentum is therefore kg·m/s. The total momentum of a system of particles is

$$\vec{P}_{tot} \equiv \sum_i \vec{p}_i = \sum_i m_i \vec{v}_i \, .$$

Problem 5A.2

Using these definitions, the equation derived above by applying Newton's third law to a system with no external forces can be rewritten as

$$\frac{d\vec{P}_{tot}}{dt} = 0 \, .$$

Problems 5B

Thus, *momentum is conserved*, meaning that the total momentum $\vec{P}_{tot}$ of a system of particles does not change if there are no external forces acting on the system. (Note that the total momentum *must* be calculated by adding the individual momenta as *vectors*. One does not add the magnitudes.) The momenta of individual particles in the system can of course change (for example, two charged particles may accelerate towards each other from rest under their mutual electrostatic attraction: their individual momenta increase in magnitude, but are oppositely directed, so the total momentum of the system is unchanged).

Momentum conservation, like energy conservation, is a fundamental law of physics which holds in all known circumstances (though when speeds approach that of light, we must be more careful about how we actually calculate the momentum). In fact, modern physicists view the third law as a consequence of momentum conservation, rather than the other way round.

The net force on a particle is, by Newton's second law, the rate of change of its momentum,

$$\vec{F} = m\frac{d\vec{v}}{dt} = \frac{d\vec{p}}{dt} \, .$$

Problem 5A.4

165

What happens if there are *external* forces acting on a system of particles? Then for each mass m_i,

$$\vec{F}_i^{\text{ext}} + \vec{f}_i = m_i \vec{a}_i \ ,$$

where $\vec{F}_i^{\text{ext}}$ is the *external* force on this mass and $\vec{f}_i$ is the *internal* force from all the other particles in the system. We can add all the equations for individual particles to get, for the whole system,

$$\sum_i \vec{F}_i^{\text{ext}} + \sum_i \vec{f}_i = \sum_i m_i \vec{a}_i \ .$$

The previous argument for the vanishing of the sum of the internal forces still applies, so the second sum on the left-hand side is zero. Thus, denoting the total external force by $\vec{F}_{\text{tot}}^{\text{ext}}$,

$$\boxed{\vec{F}_{\text{tot}}^{\text{ext}} \equiv \sum_i \vec{F}_i^{\text{ext}} = \sum_i m_i \vec{a}_i = \frac{d\vec{P}_{\text{tot}}}{dt} \ .}$$

The fact that the total force on a system is equal to the rate of change of its momentum allows us, in many cases, to treat large objects (e.g. planets) as if they were point particles. We must still explore whether we can relate the total momentum of a system to some definition of its average velocity. We could proceed using vector notation, but instead we will manipulate individual components of vectors.

Starting with the definition of the total momentum, write the x-component as

$$P_{\text{tot},x} = \sum_i m_i v_{i,x} = \sum_i m_i \frac{dx_i}{dt} = \frac{d}{dt} \sum_i m_i x_i \ ,$$

where x_i is the x-coordinate of the ith particle. Denoting the total mass of the system by $M_{\text{tot}} \equiv \sum_i m_i$, we can divide and multiply by M_{tot} to obtain

$$P_{\text{tot},x} = M_{\text{tot}} \frac{d}{dt} \left(\frac{1}{M_{\text{tot}}} \sum_i m_i x_i \right) \ .$$

Defining the *center of mass* of the system by

$$\boxed{x_{\text{cm}} \equiv \frac{1}{M_{\text{tot}}} \sum_i m_i x_i \qquad \text{(and likewise for y and z),}}$$

Problems 5C

166

the previous equation can be written as

$$P_{\text{tot},x} = M_{\text{tot}} \frac{dx_{\text{cm}}}{dt} \qquad \text{(and likewise for y and z)}.$$

Thus, the momentum of the system can be calculated as if it were a point particle carrying the total mass of the system and moving at the velocity of the center of mass. Note that if the particles have equal mass, x_{cm} is just the average of the x-coordinates. Returning to vector notation,

$$\vec{\mathbf{P}}_{\text{tot}} = M_{\text{tot}} \vec{\mathbf{v}}_{\text{cm}} ,$$

where

$$\vec{\mathbf{v}}_{\text{cm}} \equiv \frac{d\vec{\mathbf{r}}_{\text{cm}}}{dt} \qquad \text{and} \qquad \vec{\mathbf{r}}_{\text{cm}} \equiv \frac{1}{M_{\text{tot}}} \sum_i m_i \vec{\mathbf{r}}_i ,$$

and $\vec{\mathbf{r}}_i$ is the position vector of the ith particle.

Since the rate of change of the momentum is the total externally applied force, we have immediately

$$\vec{\mathbf{F}}_{\text{tot}}^{\text{ext}} = \frac{d\vec{\mathbf{P}}_{\text{tot}}}{dt} = M_{\text{tot}} \frac{d\vec{\mathbf{v}}_{\text{cm}}}{dt} = M_{\text{tot}} \frac{d^2\vec{\mathbf{r}}_{\text{cm}}}{dt^2} = M_{\text{tot}} \vec{\mathbf{a}}_{\text{cm}} .$$

The center of mass moves as if it were a point particle carrying the total mass of the system and acted upon by the sum of the external forces.

This is the reason for the name 'center of mass'. It also explains why in previous chapters we have been able to treat large objects such as the moon as if they were single point particles. As long as we know the sum of the external forces acting on each atom of a large object, we can calculate the acceleration of its center of mass. Note that even if the system consists of many disconnected chunks of matter, the center of mass moves as if it were a point particle accelerating under the influence of the total force.

In many applications one needs to calculate the center of mass of a system that decomposes simply into several parts, such as the Earth-moon system. In principle the center of mass is defined by applying the general formula above, summing over all the atoms in both celestial objects. It is shown in the solution to Problem 5C.3, however, that the problem simplifies: The center of mass can be calculated as if the system had only two particles, the Earth and the moon, each treated as a point particle located at its own center of mass.

Problems 5C.3 and 5C.4

The relation between the *total kinetic energy* of a system and its center of mass motion is a bit more complicated. As shown in the solution to Problem 5C.5, it is

$$K_{\text{tot}} = \frac{1}{2} M_{\text{tot}} v_{\text{cm}}^2 + \sum_i \frac{1}{2} m_i \left(\vec{v}_i - \vec{v}_{\text{cm}} \right)^2 \, ,$$

Problem 5C.5

Center of Mass Energy   Internal Energy

(not, as we might have guessed, $\frac{1}{2} M_{\text{tot}} v_{\text{cm}}^2$). Because kinetic energy involves a sum of squares, the internal velocities of the pieces do not cancel, so we get the second term (which is just the sum of the kinetic energies of the individual particles as seen from the center of mass). This *internal energy* of the system is the reason that energy conservation, in terms of the sum of kinetic and potential energy, often seems to fail in real-life situations—a solid object is a system of atoms, not a single particle, and can have internal energy. If we could measure the motions of the individual atoms, energy conservation would surely hold; we will see in Chapter 11 that we can demonstrate this indirectly by looking at the *temperature* of an object as a measure of its internal energy.

Although internal forces cannot change the total momentum of a system of particles, they may change its total kinetic energy: as we saw in the solution to Problem 4D.1(c), an internal force may do net work on some part of a system of particles. This means that it is not always straightforward to apply energy conservation arguments when considering the overall motion of the system. However, there are some special cases where it is clear that the work done by internal forces must cancel. One example is the normal force between two bodies in contact. By Newton's third law, $\vec{F}_{21} = -\vec{F}_{12}$. The displacement $\overrightarrow{\Delta \mathbf{r}}$ can be decomposed into a component *parallel* to the surfaces in contact, which does not contribute to the work done since it is, by definition, perpendicular to the normal forces (so

$\vec{\mathbf{F}} \cdot \overrightarrow{\mathbf{\Delta r}_{\parallel}} = 0$), and a component *perpendicular* to the surfaces. If the bodies remain in contact, this component must be the same for both objects, and so $\Delta W_{21} = -\Delta W_{12}$. (In the next chapter we will see that if there is friction between the two surfaces, then the work done by friction is related to the parallel component of $\overrightarrow{\mathbf{\Delta r}}$. This will not, however, alter the conclusion that the normal force does not do any net work.) Much the same logic applies to two objects connected by a massless, inextensible rope: if one end of the rope is displaced by an amount Δs in the same sense as the tension (i.e. towards the middle of the rope), the other end must move the same distance against the direction of the tension (away from the middle of the rope), and so the net work done is $T\Delta s + (-T\Delta s) = 0$.

The equations we have derived are valid for a system of any number of particles moving in any arbitrary way with respect to each other. However, *solving* the equations for complicated systems is usually impractical (the rest of this book will deal with ways of simplifying such problems in various special but useful cases). In this chapter we restrict ourselves to systems containing only two bodies, where the equations can be solved more easily.

Collisions of two objects are an obvious example of two-body problems. Is kinetic energy conserved in a collision? The answer in the case of point particles is "yes": we measure the part of the internal kinetic energy that corresponds to the motion of the two point particles with respect to the center of mass, and the point particles themselves have no internal structure, so this leaves nothing unaccounted for. Such collisions are called *elastic*. Elastic collisions are a good approximation to many real situations (e.g. bouncing a very springy ball, or the motion of the molecules of a gas).

Problems 5B.1, 5B.2, 5B.3, 5B.5, and 5B.6

If the colliding objects are not point particles, but have some internal structure which can be deformed or rearranged, measuring the speeds of the two colliding objects does not account for all the internal kinetic energy. In such cases, the measured kinetic energy after the collision is *not* the same as before the collision. Collisions of this type are called *inelastic*. The kinetic energy of the bodies can decrease in an inelastic collision, for example if the two bodies stick together; it can also increase, as it might if a compressed spring were released in the collision. Inelastic collisions are not really two-body collisions, since we cannot treat the colliding objects as point particles (their internal energies have become relevant to the problem).

Problems 5B.4, 5B.5, and 5B.7

Elastic collisions and other two-body interactions can often be most easily solved by working in the *center-of-mass frame*, i.e. the frame of reference which is at rest relative to the center of mass. In this frame there is zero net momentum, so at any given time the two bodies must have equal and opposite momenta.

Problems 5B.3 and 5C.6

169

Problems 5D

In collisions and similar situations where a complicated and unknown force acts for a very short time, the total transfer of momentum is more relevant to practical aspects of the problem than the details of the force. The transfer of momentum by a force $\vec{F}$ acting over a time interval t_1 to t_2 is called the *impulse* $\vec{J}$:

$$\vec{J} = \int_{t_1}^{t_2} \vec{F}\,dt = \int_{t_1}^{t_2} \frac{d\vec{p}}{dt}\,dt = \vec{p}_2 - \vec{p}_1 \;.$$

This is called the impulse-momentum theorem, and is clearly analogous to the work-energy theorem. The integral of a net force over a *displacement* gives the *kinetic energy* transferred: the integral of a net force over *time* gives the *momentum* transferred.

Impulse, like force and momentum, is a vector quantity.

170

SUMMARY

* The force exerted on a body A by another body B is equal in magnitude and opposite in direction to that exerted on B by A (Newton's third law).

* The *momentum* of a particle is defined as its mass times its velocity. Like velocity, it is a vector. The net force on a particle is equal to the rate of change of its momentum, and the total force on a system of particles is equal to the rate of change of its total momentum. Momentum, like energy, *is conserved in any closed system*.

* For any system of particles we can calculate a *center of mass*. If external forces are applied to a system of particles, the center of mass moves as if it were a point particle carrying the total mass of the system and acted upon by the sum of the external forces. The net momentum of the system is equal to the momentum that this point particle would have.

* The kinetic energy of a system of particles is equal to the kinetic energy of a single equivalent particle having the same total mass and located at the center of mass *plus* the kinetic energies of the particles making up the system *as measured relative to the center of mass*. The latter part is called the *internal energy* of the system.

* Collisions between pairs of particles may be *elastic* (the net kinetic energy is conserved) or *inelastic* (there is some conversion between kinetic energy and internal energy). Momentum is conserved in both cases.

* The change in an object's momentum over a given time interval is equal to the integral of the net force acting over that time interval, and is called the *impulse*.

* Physical concepts introduced in this chapter: momentum, center of mass, impulse.

* Mathematical concepts introduced in this chapter: none (but you may need to review some calculus and the meaning of the summation symbol $\sum$).

* Equations introduced in this chapter:

$$\vec{\mathbf{F}}_{AB} = -\vec{\mathbf{F}}_{BA} \qquad \text{(Newton's third law)};$$

$$\vec{\mathbf{p}} = m\vec{\mathbf{v}} \qquad \text{(momentum)};$$

$$\frac{d\vec{\mathbf{P}}_{tot}}{dt} = 0 \qquad \text{(conservation of momentum in absence of external force)};$$

$$\vec{\mathbf{F}} = \frac{d\vec{\mathbf{p}}}{dt} \qquad \text{(Newton's second law in terms of momentum)};$$

$$\vec{\mathbf{r}}_{cm} \equiv \frac{1}{M_{tot}} \sum_i m_i \vec{\mathbf{r}}_i \qquad \text{(position of center of mass)};$$

$$\vec{\mathbf{v}}_{cm} \equiv \frac{d\vec{\mathbf{r}}_{cm}}{dt} = \frac{1}{M_{tot}} \sum_i m_i \vec{\mathbf{v}}_i \qquad \text{(velocity of center of mass)};$$

$$\vec{\mathbf{F}}_{tot}^{ext} = M_{tot}\vec{\mathbf{a}}_{cm} = \frac{d\vec{\mathbf{P}}_{tot}}{dt} \qquad \text{(acceleration of a system of particles)};$$

$$\vec{\mathbf{P}}_{tot} = \sum_i m_i \vec{\mathbf{v}}_i = M_{tot}\vec{\mathbf{v}}_{cm} \qquad \text{(momentum of a system of particles)};$$

171

$$K_{\text{tot}} = \frac{1}{2} M_{\text{tot}} v_{\text{cm}}^2 + \sum_i \frac{1}{2} m_i \left(\vec{v}_i - \vec{v}_{\text{cm}} \right)^2 \quad \text{(K.E. of a system of particles)};$$

$$\vec{J} = \int_{t_1}^{t_2} \vec{F}\, dt = \int_{t_1}^{t_2} \frac{d\vec{p}}{dt}\, dt = \vec{p}_2 - \vec{p}_1 \qquad \text{(impulse-momentum theorem)}.$$

PROBLEMS AND QUESTIONS

By the end of this chapter you should be able to answer or solve the types of questions or problems stated below.

Note: throughout the book, in multiple-choice problems, the answers have been rounded off to 2 significant figures, unless otherwise stated.

At the end of the chapter there are answers to all the problems. In addition, for problems with an (H) or (S) after the number, there are respectively hints on how to solve the problems or completely worked-out solutions.

5A FUNDAMENTAL CONCEPTS (MOMENTUM AND NEWTON'S THIRD LAW)

5A.1 You are sitting in a chair. The forces acting include several forming equal and opposite pairs, e.g. (i) your weight and the normal force exerted on you by the chair; (ii) the weight of the chair and the gravitational force exerted by the chair on the Earth (neglecting the effect of the Earth's rotation). Which of these pairs are equal and opposite owing to Newton's third law?

(a) both (i) and (ii); (b) (i) only; (c) (ii) only; (d) neither (i) nor (ii).

5A.2 An 80 kg ice-hockey player traveling at 10 m/s collides head-on with an opposing player traveling at 7 m/s in the opposite direction. If the second player has mass 75 kg, what is the magnitude of the net momentum of the two players, to two significant figures?

(a) 280 kg·m/s; (b) 1300 kg·m/s; (c) 460 kg·m/s; (d) none of these.

5A.3 (S) A book with mass m is lying on a table of mass M. What are the forces acting (a) on the book and (b) on the table? Which pairs of forces are equal and opposite *by Newton's third law*?

5A.4 (H) A fire hydrant delivers water at a volume flow rate (i.e. volume/time) L. The water travels vertically upwards through the hydrant at speed v and then does a 90° turn to emerge horizontally at the same speed v. Assuming the pipe and nozzle have uniform cross-sections throughout, obtain an expression for the force exerted by the water on the corner of the hydrant. If the rate of delivery is $L = 800$ liters per minute at $v = 25$ m/s, what is the magnitude of the force that the structure of the hydrant has to withstand? What is the direction of that force? (One liter of water has a mass of one kilogram.)

5A.5 (S) A uniform rope of mass m and length ℓ is attached to a hook in the ceiling, and hanging from it is a mass M. Assuming that m is *not* negligible compared to M, what is the tension in the rope (i) at the hook; (ii) at the mass M; (iii) at some arbitrary point a distance y below the hook? If the rope is now removed from the hook and used to tow the mass M horizontally along a frictionless surface, what force must be applied to the end of the rope to give the mass M an acceleration a? Assume that the rope does not stretch.

5A.6 In 50 words or less, explain the difference between *internal* and *external* forces.

5A.7 (S) Two blocks of masses m_1 and m_2 are connected by a massless inextensible rope as shown. At the apex of the frictionless triangular support, the rope passes over a frictionless pulley. Find the acceleration of the blocks and the tension in the rope.

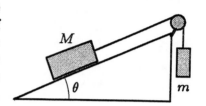

5A.8 Two blocks are connected by a massless inextensible rope over a frictionless pulley as shown. The block of mass m hangs freely, and there is no friction between the block of mass M and the slope. The experimenter finds that when she places the blocks carefully in this position they remain stationary. Find (a) the tension in the rope and (b) an expression for the mass m in terms of θ and the mass M. What will happen if the experimenter now gives the block of mass M a gentle push down the slope?

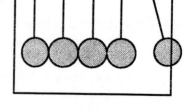

5B CONSERVATION OF MOMENTUM

5B.1 (i) A pool ball traveling at 2 m/s hits another (stationary) ball of the same mass dead center, so that the extended trajectory of the first ball passes through the center of the second. What is the velocity of the first ball after the elastic collision?

    (a) 1 m/s in the original direction;

    (b) 2 m/s at some angle to the original direction;

    (c) less than 2 m/s at some angle to the original direction;

    (d) zero.

  (ii) What is the velocity of the second ball?

    (a) 1 m/s in the same direction as the first;

    (b) 2 m/s in the original direction of the first ball;

    (c) less than 2 m/s at some angle to the direction of the first ball;

    (d) 2 m/s at some angle to the direction of the first ball.

5B.2 A Newton's cradle consists of five steel ball-bearings of equal mass suspended in a frame. You take the end ball, displace it slightly, and let it go, so that it swings into the other four balls with speed v. What happens, and why? Assume all collisions are elastic.

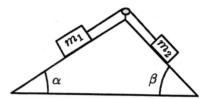

5B.3 (H) Two sliders on a linear air track are fitted with spring-loaded fenders so that their collisions will be perfectly elastic. If one has mass m and speed v and the other has mass M and is stationary, what will be the velocity of each one after the collision? Deduce from this what will be the result if the first slider collides elastically with an immovable wall.

Discuss what will happen if we extend this situation to two dimensions, so that an air puck on a frictionless table collides elastically with a wall. Assume the puck's initial velocity makes an angle θ with the wall.

5B.4 (H) You are roller-skating peacefully down a street at a constant speed of 3 m/s when someone suddenly throws a football at you from directly ahead. If your mass is 65 kg and the football's is 0.40 kg, what is your speed afterwards if (a) you catch the ball, which was thrown at you with a horizontal velocity of 15 m/s; (b) you miss it and it bounces off you with a velocity of 10 m/s (relative to the street) in the opposite direction? In each case, what is the total kinetic energy of the system comprising you and the ball before and after your interaction?

5B.5 (S) You have two sliders on a frictionless linear air track, each of mass m. One is stationary, and you slide the other one into it with a velocity v_0. What happens to the momentum and kinetic energy of each slider if (a) you have attached spring-loaded fenders so that the collision is perfectly elastic; (b) you have stuck on blobs of putty so that the two sliders stick together and move off together after the collision?

5B.6 (S) In the sport of curling, teams take turns to slide polished granite stones across an ice rink, aiming at a designated target zone. A common tactic is to dislodge well-placed opposition stones by hitting them with your own stone. Assuming that all the stones are of a standard mass, that friction can be neglected, and that the collision is elastic, is it possible to determine what will happen to a stationary stone B if it is hit by another stone A moving with velocity v? If it is not possible to determine exactly what will happen, what can be determined, and what additional information is required?

5B.7 (H) You and a friend sit motionless on sleds on frictionless ice. You slide a 10 kg block across the ice to her at 2 m/s relative to your sled (i.e. after the ice block is released, the relative velocity of the block with respect to your sled is 2 m/s), and she catches it and slides it back to you at the same speed (relative to her own sled). If you and your sled, without the 10 kg mass, together have a mass of 90 kg, and she and her sled have a mass of 70 kg, what is your speed, and that of your friend, after you catch the returned block?

5C   THE CENTER OF MASS

5C.1 A binary star system consists of two stars separated by 10^{10} km. Star 1 is three times as massive as star 2. How far from star 1 on the line joining the two stars is the center of mass of the system?

(a) 2.5×10^9 km; (b) 3.3×10^9 km; (c) 5.0×10^9 km; (d) 7.5×10^9 km.

5C.2 (S) A girl is teaching her younger brother to skate by towing him around on a rope. They finish their practice session by hauling in on the rope from each end until they meet. If her mass is 40 kg, his is 30 kg, and the rope is 5 m long, how far from her original position will they end up? Assume that they were stationary to begin with, that the rope has negligible mass, and that there is no friction.

5C.3 (S) Find the position of the center of mass of:

(a) the Earth-Moon system (masses of 6.0×10^{24} and 7.4×10^{22} kg) separated by 384 thousand kilometers;

(b) a small spherical mass m attached to the end of a long thin rod of length ℓ and mass m;

(c) three thin rods, each of mass m and length ℓ, arranged to form three sides of a square.

5C.4 (H) Find the position of the center of mass of (a) a sphere of mass m and radius r attached to a rod of mass m and length ℓ; (b) two rods of mass m and length ℓ joined at right angles; (c) two rods of mass m and length ℓ crossed as shown in the diagram.

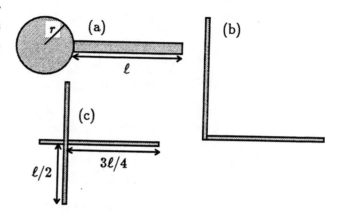

5C.5 (S) Use the definition of the center of mass to prove the expression given in the *Essentials* for the kinetic energy of a system of particles.

5C.6 (H) Two pucks of mass m_1 and m_2, moving on a level frictionless surface, undergo an elastic collision. Prior to the collision, their speeds were v_1 and v_2 respectively, as measured in their center of mass frame (i.e. the frame in which their center of mass is at rest). What are their speeds after the collision? Can you make any statement about their directions of motion after the collision?

5D IMPULSE

5D.1 A baseball approaches the batsman at 30 m/s. After he hits it, it is traveling in the opposite direction with a speed of 40 m/s. If the mass of a baseball is 0.145 kg, what was the magnitude of the impulse he applied to the ball, to three significant figures?

(a) 1.45 kg m/s; (b) 5.80 kg m/s; (c) 10.2 kg m/s; (d) none of these.

5D.2 (S) During a tennis rally, the ball approaches a player at a speed of 30 m/s. He returns the shot so that the ball has a speed of 35 m/s at an angle of 160° to the original direction. What impulse did he apply to the ball? If ball and racquet were in contact for 0.01 s, what average force (averaged over time) did he exert? A tennis ball has a mass of 60 g.

5D.3 (H) In a bat-and-ball game, the ball hits the bat at 35 m/s and is projected back in the opposite direction at 50 m/s. What is the impulse applied to the ball and the average force exerted (averaged over time) if the game is (a) tennis, involving a 60 g ball in contact with the racquet for 0.01 s; (b) baseball, with a 0.145 kg ball in contact with the bat for 0.002 s?

COMPLETE SOLUTIONS TO PROBLEMS WITH AN (S)

5A.3   *A book with mass m is lying on a table of mass M. What are the forces acting (a) on the book and (b) on the table? Which pairs of forces are equal and opposite by Newton's third law?*

Conceptualize

If we neglect the Earth's rotation, the book and the table are both stationary, so no net force can be acting on either of them. There is obviously a gravitational force $m\vec{g}$ acting on the book, and $M\vec{g}$ on the table. These must be balanced by the normal forces $\vec{n}$ and $\vec{N}$ respectively, where $\vec{n}$ is the force exerted by the table on the book, and $\vec{N}$ is the force exerted by the floor on the table.

In case (a), the book, $m\vec{g}$ and $\vec{n}$ are the only forces acting, so for zero net force they must be equal and opposite, $\vec{n} = -m\vec{g}$. But are they equal and opposite by *Newton's third law*? Clearly not: the third law states that "the force exerted by body A on body B is equal in magnitude and opposite in direction to that exerted by B on A". Two forces acting **on the same object** cannot, therefore, be a third law pair. The gravitational force $m\vec{g}$ is exerted on the book by the Earth, so its third law partner is the force exerted on the Earth by the book. Naturally this force does not cause a measurable acceleration when applied to a mass of 6×10^{24} kg, so we usually ignore it when doing practical problems.

Similarly the third law states that the normal force $\vec{n}$ exerted on the book by the table is balanced by a force $-\vec{n}$ exerted on the table by the book. These are surface forces caused by the fact that the atoms making up book and table cannot interpenetrate. They are thus manifestations of the electromagnetic fundamental force, and quite unrelated to the gravitational forces operating: the fact that the two sets of forces are numerically equal is due to the geometry of the situation (if the book were lying on a sloping surface $\vec{n}$ would no longer be $-m\vec{g}$).

For case (b), the table, we have a gravitational force $M\vec{g}$ and the normal force exerted by the book, $-\vec{n} = m\vec{g}$. Both of these act downwards, and therefore must be balanced by the normal force exerted by the floor, $\vec{N} = -(m + M)\vec{g}$, distributed in practice among the legs of the table.

Solve

(This was a conceptual problem: we have already done the small amount of formulation necessary—basically just stating the form of the gravitational force.)

(a) The forces acting on the book are gravity, $m\vec{g}$, and the normal force from the table, $\vec{n} = -m\vec{g}$. The third law partners of these forces are the gravitational force exerted on the Earth by the book, $-m\vec{g}$, and the normal force exerted by the book on the table, $-\vec{n} = m\vec{g}$.

(b) The forces acting on the table are the gravitational force $M\vec{g}$, the normal force from the book, $-\vec{n} = m\vec{g}$, and the normal force from the floor, $\vec{N} = -(m+M)\vec{g}$. Their third law partners are respectively the gravitational force exerted by the table on the Earth, the normal force exerted by the table on the book, and the normal force exerted by the table on the floor.

5A.3, continued:

Of the forces acting on the book and the table, the only third law pair is the normal forces they exert on each other. All the other third law partners act on different objects (the Earth and the floor).

Learn

Note that not all equal and opposite force pairs are manifestations of the third law! In particular, forces acting on the *same* object *cannot* be related in this way, because the third law explicitly relates a force exerted *on* an object to a force exerted *by* the object.

5A.5   *A uniform rope of mass m and length ℓ is attached to a hook in the ceiling, and hanging from it is a mass M. Assuming that m is not negligible compared to M, what is the tension in the rope (i) at the hook; (ii) at the mass M; (iii) at some arbitrary point a distance y below the hook? If the rope is now removed from the hook and used to tow the mass M horizontally along a frictionless surface, what force must be applied to the end of the rope to give the mass M an acceleration a? Assume that the rope does not stretch.*

Conceptualize

Hanging rope

Up to now we have always considered the tension in a *massless* rope, and have stated without proof that it points along the rope and is the same at all points on the rope. This is a consequence of Newton's second and third laws: if the rope is massless, there must be no net force on it (otherwise, applying $\vec{a} = \vec{F}/m$, it would have an infinite acceleration!), and by Newton's third law the force exerted *by* the rope on an object tied to its end is equal and opposite to the force exerted *on* the rope by the object. Thus if you pull with force F on one end of a massless rope, the same force F is exerted by the rope on whatever is attached to its other end.

In this case the rope is not massless, and so the argument that there can be no net force acting on it does not hold. We must apply Newton's second and third laws directly to the points we are interested in—initially, the top and bottom of the hanging rope. The forces acting are gravity (the weight of the rope and the weight of the mass M), a normal force from the hook, and the tension in the rope. All of these act in a single vertical line, along the rope, so we have only a single component equation.

Formulate

At the hook, the force exerted *on* the rope *by* the hook is the normal force N. Since the rope-plus-mass system is not accelerating, this must cancel the downward forces $mg + Mg$ acting on the system (the tension is an internal force and will cancel). The tension in the rope is the force exerted *by* the rope *on* the hook, and by Newton's third law this must be $-N$, where we define forces to be positive downward.

We do a similar analysis at the mass: the force exerted by the mass on the rope is its weight, Mg, so the tension in the rope at this point must be $-Mg$.

For part (iii) we consider a small section of rope at a distance y below the hook. We divide the rest of the rope into two pieces: the part between us and the hook, which has length y and mass my/ℓ—since the rope is uniform, its mass must be distributed

5A.5, continued:

evenly along its length—and the part between us and the mass, which has length $\ell - y$ and mass $m\left(1 - \frac{y}{\ell}\right)$. This part of the problem is then equivalent to part (ii), with a mass $M + m\left(1 - \frac{y}{\ell}\right)$ suspended from a rope of length y.

Solve

For part (i), we have $N = -(m + M)g$, and so $T(y = 0) = (m + M)g$.

In part (ii), we have already worked out that $T(y = \ell) = -Mg$.

Part (iii) gives $T(y) = -\left(M + m\left(1 - \frac{y}{\ell}\right)\right)g$.

Comparing these three equations, we see that the magnitude of the tension decreases linearly from $(m + M)g$ at $y = 0$ to Mg at $y = \ell$.

Scrutinize

This answer appears to make sense: if we put $m = 0$, returning to our familiar massless rope, the magnitude of the tension at all three points comes out to be Mg as we expect. As we worked out when conceptualizing this problem, the constancy of the tension in a massless rope is a consequence of the rope's masslessness, and not a general property of tension.

Conversely, if we let the rope hang under its own weight, setting $M = 0$, we find that the tension at the bottom end is zero. This is essential physically—if it were not true, the rope would be exerting an upward force on its own end, and would miraculously rise into the air! The tension at the top, of course, is not zero: the top of the rope feels a downward force from the rope's own mass.

We now go on to consider the second part of the problem.

Conceptualize

Tow-rope

The principles of our initial conceptualization still hold, but in this case we are using F = mass $\times$ acceleration, Newton's second law, whereas in the first part we were really using Newton's first law (the system was not accelerating, so no net force was acting on it). The vertical forces are zero (the weights are cancelled by a normal force from the surface), so we need consider only the horizontal force.

Formulate and Solve

The mass M has acceleration a, so the net force acting on it is Ma. This must be the tension in the rope at that end.

Since the rope does not stretch, it too must have an acceleration a, so the net force on the rope must be ma. As the rope is applying a force Ma to the mass, the force required on the other end of the rope is $(m + M)a$.

Scrutinize

We can check this answer by considering a system in which a mass m and a mass M are connected by massless ropes. To give such a system acceleration a, we would have to apply a force $(m + M)a$ on the massless string attached to mass m, and the string

179

5A.5, continued:

connecting m and M would have constant tension $T = Ma$ and would apply a force Ma to mass M. This agrees with our answers for the massive rope. Once again, allowing the rope to be massless gives the tension the constant value Ma, and allowing the mass on the end to go to zero sends the tension at that end to zero.

☺ *Learn*

The tension in the rope behaves in exactly the same way in both parts of the problem. We could check the tension at any point by the same method we used above, dividing the rope into smaller and smaller pieces. This suggests an alternative, calculus-based, way of calculating the tension in a massive rope:

Consider a segment of the rope of length Δx, and hence mass $\Delta m = m\Delta x/\ell$. located at a distance x from the free end of the rope. If it has acceleration a, it must be subject to a net force $F = \Delta ma$. This can only be the difference between the tension $T(x)$ pulling it forward and the tension $T(x + \Delta x) = T + \Delta T$ pulling it back towards the mass. Hence we have

$$\Delta T = -\Delta ma = -\frac{ma}{\ell}\Delta x,$$

which in the limit where $\Delta x \to 0$ becomes

$$\frac{\mathrm{d}T}{\mathrm{d}x} = -\frac{ma}{\ell}.$$

The tension decreases linearly along the rope, just as we calculated earlier. If we integrate this equation from $x = 0$ to $x = x_0$, we get

$$T(x_0) - T(0) = -\frac{ma}{\ell}x_0,$$

where $T(0)$ is the tension at $x = 0$. Putting this equal to $(M + m)a$ gives us the same equation that we had for the hanging rope above.

5A.7 *Two blocks of masses m_1 and m_2 are connected by a massless inextensible rope as shown. At the apex of the frictionless triangular support, the rope passes over a frictionless pulley. Find the acceleration of the blocks and the tension in the rope.*

Conceptualize

The difference between this problem and those we have met before is that in this case the rope changes direction when it passes over the pulley. Before we can set up the problem we need to understand the consequences of this.

By applying Newton's third law, we see that the left-hand part of the rope exerts a force on the pulley equal to the force exerted by the pulley on the left-hand rope. Similarly, the rope exerts a force on the block equal to the force that the block exerts on the rope. As the rope is massless, there can be no net force on it (otherwise it would have infinite acceleration), and thus the force exerted by the rope on the pulley is equal in magnitude

5A.7, continued:

(though opposite in direction) to the force exerted by the rope on the block. The same argument applies to the right-hand block.

Now let's consider the pulley, which has a rope tension T_L exerted on it from the left, and a tension T_R from the right. The pulley itself is a disk, and the rope runs around the rim of the disk: the pulley can therefore exert a contact force on the rope. This force is entirely radial, i.e. normal to the rim: we are told that the pulley is frictionless, so it cannot exert any tangential force. There-fore, where the rope loses contact with the pulley rim on

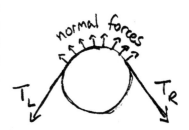

the left, we have a radial force n, a tangential force T_L, and a second tension force T acting to the right. This second force must have a tangential component equal in magnitude to T_L, since the normal force can supply no tangential component, and there can be no net force on our massless rope. We can repeat this argument all the way round the pulley until we come to the point at which the rope loses contact again, at which point we balance the tangential component of T (which is still equal to T_L) against T_R. Our conclusion is that *the frictionless pulley changes the direction of the tension, but does not change its magnitude*. (In a real pulley, friction between the pulley rim and the rope causes the pulley to turn. We will not be able to handle this situation until Chapter 8. However, the idealization of a frictionless pulley is a good approximation if the mass of the pulley wheel is very small compared to either of the blocks, and there is little friction in the bearings which allow the wheel to rotate.)

We are now in a position to formulate the problem. We can treat each block as a separate system, with two constraints:

- the magnitude of the tension T is the same for both blocks, as we have just shown;

- as the rope does not stretch, the magnitude of the acceleration $\vec{a}$ must be the same for each block (they remain the same distance apart).

$\Sigma\!\int$ *Formulate*
Treating the blocks as separate systems, we can use different coordinate systems. It is most convenient to choose a coordinate system with the x-axis parallel to the slope: in order to keep the *sign* of the acceleration the same for both blocks, we let the x-axis point uphill for the left-hand block,

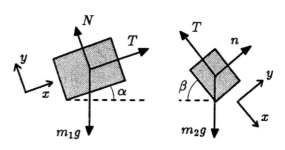

and downhill for the right-hand block. Letting a denote the x-component of the acceleration for each block (which must be the same for both blocks), we have

$$F_{x,L} = m_1 a = T - m_1 g \sin \alpha;$$
$$F_{x,R} = m_2 a = m_2 g \sin \beta - T .$$

5A.7, continued:

We thus have two equations for the two unknowns T and a, so we are ready to solve them. The y-components do not involve either T or a, and are therefore not helpful in this problem.

Solve
To find a we simply add the two equations:

$$(m_1 + m_2)a = m_2 g \sin\beta - m_1 g \sin\alpha;$$

$$\implies \quad a = \frac{m_2 \sin\beta - m_1 \sin\alpha}{m_1 + m_2} g.$$

We can then substitute in $F_{x,L}$ to find T:

$$T = m_1 g \left(\frac{m_2 \sin\beta - m_1 \sin\alpha}{m_1 + m_2} + \sin\alpha \right)$$

$$= \frac{m_1 m_2}{m_1 + m_2} g (\sin\alpha + \sin\beta).$$

Scrutinize
The dimensions are correct: a is g multiplied by the ratio of two masses, and T is g (an acceleration) multiplied by a quantity with the dimensions of mass, i.e. a force. If we set $m_2 = 0$, the acceleration comes out to $-g\sin\alpha$ and the tension to 0, which is what we would expect: the acceleration is just the downhill component of g (the normal component being balanced by the normal force exerted by the slope), and the rope is trailing freely behind the block. The minus sign is correct, because "downhill" in this case is the negative x-direction. Taking $m_1 = 0$ gives $a = g\sin\beta$, as expected. This is a particularly useful check here, because it would be quite easy to misplace a minus sign in the algebra, and dimensional analysis would not find such an error. If we wished, we could make a further check on the algebra by using the equation for $F_{x,R}$ to find T and confirming that we get the same answer.

Learn
The action of an ideal pulley is simply to change the direction of the tension, without changing its magnitude. Real pulleys are not frictionless, but they are usually very light compared to the tensions in the ropes attached to them, and thus the difference in tensions required to accelerate the non-frictionless pulley is negligible.

Changing the direction of the tension may seem fairly trivial, but it has important practical applications. For example, a typical human being can exert much more force pulling down than pulling up—consider a 100 kg couch potato, who surely cannot lift a 90 kg block of concrete off the floor, but would have no difficulty exerting a downward force of 1000 N (he just has to put his whole weight on the rope). Furthermore, we will see in Problem 7.7 that by combining several pulleys we can actually arrange to lift our 90 kg concrete block by exerting a force of much less than $g \times 90$ kg, provided that we

5A.7, continued:

exert that force over a proportionately longer distance (thereby doing the same amount of work: energy conservation is not violated).

5B.5   *You have two sliders on a frictionless linear air track, each of mass m. One is stationary, and you slide the other one into it with a velocity v_0. What happens to the momentum and kinetic energy of each slider if (a) you have attached spring-loaded fenders so that the collision is perfectly elastic; (b) you have stuck on blobs of putty so that the two sliders stick together and move off together after the collision?*

Conceptualize
Collision problems are applications of conservation laws. What we have to do is work out exactly what is conserved. The rules are:

- total momentum is *always* conserved, unless there is an external force acting on the system;

- total kinetic energy is conserved in situations where (i) no work is done on the system by an external force **and** (ii) there is no change in the internal energy of any body involved in the collision.

In this problem there is no net external force, so momentum will certainly be conserved. In case (a), where the collision is elastic, kinetic energy will also be conserved, but in case (b) it will not be—the internal energy of the blobs of putty changes when they are deformed by the collision.

$\sum\int$ *Formulate*
In case (a) we have two unknowns, the final velocities v_1 and v_2 of the first and second sliders, and two equations, one for conservation of momentum and one for conservation of kinetic energy. (This is a one-dimensional problem, so momentum conservation produces only one equation: for a three-dimensional problem we would have three equations, one for each component.) In case (b) we have only one equation, but also only one unknown, because the final velocities are known to be equal (the sliders are stuck together). We can therefore solve the equations in each case.

For case (a) the two equations are

$$mv_0 = mv_1 + mv_2$$

$$\tfrac{1}{2}mv_0^2 = \tfrac{1}{2}mv_1^2 + \tfrac{1}{2}mv_2^2$$

(where v_0 is the speed of the first slider before the collision and v_1, v_2 are the speeds of the first and second sliders after collision), while for case (b) we have

$$mv_0 = 2mv_{1+2}$$

where v_{1+2} is the final velocity of the two sliders.

Solve (a)
Squaring the momentum equation gives

$$v_0^2 = v_1^2 + v_2^2 + 2v_1v_2$$

5B.5, continued:

(dividing out the common factor of m^2). The kinetic energy equation tells us that

$$v_0^2 = v_1^2 + v_2^2,$$

and comparing these two gives

$$2v_1 v_2 = 0.$$

This means that either v_1 or v_2 is zero, and given the geometry of the situation it can only be v_1. The first slider stops, and the second slider moves off with the same speed that the first slider originally possessed. You can see this kind of collision in pool or snooker when one ball hits another square on, and also in the motion of the balls in a Newton's cradle.

Solve (b)
Clearly $v_{1+2} = v_0/2$. The final kinetic energy is $\frac{1}{2} \times 2m \times (\frac{1}{2}v_0)^2 = \frac{1}{4}mv_0^2$, half the original kinetic energy: the rest of the kinetic energy has been converted into internal energy of the system, heating and deforming the blobs of putty.

Scrutinize and Learn
The total kinetic energy in case (b) after the collision is less than that before the collision. This is reassuring: neither slider has an obvious source of additional energy, so while we can imagine *losing* kinetic energy in the collision—in this case, by doing work on the blobs of putty—it is hard to see how we could *gain* any. In case (a), during the collision we *do* do work in compressing the springs, and this *does* decrease the kinetic energy, but the spring force is conservative, so we get that kinetic energy back when the springs expand again after impact.

If we consider the center of mass frame, where slider 1 has velocity $\frac{1}{2}v_0$ and slider 2 velocity $-\frac{1}{2}v_0$ (the frame's velocity relative to the stationary frame is $\frac{1}{2}v_0$), then case (b) is trivial: the stuck-together sliders must be stationary in this frame, by definition. In case (a), the *directions* of the sliders' velocities in the center of mass frame change, but their *magnitudes* remain the same. This is also true of elastic collisions in more than one dimension, and involving objects of unequal masses. It arises because the net momentum in the center-of-mass frame is zero by definition, and so $\vec{v}_2 = -\frac{m_1}{m_2}\vec{v}_1$, i.e. $v_2 = -\frac{m_1}{m_2}v_1$. This means that the total kinetic energy is a function only of v_1, and so the elastic collision, which does not change the kinetic energy, cannot change v_1, and hence cannot change v_2.

This simplification does not hold in frames other than the center of mass frame, because in such frames $\vec{v}_2$ is not just a multiple of $\vec{v}_1$—it depends also on the total momentum $\vec{P}$. Therefore working in frames other than the center of mass frame requires more variables, and more complicated algebra. Since transforming the initial parameters of the problem into the center of mass frame is usually quite simple, it often pays to take advantage of the simpler algebra and solve collision problems in this frame.

5B.6   *In the sport of curling, teams take turns to slide polished granite stones across an ice rink, aiming at a designated target zone. A common tactic is to dislodge well-placed opposition stones by hitting them with your own stone. Assuming that all the stones are of a standard mass, that friction can be neglected, and that the collision is elastic, is it possible to determine what will happen to a stationary stone B if it is hit by another stone A moving with velocity v? If it is not possible to determine exactly what will happen, what can be determined, and what additional information is required?*

Conceptualize

This is a collision problem in two dimensions. Our system has four unknowns: the two components of the velocity of stone A after the collision, and the two components of the velocity of stone B after the collision. We can construct three equations: two for the x- and y-components of the momentum, and one for kinetic energy (since we are told the collision is elastic). Therefore we *cannot* solve this problem completely, because the number of unknowns is more than the number of equations. (In one dimension we had one fewer equation, since the momentum had only one component, but two fewer unknowns, since each velocity also had only one component: so we *could* solve the problem in one dimension.)

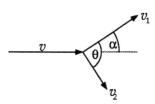

Formulate

We can, however, reduce the number of unknowns from four to one. First we write down our three equations. It turns out to be convenient to use a coordinate system in which the x-axis is along $\vec{\mathbf{v}}_1$: in this system

$$v \cos \alpha = v_1 + v_2 \cos \theta$$

$$v \sin \alpha = v_2 \sin \theta$$

$$v^2 = v_1^2 + v_2^2$$

for the x-component of momentum, the y-component of momentum, and the kinetic energy respectively (dividing out the common factor of the mass of the stones). We proceed (as in the one-dimensional case) by squaring the momentum equations:

$$v^2 \cos^2 \alpha = v_1^2 + v_2^2 \cos^2 \theta + 2v_1 v_2 \cos \theta$$

$$v^2 \sin^2 \alpha = v_2^2 \sin^2 \theta$$

and then add these together to get

$$v^2 = v_1^2 + v_2^2 + 2v_1 v_2 \cos \theta.$$

Solve

Comparing the above equation with the expression for the kinetic energy, we can deduce that

$$2v_1 v_2 \cos \theta = 0,$$

which means that one of three things must be true:

5B.6, continued:

(i) $v_1 = 0$: the first stone hit the second dead center, reducing this to the one-dimensional problem we did earlier. The first stone stops and the second goes off with velocity $\vec{v}$.

(ii) $v_2 = 0$: you missed! The first stone continues on its way and the second remains stationary.

(iii) $\cos\theta = 0$: this is the interesting case. The two stones go off such that their velocities are at right angles to each other. In this case we know that $\theta = 90°$, $v_1 = v\cos\alpha$, and $v_2 = v\sin\alpha$. Our sole remaining unknown is the angle α.

We can therefore solve this problem if we are given any of the final speeds or directions.

Scrutinize

Physically speaking, what we need to know is how glancing the collision was: it's intuitively clear that if the two stones hit head on, there will be no sideways force, and we will get case (i), whereas at the other extreme if they barely touch we will get something approaching case (ii)—the velocity of the first stone will be almost unchanged, and the second stone will go off very slowly at right angles.

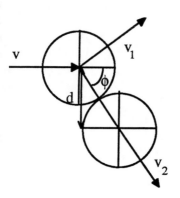

The explanation is that the forces between the stones when they collide are contact forces like those which prevent you falling through the floor, and therefore act along the line joining the centers of the stones (as in the diagram). The angle at which the second stone will go off, $\phi = \theta - \alpha$, is determined by $\sin\phi = d/2r$, r being the radius of the stones. So if we know d and r, or just the ratio d/r, we have enough information to solve the problem. The distance d (the component of the distance between the centers of the stones perpendicular to the incoming velocity) is often called the *impact parameter* of the collision.

Learn

We could have done the first part of this problem using the *vector* form of the momentum equation, $m\vec{v} = m\vec{v}_1 + m\vec{v}_2$. If we divide out the common factor of m and then take the dot product of each side with itself (effectively squaring the equation), we get $v^2 = v_1^2 + v_2^2 + 2\vec{v}_1 \cdot \vec{v}_2$. Comparing this with the energy equation leads us to deduce that $\vec{v}_1 \cdot \vec{v}_2 = 0$, yielding the same conclusions as before.

The advantage of this is that we do not need to choose a coordinate system (and in this case choosing the *wrong* coordinate system can be unfortunate—try working out this problem with the 'obvious' choice of coordinate system where the x-axis points along the incoming velocity $\vec{v}$!). Although any problem that can be solved using vectors can also be solved by taking components, it is worthwhile learning to manipulate the vector equations, because the solution is often simpler in this form.

Notice that we could solve the one-dimensional collision problem completely using only the incoming velocities and masses, whereas in two dimensions we needed one additional piece of information regarding either the collision geometry or the outgoing velocities. How many additional pieces of information would we need to solve a *three*-dimensional collision problem?

5C.2   *A girl is teaching her younger brother to skate by towing him around on a rope. They finish their practice session by hauling in on the rope from each end until they meet. If her mass is 40 kg, his is 30 kg, and the rope is 5 m long, how far from her original position will they end up? Assume that they were stationary to begin with, that the rope has negligible mass, and that there is no friction.*

Conceptualize
This problem is most easily solved by thinking about the center of mass of the children-plus-rope system. No external force is acting on this system, and therefore the center of mass must obey Newton's first law. As it is initially stationary, it will remain stationary while the children haul in on the rope. When both children are in the same place, they must be *at* the center of mass, so calculating its position at the beginning of the problem will give the children's position at the end.

We can treat the children as point particles for the purposes of calculating the center of mass, but, as discussed in Problem 4D.1(c), they can't be point particles for the purpose of pulling on the rope.

Formulate
This is effectively a one-dimensional problem, since all the movement takes place along the line of the rope. The location of the center of mass is therefore given by

$$x_{\text{cm}} = \frac{\sum m_i x_i}{\sum m_i}.$$

Since we want the final position relative to the initial position of the girl, it makes sense to choose that as the origin of coordinates.

Solve
The position of the center of mass of the system relative to the girl's position when they start to pull is

$$x_{\text{cm}} = \frac{(m_{\text{girl}} \times 0) + (m_{\text{boy}} \times L_{\text{rope}})}{m_{\text{girl}} + m_{\text{boy}}} = \frac{30\text{kg} \times 5\text{m}}{70\text{kg}} = 2.1\text{m}.$$

Therefore, rounding to the nearest half meter (realistically we can hardly specify to the nearest centimeter the position of a mass consisting of two children!) their final location is 2 m from the girl's original position.

Scrutinize
The dimensions are very simple and obviously correct. The final answer is closer to the girl's starting point, since she is more massive than her brother. If we replace the girl by a pet dog of negligible mass, the formula correctly implies that the system center of mass is at the boy's starting point, and conversely if we replace the boy by the dog we wind up where the girl started (but note that a very small mass *at a very large distance* can have a significant effect on the position of the center of mass: the important quantity is not *m*, but the product *mr*).

Learn
Note that it doesn't matter who actually hauls in the rope. The force the girl exerts on the rope is always equal and opposite to the force the rope exerts on her, and the same

187

5C.2, continued:

is true for her brother. Since for a massless rope the tension is the same at each end, it follows that both children exert an equal force on the rope, even if one is actively hauling in and the other merely holding on.

What happens if the rope is not massless? Our center-of-mass argument above still holds, but the equal-tension one does not. We also have to worry about what happens to the pile of rope left when hauling in, because that has an effect on the position of the center of mass. If the children coil the rope up as they go, they will indeed end up at the position of the center of mass; if they leave the rope trailing behind them, they won't (and it will matter who hauled and who hung on). To see this, consider the extreme case of replacing the rope by a large tree-trunk which is much more massive than either child: if the log is initially stationary, it will stay that way, and the children (pulling themselves hand-over-hand along the log) may wind up anywhere along its length. The center of mass of the system still stays fixed, but it is now determined primarily by the position of the tree and not by the positions of the children.

5C.3   *Find the position of the center of mass of:*

(a) *the Earth-Moon system (masses of 6.0×10^{24} and 7.4×10^{22} kg) separated by 384 thousand kilometers;*

(b) *a small spherical mass m attached to the end of a long thin rod of length ℓ and mass m;*

(c) *three thin rods, each of mass m and length ℓ, arranged to form three sides of a square.*

Conceptualize
This question is so specifically posed that we can consider the conceptualization already done, and proceed to:

Formulate
The equation for the position of the center of mass of *any* system is

$$M\vec{r}_{cm} = \sum_i m_i \vec{r}_i,$$

where M is the total mass of the system and m_i, $\vec{r}_i$ are the mass and position of the ith individual mass. For this question, the important point is that we can break this into pieces:

$$M\vec{r}_{cm} = \sum_{i=1}^{k-1} m_i \vec{r}_i + \sum_{i=k}^{\ell-1} m_i \vec{r}_i + \sum_{i=\ell}^{n} m_i \vec{r}_i,$$

$$= M_1 \left\{ \frac{1}{M_1} \sum_{i=1}^{k-1} m_i \vec{r}_i \right\} + M_2 \left\{ \frac{1}{M_2} \sum_{i=k}^{\ell-1} m_i \vec{r}_i \right\} + M_3 \left\{ \frac{1}{M_3} \sum_{i=\ell}^{n} m_i \vec{r}_i \right\},$$

$$= M_1 \vec{r}_{cm,1} + M_2 \vec{r}_{cm,2} + M_3 \vec{r}_{cm,3} .$$

5C.3, continued:

i.e. if we have a system which is made up of several subsystems, we can calculate the center of mass of each subsystem separately and then combine them to find the center of mass of the whole system.

Solve (a)
For the Earth-Moon system we assume that both Earth and Moon are spherical and that their densities either are uniform (a fair approximation for the Moon) or at least depend only on the distance from the center, and not on direction (OK for the Earth). In this case the center of mass of the sphere is located at the center of the sphere, since for each small element of mass at position $\vec{r}$ relative to the center there is a corresponding piece at $-\vec{r}$. Hence, taking $\vec{r} = 0$ at the center of the Earth, our equation reduces to

$$(M_{\text{Earth}} + M_{\text{Moon}})r_{\text{cm}} = (M_{\text{Earth}} \times 0) + (M_{\text{Moon}} \times r),$$

where r is the distance between the Earth's center and the Moon's. This gives us $r_{\text{cm}} = 4700$ km. The Earth-Moon center of mass is 4700 km Moonwards from the center of the Earth, which puts it actually inside the Earth (radius 6400 km).

Solve (b)
The same technique applies to the sphere-and-rod system. We are told the sphere is small, and can thus regard it as a point mass; the center of mass of the rod is at its center, a distance $\ell/2$ from the sphere (this should be obvious from its symmetry; if you're not convinced, see the note to the solution of problem 6.9). Combining these gives us

$$2mr_{\text{cm}} = (m \times 0) + (m \times \tfrac{1}{2}\ell)$$

if we put the origin of coordinates at the center of the small sphere. The center of mass is therefore located at $\ell/4$, or $\frac{1}{4}$ of the way along the rod from the weighted end.

Solve (c)
The third problem is slightly more complicated because it is two-dimensional. The center of mass of each rod is halfway along its length, so we can reduce our structure to three point particles at coordinates $(0, \ell/2)$, $(\ell/2, \ell)$ and $(\ell, \ell/2)$, putting the origin at one corner (see diagram). Using the equation for the center of mass in coordinate form gives us

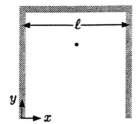

$$3mx_{\text{cm}} = (m \times 0) + (m \times \tfrac{1}{2}\ell) + (m \times \ell)$$

$$3my_{\text{cm}} = (m \times \tfrac{1}{2}\ell) + (m \times \ell) + (m \times \tfrac{1}{2}\ell)$$

so the center of mass is located at $(\ell/2, 2\ell/3)$.

Scrutinize and Learn
Note that it doesn't matter what coordinate system we choose: if I displace my coordinate origin by an amount $\vec{R}$, the equation for the center of mass becomes

$$M\vec{r}_{\text{cm}} = \sum_i m_i\left(\vec{r}_i + \vec{R}\right) = \sum_i m_i\vec{r}_i + M\vec{R},$$

189

5C.3, continued:

so the calculated value of $\vec{r}_{cm}$ is just displaced by the same amount $\vec{R}$, as it should be. We are therefore free to choose the most convenient coordinate system to do the calculation.

There is something familiar about the location of the center of mass in these examples. In part (b) especially, it seems to be located at the point where you would support the object if you wanted to balance it on a knife-edge or hang it from a hook. In fact this is absolutely true, although we will not have the technology to prove it until Chapter 8: the force of gravity on an object behaves as if it acts through the center of mass (which is often called the *center of gravity* for that reason).

5C.5   *Use the definition of the center of mass to prove the expression given in the Essentials for the kinetic energy of a system of particles.*

Conceptualize
This is another highly specific problem needing little additional conceptualization. The formulas we will use to solve it are the total kinetic energy of a system of particles and the equation defining the center of mass.

Formulate
The total kinetic energy is just the sum of the individual kinetic energies:

$$K = \sum_i \tfrac{1}{2} m_i v_i^2,$$

and the position of the center of mass is given by

$$M\vec{r}_{cm} = \sum_i m_i \vec{r}_i,$$

where M is the total mass.

Solve
If the center of mass is moving with velocity $\vec{v}_{cm}$, we can write K as

$$K = \sum_i \tfrac{1}{2} m_i \left(\vec{v}_{cm} + \left(\vec{v}_i - \vec{v}_{cm} \right) \right)^2 .$$

Expanding the square gives us

$$K = \tfrac{1}{2} M v_{cm}^2 + \sum_i \tfrac{1}{2} m_i \left(\vec{v}_i - \vec{v}_{cm} \right)^2 + \sum_i m_i \vec{v}_{cm} \cdot \left(\vec{v}_i - \vec{v}_{cm} \right) .$$

If we compare this with what we want, we see that the first two terms are the "right answer" and the third term is an unwanted addition. Proving the given equation therefore depends on showing that this extra term is actually zero. The only obvious line of

5C.5, continued:

attack is to use the center-of-mass definition again, so let's rewrite our extra piece in terms of $\vec{r}$ instead of $\vec{v}$:

$$\sum_i m_i \vec{v}_{cm} \cdot (\vec{v}_i - \vec{v}_{cm}) = \vec{v}_{cm} \cdot \sum_i m_i \left(\frac{d\vec{r}_i}{dt} - \frac{d\vec{r}_{cm}}{dt} \right).$$

Since the masses don't change with time, we can take the differentiation outside the sum to get

$$\vec{v}_{cm} \cdot \frac{d}{dt} \left(\sum_i m_i \vec{r}_i - M\vec{r}_{cm} \right).$$

But if we recall the definition of the center of mass, the term in the brackets is just $M\vec{r}_{cm} - M\vec{r}_{cm}$, which is obviously zero independent of time, so its derivative is zero, and hence this whole term is zero. We are left with what we wanted, namely

$$K = \tfrac{1}{2} M v_{cm}^2 + \sum_i \tfrac{1}{2} m_i \left(\vec{v}_i - \vec{v}_{cm} \right)^2.$$

The kinetic energy consists of the kinetic energy that the system would have if it were a point particle, plus the kinetic energies that the individual particles have *relative* to their center of mass.

Scrutinize

Our final expression is presumably correct, since it is quoted in the *Essentials,* but as an exercise we should convince ourselves that it has sensible properties. Firstly, if all the particles coalesce into a single point mass, their velocities relative to the center of mass will be zero, and K reduces to the usual formula for a single mass. The same occurs if the particles are all fixed relative to one another, even if they have non-zero separations. This explains why we can often treat extended (but rigid) objects as if they were point particles. Secondly, if we are already working in the center-of-mass frame, our final result is the same as our starting point, namely $K = \sum_i \tfrac{1}{2} m_i v_i^2$: in this frame the system has no overall motion, so all the kinetic energy comes from the internal movement of its components.

Learn

This derivation is an exercise in manipulating vector equations and derivatives. If you are confused, try rewriting it in component form. It is always possible and legitimate to decompose a vector equation into components, although it is usually easier to keep track of what is going on if you can manipulate the vectors directly.

5D.2 *During a tennis rally, the ball approaches a player at a speed of* 30 m/s. *He returns the shot so that the ball has a speed of* 35 m/s *at an angle of* 160° *to the original direction. What impulse did he apply to the ball? If ball and racquet were in contact for* 0.01 s, *what average force (averaged over time) did he exert? A tennis ball has a mass of* 60 g.

Conceptualize

This problem is primarily concerned with change in momentum. We have the mass of the tennis ball and its initial and final velocities, and can therefore calculate its change in momentum. According to the impulse-momentum theorem, this The force applied will actually vary during the time that the ball and the racquet are in contact (the face of the racquet acts very much like a spring), but the *average* force is simply the total impulse delivered divided by the total time for which the force acts.

Formulate

If we define the x and y axes as shown (z is perpendicular to the plane defined by the two momentum vectors, and is zero throughout), then the initial and final momenta are

$$\vec{\mathbf{p}}_i = [p_i, 0, 0]$$

$$\vec{\mathbf{p}}_f = [p_f \cos\theta, p_f \sin\theta, 0].$$

The impulse is

$$\vec{\mathbf{J}} = \vec{\mathbf{p}}_f - \vec{\mathbf{p}}_i,$$

and the average force exerted is

$$\vec{\mathbf{F}}_{\text{ave}} = \frac{\int_{t_i}^{t_f} \vec{\mathbf{F}}\, dt}{t_f - t_i} = \frac{\vec{\mathbf{J}}}{t_f - t_i}.$$

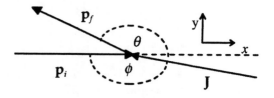

Solve

The impulse applied was

$$\vec{\mathbf{J}} = [p_f \cos\theta - p_i, p_f \sin\theta, 0]$$
$$= [J \cos\phi, J \sin\phi, 0],$$

where

$$p_i = (0.060\,\text{kg}) \times (30\,\text{m/s}) = 1.8\,\text{kg} \cdot \text{m/s},$$
$$p_f = (0.060\,\text{kg}) \times (35\,\text{m/s}) = 2.1\,\text{kg} \cdot \text{m/s},$$
$$\text{and} \quad \theta = 160°.$$

This gives

$$J = \sqrt{(-3.77)^2 + (0.72)^2}\,\text{kg} \cdot \text{m/s} = 3.8\,\text{kg} \cdot \text{m/s}$$

$$\text{and} \quad \phi = \tan^{-1}\left(\frac{0.72}{-3.77}\right) = 169°$$

5D.2, continued:

(angles with positive sine and negative cosine are in the second quadrant, between 90° and 180°). The average force is $(3.8 \text{ kg} \cdot \text{m/s})/(0.01 \text{ s}) = 380$ N, in the same direction as the impulse; that is, at 169° to the original direction of the ball.

Scrutinize
Since $1 \text{ N} = 1 \text{ kg} \cdot \text{m/s}^2$, it is clear that mass $\times$ velocity has the same dimensions as force $\times$ time, so equating impulse and (change of) momentum is dimensionally correct. In this problem we have a large change in the x-component of velocity (the ball almost reverses direction) and a comparatively small change in the y-component, so the magnitude of the change is approximately double the incoming momentum. Our values are in agreement with this expectation.

Learn
We have now defined two different integrals of the force: the force integrated over a *distance* interval, which is the work done (a dot product of two vectors, therefore a scalar), and the force integrated over *time*, which is the impulse (a vector multiplied by a scalar, therefore a vector). Note that either one of these can be zero without implying that the other one is also zero: for example, a force applied at right angles to the direction of motion does no work, but can nonetheless apply a non-zero impulse.

HINTS FOR PROBLEMS WITH AN (H)
The number of the hint refers to the number of the problem

Note: In dealing with collision problems, the algebra can become *very* tedious if you make a bad choice of reference frame. If you think you have set up the problem properly, but can't see how to extract a useful result from your equations, don't immediately conclude that you have done something hopelessly wrong—try looking for an alternative frame of reference. The frame most likely to be useful is the center of mass frame, or possibly the rest frame of one of the colliding objects.

5A.4 Do you have to apply a force to change the direction of motion of an object? If so, why?

In terms of L and v, what is the magnitude of the momentum carried by the water that flows into the hydrant in 1 s? As a result of flowing round the bend, what is the change in the x component of momentum every second? The y-component? The total momentum?

5B.3 The two sliders form an isolated system. What is meant by 'isolated system'? What is conserved in the motion of the objects which comprise an isolated system?

What is meant by 'elastic collision'? What is conserved in an elastic collision?

To solve this problem, try working in the center of mass frame.

Think of an immovable wall as a slider of infinitely large mass. What happens to your two velocities if you make M very large?

Is there a frame of reference in which the initial situation in your two-dimensional system is identical to the one you have just solved?

5B.4 What quantity (or quantities) is conserved in these collisions?

5B.7 At every step of the problem, think carefully about which objects you should consider as an isolated system. What is conserved in any isolated system? Just after a throw what is the sum of the magnitudes of the velocities of the sled and the block? What is relation between the total momentum of a sled plus block just before a throw and just after? If you are consistently getting the wrong answer, try checking the motion of the center of mass after each catch—what should it be doing?

Note: In most problems it is better to assign symbols for given numerical quantities and then first solve the problem algebraically. This problem is an exception to that "rule". The problem has 4 layers, each of which uses the answers from the previous layer. It gets very complicated to proceed in terms of the original variables. If you are getting the wrong answer, see that you are correctly doing the first step by checking the answer to the following: After you slide the block, what is your speed and what is the speed of the block?

194

5C.4 How is the center of mass defined? If you're confused, review the solution to problem 5C.3.

5C.6 What is the meaning of 'center of mass frame'? What does this imply about the total momentum of an isolated system considered in its center of mass frame? Use this to find v_2 in terms of v_1. Now do the same thing for *after* the collision. Can you now solve the kinetic energy equation?

5D.3 What is the meaning of 'impulse applied to the body'? How does this relate to momentum? In each case, what is the momentum of the ball before and after it is hit?

If you're still stuck, study the solution to problem 5D.2.

ANSWERS TO HINTS

5A.4 Yes, because the direction of the velocity vector changes (i.e., there is an acceleration); equivalently, the momentum changes (an impulse has been applied).

$\rho L v$; $\rho L v$, $-\rho L v$, $\sqrt{2}\rho L v$.

5B.3 One where there is no net external force acting; momentum.

One where there is no change in the internal energy of the colliding objects (no heating or deformation); kinetic energy and momentum.

Velocity of mass m tends to $-v$; velocity of mass M tends to zero.

Yes.

5B.4 Momentum.

5B.7 Momentum; 2 m/s; they are equal; it remains stationary; recoiling at 0.2 m/s; moving forward at 1.8 m/s.

5C.4 Its coordinates are such that

$$x_{\text{cm}} = \frac{\sum_i m_i x_i}{\sum_i m_i},$$

and likewise for y and z.

5C.6 The frame in which the center of mass is stationary; it is always zero.

$$v_2 = \frac{m_1 v_1}{m_2} \qquad \text{(both times)};$$

$$\left[v_1^2\right]_{\text{after}} = \left[v_1^2\right]_{\text{before}}$$

5D.3 $\vec{J} = \int \vec{F}\, dt$; impulse is total change in momentum.

(a) 2.1 and -3.0 kg m/s;

(b) 5.1 and -7.2 kg m/s (taking the positive x-axis in direction of incoming ball in both cases).

ANSWERS TO ALL PROBLEMS

5A.1 c

5A.2 a

5A.3 See complete solution.

5A.4 $\sqrt{2}\rho Lv$, where ρ is the density of water; 470 N, directed upwards 135° from direction of spray.

5A.5 See complete solution.

5A.6 An acceptable answer would be:

"An internal force is exerted by one body in the system under consideration on another body in the system. Such a force does not change the momentum of the system as a whole. An external force is exerted by something outside the system, and does change the system momentum."

5A.7 See complete solution.

5A.8 (a) $T = mg$; (b) $m = M\sin\theta$. The experimenter's gentle push will impart a small downward velocity to the block. After the push has been applied the force equations will resume the form they had before the push, which means that the acceleration will again be zero. The block of mass M will therefore continue down the hill until either it reaches the bottom, or the hanging block reaches the pulley.

5B.1 d; b

5B.2 The displaced ball stops when it hits the other four, and the ball at the other end comes off with the same speed v (only way to conserve both momentum and kinetic energy). This ball then swings out to the same displacement given the first ball (conservation of energy, as in simple pendulum), swings back to hit the rest with the same speed v, and the process repeats (indefinitely, in the absence of friction). Note that the collisions all take place in the horizontal plane, so there is no net external force (gravity is balanced by tension in suspending wires), hence we can use momentum conservation.

5B.3 $\frac{m-M}{m+M}v$ (slider of mass m) and $\frac{2mv}{m+M}$ (slider of mass M).

Slider will rebound from wall with velocity $-v$.

In two dimensions, component of velocity perpendicular to wall will be reversed, but parallel component unchanged. Puck will bounce back from wall at angle $180° - \theta$.

5B.4 (a) 2.89 m/s; (b) 2.85 m/s. (to 2 significant figures, 2.9 and 2.8 m/s, respectively)
Before: 340 J; after: (a) 270 J, (b) 280 J.

5B.5 See complete solution.

5B.6 See complete solution.

5B.7 0.33 m/s and 0.48 m/s, in opposite directions

5C.1 a

5C.2 See complete solution.

5C.3 See complete solution.

5C.4 (a) $\frac{1}{2}\left(r + \frac{1}{2}\ell\right)$ measured from center of sphere;

　　(b) at point $\left(\frac{1}{4}\ell, \frac{1}{4}\ell\right)$ in a coordinate system where one rod is the x-axis and the other the y-axis;

　　(c) $3\ell/8$ measured from left-hand end of horizontal rod in diagram.

5C.5 See complete solution.

5C.6 v_1 and v_2 respectively, in opposite directions (but angle with original direction unknown).

5D.1 c

5D.2 See complete solution.

5D.3 (a) 5.1 kg m/s; 510 N.

　　(b) 12.3 kg m/s; 6.2 kN.

SUPPLEMENTARY NOTES

SOLVING REAL PROBLEMS

In this chapter we begin to see why the simplifications and idealizations we have been using in our problems do not prevent us from gaining physical insight which can be applied to real situations. This works in real life largely because of the set of equations in this chapter giving the acceleration, momentum and kinetic energy of a system of particles. In terms of application to problem solving, these tell us that

- we can calculate the momentum and acceleration of a macroscopic object (e.g. a car) by treating it as a point particle of the same mass;

- momentum is conserved in all situations, even those involving forces like friction where the sum of kinetic and potential energy is not constant (e.g. inelastic collisions);

- apparent failures of energy conservation in situations involving real physical objects can be understood in terms of changes in the internal energy of the system.

The first two points are consequences of the third law, or more generally of momentum conservation, and are vital to the development of physical science since the Renaissance. It is clear that if one had to consider the detailed structure of every object on which a force acts before predicting the motion of the object, it would be impossible to make useful predictions for real objects. (This is a problem which bedevils calculations involving the strong fundamental force, where, for a complicated set of reasons involving the detailed structure of the force, the current theory only yields exact predictions for a very restricted class of simple interactions. As a result most experimental results cannot be interpreted cleanly in terms of the theory, which has consequently been very difficult to develop and test properly.) The third point shows us how to test our theories more rigorously: if it is correct, then if we can find a way of measuring the internal energy of a system of particles (more particularly, of the atoms making up a physical object) we should find that the change in that internal energy after an interaction balances the change in mechanical (kinetic plus potential) energy we observe. Internal energy in fact often manifests itself as heat, and its behavior is studied in a branch of physics called thermodynamics. We will introduce some of the basic concepts of thermodynamics in Chapter 11, but it is far too large a subject in its own right to be considered as a subset of classical mechanics.

The conservation laws for energy and momentum are another important weapon in practical applications. As discussed in the notes to Chapter 4, the great advantage of these principles is that we can often apply them when our knowledge about the system we are studying is incomplete, or when the equations that describe it are mathematically intractable. Although we generally cannot solve a problem completely using conservation laws (for example, we have already seen that a two-body collision in two dimensions is not completely soluble), we can put severe restrictions on the possible solutions. This may in itself be sufficient for the purposes of the practical application (for example, in making sure that a particular effect cannot be large enough to distort the results of an experiment); if not, it at least provides a useful starting point for more detailed calculations, perhaps involving numerical integration.

FIELDS AND THE THIRD LAW

We have quoted the third law in Newton's terms, involving the actions of two objects on each other. In the case of forces like gravity and the electrostatic force, this requires the concept of *action at a distance*, i.e. body A somehow affects body B despite the fact that they are not in contact. We saw in the Supplementary Notes to Chapter 4 that an alternative viewpoint is to say that body A actually creates a *field* with which body B then interacts (and vice versa). Modern particle physics indicates that the microscopic description of this field is a cloud of force-carrying particles which are constantly being emitted and absorbed by the interacting bodies.

This suggests that the proper formulation of the third law would be that the force exerted by body A on the field with which it interacts is equal and opposite to that exerted by the field on A, and likewise for B. For nearly static fields this makes no real difference. Suppose, as an analogy, that body A and body B were connected by a massless rope. We could then argue that the third law applies *either* directly to the two tension forces *or* individually to the tension force applied to A (or B) by the rope and the force applied to the rope by A (or B). The former is not strictly correct, but as long as the rope is massless it gives the same answer as the latter.

However, if the rope joining A and B is *not* massless, then only the second interpretation works, since the tension is no longer constant along the rope. In this case there is a net force on the rope, so the rope itself acquires a nonzero momentum. It turns out that there are circumstances, particularly in the forces felt and exerted by moving electrically charged particles, where the same thing happens for fields, and we *must* treat the third law as acting locally, in the interaction of each body with the local electromagnetic field. We will avoid such situations here, but they are quite common in electromagnetic theory.

ESSENTIALS OF INTRODUCTORY CLASSICAL MECHANICS

CHAPTER 6

MACROSCOPIC FORCES AND NON-INERTIAL REFERENCE FRAMES

OVERVIEW

The concept of the internal kinetic energy of a system of particles has several interesting consequences when applied to the motion of physical objects. Since real objects are made up of atoms, even a single macroscopic body can be thought of as a system of many particles. In this chapter we consider the treatment of physical forces which cause unmeasured changes in the internal energy of such a system, and which therefore lead to an apparent non-conservation of mechanical energy. These are known as *dissipative forces*, the most common being friction. We shall see later that the change in the internal energy of the system caused by the action of a dissipative force can often be detected experimentally as a change in temperature.

We have noted in earlier chapters that Newton's laws are only valid in inertial reference frames. However, in some circumstances it is more natural to work in a non-inertial frame. This can be done by introducing fictitious forces to account for that component of the observed acceleration which is due to the acceleration of the reference frame.

When you have completed this chapter you should:

✔ understand what is meant by a dissipative force;

✔ recognize the distinction between static and kinetic friction;

✔ understand the procedures for determining the forces of static and kinetic friction in various situations;

✔ be able to solve problems involving other types of dissipative forces, such as air friction, when the nature of the dissipative force is described in the problem;

✔ know what is meant by the term "fictitious force" and be able to use fictitous forces to do calculations involving non-inertial reference frames.

ESSENTIALS

If two physical surfaces come into contact the atoms making up those surfaces interact by the electromagnetic force. We have already met one consequence of this—the normal force which prevents solid objects from sinking into each other.

When a moving body slides on a stationary body, we observe another aspect of these interatomic forces: a frictional force acts to resist the relative motion. The actual mechanism of friction is extremely complex, involving the formation of temporary bonds between surfaces and the deformation of tiny irregularities on each face. Experimentally we find that, to a good approximation, the magnitude of the frictional force exerted by one surface on the other is proportional to that of the normal force exerted by that surface. We can then write

Problems 6B and 6E.7

$$\left|\vec{\mathbf{F}}_k\right| = \mu_k \left|\vec{\mathbf{N}}\right| \, ,$$

where the dimensionless constant μ_k is called the *coefficient of kinetic friction*, and its value depends on the nature of the surfaces. The subscript k appears on $\vec{\mathbf{F}}_k$ and μ_k because the case discussed here is called *kinetic friction*, since one surface is moving relative to the other. The force on the moving body is directed opposite its velocity, and then, by Newton's third law, the force on the stationary body is in the direction of the moving body's velocity. Notice that, like Hooke's 'law', this relation is not a physical law: it is an experimentally valid approximation to a very complicated physical process.

A force of friction can also be transmitted between two surfaces when both are stationary, in which case it is called *static friction*. The method of calculation is somewhat different, since the force of friction will depend on what other forces are acting. The force of static friction is denoted by $\vec{\mathbf{F}}_s$, and is determined by the following rules:

Problems 6A

(1) Newton's third law applies, so the force on one surface is equal in magnitude but opposite in direction to the force on the other surface.

(2) The force will be in the plane of the two surfaces in contact.

(3) Within the plane of the two surfaces, both the direction and magnitude of the frictional force will adjust to cancel all other forces, so that there is no net force that would cause one surface to slide along the other.

(4) The force of static friction obeys the inequality

$$\left|\vec{\mathbf{F}}_s\right| \le \mu_s \left|\vec{\mathbf{N}}\right| ,$$

where μ_s is called the *coefficient of static friction*. If the force determined by criteria (1)–(3) fails to obey this inequality, then it means that friction is not strong enough to hold the surfaces stationary. The surfaces will start to slide, and the rules governing kinetic friction will then apply. Hence for a given situation μ_s can be determined by measuring the force needed to cause the object to begin to move. It is impossible to have $\mu_s < \mu_k$: they can be equal, but usually $\mu_s > \mu_k$, which means that it is usually easier to keep something sliding than to start it sliding.

Occasionally we deal with situations in which neither surface in a friction problem is stationary, such as a suitcase dropped on a moving conveyor belt. For the case of kinetic friction, the magnitude of the force is still given by

$$\left|\vec{\mathbf{F}}_k\right| = \mu_k \left|\vec{\mathbf{N}}\right| .$$

The force on each surface is directed opposite to the velocity of that surface *relative to the other surface*. For the case of static friction, only item (3) needs modification. The force will again be whatever is needed to prevent sliding (subject to the inequality in (4)), but with moving surfaces that does not necessarily mean that the force of friction cancels all other forces. If the conveyor belt is accelerating, for example, the force of static friction acting on the suitcase will cause it to accelerate at the same rate, to prevent sliding.

If we measure only the overall kinetic and potential energy of the body considered as a point particle, we will not record the changes in motion and position of the surface atoms caused by the frictional forces. Therefore, instead of finding

Problems 6C

$$K + U = \text{constant} ,$$

where U is the potential energy associated with any conservative forces acting on the body, we will see that

$$K_{\text{final}} + U_{\text{final}} = K_{\text{initial}} + U_{\text{initial}} + W_{\text{friction}} ,$$

where W_{friction} is the work done by friction, which corresponds to the unobserved change in the system's internal energy.

The total work W_{friction} done by friction for a closed system is always negative, since friction can convert kinetic energy to heat, but

205

never vice versa. It is possible, nonetheless, for friction to do positive work in cases where we are not discussing a closed system. When one places a suitcase with zero velocity on a moving conveyor belt, kinetic friction does positive work on the suitcase as the suitcase accelerates to the speed of the belt. Once the suitcase reaches the speed of the belt, then the rules of static friction apply. If the belt moves at constant velocity, then no force is necessary to prevent sliding, and the force of static friction will be zero (not $\mu_s|\vec{\mathbf{N}}|$!). If the belt then starts to accelerate, static friction will cause the suitcase to accelerate, so static friction will do positive work on the suitcase. If the conveyor belt accelerates so fast that the force necessary for the suitcase to keep up exceeds the inequality of item (4) above, then the suitcase will start to slip.

Forces which produce apparent changes in the total mechanical energy in this way are called *dissipative* (or *non-conservative*) forces. Another common example is the drag force exerted on an object moving through a liquid or gas. Dissipative forces always arise as experimental approximations to more complex underlying physical forces: at the fundamental level we believe that energy is always conserved.

Problems 6D, 6E.8, 6E.9, and 6E.10

For a conservative force, the work done by the force as an object traverses a closed path is always zero. So if we put energy into a stone by lifting it, we will be able to retrieve the energy when the stone is lowered, because the work done by gravity on the stone must be zero for the closed path. Since the energy put into a stone by lifting it remains available, we defined the concept of potential energy to account for it. For dissipative forces, however, the work done as an object traverses a closed path is not zero. If a body is slid from point A to point B and back, friction opposes the motion in both directions, and the net work done by friction is negative. The energy is converted to heat, but it cannot be retrieved as kinetic energy, and there is no way to describe it as a potential energy.

The approximations involved in treating friction and similar effects in terms of dissipative forces, and the lack of an associated potential energy, do not affect the status of such forces as 'real', well-behaved examples of the concept of force: they obey Newton's laws in inertial reference frames. However, many 'forces' which are familiar in everyday life—for example, the force which pushes you back into the car seat during acceleration—are *not* real forces in this sense: instead, they are the observable consequence of making measurements in a non-inertial reference frame.

Consider a particle of mass m moving with constant velocity $\vec{v}$. Problems 6F.
Its momentum is $\vec{p} = m\vec{v}$, and the net force acting on it is $\dfrac{d\vec{p}}{dt} = 0$.
If we observe from a reference frame moving with constant velocity $\vec{V}$, the observed momentum becomes $m(\vec{v} - \vec{V})$, and if both $\vec{v}$ and $\vec{V}$ are constant the observed force is still zero. However, if our reference frame is acclerating, so that $\vec{V} = \vec{V}_0 + \vec{a}t$, the observed momentum is time-dependent, and to the accelerating observer it appears that the particle is being acted on by a force $\dfrac{d\vec{p}}{dt} = -m\vec{a}$. If the observer assumes that such a force is indeed acting, her calculations using Newton's laws will give the correct answers: the *fictitious force* $-m\vec{a}$ gives the particle an acceleration $-\vec{a}$ which compensates for the acceleration $\vec{a}$ of the observer's frame of reference.

If the non-inertial frame of reference is undergoing linear acceleration $\vec{a}(t)$, which could be time dependent, then the fictitious force is simple to write down:

$$\boxed{\vec{F}_{\text{fict}} = -m\vec{a}(t) \ ,}$$

where m is the mass of the object on which the force is acting. Beware, however, of rotating frames of reference. In such frames the fictitious force includes not only the *centrifugal* force, but also a velocity-dependent term called the *Coriolis* force, which is beyond the scope of this book.

In principle, it is never necessary to use the concept of a fictitious force: we can simply choose not to try to do force calculations in non-inertial reference frames. However, there are applications where the use of an accelerated frame is more natural: if we wish to design a seat belt or an airbag, it makes sense to work in the non-inertial reference frame of the rapidly decelerating car; if we are doing weather forecasts, and therefore want to study the motion of large masses of air relative to the ground, the only sensible reference frame to use is one which is fixed relative to the surface of the rotating Earth. (Note that for small-scale problems such as blocks sliding down inclined planes, it is a very good approximation to regard the Earth's surface as defining an inertial reference frame, but this approximation will not work for large-scale phenomena such as weather patterns.) In these cases we can only use Newton's laws successfully if we introduce appropriate fictitious forces.

Because the purpose of a fictitious force is to compensate for the acceleration of the observer's reference frame, it must produce the same acceleration for particles of different masses, so it must have the form $m\vec{a}$. We are already familiar with one real force that has exactly this form, namely gravity. Over small length scales, the motion of objects viewed from an accelerating reference frame without gravity is indistinguishable from that seen from an inertial frame with a gravitational field. This is an alternative statement of the Principle of Equivalence (see Chapter 2), that the inertial mass is equal to the gravitational mass—an unexplained coincidence in Newtonian mechanics, but a fundamental principle of General Relativity.

SUMMARY

* Frictional forces are contact forces produced by atomic interactions at the surfaces of physical objects. Since the changes in position and motion of surface atoms are not generally measured, the action of frictional forces when one object slides on another causes an apparent loss of mechanical energy from the system. Forces which behave in this way are called *dissipative* (or *non-conservative*) forces.

* When two surfaces slide along each other, the force of *kinetic friction* acts on each. To a good approximation, the magnitude of the force is equal to the *coefficient of kinetic friction* times the magnitude of the normal force between the surfaces. The direction of the force on each surface is opposite the direction of the velocity of that surface relative to the other surface.

* If two surfaces are in contact with no relative velocity, the force of *static friction* can act between them. This force is in the plane of the two surfaces, and has a direction and magnitude equal to whatever is necessary to prevent the surfaces from sliding, up to a maximum given by the *coefficient of static friction* times the magnitude of the normal force. If this maximum is not sufficient to prevent sliding, then the surfaces will slide and the rules of kinetic friction will apply.

* Newton's laws can be applied in non-inertial reference frames by introducing *fictitious forces* to account for the acceleration of the reference frame.

* Physical concepts introduced in this chapter: dissipative force, static friction, kinetic friction, coefficient of static friction, coefficient of kinetic friction.

* Mathematical concepts introduced in this chapter: none.

* Equations introduced in this chapter:

$$\left|\vec{\mathbf{F}}_k\right| = \mu_k \left|\vec{\mathbf{N}}\right| \qquad \text{(kinetic friction)};$$

$$\left|\vec{\mathbf{F}}_s\right| \le \mu_s \left|\vec{\mathbf{N}}\right| \qquad \text{(static friction)};$$

$$\vec{\mathbf{F}}_{\text{fict}} = -m\vec{\mathbf{a}}(t) \qquad \text{(fictitious force in linearly accelerating frame)}.$$

PROBLEMS AND QUESTIONS

By the end of this chapter you should be able to answer or solve the types of questions or problems stated below.

Note: throughout the book, in multiple-choice problems, the answers have been rounded off to 2 significant figures, unless otherwise stated.

At the end of the chapter there are answers to all the problems. In addition, for problems with an (H) or (S) after the number, there are respectively hints on how to solve the problems or completely worked-out solutions.

6A   STATIC FRICTION

6A.1   You are asked to drag a 45 kg crate across a warehouse floor. You find that in order to start the crate moving you have to apply a horizontal force of 250 N. Taking $g = 10$ m/s^2, what is the coefficient of static friction between the crate and the floor?

(a) 0.06; (b) 0.56; (c) 1.8; (d) 0.18.

Your six-year-old cousin tries to help you by dragging the next crate, but she can only apply a force of 50 N. What frictional force opposes her efforts?

(a) 50 N; (b) 250 N; (c) 450 N; (d) none of these.

6A.2 (H)   A small weight of mass 50 g is placed on the turntable of a record player, 10 cm from the center. If the player is set for 33.3 rpm, what is the minimum coefficient of static friction required if the weight is to stay put? (Take $g = 10$ m/s^2.)

6B   KINETIC FRICTION

6B.1   A train of total mass 100,000 kg is moving at 15 m/s when the engineer spots a cow on the line ahead. He pulls the emergency brake lever and locks the wheels of the train. If the coefficient of kinetic friction between the wheels and the rails is 0.6, how long does the train take to stop? (Take $g = 10$ m/s^2; the track is level.)

(a) 0.25 s; (b) 1.0 s; (c) 2.5 s; (d) 4.0 s.

6B.2 (S)   You have just moved into a new apartment, and you are attempting to shift a 60 kg desk from one side of a (fortunately uncarpeted) room to the other. Are you better off pulling horizontally, or at some angle to the horizontal? If the coefficient of kinetic friction between the desk and the floor is 0.45, what is the smallest force you can apply to move the desk at a constant speed?

6B.3   Explain in 50 words or less the distinction between static and kinetic friction.

6C   WORK DONE BY FRICTION

6C.1 (S)   A child slides down a slide in a children's playground. The slide makes an angle of 40° to the horizontal and is 3 m high. If the coefficient of kinetic friction between the child and the surface of the slide is 0.15, what is the child's speed at the bottom? How much work has been done (a) by gravity; (b) by friction? What is the sum of kinetic and gravitational potential energy of the child, whose mass is 30 kg, at the top and bottom of the slide? What has happened to the 'lost' energy?

6C.2 (H)   You pull a mass M up a ramp inclined at an angle θ to the horizontal. If you exert just enough force to move the mass at constant speed and you always pull parallel to the slope, how does (a) the force you exert, (b) the work you do in raising the mass through a vertical height h, depend on the angle of the slope and on the coefficient of friction between the mass and the ramp? Take $g = 10$ m/s^2.

6D   OTHER DISSIPATIVE FORCES

6D.1   Air resistance at high speeds can be approximated by $\vec{\mathcal{F}} = -kv^2\hat{\mathbf{v}}$, where $\vec{\mathbf{v}}$ is the velocity vector of the moving object, $\hat{\mathbf{v}}$ is the unit vector parallel to $\vec{\mathbf{v}}$, and k is a constant whose value depends on the object's shape. Using this information, (a) describe qualitatively the behavior of an object falling freely in air and (b) derive an expression for the maximum velocity attained by an object of mass m falling in air through some very long vertical distance h.

6D.2   The exact value of k (as defined above) for a given object depends on many details of its shape, but the most important determining factor is the cross-sectional area perpendicular to the direction of motion (this is why objects designed to minimize air drag tend to be long and slim). In view of this, discuss (a) the action of parachutes; (b) why cats generally survive falls from high-rise apartment balconies whereas human beings generally do not; (c) the result Galileo would have gotten if he really had dropped one wooden and one lead cannonball off the Leaning Tower of Pisa.

6E   MOTION WITH DISSIPATIVE FORCES

6E.1 (S)   Two blocks are connected by a light rope over a pulley as shown. The pulley is frictionless, but the coefficient of friction between block A and the slope is 0.40 for static friction and 0.30 for kinetic friction. If the mass of block A is 5 kg, what is the smallest mass B needed (a) to start block A sliding up the slope from rest; (b) to keep it moving if it has been started by an external push; (c) to prevent A from sliding *down* the slope? (d) What is the frictional force acting on block A if block B has a mass of 2 kg? Take $g = 10$ m/s^2.

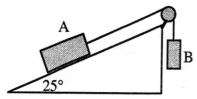

6E.2 (H)   Thutmose, Pharaoh's chief pyramid builder, needs to drag a block of stone of mass 10,000 kg up an earth ramp during the construction of Pharaoh's latest project. The coefficient of static friction between the stone and the ramp is 0.6, and the kinetic friction coefficient is 0.4. He has available a large corps of slaves, each capable of exerting a force of 300 N. If the ramp makes an angle of 20° to the horizontal, how many slaves does he need to get the stone to start to move? Once it has started moving, how many can he divert to work on the next stone? Take $g = 10$ m/s^2.

6E.3   In the context of the physics of this chapter, explain why, if you need to stop quickly, it is bad to lock the wheels of your car.

6E.4   An object of mass m rests on a slope making an angle θ with the horizontal. The coefficient of static friction between the object and the slope is μ_s, and the coefficient of kinetic friction is μ_k. As usual, μ_s is larger than μ_k. How steep does the slope have to be before the object starts to slide? If the slope is such that it will just start to slide, what will its acceleration be once it has begun to move?

6E.5 (H) A 500 g block rests on a level table. The coefficients of friction between block and table are $\mu_s = 0.35$ and $\mu_k = 0.25$. The block is attached to a wall by means of a horizontal spring of spring constant $k = 100$ N/m. An experimenter pulls on the block to stretch the spring and then lets go, with the block initially at rest. Take $g = 10$ m/s^2.

(a) What is the maximum extension of the spring for which the block will remain stationary when released?

(b) If the block is placed in this position and then given a very gentle push towards the wall, describe in words what will happen. What is the initial acceleration of the block? At what position (relative to its starting point) does it reach its maximum speed?

6E.6 (S) A curve on a freeway has radius 300 m, and has been banked for a design speed of 80 km/h (i.e. the inward component of the normal force provides the necessary centripetal acceleration at this speed). The freeway is presently occupied by the getaway car from a bank robbery, with the police in hot pursuit. In dry conditions, how fast can the crooks safely take the bend? What if they had chosen to commit their robbery on the proverbial dark and stormy night? [The coefficients of friction for rubber on dry concrete are $\mu_s = 1.0$, $\mu_k = 0.8$; for wet concrete they are 0.30 and 0.25 respectively.]

6E.7 (S) Two cars collide at an intersection. They remain locked together after the collision, and by measuring the skid marks the police conclude that the wreckage traveled 4.4 m at an angle of 43° to car 1's original direction. Car 1 had mass 1000 kg and car 2 1300 kg. If the accident happened in dry conditions when the coefficient of kinetic friction between rubber and concrete is 0.8, calculate the speeds of the two cars immediately before the collision.

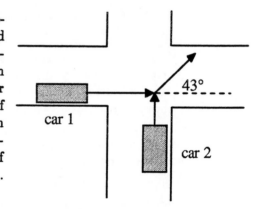

6E.8 (H) At very slow speeds (especially in liquids rather than gases) the drag force is proportional to the speed rather than its square, i.e. , $\vec{f} = -k\vec{v}$ where k is a constant. Suppose that a small ball of mass m is projected into such a liquid so that it initially has a horizontal velocity $[u, 0, 0]$. If the y-direction is defined to be vertically upwards, what is the ball's velocity vector $\vec{v}$ at some later time t? Describe in words the motion of the ball. (Assume all effects other than gravity and fluid resistance can be neglected.)

6E.9 The diagram shows the path of a projectile. The interval between adjacent points is 0.1 s, and the diagram was constructed with an initial velocity vector $[10, 10, 0]$ m/s and $k/m = 0.35$ m^{-1} (where m is the projectile mass and the air drag is $\vec{f} = -kv^2\hat{v}$). Discuss qualitatively how this trajectory differs from the motion of projectiles as analyzed in Chapter 1.

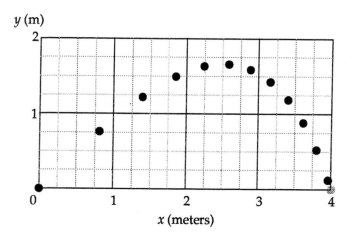

In the absence of air drag, the range of a projectile is maximized by firing it at 45° to the horizontal. To maximize the range for the projectile shown here, should you fire it at (a) 45°, (b) < 45°, or (c) > 45°? Do not attempt a detailed mathematical analysis, but do try to justify your answer with a reasonably persuasive argument.

6E.10 (S)   A particle of mass m is launched vertically upward at time $t = 0$ with initial speed v_0. If the air drag is $\vec{\mathcal{F}} = -kv^2\hat{\mathbf{v}}$, show that the particle reaches its maximum height at time

$$t = \sqrt{\frac{m}{kg}}\, \tan^{-1}\left(v_0\sqrt{\frac{k}{mg}}\right).$$

What is the maximum height reached? How does this compare with the height reached in the absence of air resistance, for a projectile with $k/m = 0.35$ m^{-1} and $v_0 = 10$ m/s vertically upwards? Take $g = 10$ m/s^2.

You may find it useful to know that:

$$\int \frac{\mathrm{d}x}{1 + x^2} = \tan^{-1} x\ ;$$

$$\int \tan\theta\, \mathrm{d}\theta = \ln(\sec\theta)\ .$$

6F   NON-INERTIAL REFERENCE FRAMES

6F.1 (H)   An experiment aboard a space probe includes a mass M which is attached to a spring of spring constant k and natural length ℓ_0. The other end of the spring is fixed. While the space probe is making a course correction, an astronaut notices that the mass M appears to be stationary, but the spring has stretched to length ℓ. Derive an expression for the acceleration of the space probe:

(a) using an appropriate inertial reference frame

(b) using the rest frame of the accelerating spacecraft.

213

6F.2 (H)   A train is accelerating in a horizontal straight line. A passenger holds a plumb bob consisting of a mass M on a light string of length ℓ.

(a) If the magnitude of the train's acceleration is a, derive an expression for the angle which the string of the plumb bob makes with the vertical.

(b) If the bob is slightly displaced from its equilibrium position, what is the period of the resulting oscillations?

COMPLETE SOLUTIONS TO PROBLEMS WITH AN (S)

6B.2   *You have just moved into a new apartment, and you are attempting to shift a 60 kg desk from one side of a (fortunately uncarpeted) room to the other. Are you better off pulling horizontally, or at some angle to the horizontal? If the coefficient of kinetic friction between the desk and the floor is 0.45, what is the smallest force you can apply to move the desk at a constant speed?*

Conceptualize

It may seem obvious that you should apply a horizontal force, since you want the desk to move horizontally. However, recall that the frictional force is proportional to the normal force. Looking at the force diagram, we can see that if you apply a force with some upward component, you will decrease the normal force. You can trade a reduced horizontal component of $\vec{f}$ off against a reduced frictional force opposing it. To find the minimum force required, i.e. to minimize f, we will have to construct an equation for the net force in terms of our known quantities (m and μ_k) and the unknown angle θ. We can then differentiate this to find the value of θ which minimizes f.

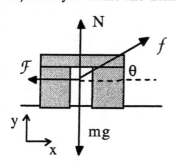

Formulate

The components of the net force are

$$F_x = f \cos\theta - \mathcal{F}_k$$
$$F_y = f \sin\theta + N - mg \,,$$

assuming you apply a force of magnitude f at an angle θ to the horizontal.

Since we are considering a situation where the desk is *moving*, we want *kinetic* friction, so the magnitude of the frictional force is $\mathcal{F}_k = \mu_k N$. We want the desk to move horizontally at a constant speed, so there will be no net force acting either horizontally or vertically: $F_x = F_y = 0$

Our unknowns are N, f and θ, three in all, and we have two equations. However, the condition that we want the *minimum* value of f will give us a third equation, $\mathrm{d}f/\mathrm{d}\theta = 0$, and so we can solve this problem.

Solve

The condition that $F_y = 0$ tells us that $N = mg - f\sin\theta$. Furthermore $\mathcal{F}_k = \mu_k N$, so $F_x = 0$ implies that

$$f\cos\theta = \mu_k(mg - f\sin\theta)$$
$$\Rightarrow f = \frac{\mu_k\, mg}{\cos\theta + \mu_k \sin\theta}.$$

To find the minimum value of f, we differentiate with respect to θ:

$$\frac{\mathrm{d}f}{\mathrm{d}\theta} = -\frac{\mu_k\, mg}{(\cos\theta + \mu_k \sin\theta)^2}\left(-\sin\theta + \mu_k \cos\theta\right).$$

215

6B.2, continued:

This is zero when the last term is zero, i.e. when $\tan\theta = \mu_k$. For $\mu_k = 0.45$, our force is best applied at 24° to the horizontal. To find the magnitude of f, we substitute the numerical values into our equation:

$$f = \frac{0.45 \times (60\,\text{kg}) \times (9.8\,\text{m/s}^2)}{\cos 24° + 0.45 \sin 24°} = 240\,\text{N}.$$

If you choose to pull horizontally, you need $f = \mu_k\, mg = 265$ N, about 10% more.

Scrutinize

Calculating the force required to move the desk pulling horizontally does two things: it confirms that the value we found by setting the derivative to zero is a minimum (remember that the derivative would also be zero for a maximum), and it assures us that the numerical value is reasonable.

Learn

Experience tells us that another reason not to pull horizontally (especially in the case of a tall object like a bookcase, rather than a desk) is that the object is more likely to topple over than to slide. This is because our force diagram, which shows all the forces acting at the same point, is not very realistic: you would probably pull near the top of the desk, while the frictional force acts on its base. The result of this is that the object develops a tendency to rotate, rather than to remain in the same orientation. This will be the topic of Chapter 8.

6C.1   *A child slides down a slide in a children's playground. The slide makes an angle of 40° to the horizontal and is 3 m high. If the coefficient of kinetic friction between the child and the surface of the slide is 0.15, what is the child's speed at the bottom? How much work has been done (a) by gravity; (b) by friction? What is the sum of kinetic and gravitational potential energy of the child, whose mass is 30 kg, at the top and bottom of the slide? What has happened to the 'lost' energy?*

Conceptualize

The work done by a force on an object is the dot product of the force and the displacement of the object. Looking at the force diagram for the child, we can see that the normal force will do no work (it is perpendicular to the displacement), friction will do work $-\mathcal{F}x$, where x is the distance the child slides (the friction and the displacement are antiparallel), and gravity will do work mgh, where m is the child's mass and h is the vertical height of the slide.

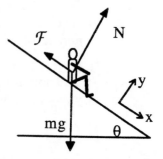

To calculate the work done by friction, we shall first have to calculate the magnitude of $\mathcal{F}$. Once this is done, we can use energy conservation to calculate the kinetic energy, or we can do it from Newton's laws (since in the process of calculating the friction we shall have found the net force on the child).

216

6C.1, continued:

Formulate
The free-body diagram for the child is shown above right. The net force is

$$F_x = mg \sin \theta - \mathcal{F}$$
$$F_y = N - mg \cos \theta$$

and in this case, since the child is moving, we are dealing with kinetic friction. Hence $\mathcal{F} = \mu_k N$, and from the fact that the y-component of the net force must be zero we know $N = mg \cos \theta$.

Solve
The distance traveled down the slide is $h/\sin \theta$. Therefore the work done by friction is

$$W_{\mathcal{F}} = -\mu_k mgh \cot \theta$$
$$= -(0.15) \times (30 \text{ kg}) \times (9.8 \text{ m/s}^2) \times (3 \text{ m}) \times \cot 40° = -160 \text{ J} .$$

The work done by gravity is $mgh = 880$ J, which is, by definition, equal to minus the change in the child's gravitational potential energy. We have

$$K_{\text{final}} = U_{\text{initial}} + W_{\mathcal{F}} = mgh + W_{\mathcal{F}}$$

(since the initial kinetic energy is zero, and so is the final gravitational potential energy). So the sum of kinetic and gravitational potential energy is 880 J at the top of the slide and 720 J at the bottom. The 'lost' energy is equal to the work done by friction, and has been transformed into internal energy—specifically, into heating the surfaces involved (this is why you can burn yourself by sliding down a rope, and why a match lights when struck).

Scrutinize
We can check our result using kinematics. The net force on the child is

$$F_x = mg(\sin \theta - \mu_k \cos \theta) ,$$

so the child's acceleration is $g(\sin \theta - \mu_k \cos \theta)$. Using $v = at$ and $x = \frac{1}{2}at^2$, we have $x = v^2/2a$, and since $x = h/\sin \theta$ this gives

$$v = \sqrt{2gh(1 - \mu_k \cot \theta)} = 6.9 \text{ m/s} ,$$

and so $K_{\text{final}} = \frac{1}{2}mv^2 = 720$ J, as before.

Learn
Note that the work done by gravity is independent of the slope of the slide, but the work done by friction is not—a shallower chute of the same height would involve sliding a longer distance, and thus increase the magnitude of the (negative) work done by friction. The child would end up with a smaller final velocity. It is typical of dissipative forces that the work done in moving from point A to point B *does* depend on the path

6C.1, continued:

taken between A and B, in contrast to conservative forces. As a result we *cannot* define a 'potential energy' associated with a dissipative force, and thus we see an *apparent* loss of energy if we only take into account so-called mechanical energy (i.e. kinetic plus potential). In fact this energy is not lost, but simply transformed into a different form (usually heat).

6E.1 *Two blocks are connected by a light rope over a pulley as shown. The pulley is fric-tionless, but the coefficient of friction between block A and the slope is 0.40 for static friction and 0.30 for kinetic friction. If the mass of block A is 5 kg, what is the smallest mass B needed (a) to start block A sliding up the slope from rest; (b) to keep it moving if it has been started by an external push; (c) to prevent A from sliding down the slope? (d) What is the frictional force acting on block A if block B has a mass of 2 kg? Take $g = 10$ m/s^2.*

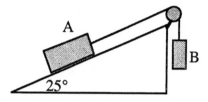

Conceptualize

From the point of view of block A, it doesn't really matter that the source of the tension in the rope is the weight of block B. We can therefore divide this problem into two pieces: the forces on block A (which will determine the motion of block A) and those on block B (which will determine the tension). As the rope is "light" (i.e., of negligible mass) and the pulley frictionless, we can assume that the magnitude of the tension is constant.

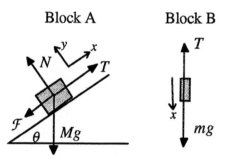

To solve the problem, we therefore draw *separate* force diagrams (*free-body diagrams*) for blaocks A and B, choose appropriate coordinate systems, and write down the component equations of the net force.

Formulate

The free-body diagrams are shown above right. Block B forms a one-dimensional system with net force

$$f_B = mg - T \ .$$

Block A has a somewhat more complicated force diagram. The components of the net force acting on A are

$$F_x = T - \mathcal{F} - Mg\sin\theta$$

$$F_y = N - Mg\cos\theta \ .$$

The two blocks are connected by a rope of negligible mass, so the tension T is the same for both. The acceleration produced, if any, will also be the same for both, since we can assume the rope doesn't stretch (ropes in physics problem land don't stretch unless you are explicitly told that they do!). We choose to draw the friction force pointing *down* the slope because we are investigating the case where block A is expected to move *up* the slope, and the frictional force will act to oppose this.

218

6E.1, continued:

Solve (a) & (b)

For case (a), consider the situation when block A is just about to start sliding. The system is still stationary, so we know that (i) the net force on both A and B must be zero and (ii) we are dealing with static friction. The first point tells us (from B's force diagram) that $T = mg$, and the second that (since the block is about to slide) $\mathcal{F}_s = \mu_s N$. From the y component of the force on block A we also know that $N = Mg\cos\theta$. Putting all this information together, we have

$$F_x = mg - \mu_s Mg\cos\theta - Mg\sin\theta \ ,$$

and this is zero when

$$m = M(\mu_s\cos\theta + \sin\theta) = 3.9 \text{ kg} \ ,$$

for $M = 5$ kg and $\theta = 25°$. Any mass B larger than 3.9 kg will thus cause block A to start sliding.

For case (b) the system is moving at constant speed, so again there is no net force, but this time we are dealing with kinetic friction. We simply replace μ_s by μ_k in the above formula to find $m = 3.5$ kg.

Formulate and Solve (c)

For case (c) we need a new force diagram for block A. A's motion is now *down* the slope, so the frictional force will act in the opposite direction. The net force on A is now

Block A

$$F_x = T + \mathcal{F} - Mg\sin\theta$$

$$F_y = N - Mg\cos\theta \ .$$

In the case where A is just about to start sliding down the slope, we again have no net force and the maximum possible amount of static friction. B's force diagram is unchanged, so T is still mg and we have

$$F_x = mg + \mu_s Mg\cos\theta - Mg\sin\theta \ ,$$

giving

$$m = M(\sin\theta - \mu_s\cos\theta) = 0.3 \text{ kg} \ .$$

Formulate (d)

For the final part, we note that a mass of 2 kg is more than required to prevent A from moving downhill, but not sufficient to move it uphill. Therefore the blocks will be stationary and static friction operates. Block A is not on the point of sliding, so the size of the frictional force is determined by the condition that there is no net force acting. It is not immediately apparent what direction $\mathcal{F}$ acts in: for convenience we shall use the second of our two free-body diagrams (if we are wrong, $\mathcal{F}$ will come out negative).

219

6E.1, continued:

Solve (d)

Using $F_x = 0$ and $T = mg$ as before, we have

$$F_x = mg + \mathcal{F} - Mg\sin\theta = 0 \ ,$$

i.e.

$$\mathcal{F} = Mg\sin\theta - mg = 1.1 \text{ N} \ .$$

Since this is positive we were in fact correct about the direction of the force: in the absence of friction block A would slide downwards. A slightly more massive block B, say 2.5 kg, would result in a frictional force directed the other way (in the absence of friction, A would then slide upwards). Notice that the frictional force is very much less than $\mu_s N = \mu_s Mg\cos\theta = 18$ N.

Scrutinize

In the absence of friction the mass m needed to give no net force on Block A is $M\sin\theta = 2.1$ kg. Any greater mass would cause A to accelerate uphill; smaller values would let it accelerate downhill. In the presence of friction we need a greater mass to move A uphill (reasonable, as a greater tension force is needed to overcome the additional force of friction), and less mass to stop it moving downhill (here friction is 'helping' block B).

If $\theta = 90°$, there is no normal force on Block A, and the results should be independent of friction. Our equations satisfy this criterion for parts (a)–(c), as $\cos 90° = 0$. In part (d) we can still calculate a value for $\mathcal{F}$, because we are simply calculating the value required by the condition of zero net force, but in fact the assumption made in part (d)—that neither block moves, because of the effects of static friction—does not hold for $\theta = 90°$, and so the value we obtain is not valid.

☺ **Learn**

This example demonstrates most of the ways in which friction can enter a force problem. Note that the techniques we apply to solve the problem are exactly the same as those we used in earlier chapters—we just have to decide when drawing the free-body diagram where friction is operating, and when calculating the net force whether we need to apply static friction at its maximum value, static friction at some smaller value, or kinetic friction. We must also consider the direction in which the frictional force acts, as we saw in drawing the free-body diagrams for parts (a) and (c) above: to determine this, we apply the rule that friction between two surfaces always acts to oppose the *relative* motion of the surfaces in question.

6E.6   *A curve on a freeway has radius 300 m, and has been banked for a design speed of 80 km/h (i.e. the inward component of the normal force provides the necessary centripetal acceleration at this speed). The freeway is presently occupied by the getaway car from a bank robbery, with the police in hot pursuit. In dry conditions, how fast can the crooks safely take the bend? What if they had chosen to commit their robbery on the proverbial dark and stormy night? [The coefficients of friction for rubber on dry concrete are $\mu_s = 1.0, \mu_k = 0.8$; for wet concrete they are 0.30 and 0.25 respectively.]*

6E.6, continued:

Conceptualize

While the car is on the bend, it is engaged in circular motion, and if it is moving with speed v its acceleration must be v^2/r, where r is the radius of the bend. In the absence of friction, this acceleration could only be produced by the horizontal component of the normal force from the banked bend, and there would be only one speed at which the corner could be negotiated successfully: the question states that this speed is 80 km/h. With friction acting, we have an additional horizontal force which will allow the car to take the bend at speeds higher than 80 km/h.

At these higher speeds, the inward component of the normal force will not provide a large enough centripetal acceleration. In the absence of frictional forces, the car will turn less sharply than required (r will increase) and will run off the outside of the bend. The frictional force acts to resist this motion, and is therefore directed inward, as shown on the diagram. Since the car is *not* skidding, the part of the tire in contact with the road is *not* sliding on the road surface, and therefore we want the *static* friction. Further, since we are interested in the maximum possible speed, the static friction must be at its maximum possible value, i.e. $\mu_s N$. We thus have three independent unknowns, θ, v, and N. Our strategy will be to find θ from the known design speed of the bend, and then use the two component equations of the net force to find v and N.

Formulate

Putting $\mathcal{F} = \mu_s N$, the components of the net force are

$$
\begin{aligned}
F_y &= N\cos\theta - mg - \mu_s N \sin\theta &= 0 \\
F_x &= N\sin\theta + \mu_s N \cos\theta &= mv^2/r\,.
\end{aligned}
\quad (1)
$$

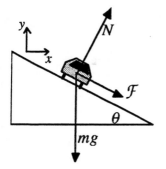

To solve these for v and N we need the value of θ, which we obtain by considering the case where $\mathcal{F} = 0$ and the bend is taken at its design speed of $v_0 = 80$ km/h. Our equations then become:

$$N\cos\theta - mg = 0$$

$$N\sin\theta = \frac{mv_0^2}{r}\,,$$

from which

$$\tan\theta = \frac{v_0^2}{rg}\,.$$

Solve

From Eq. 1 we have

$$N\left(\cos\theta - \mu_s \sin\theta\right) = mg$$

$$N\left(\sin\theta + \mu_s \cos\theta\right) = \frac{mv^2}{r}\,,$$

221

6E.6, continued:

giving

$$v^2 = rg \frac{\sin\theta + \mu_s \cos\theta}{\cos\theta - \mu_s \sin\theta} \, .$$

By dividing numerator and denominator by $\cos\theta$ we could, if we wished, express this equation in terms of $\tan\theta$, and hence in terms of our given parameters v_0, r and g, but there is no real need to do this—we can simply substitute the numerical values into the equation for θ, giving, for $g = 9.8$ m/s^2, $\tan\theta = 0.168$, or $\theta = 9.5°$. Under dry conditions, $v = 64$ m/s $= 230$ km/h (which isn't very likely to cause the crooks any problems), while for wet conditions we get $v = 38$ m/s $= 140$ km/h, or about 80 mph (which might lead to disaster).

Scrutinize
Our equation for v^2 clearly reduces to the frictionless case for $\mu_s = 0$, as it should. The dimensions are correct: $[rg] = $ [length] $\times$ [length]/[time]^2, which is the same as v^2. The units require some care: 80 km/h must be converted to 22.2 m/s before using the formula for $\tan\theta$.

Looking at the equation, we see that a larger coefficient of friction would increase the numerator and decrease the denominator, increasing v (as we see in comparing wet and dry conditions). If we express v^2 in terms of $\tan\theta$, giving $rg(\tan\theta + \mu_s)/(1 - \mu_s \tan\theta)$, we see that an increase in θ also increases v: this is sensible, as a larger θ corresponds to a curve with a higher design speed.

Learn
In problems involving friction we must always ask ourselves two questions: are we dealing with static or kinetic friction, and in which direction does the frictional force act? The answers may seem obvious, but there are pitfalls—in this example we have a *moving* car, but must apply *static* friction, and the horizontal component of the frictional force acts in the *same* direction as the horizontal component of the normal force, not opposed to it. Frictional forces invariably act to resist relative *motion* of the two surfaces: generally this means opposing an applied force, but not always!

For *static* friction problems, we must also ask whether the size of the frictional force is determined by μ_s or by the condition that the object is not moving. In this example, μ_s is the same for the car doing 80 km/h as it is for the one doing 230 km/h, but in the first case the frictional force is actually zero, because there is no force tending to slide the surfaces of the tires on the surface of the road. For intermediate speeds, there is a frictional force, but its size is determined by the value of v^2/r, not by μ_s. (What happens to the frictional force if the car is doing *less* than 80 km/h?)

For rubber on concrete, as for most pairs of surfaces, $\mu_k < \mu_s$. If the car does start to skid, its sideways motion will accelerate as static friction is replaced by kinetic friction. This is why it is so easy to lose control of a skidding auto.

6E.7   *Two cars collide at an intersection. They remain locked together after the collision, and by measuring the skid marks the police conclude that the wreckage traveled 4.4 m at an angle of 43° to car 1's original direction. Car 1 had mass 1000 kg and car 2 1300 kg. If the accident happened in dry conditions when the coefficient of kinetic friction between rubber and concrete is 0.8, calculate the speeds of the two cars immediately before the collision.*

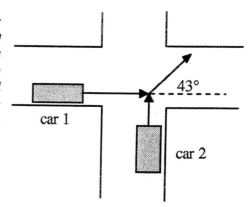

Conceptualize

We have two distinct problems here: the collision itself, and the subsequent deceleration of the wreckage due to friction with the road. Our information relates most directly to the second part, so we shall deal with that before tackling the collision.

The only horizontal force acting on the wreckage during its deceleration is friction. The work-energy theorem implies that the work done by friction must therefore equal the change in kinetic energy of the wreck, so by calculating the magnitude of $\mathcal{F}$ we can deduce the initial speed of the wreck. Our collision problem will then have two equations (conservation of momentum in two dimensions) and two unknowns (the magnitudes of the velocities of car 1 and car 2—we know their directions), and we should therefore be able to solve it.

Formulate

 The force diagram for the wreck involves three forces: gravity and the normal force from the road, which must balance each other, and kinetic friction. We conclude that the vertical and horizontal components of the net force are respectively

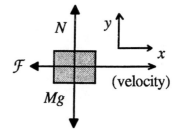

$$F_{\text{v}} = N - (m_1 + m_2)g = 0$$
$$F_{\text{h}} = -\mathcal{F} = -\mu_k N = -\mu_k(m_1 + m_2)g \ .$$

The work done by friction is $\vec{\mathcal{F}} \cdot \vec{\mathbf{r}}$, where $\vec{\mathbf{r}}$ is the displacement of the wreck. As the wreck moves horizontally, the vertical forces do no work, so by the work-energy theorem the work done by friction must be equal to the change in kinetic energy of the wreck.

Solve

 As $\vec{\mathcal{F}}$ is antiparallel to $\vec{\mathbf{r}}$, the work done is

$$\vec{\mathcal{F}} \cdot \vec{\mathbf{r}} = -\mathcal{F}r = -\mu_k(m_1 + m_2)gr.$$

The change in kinetic energy is $-\frac{1}{2}(m_1 + m_2)v_0^2$, where v_0 is the speed of the wreck immediately after the collision (as the wreck comes to a halt, clearly $K_{\text{final}} = 0$). The

6E.7, continued:

work-energy theorem then gives

$$v_0 = \sqrt{2\mu_k gr} = \sqrt{2 \times 0.8 \times 9.8 \text{ m/s}^2 \times 4.4 \text{ m}} = 8.3 \text{ m/s, or } 30 \text{ km/h.}$$

Scrutinize

We can also do this using kinematics. If the speed of the wreckage immediately after the collision is v_0, then when it stops $v^2 = 0 = v_0^2 + 2ar$, where r is the distance traveled and $a = -\mu_k g$ is the acceleration. Therefore $v_0 = \sqrt{2\mu_k gr}$, in agreement with our value from energy conservation.

Conceptualize

Our next task is to deal with the collision. Although friction is obviously present, the collision takes place very quickly over a very short distance, and thus both the impulse applied and the work done by friction during the collision itself are small compared to the contact forces between the cars. We shall therefore neglect frictional effects and treat the collision as an isolated two-body system. This is an inelastic collision (the two cars stick together), so only momentum is conserved.

Formulate and Solve

We define a coordinate system so that x points in the direction of car 1's incoming velocity, and y in the direction of car 2. Momentum conservation then gives us

$$(m_1 + m_2)v_0 \cos 43° = m_1 v_1$$
$$(m_1 + m_2)v_0 \sin 43° = m_2 v_2$$

where v_1 and v_2 are the speeds of car 1 and car 2 immediately before the collision. Putting in the masses and our calculated value of v_0 gives

$$v_1 = 14 \text{ m/s} = 50 \text{ km/h},$$
$$v_2 = 10 \text{ m/s} = 36 \text{ km/h}.$$

Scrutinize

Is it fair to neglect friction during the collision? We may argue as follows: the frictional force on the wreck is $\mu_k(m_1 + m_2)g = 18$ kN. The loss of kinetic energy as a result of the collision is 84 kJ. Even if the two cars crumpled by as much as one meter during the collision (unlikely at such comparatively low speeds), the average contact force exerted during the collision must therefore be 84 kN (equating the work done by the dissipative forces involved in the collision to the loss of kinetic energy), which is some five times the frictional force. (Notice that the more the cars crumple, the smaller the average force exerted during the collision—this is why auto engineers design cars with 'crumple zones' to protect passengers.)

6E.10   *A particle of mass m is launched vertically upward at time $t = 0$ with initial speed v_0. If the air drag is $\vec{\mathcal{F}} = -kv^2\hat{\mathbf{v}}$, show that the particle reaches its maximum height at time*

$$t = \sqrt{\frac{m}{kg}}\, \tan^{-1}\left(v_0\sqrt{\frac{k}{mg}}\right).$$

What is the maximum height reached? How does this compare with the height reached in the absence of air resistance, for a projectile with $k/m = 0.35$ m^{-1} and $v_0 = 10$ m/s vertically upwards? Take $g = 10$ m/s^2.

Conceptualize

The force diagram for this problem looks very simple. The difficulty is that the air drag force is dependent on the velocity, which in turn depends on the past history of the acceleration, which depends on the air drag force. So we are going to end up with a differential equation relating the acceleration, dv/dt, to the speed v.

Formulate

Taking up to be positive, the acceleration is

$$a = -g - \frac{k}{m}v^2\,,$$

so our differential equation for v is

$$\frac{dv}{dt} = -g\left(1 + \frac{k}{mg}v^2\right).$$

Solve

The maximum height is reached when $v = 0$, so we need to integrate our equation from $v_i = v_0$ to $v_f = 0$. We have

$$\int_{v_0}^{0} \frac{dv}{1 + A^2v^2} = -g\int_{0}^{t_f} dt\,,$$

where $A^2 = k/mg$. To solve this we write

$$Av = \tan\theta$$

$$A\,dv = \sec^2\theta\,d\theta\,,$$

and note that $\sec^2\theta = 1 + \tan^2\theta$ for any θ. The integral then reduces to

$$\int_{\theta_i}^{0} \frac{d\theta}{A} = -\frac{\theta_i}{A} = -gt_f\,,$$

6E.10, continued:

where $\theta_i = \tan^{-1}(Av_0)$. Solving for t_f,

$$t_f = \frac{1}{gA}\theta_i = \sqrt{\frac{m}{kg}}\tan^{-1}\left(v_0\sqrt{\frac{k}{mg}}\right) \ ,$$

as required.

To find the corresponding height $y_{\max}$, we first write the solution of our integration in a more general form to get an equation for v at any time t:

$$\theta(t) - \theta_i = \tan^{-1}\left(v\sqrt{\frac{k}{mg}}\right) - \theta_i = -\sqrt{\frac{kg}{m}}\,t \ ,$$

i.e.

$$v(t) = \sqrt{\frac{mg}{k}}\tan\left(\theta_i - \sqrt{\frac{kg}{m}}\,t\right) \ ,$$

and then integrate this from $t = 0$ to $t = t_f$. To do this we need the integral of $\tan\theta$. This is most easily done by putting $u = \cos\theta$, $du = -\sin\theta\,d\theta$, from which

$$\int\tan\theta\,d\theta = \int\frac{\sin\theta}{\cos\theta}d\theta = -\int\frac{du}{u} = -\ln u = \ln(\sec\theta) \ .$$

Our integral can be cast into this form by putting

$$s = \theta_i - \sqrt{\frac{kg}{m}}\,t$$

$$ds = -\sqrt{\frac{kg}{m}}\,dt \ ,$$

from which

$$\int_0^{t_{\max}} v(t)\,dt = y_{\max} = -\frac{m}{k}\int_{s_0}^{s_f}\tan s\,ds = -\frac{m}{k}\left(\ln(\sec s_f) - \ln(\sec s_0)\right) \ .$$

Now

$$s_0 = \tan^{-1}\left(v_0\sqrt{\frac{k}{mg}}\right)$$

and

$$s_f = \tan^{-1}\left(v_0\sqrt{\frac{k}{mg}}\right) - \sqrt{\frac{kg}{m}}\sqrt{\frac{m}{kg}}\tan^{-1}\left(v_0\sqrt{\frac{k}{mg}}\right) = 0 \ ,$$

so

$$y_{\max} = \frac{m}{k}\ln\sqrt{1 + \frac{kv_0^2}{mg}} \ ,$$

6E.10, continued:

using the identity $\sec^2\theta = 1 + \tan^2\theta$.

Putting in the numbers gives

$$y_{max} = \frac{1}{0.35 \text{ m}^{-1}} \ln\sqrt{1 + (10 \text{ m/s})^2\frac{0.35 \text{ m}^{-1}}{10 \text{ m/s}^2}}$$

$$= (2.86 \text{ m}) \times \ln(2.12) = 2.2 \text{ m} \ .$$

Scrutinize

This is rather higher than the ball in Problem 6E.9, which started off with an identical v_y and had identical k/m. The reason is that the air drag on that projectile is larger because its *overall* speed is larger. The differential equations for its motion mix up x- and y-components, and are very awkward to solve—problems of this sort tend to be done numerically, by computer.

We can check that the hideous expressions we have derived do in fact reduce to the right forms when k/m is small by using various small-number approximations: for small ϵ

$$\sin\epsilon \approx \epsilon \qquad\qquad \sec\epsilon \approx 1 + \tfrac{1}{2}\epsilon^2$$
$$\tan\epsilon \approx \epsilon \qquad\qquad \ln(1+\epsilon) \approx \epsilon$$

and so

$$t_f \approx \sqrt{\frac{m}{gk}}\left(v_0\sqrt{\frac{k}{mg}}\right) = \frac{v_0}{g}$$

$$y_{max} \approx \frac{m}{k}\ln\left(1 + \tfrac{1}{2}t_f^2\frac{kg}{m}\right) \approx \tfrac{1}{2}gt_f^2 \ .$$

These are indeed the equations we expect.

Learn

Note that although the mathematics of this realistic problem was much more complicated than our idealized systems, the concepts and techniques involved were just the same. This is why we use idealized systems—they illustrate the physics without requiring the additional mathematical baggage.

HINTS FOR PROBLEMS WITH AN (H)
The number of the hint refers to the number of the problem

6A.2 What is the weight's motion if it is *not* sliding? What is its acceleration? What force produces this acceleration?

6C.2 Draw a force diagram for the block. What is the net force acting if it moves at constant speed?

What is the definition of work done by a force? What is the direction of the frictional force?

Still stuck? Study the solution to problem 6C.1.

6E.2 Draw a force diagram for the stone. What determines the frictional force? If you're still stuck, review the solution to problem 6E.1.

6E.5 What forces are acting on the block (a) before release; (b) after release? Draw a force diagram for the block at the instant of release. What force makes it possible that the block will remain stationary? What condition must hold if it does?

Draw another force diagram for the moving block. How does the net force depend on its position? What is the net force at the point where the block reaches its maximum speed?

6E.8 What are the horizontal (x) and vertical (y) components of the acceleration at time t?

To integrate the y equation you may find it useful to change variables from v_y to $w = g - \dfrac{k}{m}v_y$.

6F.1 (a) In an inertial frame of reference, what force is acting on the mass? How does the acceleration of the mass compare with the acceleration of the space probe?

(b) In the space probe's frame of reference, what is the net force on the mass M? What is the value of the fictitious force which must be introduced to achieve this?

6F.2 (a) What is the fictitious force acting on the plumb bob? Draw a force diagram for the bob including the fictitious force.

(b) Define a coordinate system so that the y-axis is directed parallel to the string of the plumb bob in its equilibrium position. If the bob is displaced from equilibrium by a small angle $\Delta\theta$, what is the x-component of the force on the bob?

ANSWERS TO HINTS

6A.2 Circular motion at 33.3 rpm; v_2/r; static friction.

6C.2 Force diagram:

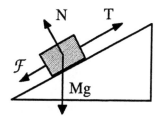

Zero.

$\int \vec{F} \cdot d\vec{r}$;

opposite to direction of motion of block.

6E.2 Force diagram as for 6C.2. Size of static friction force is determined by $\mu_s N$ or size of opposing force, whichever is less; kinetic friction is $\mu_k N$. Here we want the point at which the block just starts to move, so static friction is $\mu_s N$.

6E.5 Vertically, gravity and normal force from table; horizontally, spring force and force applied by experimenter. After release static friction replaces the last of these.

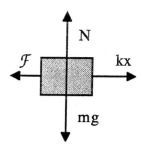

Static friction; zero net force, i.e. $kx = \mathcal{F}_s$.

Diagram is the same for moving block, but kinetic friction replaces static friction; $F(x) = \mu_k mg - kx$ where x is measured from the point at which the spring is not stretched; zero.

6E.8 $\dfrac{dv_x}{dt} = -\dfrac{k}{m}v_x$; $\dfrac{dv_y}{dt} = -\left(g - \dfrac{k}{m}v_y\right)$

6F.1 (a) $|\vec{F}| = k(\ell - \ell_0)$, directed along spring toward the fixed end; accelerations are equal.

(b) Net force = zero; $\vec{F}_{\text{fict}}$ must oppose force of spring, so must have magnitude $k(\ell - \ell_0)$ and must point along spring, away from fixed end.

6F.2 (a) $\vec{F}_{\text{fict}} = -M\vec{a}$, where $\vec{a}$ is the train's acceleration.

(b) $F_x \simeq -T\Delta\theta = -M\Delta\theta\sqrt{g^2 + a^2}$.

ANSWERS TO ALL PROBLEMS

6A.1 b; a

6A.2 0.12

6B.1 c

6B.2 See complete solution.

6B.3 An acceptable answer would be:

"Kinetic friction acts to oppose the relative motion of two surfaces which are already moving. It has a fixed magnitude of $\mu_k N$. Static friction acts to prevent relative motion of two surfaces at rest. It has whatever magnitude is necessary to do this, up to a maximum of $\mu_s N$."

6C.1 See complete solution.

6C.2 (i) $Mg(\sin\theta + \mu_k \cos\theta)$;

(ii) $Mgh(1 + \mu_k \cot\theta)$.

For a given μ_k you need minimal force for a slope with $\tan\theta = \mu_k$; but you do least work simply lifting the object vertically—the shallower the slope, the more work you have to do.

6D.1 (a) Initially, as long as $kv^2 \ll mg$, the effect of the air resistance is small, so the motion is close to a trajectory of uniform acceleration g downward. As kv^2 becomes comparable to mg, the magnitude of the downward acceleration decreases, and the projectile approaches a constant speed, called the **terminal speed**.

(b) $v_{\text{terminal}} = \sqrt{\dfrac{mg}{k}}$

6D.2 (a) A parachute is basically a device to increase the surface area of a freely falling object (human being, crate of supplies, descending space-probe, etc.) while not greatly increasing its mass. Thus $\sqrt{mg/k}$ is greatly reduced, and the object has a much lower terminal speed (and hence a very much decreased risk of suffering damage on landing).

(b) Cats and humans have similar silhouettes and are made of similar materials, One would therefore expect that $k_{\text{cat}}/k_{\text{human}} \simeq A_{\text{cat}}/A_{\text{human}}$, where A is the surface area of the being in question. Similarly, the density of a cat should be similar to that of a human, so $m_{\text{cat}}/m_{\text{human}} \simeq V_{\text{cat}}/V_{\text{human}}$, where V is the volume. Surface area is basically ℓw, where ℓ is the length of the object and w is its width; volume is $\ell w t$, where t is the thickness. Therefore $(k/m)_{\text{cat}}/(k/m)_{\text{human}} \propto t_{\text{cat}}/t_{\text{human}}$, which is significantly less than one, and so the terminal speed of a human is higher than that of a cat. (This effect, namely that volume increases with increasing size of animal more rapidly than surface area does, is important in a wide range of biological issues: small animals lose heat more quickly (and therefore, if warm-blooded, need faster matabolisms), absorb gas more easily (insects don't need lungs), and are much more affected by surface forces (insects can walk on water; insects and small lizards can walk up walls); also, since muscle strength is proportional to cross-sectional area, small animals seem astonishingly strong, able to leap many times their own body length and so forth.)

(c) Galileo's cannonballs would presumably have had similar size and shape, and therefore similar k, but the lead ball would clearly be much heavier than the wooden ball. Hence the lead ball's terminal speed would be higher, and it would hit the ground first. This effect is probably what caused the ancient Greeks and other pre-Renaissance scientists/philosophers to believe that heavy objects fell faster than light ones.

6E.1 See complete solution.

6E.2 302; 62.

6E.3 If you lock the wheels of your car, the tire surfaces are sliding on the road surface, and therefore the force that is slowing you down is kinetic friction, $\mu_k Mg$, where M is the mass of your car. On wet or icy roads, μ_k may be rather small, and you will not stop very quickly; also, while the wheels are sliding, you have no control over either the rate of deceleration (pushing the brake down harder will not affect the forces acting at all), nor the direction of motion (turning the wheels will not affect the direction of the force, which simply opposes the relative motion of car and road). The goal, then, is to press on the brake as hard as one can without letting the car skid, so one can take advantage of the maximum force of static friction.

6E.4 $\tan\theta = \mu_s$; $\dfrac{g(\mu_s - \mu_k)}{\sqrt{1+\mu_s^2}}$

6E.5 (i) 1.75 cm; (ii) The block will initially accelerate, since $\mu_k < \mu_s$. As the spring extension reduces, the spring force will become smaller, while kinetic friction remains the same: thus at some point the net force will change sign, and the block will decelerate and eventually stop. At this point the spring compression will be less than the starting extension (since the frictional force has done negative work, and reduced the kinetic energy of the block more than the spring acting alone), and therefore the spring force will be insufficient to overcome static friction: once the block stops, it will remain stationary.

1 m/s² towards wall; 0.5 cm towards wall.

6E.6 See complete solution.

6E.7 See complete solution.

6E.8 $v_x = u\exp\left(-\dfrac{k}{m}t\right)$; $v_y = \dfrac{mg}{k}\left(1 - \exp\left(-\dfrac{k}{m}t\right)\right)$

The ball's trajectory will tend towards a situation where it is traveling vertically downwards with speed mg/k.

6E.9 The trajectory is asymmetric, with steeper descent, not a parabola, because the horizontal component of velocity is no longer constant. In the absence of air resistance we would expect a range of 20 m (4 m in diagram) and maximum height of 5 m (1.7 m). Air resistance has had a dramatic effect on both, though range has been more affected than height.

In the absence of air resistance, the optimum 45° angle is the result of a tradeoff between the benefits of vertical velocity, which increases flight time, and horizontal velocity, which measures the rate of progress toward the destination. With air resistance, one can see from the diagram that the horizontal velocity is rapidly reduced (recall that the circles are evenly spaced in time), so most of the forward progress is made during the earlier part of the flight. The benefit of increased flight time is therefore reduced, so the tradeoff is skewed in favor of increased horizontal velocity. We conclude that the range is likely to be maximized by aiming the projectile at *less than 45°* to the horizontal—option (b). (In fact, numerical simulation indicates that the range is maximal for $\theta \simeq 35°$. It should be pointed out, however, that the projectile described here has an unusually high air drag. Its terminal speed (see Problem 6D.1) is 5.3 m/s, slightly slower than the descent rate of a standard military parachute.)

6E.10 See complete solution.

6F.1 $|\vec{a}| = \dfrac{k}{M}(\ell - \ell_0)$, directed along spring toward the fixed end.

See the hints to follow the two alternative arguments.

6F.2 (a) $\theta = \tan^{-1}\left(\dfrac{a}{g}\right)$.

(b) $T = 2\pi\sqrt{\dfrac{\ell}{\sqrt{g^2 + a^2}}}$.

ESSENTIALS OF INTRODUCTORY CLASSICAL MECHANICS

CHAPTER 7

ENERGY, MOMENTUM AND MACROSCOPIC FORCES

OVERVIEW

This chapter contains no new ideas. Instead, we take the material covered in Chapters 4, 5 and 6 and use it to solve more complicated problems. Notice that in this chapter we will not divide the problems up into sections dealing with specific topics; instead you will have to decide for yourself which of the physical principles you have learned are relevant to a given problem.

When you have completed this chapter you should:

> ✔ be able to extract the essential features of a problem and express them in mathematical equations;
>
> ✔ be capable of manipulating the equations relevant to a problem to obtain an expression for the required quantity, either symbolically or numerically;
>
> ✔ be able to analyze a hypothetical situation in terms of the physics presented in previous units, and explain that analysis clearly in non-mathematical terms.

PROBLEMS AND QUESTIONS

By the end of this chapter you should be able to answer or solve the types of questions or problems stated below.

At the end of the chapter there are answers to all the problems. In addition, for problems with an (H) or (S) after the number, there are respectively hints on how to solve the problems or completely worked-out solutions.

7.1 (H)   The cars on a rollercoaster ride at a fairground start from rest a height h above ground level, descend to ground level and then execute an essentially circular loop of radius r.

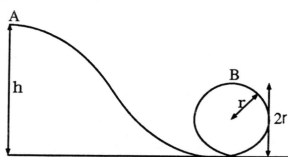

(a) At point B, the top of the loop, passengers feel a sensation of "weight" acting upwards, i.e. towards the outside of the loop. Explain, in terms of the forces acting, the origin of this feeling.

(b) If the "weight" sensation felt by a passenger of mass m is half her normal weight, calculate, in terms of g and r, (i) the speed of the car at point B and (ii) the height h of the starting point A.

7.2   What is the potential energy of the Earth due to its position in the gravitational field of the Sun, if we define the potential energy such that it would be zero if the Earth were infinitely far from the Sun? What is the Earth's kinetic energy if we treat it as a point mass (i.e. neglect all effects of its rotation)? With the same assumption, what is the Earth's total energy? Comment on your result.

[The mass of the Sun is 2×10^{30} kg, that of the Earth is 6×10^{24} kg, and the distance between them is 150 million kilometers. The gravitational constant $G = 6.67 \times 10^{-11}$ N· m²/kg².]

7.3 (H)   An Eskimo child is using her parents' hemispherical igloo as a slide. She starts off from rest at the top and slides down under the influence of gravity. The surface of the igloo is effectively frictionless.

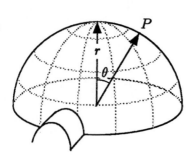

(a) What is her potential energy at point P (see diagram)? Define the potential energy so that it is zero when the child is on the ground.

(b) Draw a force diagram for her at point P.

(c) Does she remain in contact with the igloo all the way to the ground? If not, at what angle θ does she lose contact?

7.4 (S) Prior to the Industrial Revolution, water-wheels were commonly used to power machines (particularly mills for grinding flour). Suppose that a waterwheel is driven by a stream which is 2 m wide and 1.5 m deep and which flows at 1 m/s. The stream is made to flow over a weir with a vertical fall of 3 m immediately before striking the wheel. After the weir, the stream is observed to continue with the same width and depth as before the weir. Explain what is happening to the energy of the water and the wheel, and calculate how much energy per second is available to power the mill. The density of water is 1000 kg/m^3.

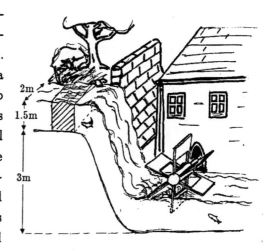

7.5 (S) The potential energy of an atom bound in a molecule or crystalline solid is given by a function with the general shape shown in the diagram. The zero is chosen so that an atom infinitely distant from the other atoms making up the compound would have zero potential energy.

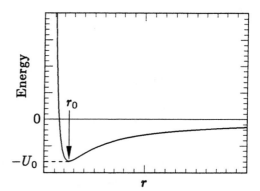

(a) What force acts on an atom located (i) closer than r_0; (ii) at r_0; (iii) beyond r_0?

(b) What would happen to an atom initially at r_0 if it had a small kinetic energy K? What if it had a large kinetic energy $K > U_0$?

7.6 (H) A man tows his daughter on a sled on level ice, and she in turn tows her teddy-bear behind her on a toy sled. The girl and her sled have a combined mass M; Teddy and its sled have a mass m. Dad's tow-rope is inclined at an angle of θ to the horizontal, while the rope joining the two sleds is horizontal. Friction between the sled runners and the ice is negligible, as is the mass of each rope.

(a) Draw free-body diagrams for each sled. Which forces are Third Law pairs?

(b) Derive expressions for the tension in each rope when the acceleration of the sleds is a (obviously directed forwards). If $M = 30$ kg, $m = 8$ kg, $\theta = 30°$ and the sleds accelerate at 1 m/s^2, what is the magnitude of each tension?

(c) Suppose that there is in fact some non-zero coefficient of kinetic friction μ_k between the sleds and the ice. In terms of m, M, g, $\cos\theta$ and μ_k, what tension does Dad have to exert to keep the sleds moving at constant velocity?

7.7 (S)   A common piece of lifting gear is the *block and tackle*, consisting of a system of pulleys arranged as in the schematic diagram on the right. Assuming that the pulleys are frictionless and that the angle the rope makes with the vertical is always negligible, what force must you apply, and what work must you do, to lift a load of mass $M = 30$ kg a vertical distance of 1 m? Take $g = 10$ m/s², and treat the rope as massless.

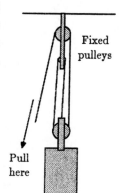

Why is it easier to lift a heavy object using this device?

7.8   A suitcase of mass M is placed on a level conveyor belt at an airport. The coefficient of static friction between the suitcase and the conveyor belt is μ_s, and the coefficient of kinetic friction is μ_k, with $\mu_k < \mu_s$.

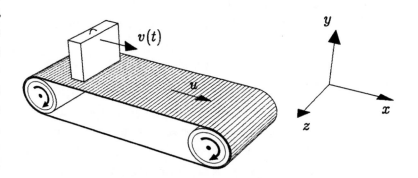

The conveyor belt moves with constant speed u, and at time $t = 0$ the suitcase is placed on the conveyor with speed $v = 0$. At $t = 0$, what is the total force $\vec{\mathbf{F}}$ acting on the suitcase? How long does the suitcase take to reach the speed of the conveyor belt (i.e. at what time t does $v(t) = u$)? What is the work done by friction on the suitcase during this time? Comment briefly on the direction of the frictional force and the sign (positive or negative) of the work done. After the suitcase reaches the speed of the conveyor belt, what is the force of friction that acts on it?

7.9   The level conveyor belt of Problem 7.8 is part of an airport baggage delivery system. The bags are delivered onto the level belt by an inclined conveyor belt which lifts them from the tarmac to the baggage collection region. This 'delivery' conveyor is inclined at an angle θ to the horizontal, and moves with constant speed $u_0 < u$.

(a) What is the minimum coefficient of static friction between bags and delivery conveyor needed to ensure that bags do not slip as they are delivered to the collection hall? In which direction does the frictional force act?

(b) The delivery conveyor is oriented at right angles to the level conveyor, so our suitcase of mass M lands on the level conveyor with velocity $\vec{\mathbf{v}}(0) = [0, 0, u_0 \cos \theta]$. What is the frictional force $\vec{\mathbf{F}}$ acting on the suitcase just after it lands. At what time t does $v_x(t) = u$, and how far across the conveyor (in the z direction) has the suitcase traveled at that point?

(c) Some way along the level conveyor, maintenance men working on an overhead light fixture have erected a scaffold which passes over the top of the belt. The strap of a hiker's backpack has caught on the scaffold, causing it to get firmly stuck. Our suitcase collides with the backpack and gets jammed behind it, so that both are now stationary with respect to the airport. What contact force is being exerted by the backpack on the suitcase? If the backpack has mass M_2, what is the magnitude of the horizontal component of the tension in the strap that is caught on the overhead scaffold?

7.10 (S) Two masses m and M are connected by a massless rope which passes over a frictionless pulley. If $M > m$ and the rope does not stretch, what is the acceleration of the mass M?

7.11 (S) (a) Two blocks of mass 1 kg and 2 kg are connected by a light string passing over a pulley as shown. Assuming that there is no friction anywhere in the system, what is the acceleration of the blocks? Take $g = 10$ m/s^2.

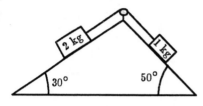

(b) Assuming that the pulley remains frictionless, what is the minimum coefficient of static friction between blocks and slope required to allow the blocks in part
(a) to remain motionless? Suppose that the coefficient of static friction has this value, but the coefficient of kinetic friction is smaller. What would happen if the blocks were started in motion sliding towards the left (i.e., downhill for the block on the left, uphill for the block on the right)?

(c) Suppose that the coefficient of static friction between blocks and slope is 0.12. Is it possible for the blocks described in part (b) to be stationary? If so, what is the range of possible values for the tension in the string?

(d) Now suppose that a heavy uniform rope (i.e. a rope with constant mass per length) is laid over a frictionless triangular block as shown. Assume that the peak of the triangle behaves as a frictionless pulley. Will the rope slip?

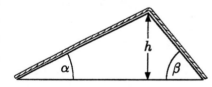

7.12 (H) The setup in the diagram uses massless, frictionless pulleys and a rope of negligible mass. What mass M is required to balance the 2 kg mass, so that if the masses are initially stationary they will remain so? Describe qualitatively what will happen if the mass M is then given a small downward impulse.

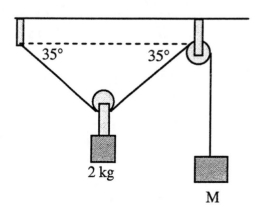

7.13 (H) A rifle of mass 10 kg fires a 10 g bullet into a 3 kg block of wood which is suspended by a thin wire, forming a *ballistic pendulum*. The bullet remains embedded in the block of wood, which is observed to swing so that it reaches a vertical height of 20 cm above its starting point. What was the speed of the bullet, and with what speed did the rifle recoil?

Ignore air resistance, friction in the suspension, and the vertical motion of the bullet, and assume that the block of wood is small relative to the length of the wire (we will see why this is necessary in Chapter 8).

7.14   Two masses A and B are connected by a spring. A has mass M, B has mass $2M$, and the spring has negligible mass. The spring is compressed so that the potential energy stored in it is U_0. The system is placed on a level horizontal air table (which provides a frictionless surface), given a velocity $\vec{u}$ in the x-direction as shown, and the spring is released. In the subsequent motion the line BA always points in the positive y-direction.

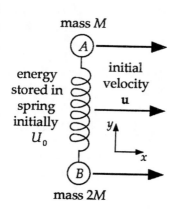

(a) The diagram shows, to scale, the initial position of A and the path followed by B over a certain length of time. Make a similar drawing which also includes the path followed by A. Mark on your drawing the initial position and subsequent motion of the center of mass of the system.

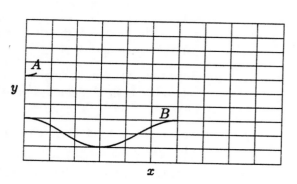

(b) In terms of the given quantities, what is the initial total energy of the system (A, B and the spring)?

(c) How much potential energy is stored in the spring when A and B have kinetic energies K_A and K_B respectively?

(d) At some point in the motion, the y-component of the velocity of mass B is v_y. Write down the velocity vector $\vec{v}_A$ of A at that instant, expressing your answer in terms of v_y and the quantities given above.

7.15 (H)   A block of mass M rests on a horizontal surface. The coefficient of kinetic friction between the block and the surface is μ_k, and the coefficient of static friction is μ_s, with $\mu_s > \mu_k$. The block is pulled horizontally by a massless inextensible rope, with a tension T that is gradually increased until the block starts to slide.

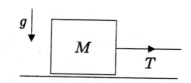

(a) What is the value of the tension T_1 at which the block begins to slide?

(b) When the tension was only $\frac{1}{2}T_1$, before the block began to slide, what was the magnitude and direction of the force of friction?

(c) If the tension is maintained at the value T_1, what is the acceleration of the block?

(d) A second block, identical to the first, is placed directly on top of the first block while both are at rest. The coefficients of friction between the two blocks are $\bar{\mu}_k$ for kinetic friction and $\bar{\mu}_s$ for static friction. As before, a horizontal rope is attached to the first (lower) block, and the tension in the rope is increased gradually from zero. At some value of the tension the two blocks begin to move, but there is initially no relative velocity between the two. As the steady increase in the tension is maintained, they accelerate faster and faster. At what value of the tension will the second block begin to slip relative to the first block? In what direction will it slip, relative to the block below?

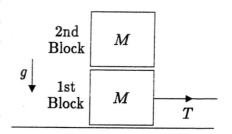

7.16 (S)   A rocket is a 'Newton's Third Law machine'—it operates by ejecting a high velocity exhaust at one end. Suppose that a rocket with initial mass M_i burns its fuel at a constant rate dm/dt and expels the combustion products with speed u relative to itself. By how much has the rocket's speed increased when its mass has decreased to M_f (the difference having been ejected as exhaust)? (Assume the rocket is in interstellar space, with no other forces acting.)

A deep space probe will be placed in low Earth orbit by a shuttle launch, and will then fire its own booster rocket to leave orbit. You are in charge of designing the booster. If the probe's mass is 500 kg and it needs a velocity change of 5 km/s, what minimum mass of fuel will you need to specify if the exhaust velocity is to be 2500 m/s?

7.17   A spaceship is stationary in outer space, far away from any matter. It is facing a very distant star. At some instant it starts its rocket engines. The hot gases are ejected from the engines with speed v, relative to the spaceship. After some time the spaceship attains a speed greater than v. From that time on, in which direction is the hot gas ejected from the engines moving? In which direction is the overall center of mass of the spaceship and all ejected gas moving? Explain.

Explain also why you would expect the speed v of the ejected gases to be approximately constant relative to the engines, and not relative to the fixed frame of reference.

7.18 (H)   A train moving in the x-direction is uniformly accelerating with acceleration $\vec{a} = [a, 0, 0]$. In one of the train carriages, Alice and Betty stand opposite one another, a distance w apart: in Alice's frame of reference they have coordinates $[0, 0, 0]$ and $[0, w, 0]$ respectively (the z axis points vertically up). Alice throws a ball across the carriage to Betty.

(a) If Alice throws the ball at an angle θ to the horizontal with initial speed v, what must the initial velocity vector $\vec{v}$ be, in Alice's frame of reference, if the ball is to land precisely

241

in Betty's hands (i.e. the initial and final positions of the ball are the coordinates of Alice and Betty respectively)?

(b) If $\theta = 45°$, at what speed v should Alice throw the ball, and how long will its flight last? Express your answers in terms of g, a and w.

7.19 (H) Two identical small balls, A and B, are connected by a string of length ℓ and negligible mass. Ball A is placed on a frictionless table (with a frictionless edge), and B is held a distance $\ell/2$ from the edge of the table so that the string is horizontal and just taut.

If mass B is now released, will it hit the side of the table before A falls off the edge, or vice versa?

Explain your reasoning clearly!

Note: This problem can be solved by reasoning. It is **not** necessary to solve the equations of motion explicitly.

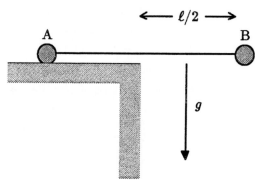

COMPLETE SOLUTIONS TO PROBLEMS WITH AN (S)

7.4   *Prior to the Industrial Revolution, waterwheels were commonly used to power machines (particularly mills for grinding flour). Suppose that a waterwheel is driven by a stream which is 2 m wide, 1.5 m deep and flows at 1 m/s. The stream is made to flow over a weir with a vertical fall of 3 m immediately before striking the wheel. After the weir, the stream is observed to continue with the same width and depth as before the weir. Explain what is happening to the energy of the water and the wheel, and calculate how much energy per second is available to power the mill. The density of water is 1000 kg/m^3.*

Conceptualize

We can look at this problem in two ways: by considering the work done on and by the water as it flows over the weir and past the waterwheel, or in terms of energy conservation in the system consisting of water, wheel and Earth. In terms of energy conservation, the water above the waterfall has greater gravitational potential energy in the water-Earth system than does the same amount of water in the pool at the bottom of the waterfall. However, in steady-state the water has to flow out of the millpool at the same rate as it flows in, since the millpool can neither produce water nor cause it to disappear. Since the dimensions of the steam after the weir are the same as before, the water must flow at the same speed. Therefore the loss in potential energy is not balanced by a gain in kinetic energy *of the water*, so it must be balanced by a gain in energy of the waterwheel. In terms of work done on and by the water, the same series of events can be described as follows:

- Work is done by gravity on the water as it descends the waterfall. Its kinetic energy at the bottom of the fall has increased by an amount corresponding to the work done.

7.4, continued:

- When the water leaves the pool, its kinetic energy has decreased back to its initial value. Therefore work must have been done by the water on some intervening object. The only obvious candidate object is the waterwheel.

These two pictures are entirely equivalent, since the work done by gravity on the water is, by definition, equal to the loss of gravitational potential energy from the water-Earth system. This amount of energy is transferred from the water-Earth to the waterwheel, and within the mill the kinetic energy of the wheel is used to drive the mill mechanism by processes too complicated for us to deal with them at this point.

Formulate and Solve

The amount of water passing over the weir in one second is $(2\,\mathrm{m}) \times (1.5\,\mathrm{m}) \times (1\,\mathrm{m}) = 3\,\mathrm{m}^3$ (for example, the shaded area in the figure). Its mass is 3000 kg, so its kinetic energy at this point is $\frac{1}{2}mv^2$, or 1.5 kJ. If we treat this water as a point mass located at the position of its center of mass, it also has potential energy $mgh = 88.2$ kJ, compared to a similar mass of water—also considered as a point mass—in the millpond at the bottom of the weir. As the water descends the weir this potential energy is converted to kinetic energy, so at the bottom of the weir its kinetic energy is 89.7 kJ. When the water leaves the millpond it carries with it its original 1.5 kJ of kinetic energy, so the energy available to power the mill, rounded to two significant figures, is 88 kJ/s, or 88 kW.

Scrutinize

If we consider the work done on the water by gravity instead of the potential energy lost, we of course obtain the same result: $(mg) \cdot (h) = mgh$.

Learn

In practice the mill will not be able to use all the 88 kJ of energy lost by the water. Much of this will be 'wasted' by being transformed into forms such as heat which do not contribute to the turning of the mill.

7.5   *The potential energy of an atom bound in a molecule or crystalline solid is given by a function with the general shape shown in the diagram on the next page. The zero is chosen so that an atom infinitely far away from the other atoms making up the compound would have zero potential energy.*

(a) *What force acts on an atom located (i) closer than r_0; (ii) at r_0; (iii) beyond r_0?*

(b) *What would happen to an atom initially at r_0 if it had a small kinetic energy K? What if it had a large kinetic energy $K > U_0$?*

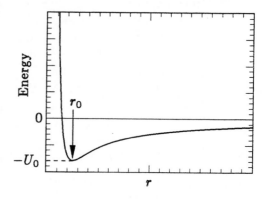

Conceptualize

We have been given a potential energy and asked for (a) a force and (b) the motion of a particle of a given kinetic energy. We can deal with part (a) by recalling that the force is simply $(-1) \times$ the derivative of the corresponding potential energy with respect to r. We do not have the exact functional form of the potential, so we cannot solve this in a quantitative fashion, but we can deduce the

7.5, continued:

direction of the force by considering the *sign* of the slope of U, and estimate its *magnitude* by looking at the *steepness* of the slope.

Part (b) is an energy conservation problem: we solve it by using the fact that the particle's total energy must remain constant to deduce how its kinetic energy varies with r.

Solve (a)

The slope of $U(r)$ is negative for $r < r_0$, positive for $r > r_0$, and zero at r_0. The corresponding force is large and positive for $r < r_0$, smaller and negative for $r > r_0$ where the slope is less steep, and zero at r_0. In each case, therefore, the force tends to accelerate the atom towards r_0, which is a position of stable equilibrium.

Solve (b)

An atom with a small kinetic energy K would move outwards or inwards from r_0, gaining potential energy and losing kinetic energy as it did so. Its total energy remains constant at $K - U_0$, and it will therefore have zero kinetic energy when its potential energy is equal to $K - U_0$. At this point there will be a force acting on it which will cause it to accelerate back towards r_0. As a result the atom oscillates about the equilibrium position. If the kinetic energy is small enough that the maximum displacement from r_0 is a small fraction of r_0, the atom will perform simple harmonic motion (it will be possible to approximate the shape of the potential energy curve by a quadratic); if it is larger, the motion will still be oscillatory, but its mathematical form will be more complicated.

If the atom's kinetic energy is larger than U_0, and it is moving outwards (towards larger r) it will never reach a point where its potential energy is $K - U_0$, and therefore it will never stop. If it is initially moving inwards, it will reach a point where it has zero kinetic energy, and will then turn round under the influence of the force acting on it and move outwards. Since its total energy is unchanged, it will then be able to move outwards to infinite r. We see that regardless of its initial direction, the atom will eventually wind up infinitely far from the rest of its molecule or solid—it is no longer part of the compound.

Scrutinize and Learn

This is a simplified (we have ignored quantum mechanical effects and reduced the problem to one dimension) but essentially correct analysis of the behavior of bound atoms. We will see later that kinetic energy can be supplied to atoms by heating the material: the escape of our atom when it gains enough kinetic energy thus corresponds to the melting of a solid or the thermal breaking up of a molecule. We could have performed a similar analysis for gravitationally bound systems: a deep-space probe like Pioneer or Voyager has enough kinetic energy to escape from the solar system, whereas a communications satellite does not. (Since the gravitational force does not change sign, there is no equivalent of r_0 in this system.) In general, a particle moving in a particular potential energy is bound (restricted to a limited range of position) if its total energy is less than the maximum value of the potential energy in all directions.

7.7

*A common piece of lifting gear is the **block and tackle**, consisting of a system of pulleys arranged as in the schematic diagram on the right. Assuming that the pulleys are frictionless and that the angle the rope makes with the vertical is always negligible, what force must you apply, and what work must you do, to lift a load of mass $M = 30$ kg a vertical distance of 1 m? Take $g = 10$ m/s², and treat the rope as massless.*

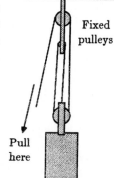

Fixed pulleys

Pull here

Why is it easier to lift a heavy object using this device?

Conceptualize

From the schematic, we have three segments of rope exerting an upward force on the block—two on the pulley and one on the pulley frame. You apply a force to a fourth segment of rope, that leading to the upper pulley. To solve this problem we need to relate the force you exert on the rope to the forces the various bits of rope exert on the block.

We stated in Chapter 2, and proved in Problem 5A.5, that the tension along a massless rope is constant. By Newton's third law, the tension T in the segment of rope you pull on is equal to the force you exert on the rope. The tension in the rope at the upper pulley is therefore T. As the rope goes round the pulley, the pulley exerts a normal force perpendicular to the surface of the pulley, and therefore perpendicular to the line of the rope. Since it is a *frictionless* pulley, it does not exert any force *along* the line of the rope, and so it does not change the magnitude of T (the tension is always directed along the line of the rope). Therefore the magnitude of the tension at the other side of the pulley is still T, although the direction has changed The same logic applies to the other two pulleys of the block and tackle, so we conclude that all three tension forces applied to the load M are equal to T.

Formulate

If the dimensions of the pulleys are small compared to the distance between the upper and lower parts of the block and tackle, all the rope segments will be essentially vertical, and so the problem reduces to one dimension. The force diagram for the load is as shown. The minimum force required to lift the mass just balances the gravitational force on the mass:

$$Mg = 3T.$$

So the force that you must apply is $T = \frac{1}{3}Mg$.

The work done on the block by the rope in raising it a distance s is the dot product of the force exerted by the rope, $[0, 3T, 0]$, and the displacement of the block, $[0, s, 0]$. Since these are parallel, the work done is simply the product of their magnitudes, $3Ts = Mgs$.

Alternatively, one can directly calculate the work that you do on the rope. In raising the block a distance s, each of the three rope segments leading to the block are shortened by a distance s, so the rope end that you are holding moves a distance $3s$. Since you are applying a force of magnitude $\frac{1}{3}Mg$ in the same direction, the work that you do is Mgs.

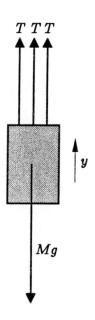

$T\ T\ T$

y

Mg

7.7, continued:

Solve

Putting in the numbers, to lift a 30 kg load through 1 m (at constant speed) you would need to exert a force of 100 N and do 300 J of work.

If you had simply lifted the mass, you would have had to exert a force $Mg = 300$ N, and you would have done work $Mgs = (300\,\text{N}) \times (1\,\text{m}) = 300$ J. The block and tackle does not decrease the work you have to do (as physicists, we would be extremely surprised if it did, since this would violate energy conservation!), but it does decrease the force you must exert. It is physiologically easier to exert a small force over a long distance than a large force over a short distance, so you find it easier to lift the load using the block and tackle.

Scrutinize

In terms of work and energy, you have done $3Ts$ of work on the rope, and the rope has done $3Ts$ of work on the mass. The mass's kinetic energy has not changed, because no net work has been done on it (gravity, acting downwards, has done work $-3Ts$). Looking at the mass-Earth system, $3Ts$ of work has been done by an external force (you), and the mass's gravitational potential energy has increased by $Mgs = 3Ts$. Energy conservation is thus satisfied in this problem.

Learn

As long as there is no friction in the system, the magnitude of the tension along a massless rope is constant. The direction of the tension is always along the direction of the rope.

7.10   *Two masses m and M are connected by a massless rope which passes over a frictionless pulley. If $M > m$ and the rope does not stretch, what is the acceleration of the mass M?*

Conceptualize

The force diagram for this problem is shown on the right. As this is another massless rope and frictionless pulley, the two tension forces are equal in magnitude (and in this case also in direction). Since all the forces act vertically, this is essentially a one-dimensional problem.

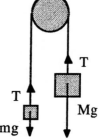

Formulate

We treat the two masses as separate problems, linked by the facts that (i) the tension in the rope is the same for both, because the rope is massless, and (ii) the magnitude of the acceleration is the same for both, because the rope does not stretch. Taking up to be positive, the net force F on the large mass M is

$$F = T - Mg,$$

and by Newton's second law $F = Ma$, so

$$Ma = T - Mg.$$

7.10, continued:

Similarly, for the net force f on the small mass m

$$f = T - mg = ma'.$$

Solve

Since the rope is of fixed length, the acceleration of the small mass must be equal in size to the acceleration of the large mass, but opposite in direction (if one goes up, the other goes down), i.e. $a' = -a$. Hence we can eliminate T by subtracting our two equations:

$$F - f = (m + M)a = (m - M)g.$$

The acceleration is

$$a = -\frac{M - m}{M + m}g,$$

where the minus sign indicates (since we took up to be positive) that the large mass is accelerating downwards.

Scrutinize

Does our result make sense? We can conduct a mental check by looking at some special values. If $m = 0$, then $a = -g$, which is obviously right (the large mass is then a freely falling body). If $m = M$, there is no acceleration, which is sensible enough, and if $m > M$, the acceleration is positive, which means M is going up and m is going down, as we would expect.

Learn

Notice that if we make m and M nearly equal, a will be very small. Provided we can really make the effects of friction unimportant, this would be a good way to measure the value of g without needing accurate timing equipment—for instance, if we choose $M = 1$ kg and $m = 0.99$ kg, the acceleration will be only about 5 cm/s^2, and the mass will take more than 6 s to fall one meter. In fact this type of experimental arrangement, called an Atwood's machine, has indeed been used to make accurate measurements of g.

7.11 (a) *Two blocks of mass 1 kg and 2 kg are connected by a light string passing over a pulley as shown. Assuming that there is no friction anywhere in the system, what is the acceleration of the blocks? Take $g = 10$ m/s^2.*

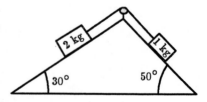

Conceptualize

This is a problem very much like 5A.7. We saw in that problem that the action of the frictionless pulley is to change the direction of the string without changing the magnitude of its tension. Because the string does not stretch, the magnitude of the acceleration is also the same for each block.

7.11, continued:

$\sum \int$

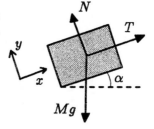

Formulate

For the $M \equiv 2$ kg block we define a coordinate system with the x-axis pointing up the slope. In these coordinates the x- and y-components of the net force are

$$F_x = T - Mg \sin \alpha \qquad (1)$$

$$F_y = N - Mg \cos \alpha \ , \qquad (2)$$

where $\alpha = 30°$. The y-component must be zero, because we know the block will not accelerate perpendicular to the slope.

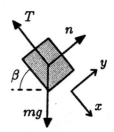

For the $m \equiv 1$ kg block we choose a coordinate system with the x-axis pointing down the slope. Notice that since we are treating the blocks as separate entities, there is no requirement to choose the same coordinate system for both blocks; for convenience, however, we have chosen the x directions so that a positive acceleration for one block corresponds to a positive acceleration for the other. With this choice of coordinates, the components of the net force are

$$f_x = mg \sin \beta - T \qquad (3)$$

$$f_y = n - mg \cos \beta \ , \qquad (4)$$

where $\beta = 50°$. Again, the y-component is zero. Applying Newton's second law for each block, we can write the equations of motion as

$$Ma = T - Mg \sin \alpha \qquad (1')$$

$$0 = N - Mg \cos \alpha \qquad (2')$$

$$ma = mg \sin \beta - T \qquad (3')$$

$$0 = n - mg \cos \beta \ , \qquad (4')$$

where a denotes the x-component of the acceleration, which must be the same for both blocks, since the string has constant length. Thus we have four equations for the four unknowns, a, T, N, and n. Because we don't need to know N or n, we can forget the y equations $(2')$ and $(4')$, leaving two equations in two unknowns.

Solve

Adding the x-component equations $(1')$ and $(3')$, one finds

$$(M + m)\, a = mg \sin \beta - Mg \sin \alpha \ . \qquad (5)$$

The acceleration is therefore

$$a = \frac{mg \sin \beta - Mg \sin \alpha}{M + m} = \frac{(1 \text{ kg}) \sin 50° - (2 \text{ kg}) \sin 30°}{(3 \text{ kg})} \times (10 \text{ m/s}^2) = -0.78 \text{ m/s}^2.$$

7.11, continued:

This is negative, so the acceleration is directed in the negative x-direction: downhill for M, uphill for m.

Scrutinize

The dimensions of our final expression for acceleration are correct, since the numerator has the dimensions of mass times acceleration, and the denominator has the dimension of mass. The answer can be checked for special cases: if we put either mass equal to zero, the other has acceleration $g \sin \beta$ (or $-g \sin \alpha$), as we would expect for a free body sliding down an inclined plane.

(b) *Assuming that the pulley remains frictionless, what is the minimum coefficient of static friction between blocks and slope required to allow the blocks in part (a) to remain motionless? Suppose that the coefficient of static friction has this value, but the coefficient of kinetic friction is smaller. What would happen if the blocks were started in motion sliding towards the left (i.e., downhill for the block on the left, uphill for the block on the right)?*

Conceptualize

The situation is essentially as in part (a), but we must add the frictional forces to our free-body diagrams. In the absence of friction, we saw that the blocks move in the negative x-direction, i.e. the 2 kg block moves downhill. The frictional forces will both act to oppose this motion, pointing uphill for the 2 kg block and downhill for the 1 kg block. Because we are dealing with static friction, we do not immediately know the magnitudes of the frictional forces. However, since we are looking for the minimum value of μ_s, we can expect that at least one frictional force will have its maximum magnitude of $\mu_s N$.

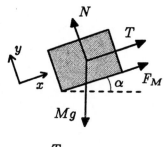

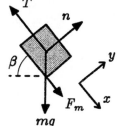

Formulate

The x-component equations (1') and (3') become

$$Ma = T - Mg \sin \alpha + F_M \qquad (6)$$

$$ma = mg \sin \beta - T + F_m , \qquad (7)$$

where F_M and F_m are the x-components of the frictional forces on the two blocks. Since we seek a solution for which the blocks are not sliding, we can set $a = 0$. We can then add the two equations to obtain

$$F_M + F_m = Mg \sin \alpha - mg \sin \beta . \qquad (8)$$

Solve

In general the force of static friction obeys the inequality $|\vec{F}_s| \le \mu_s |\vec{N}|$, so in this case

$$|F_M| \le \mu_s N = \mu_s Mg \cos \alpha \qquad (9)$$

$$|F_m| \le \mu_s n = \mu_s mg \cos \beta , \qquad (10)$$

7.11, continued:

where we have obtained the values of N and n from the y-component equations $(2')$ and $(4')$. If we insert these inequalities for F_M and F_m into Eq. (8), we obtain

$$|Mg \sin \alpha - mg \sin \beta| = |F_M + F_m| \leq |F_M| + |F_m| \leq \mu_s (Mg \cos \alpha + mg \cos \beta) ,$$

so

$$\mu_s \geq \frac{|M \sin \alpha - m \sin \beta|}{M \cos \alpha + m \cos \beta} .$$

We were asked to find the *minimal* value for μ_s which allows a static configuration, so that question is answered by

$$\mu_s|_{\min} = \frac{|M \sin \alpha - m \sin \beta|}{M \cos \alpha + m \cos \beta} . \tag{11}$$

Putting in the numbers,

$$\mu_s|_{\min} = \frac{|(2 \text{ kg}) \sin 30° - (1 \text{ kg}) \sin 50°|}{(2 \text{ kg}) \cos 30° + (1 \text{ kg}) \cos 50°} = 0.099 .$$

We were also asked what would happen if $\mu_s = \mu_s|_{\min}$, with $\mu_k < \mu_s$, and the blocks were started in motion sliding towards the left. Recall that this is the same direction in which the blocks would slide if there were no friction, as we found in part (a). Once the blocks are in motion the frictional force on the two blocks will have magnitudes $\mu_k N$ and $\mu_k n$, respectively. These forces are smaller than $\mu_s N$ and $\mu_s n$, which together are just barely enough to prevent the blocks from sliding. Thus the blocks will continue to slide, accelerating in the negative x-direction, until the 2 kg mass reaches the bottom of the incline.

Scrutinize
The expression (11) for $\mu_s|_{\min}$ is dimensionless, as it must be since μ_s is a pure number (being a ratio of two forces). If we set $m = 0$, the required coefficient of friction is simply $\tan \alpha$, as in Problem 6E.4; if we put $M = 0$, we get $\tan \beta$, which is also in agreement with Problem 6E.4.

Learn
Signs can be very tricky in problems involving friction. The direction of both static and kinetic friction forces generally depends on the values of other quantities in the problem, so one frequently uses formulas that are valid only for a restricted range of values. In the above derivation we have taken pains to make no assumptions about the signs of the expressions, so Eq. (11) is valid for all values of α and β, from 0 to 90°, and for all values of M and m. However, we knew that $M \sin \alpha - m \sin \beta$ is positive for the numbers given in the problem, so we could have concluded that F_M and F_m are positive. If we had used this knowledge, we could have obtained a formula just like Eq. (11), but without the absolute value signs. In that case, however, we would have found a negative value for $\mu_s|_{\min}$ when we applied the equation to the special case $M = 0$. Coefficients of friction are never negative, so such an answer would have been

7.11, continued:

a mistake. Thus, it is important to keep track of any assumptions that you make about the signs of the quantities in your equations, and you should expect your equations to fail when they are applied to cases that violate those assumptions.

(c) *Suppose that the coefficient of static friction between blocks and slope is 0.12. Is it possible for the blocks described in part (b) to be stationary? If so, what is the range of possible values for the tension in the string?*

Conceptualize

Since we have learned from part (b) that a coefficient of static friction of 0.099 is sufficient to allow a static configuration of the blocks, the value of 0.12 given in this part is clearly sufficient. So the nontrivial part of the problem is to find the range of possible values of the tension. This problem is unusual, as most of the problems we encounter have unique answers, while in this problem we are asked to find a range of possible answers.

Formulate

Although the question is different, the physical situation is identical to that of part (b). Thus, Eqs. (6), (7), (9), and (10) are all still valid. The first two of these equations allow us to relate the tension to the frictional forces, while the latter two give us the range of possibilities for the frictional forces.

Solve

We are describing a static situation, so $a = 0$. From Eqs. (6) and (7), it follows that

$$T = Mg \sin \alpha - F_M$$
$$T = mg \sin \beta + F_m \; .$$

Eqs. (9) and (10) can be rewritten as

$$-\mu_s Mg \cos \alpha \le F_M \le \mu_s Mg \cos \alpha$$
$$-\mu_s mg \cos \beta \le F_m \le \mu_s mg \cos \beta \; .$$

Combining with the previous equations, we have the inequalities

$$Mg \sin \alpha - \mu_s Mg \cos \alpha \le T \le Mg \sin \alpha + \mu_s Mg \cos \alpha$$
$$mg \sin \beta - \mu_s mg \cos \beta \le T \le mg \sin \beta + \mu_s mg \cos \beta \; .$$

Numerically,

$$7.9 \text{ N} \le T \le 12.1 \text{ N}$$
$$6.9 \text{ N} \le T \le 8.4 \text{ N} \; .$$

Since both of these must hold, the final answer is the intersection of the ranges given by the first and second inequalities:

$$7.9 \text{ N} \le T \le 8.4 \text{ N} \; .$$

7.11, continued:

 Scrutinize
The dimensions are clearly correct, since each term is a mass times an accleration. The dependence on μ_s can also be seen to be at least qualitatively correct: as μ_s is increased the lower limits get lower and the upper limits get higher, so the range is monotonically increased. This behavior agrees with our intuition, because a larger amount of friction should increase the range of parameters for which a stationary solution exists. Finally, we can check that the range of values disappears at precisely the value of μ_s that was calculated in (b). For the numerical values in this problem, the most restrictive of the above inequalities give

$$Mg \sin \alpha - \mu_s Mg \cos \alpha \leq T \leq mg \sin \beta + \mu_s mg \cos \beta \ .$$

The upper and lower limits are equal, and hence the range disappears, precisely when

$$\mu_s = \frac{Mg \sin \alpha - mg \sin \beta}{mg \sin \beta + mg \cos \beta} \ ,$$

which is exactly the value of $\mu_s|_{\min}$ found in part (b).

 Learn
It is unusual to have a problem with a range of answers, but this situation can arise when there are forces—such as static friction, normal forces, or the tension in an inextensible string—which have magnitudes that adjust to the other forces that are acting. A classic example of such a problem, which we will learn how to analyze in Chapter 9, is the distribution of weight among the four legs of a rigid table. For a three-legged table, on the other hand, the answer is unique.

If one were to physically construct the system described in this question, one would of course expect that the tension in the string would have some definite value. But how can the physical system pick out a definite value, when our calculation could not? The answer is that our calculation was overly idealized. In reality there is no such thing as an inextensible string, but any real string has some elasticity. The string stretches slightly, and the amount of stretching increases with the tension. So the tension in the string would depend on the precise distance between the blocks.

(d) *Now suppose that a heavy uniform rope (i.e. a rope with constant mass per length) is laid over a frictionless triangular block as shown. Assume that the peak of the triangle behaves as a frictionless pulley. Will the rope slip?*

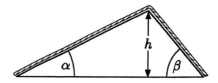

Conceptualize
We know that a system of particles accelerates under the influence of external forces as if all its mass were concentrated at the center of mass. By treating the pieces of string on either side of the peak as two separate systems, we can reduce this problem to something equivalent to part (a).

253

7.11, continued:

Formulate

The length of the left-hand segment of rope is

$$\ell_1 = \frac{h}{\sin \alpha} ,$$

while the length of the right-hand segment is

$$\ell_2 = \frac{h}{\sin \beta} .$$

If we let σ denote the mass per length of the system, then the masses of the left- and right-hand segments are

$$m_1 = \frac{\sigma h}{\sin \alpha}$$

$$m_2 = \frac{\sigma h}{\sin \beta} .$$

If we model the peak of the triangular block as a frictionless pulley, then we can apply Eqs. (1′) and (3′) from part (a), using these masses:

$$m_1 a = T - m_1 g \sin \alpha = T - \sigma h g$$

$$m_2 a = m_2 g \sin \beta - T = \sigma h g - T ,$$

where T is the tension of the rope at the peak, which determines the magnitude of the tension force acting on each segment of the rope. Adding the equations gives

$$(m_1 + m_2)a = 0 ,$$

so the rope will remain stationary if it starts stationary. On the other hand, if it is given a small nudge, say to the right, it will not only continue to move, but will actually accelerate. This is because the mass of rope on the right will increase while the mass on the left decreases, so a net force to the right will develop. Our rope is in a position of unstable equilibrium.

Scrutinize

The crucial point is that the length of rope on each side is inversely proportional to $\sin \alpha$ (or $\sin \beta$), whereas the component of $\vec{g}$ down the slope is directly proportional to $\sin \alpha$ (or $\sin \beta$). Hence the component of the gravitational force down the slope is independent of the angle.

Learn

The rope problem gives an interesting illustration of how one can take advantage of the freedom to call any selection of particles a system. No matter what system we choose, we always know that the acceleration of the center of mass is given by the total force acting on it divided by the its total mass. Here we started with one rope, but found it

7.11, continued:

useful to treat it as *two* systems, separately considering the segments of rope on either side of the peak.

7.16   *A rocket is a 'Newton's Third Law machine'—it operates by ejecting a high velocity exhaust at one end. Suppose that a rocket with initial mass M_i burns its fuel at a constant rate dm/dt and expels the combustion products with speed u relative to itself. By how much has the rocket's speed increased when its mass has decreased to M_f (the difference having been ejected as exhaust)? (Assume the rocket is in interstellar space, with no other forces acting.)*

A deep space probe will be placed in low Earth orbit by a shuttle launch, and will then fire its own booster rocket to leave orbit. You are in charge of designing the booster. If the probe's mass is 500 kg and it needs a velocity change of 5 km/s, what minimum mass of fuel will you need to specify if the exhaust velocity is to be 2500 m/s?

Conceptualize

This is an application of conservation of momentum. The rocket and its exhaust together form an isolated system, with no external force acting, so their combined momentum must be conserved. The difficulty is that the masses of rocket and exhaust are not constant: the rocket is losing mass continuously, and the total mass of combustion products expelled is increasing. Because this is a continuous process, it is necessary to use calculus to solve this problem.

Formulate

Consider a time t at which the rocket's mass is m and its speed is v. A short time interval Δt later its mass is $m + \Delta m$ and its speed is $v + \Delta v$; its momentum has changed by an amount $v\Delta m + m\Delta v$. (Notice that Δm will be a negative number, because the rocket's mass is decreasing—we do it this way because we want the differential dm/dt (i.e. $\lim\limits_{\Delta t \to 0}(\Delta m/\Delta t)$) to be the rate of change of the rocket's mass, which is what interests us, and not the rate of change of the amount of mass ejected as exhaust. Also note that the term $\Delta m \Delta v$ in the momentum change is neglected: if Δt is small, $|\Delta m| \ll m$ and $|\Delta v| \ll v$, so $\Delta m \Delta v$ is much smaller than either of the other two terms.)

The rocket's momentum change is balanced by the momentum $(v - u)(-\Delta m)$ of the exhaust ejected during this time interval, $v - u$ being the speed of the exhaust in a stationary reference frame. (A change of Δm in the mass of the rocket clearly implies ejection of $-\Delta m$ of fuel.) This gives us

$$v\Delta m + m\Delta v - v\Delta m + u\Delta m = 0,$$

$$\Rightarrow m\Delta v = -u\Delta m.$$

If we divide this by the time interval Δt and take the limit as $\Delta t \to 0$ it tells us that the net force on the rocket (i.e. its mass times its acceleration dv/dt) is its exhaust velocity times the rate at which it burns and expels fuel, $u\,dm/dt$. This is called the *thrust* of the rocket.

7.16, continued:

Solve

If we divide the equation above by m, we obtain the equation for Δv:

$$\Delta v = -\frac{u}{m}\Delta m \ .$$

The equation means that for any small interval during which the mass of the rocket changes by Δm, the speed changes by $-(u/m)\Delta m$. If we are interested in calculating the change in the speed of the rocket over time, we could imagine dividing the time interval into a huge number of small increments, and then applying the above formula to each increment in sequence. For each increment we would have a different value of m, since the mass decreases as exhaust is ejected. The total change in speed would be the sum of the small increments, which is exactly how one defines an integral:

$$v_f - v_i = -u \int_{M_i}^{M_f} \frac{dm}{m} \ .$$

Doing the integration gives $v_f - v_i = -u \ln\left(M_f/M_i\right) = u \ln\left(M_i/M_f\right)$. Note that if the rocket carries enough fuel, we can have $v > u$, since $\ln(M_i/M_f)$ can be greater than 1. Assuming we are not dealing with velocities near the speed of light, the limiting factor is the ratio of payload mass to fuel mass. This ratio is improved if fuel tanks etc. can be discarded when they are empty, hence the use of multi-stage rockets in satellite launches.

Applying this formula to our probe booster, we have $u = 2500$ m/s, $M_f = 500$ kg, and $v_f - v_i = 5000$ m/s. To extract M_i, we take the antilog of our formula:

$$\frac{M_i}{M_f} = \exp\left(\frac{v_f - v_i}{u}\right) \ .$$

This gives $M_i = (500 \text{ kg}) \times \exp(2) = 3700$ kg. The minimum mass of fuel is thus 3200 kg, assuming that this is a single-stage rocket and that the original 500 kg already included the mass of the necessary fuel tanks.

Scrutinize

The impulse applied to the 500 kg payload is 2.5 MN·s. If we had done this by ejecting the whole of the 3200 kg of fuel in one instantaneous pulse, the required exhaust velocity would be $(2.5 \times 10^6 \text{ kg} \cdot \text{m/s})/(3200 \text{ kg}) = 780$ m/s, which is considerably less than the actual exhaust velocity. This makes sense, because such an instantaneous ejection is more efficient than our continuous boost—in the early stages of acceleration, what we are accelerating is mainly fuel rather than payload. (The disadvantage of the instantaneous-boost approach is that the instantaneous *force* applied to the payload approaches infinity, so what actually gets launched is a squashed heap of wreckage rather than a delicate scientific instrument!)

Although the overall *momentum* change of the system of rocket plus exhaust is zero, the overall change in *kinetic energy* is large. The source of this energy is the chemical potential energy liberated by burning the fuel.

7.16, continued:

Learn

The rocket problem is a classic example of a problem involving the continuous transfer of material. A similar problem is that of a railroad flatcar onto which is poured a continuous stream of water or sand. In all such problems, the key idea is to think incrementally. Don't try to see through the problem in one step, but instead begin by considering an arbitrarily short interval of time Δt. If you can figure out how the conditions at the end of Δt are related to what they were at the start, then the mechanical manipulations of calculus will usually do the rest of the work for you.

Another fascinating feature of the rocket problem is the fact that the velocity of the center of mass of the whole system—rocket plus exhaust—can never change. If the rocket begins at rest in empty space, then the center of mass will always remain at its initial location, no matter how far the payload might travel.

HINTS FOR PROBLEMS WITH AN (H)
The number of the hint refers to the number of the problem

7.1 What is the acceleration of the car at point B? What forces could be acting to cause this acceleration? Do any of these forces have Third Law partners which are relevant to the problem?

7.3 (c) What quantity is conserved throughout the child's motion? If at point P she is sliding with speed v, what is v in terms of g, r and θ?

What is her centripetal acceleration at point P? What is the net centripetal force on her?

What would the normal force on the child be if she were not in contact with the igloo? What do you think the normal force would be at the exact point where she loses contact with the igloo?

7.6 For both part (a) and part (c), ask yourself the following questions.

Which quantities are the same for the two sleds?

What is the net horizontal force on each sled? The net vertical force?

If you're still stuck, try reviewing the solutions to problems 7.10 and 7.11.

7.12 Draw free-body diagrams for each mass. What is the condition for balance?

If the mass M descends slightly, what happens to (a) the position of the 2 kg mass; (b) the forces acting on the 2 kg mass?

7.13 There are three stages to this problem: (i) firing the rifle; (ii) the impact of the bullet; (iii) the motion of the block (and bullet) after impact. In each case, which quantity is conserved? Which is not conserved?

7.15 For part (d), what is the horizontal force acting on the upper block? Before the block starts to slip, how is the value of this force related to (i) the acceleration, (ii) the tension?

7.18 In Alice's frame of reference, what is the acceleration of the ball? What is the position of the ball at time t?

7.19 It may help to draw a force diagram for the system after mass B has fallen some distance. Study the directions of all the forces involved (do not try to calculate their magnitudes, but do consider which forces must be equal in magnitude). You may also find it useful to list the external forces acting on the system of two balls and a string, and to visualize their directions.

258

ANSWERS TO HINTS

7.1 v^2/r; gravity and a normal force from the track; yes, the Third Law pair of the normal force exerted by the track on the car is a force exerted by the car on the track.

7.3 Mechanical energy (kinetic plus potential); $\sqrt{2rg(1-\cos\theta)}$

v^2/r; $mg\cos\theta - N$, where N is the normal force from the igloo.

Zero; zero.

7.6 The acceleration, and the magnitude of the tension in the rope between them.

For parts (a) and (b), $ma = 30$ N for the girl's sled and 8 N for Teddy's. The vertical components are both zero.

For part (c), net force is zero in both horizontal and vertical directions. Horizontal force is $T\cos\theta - t - \mu_k N$ for girl's sled, and $t - \mu_k n$ for Teddy, where T and t are the tensions in the first and second ropes and N and n are the respective normal forces.

7.12

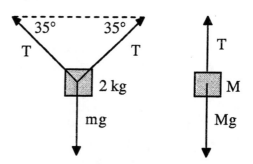

$2T\sin 35° - mg = 0$ (2 kg mass); $T - Mg = 0$ (mass M).

2 kg mass moves upwards; downward force unchanged, upward forces decrease (because angle decreases).

7.13 Conserved: (i), (ii) momentum; (iii) mechanical (kinetic plus potential) energy.

Not conserved: (i), (ii) kinetic energy; (iii) momentum.

7.15 Static friction, F_s; $F_s = Ma$; $F_s = \frac{1}{2}(T - 2\mu_k Mg)$.

7.18 Acceleration $= [-a, 0, -g]$; position given by $x = vt\cos\theta\sin\alpha - \frac{1}{2}at^2$, $y = vt\cos\theta\cos\alpha$, $z = vt\sin\theta - \frac{1}{2}gt^2$, where α is the angle between the ball's direction and the y-axis.

7.19 Forces you should have on your diagram: gravity; normal force from surface of table; normal force from edge of table; tension.

ANSWERS TO ALL PROBLEMS

7.1 (a) The downward force acting on each passenger must be mv^2/r, to maintain the circular motion. If $v^2/r > g$, some of this downward force must come from a normal force exerted by the track on the car (and by the car seats on the passengers). The Third Law pair to this normal force, which is exerted by the car on the track (and by the passengers on the seats), acts outward, and is responsible for the feeling of weight.

   (b) $v = \sqrt{\frac{3}{2}gr}$; $h = \frac{11}{4}r$

7.2 -5.3×10^{33} J; 2.7×10^{33} J; -2.7×10^{33} J. Total energy is negative, as expected for a bound state—cf. problem 7.5. [In fact, in this case the kinetic energy is exactly half the magnitude of the potential energy: $K = -\frac{1}{2}U$.]

7.3 (a) $mgr\cos\theta$.

   (b) see diagram at right.

   (c) No; at $48.2°$ ($\cos\theta = \frac{2}{3}$)

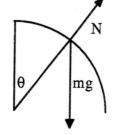

7.4 See complete solution.

7.5 See complete solution.

7.6 Tension t in the rope between the two sleds forms a Third Law pair with the force exerted by the child's sled on the rope, and another pair with the force exerted by Teddy's sled on the rope.

   $T = 44$ N; $t = 8$ N.

   $T = \dfrac{\mu_k(m+M)g}{\cos\theta + \mu_k\sin\theta}$.

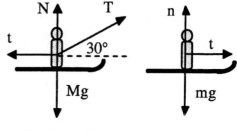

Child's sled   Ted's sled

7.7 See complete solution.

7.8 $\vec{F} = [\mu_k Mg, 0, 0]$; $\dfrac{u}{\mu_k g}$; $\frac{1}{2}Mu^2$. Because friction always acts to oppose *relative* motion, the frictional force in this case acts to **accelerate** the suitcase, and does positive work. After the suitcase reaches the speed of the conveyor belt, the force of friction acting on it is zero.

7.9 (a) $\mu_s = \tan\theta$; in the direction of motion of the conveyor.

   (b) $\vec{F} = \mu_k Mg \left[\dfrac{u}{\sqrt{u^2 + u_0^2 \cos^2\theta}}, 0, -\dfrac{u_0 \cos\theta}{\sqrt{u^2 + u_0^2 \cos^2\theta}} \right]$; $t = \dfrac{\sqrt{u^2 + u_0^2 \cos^2\theta}}{\mu_k g}$; $z(t) = \dfrac{u_0 \cos\theta \sqrt{u^2 + u_0^2 \cos^2\theta}}{2\mu_k g}$.

   (c) $\vec{F} = [-\mu_k Mg, 0, 0]$; $\mu_k(M + M_2)g$.

7.10 See complete solution.

7.11 See complete solution.

7.12 1.7 kg. The system will oscillate.

7.13 600 m/s; 0.6 m/s (taking $g = 9.8$ m/s^2).

7.14 (b) $U_0 + \frac{3}{2}Mu^2$; (c) $U_0 + \frac{3}{2}Mu^2 - K_A - K_B$ (d) $[u, -2v_y, 0]$.

7.15 (a) $\mu_s Mg$.

   (b) $\frac{1}{2}\mu_s Mg$, in direction opposite the tension force.

   (c) $(\mu_s - \mu_k)g$, in direction of tension force.

   (d) $2(\bar{\mu}_s + \mu_k)Mg$; backwards (opposite to direction of motion).

7.16 See complete solution.

7.17 towards the star; stationary.

If we let $\hat{u}$ denote a unit vector pointing toward the point A, then the velocity vector of the spaceship can be written as $V\hat{u}$, where V is the spaceship's speed. The exhaust gas moves with velocity $-v\hat{u}$ relative to the spaceship, and therefore with velocity $(V - v)\hat{u}$ relative to a stationary observer. If $V > v$, the exhaust velocity vector therefore points towards A.

There is no external force acting on the system, so the system center of mass has no acceleration. Since the center of mass was at rest before the spaceship fired its rocket engines, it must remain at rest. (Note that the internal kinetic energy of the system certainly increases, but this is not a violation of energy conservation: the increase in kinetic energy is balanced by a decrease in the chemical potential energy of the fuel.)

The speed v of the exhaust gases is determined by the chemical potential energy of the fuel and the design of the engines. If we knew the parameters, we could calculate v for the case when the spaceship is at rest. If we now consider the instant when the rocket has attained velocity $\vec{V}$, and repeat this calculation in a reference frame moving at the same velocity (so that the spacecraft is instantaneously at rest in this frame*), we will be doing essentially the same calculation as the first one. That is, since everything relevant to the calculation (e.g., the fuel tanks, the pumps, and the combustion chamber) is moving with the spaceship, everything will be at rest in the new frame of reference. As long as nothing has happened in the meantime to affect the behavior of the engine, then the calculation will be unchanged, and we will get the same answer for the exhaust speed. Therefore the exhaust speed must be approximately constant relative to the rocket engine.

There is, however, one further complication that is worth exploring. The above argument shows that if nothing relevant to the mechanics of the rocket changes as the rocket accelerates, then the change in the speed of the rocket will have no effect on the speed of the exhaust relative to the rocket. There is, however, one property of a rocket that typically changes dramatically over the course of a flight: its mass. Most of the mass of a typical

---

* The spacecraft itself defines an accelerating, non-inertial, reference frame, but at any given moment it is at rest relative to an inertial frame moving with the same instantaneous velocity $\vec{V}$.

rocket is fuel, so the mass of the rocket decreases very significantly with time. The above argument does not tell us whether the change in the rocket mass will change the exhaust speed, so to check that we need to do a more quantitative calculation by using conservation of energy and momentum. Suppose that at time t the rocket plus its remaining fuel has mass $m + \Delta m$. In the short time interval Δt it burns Δm of fuel, converting ΔE of chemical potential energy to kinetic energy and ejecting Δm of exhaust gas at speed v relative to the rest frame of the rocket at time t. By conservation of momentum, the rest of the rocket must move in the opposite direction with speed V, where $mV = \Delta m v$. By conservation of energy, $\Delta E = \frac{1}{2}mV^2 + \frac{1}{2}\Delta m v^2$. Combining these two equations,

$$\Delta E = \frac{1}{2}m\left(\frac{\Delta m}{m}v\right)^2 + \frac{1}{2}\Delta m v^2$$

$$= \frac{1}{2}\Delta m v^2\left(\frac{\Delta m}{m} + 1\right)$$

$$\implies \quad v = \sqrt{\frac{2E}{\Delta m\left(1 + \frac{\Delta m}{m}\right)}}.$$

As Δm was the fuel burned in a short time interval, we can safely assume that Δm is small compared to m, and so $1 + \Delta m/m \simeq 1$. Hence the exhaust speed is approximately constant in the rest frame of the rocket (it depends only on the amount of gas expelled in time Δt and the amount of energy liberated by burning that amount of fuel).

7.18 (a) $\vec{v} = v\left[\dfrac{a}{g}\sin\theta, \sqrt{\cos^2\theta - \dfrac{a^2}{g^2}\sin^2\theta}, \sin\theta\right]$.

(b) $v = \sqrt{\dfrac{gw}{\cos\alpha}}$, $t = \sqrt{\dfrac{2w}{g\cos\alpha}}$, where $\sin\alpha = \dfrac{a}{g}$.

7.19 Ball A falls off the edge before ball B hits it. There are at least two conclusive arguments: (i) the only horizontal force on the two-ball-plus-string system is the force of the table edge on the string, which has a component to the right; therefore the center of mass must move to the right; (ii) thinking of the balls one at a time, the only horizontal force is from the tension in the string; the tension force has equal magnitude on the two balls, but only for the left ball is the force purely horizontal.

ESSENTIALS OF INTRODUCTORY CLASSICAL MECHANICS

CHAPTER 8

ROTATION IN TWO DIMENSIONS

OVERVIEW

We have seen in earlier chapters that dealing explicitly with a system of many bodies becomes increasingly difficult as the number of individual bodies increases. In Chapter 6 we looked at one way of handling this problem — approximating the individual interactions of the surface atoms of two bodies by a single macroscopic force, i.e. friction. This chapter introduces the idea of *rigid bodies*, where the configuration of the system (the shape of the body) remains fixed at all times. Rigid bodies can move as point particles; they can also *rotate* about some axis.

In this chapter we shall deal with rigid bodies moving in a two-dimensional plane and rotating about an axis perpendicular to this plane. This is the rotational analogue of one-dimensional linear motion — it simplifies the algebra but still allows us to develop all the new physical concepts we need. Since the direction of the axis of rotation is fixed, we will not have to describe the direction in the course of our calculations. This means that we will be able to use scalars to represent quantities — such as *angular velocity*, *torque*, and *angular momentum*, which under more general circumstances would require vectors. In the following chapter we will extend our discussion to cases in which the axis is not fixed, and then we will introduce the full vector formalism needed to describe the rotations of rigid bodies in three dimensions.

When you have completed this chapter you should:

✔ be able to explain the concept of a rigid body and recognize its similarities to and differences from a real physical object;

✔ know what is meant by the terms angular velocity, angular acceleration, rotational kinetic energy, moment of inertia, torque, and angular momentum;

✔ be able to calculate the moment of inertia of a simple solid object about a fixed axis;

✔ be aware that two-dimensional motion of a rigid body can always be regarded as a combination of translation and rotation about an axis through the center of mass and perpendicular to the plane of motion;

✔ know how to use the rotational equivalents of Newton's laws to predict the outcome of motion involving translation and rotation about an axis with fixed orientation.

ESSENTIALS

Many solid bodies, such as blocks of wood or bars of steel, assume a shape that is maintained under a wide variety of conditions. The idealized solid object for which this is exactly true is called a *rigid body*. In an ideal rigid body, the distance between any two constituent parts remains exactly constant over time. Rigid bodies cannot bend, twist, expand, or contract.

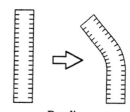

Bending
In a bent bar, the distances between constituent particles are stretched on one side and shortened on the other. In a rigid body such distances cannot change.

A rigid body can move in space while retaining the same orientation, a form of motion called *translation*. A translation can be described in the same way that we describe the motion of point particles. A rigid body can also change its orientation, a form of motion called *rotation*. The most general motion of a rigid body involves simultaneous translation and rotation, but for simplicity we begin our discussion by considering rotations alone, without any translation. We therefore assume for now that one point on the rigid body, which we call P, is held fixed. The motion of the rigid body is then called a *rotation about the point P*.

Although the definition of a rotation requires only that a single point P be held fixed, it can be shown that for any such motion there is an entire line of points that remains fixed. This line of fixed points is called the *axis* of the rotation. The fixed point P and perhaps even the entire axis will sometimes lie outside the physical body, but one can always imagine extending the rigid body to avoid this complication.

In studying translational motion we started by confining ourselves to motion in one dimension. For similar reasons, we begin our discussion of rotations by considering cases in which the axis is fixed. That is, we assume that the physical device is constructed so that the only possible motion is rotation about a specified axis. An example would be a wheel, rotating about an axle rigidly attached to a stationary table. In this case the motion of the wheel can be described by a single coordinate, giving the angle at which the wheel is oriented at any given time. For definiteness, we can introduce a Cartesian coordinate system with the z-axis along the axis of rotation, and we can choose a reference point Q which is on the rigid body and in the xy-plane. We then define the coordinate θ as the angle between the x-axis and the line joining the rotation axis to the point Q. By convention the angle is defined to increase as the reference point Q moves in the counterclockwise direction, from the x-axis towards the y-axis.

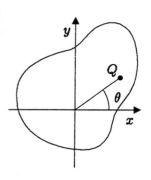

Following the analogy with one-dimensional motion, we refer to the first and second time-derivatives of the coordinate as a velocity and an acceleration, respectively. Specifically, for rotational motion we define the *angular velocity* (measured in *radians per second*)

$$\omega \equiv \frac{d\theta}{dt} \, .$$

We also define the *angular acceleration* (measured in *radians per second*^{2})

$$\alpha \equiv \frac{d\omega}{dt} \, .$$

Problem 8A.1

For clarity we emphasize that angular velocity and angular acceleration are not the same quantities as the (linear) velocity and acceleration that we have been discussing since Chapter 1; the connection is only by analogy.

While a rigid body rotates about a fixed axis, each point particle that makes up the rigid body is moving on a circular trajectory. Since each point particle moves according to Newton's laws of motion, we can deduce the laws that govern rigid body motion from the laws that we already know for point particles. To do this, we begin by relating the velocity and acceleration of the point particles to the angular velocity and angular acceleration of the rigid body.

Consider a point particle on the rigid body, located a distance R from the fixed axis. (Whenever we speak of the distance between a point and a line, we mean the distance measured perpendicularly to the line.) In a small time interval Δt, the point will rotate through a small angle $\Delta\theta = \omega\Delta t$. The particle moves along the arc of a circle, moving tangentially (i.e., perpendicular to the radial direction) through an arc length $\Delta s = R\,\Delta\theta$. Therefore, if $\omega > 0$, the particle's velocity $\vec{\mathbf{v}}$ has magnitude

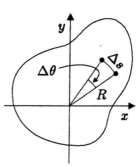

$$v = |\vec{\mathbf{v}}| = \frac{\Delta s}{\Delta t} = R\frac{\Delta\theta}{\Delta t} = R\omega \, .$$

Denoting the outward radial component of a vector by a subscript r, and the counterclockwise tangential component of a vector by a subscript $\perp$, the velocity of the particle can be specified by

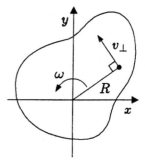

$$v_r = 0 \, ; \qquad v_\perp = R\omega \, .$$

The equation above holds for either sign of ω.

267

The acceleration is a bit more complicated. If ω is constant then the particle is undergoing uniform circular motion, so we already know that the acceleration is directed towards the origin, with magnitude v^2/R. When ω is not constant, it is shown in Problem 8A.2 that the centripetal acceleration is unchanged, but there is also a tangential component to the acceleration given by $dv/dt = R\alpha$, so the full acceleration vector is described by

Problem 8A.2

$$a_r = -\frac{v^2}{R} = -R\omega^2 \; ; \qquad a_\perp = R\alpha \; .$$

We now want to relate the motion of the rigid body to the applied forces. The most straightforward approach is to study the kinetic energy of the rotating rigid body, which is an example of a system of particles, as discussed in Chapter 5. The kinetic energy of such a system is given by

$$K = \sum_i \frac{1}{2} m_i v_i^2 \; ,$$

the sum of the kinetic energies of the individual particles. For a rigid body rotating about a fixed axis, we can replace each v_i by $R_i\omega$ to obtain

$$K = \frac{1}{2} \left(\sum_i m_i R_i^2 \right) \omega^2 \; .$$

We call this the rotational kinetic energy of the body, and define the quantity in parentheses to be the **moment of inertia** of the rigid body about the specified axis:

$$I = \sum_i m_i R_i^2 \; .$$

Problems 8C.1 and 8C.2

(For a solid body, we replace the sum over R_i by an integral over volume.)

The rotational kinetic energy is therefore given by

$$K = \frac{1}{2} I \omega^2 \; ,$$

Problem 8D.1

which is closely analogous to the formula $\frac{1}{2}Mv^2$ for ordinary translational kinetic energy. While angular velocity and angular acceleration are concepts that are **analogous** to the concepts of velocity and acceleration discussed earlier in the book, rotational kinetic energy is not analogous to kinetic energy—it really *is* kinetic energy, as defined in Chapter 4.

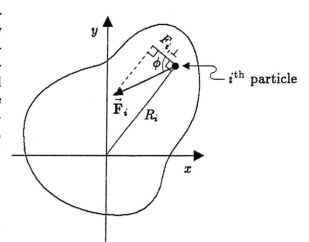

Having obtained a simple expression for the kinetic energy, we can now use the work-energy theorem of Chapter 4 to relate the change in kinetic energy of the rotating body to the total work done by external forces. If the rigid body moves through a small angle $\Delta\theta$, the work done on the ith point particle is given by

$$\Delta W_i = \vec{\mathbf{F}}_i \cdot \overrightarrow{\Delta R_i} = |\vec{\mathbf{F}}_i||\overrightarrow{\Delta R_i}|\cos\phi \ ,$$

where $\vec{\mathbf{F}}_i$ is the total force (both internal and external) applied to the ith particle, $|\overrightarrow{\Delta R_i}| = R_i\Delta\theta$ is the distance the particle moves, and ϕ is the angle between the force and the displacement vector $\overrightarrow{\Delta R_i}$. Since $\overrightarrow{\Delta R_i}$ is tangential, $|\vec{\mathbf{F}}_i|\cos\phi$ is just the tangential component of $\vec{\mathbf{F}}_i$, which we call $F_{i,\perp}$. (Note that although the particle motion in the rotating body is purely tangential, the acceleration of a particle, and hence the force acting on it, can have a radial component as well. Only the tangential component, however, can do work on the body.) Summing over all the particles, the total work done on the rigid body is

$$\Delta W = \sum_i F_{i,\perp} R_i \Delta\theta \ .$$

The quantity $F_{i,\perp} R_i$ will play an important role in rotational motion, so it is given a name, the *torque* τ:

$$\tau_i \equiv F_{i,\perp} R_i \ ; \qquad \tau_{\text{tot}} = \sum_i \tau_i = \sum_i F_{i,\perp} R_i \ .$$

Problems 8B

Recalling the definition of $\perp$ on page 267, we see that torque, like angle, is positive when counterclockwise.

In terms of the torque, the work done on the rigid body as it rotates through a small angle $\Delta\theta$ can be written as

$$\Delta W = \tau_{\text{tot}} \Delta\theta \ .$$

By the work-energy theorem, this work must equal the change in the kinetic energy of rotation. We can obtain an expression for the

269

power applied to the rotating body by dividing the above equation by Δt and then taking the limit as $\Delta t \to 0$:

$$P = \frac{dW}{dt} = \tau_{\text{tot}} \frac{d\theta}{dt} = \tau_{\text{tot}} \omega \ .$$

Equating this expression to the rate of increase of the kinetic energy of the body, we find

$$\tau_{\text{tot}} \omega = \frac{d}{dt}\left(\frac{1}{2} I \omega^2\right) = I\omega \frac{d\omega}{dt} = I\omega\alpha \ ,$$

from which we can see that

$$\boxed{\tau_{\text{tot}} = I\alpha \ .}$$

With this formula we have achieved our goal of determining the angular acceleration of the rigid body from the forces acting on it. In the process, we have discovered the torque, a quantity which for rotational motion is the analogue of the force.

The angular acceleration of a rotating rigid body is proportional to the total torque acting on it, just as the linear acceleration of an object is proportional to the total force acting on it. Similarly, the angular acceleration is inversely proportional to the moment of inertia, just as the linear acceleration is inversely proportional to the mass. The unit of torque is the newton-meter, abbreviated $N \cdot m$. (This is actually the same as the unit of energy, but to emphasize that torque is analogous to force we always use $N \cdot m$ for its unit, never J.) Both the moment of inertia and the torque depend upon the choice of the rotation axis, since the R_i appearing in the definitions are measured from the axis.

While we derived the above equation from the work-energy theorem, it is easy to verify that it also follows as a consequence of Newton's second law. Replacing $\vec{F}_i$ by $m_i \vec{a}$ in the definition of the torque, we find

$$\tau_{\text{tot}} \equiv \sum_i F_{i,\perp} R_i = \sum_i m_i R_i a_{i,\perp} = \sum_i m_i R_i^2 \alpha = I\alpha \ ,$$

where in the last step we used $a_\perp = R\alpha$ and the definition of I.

270

In calculating the torque, it is sometimes useful to express it in a slightly different way. Since $F_{i,\perp} R_i = |\vec{F}_i| R_i \cos\phi$, where ϕ is the angle between $\vec{F}_i$ and the tangential direction, one can instead write the contribution to the torque from the force on the ith particle as

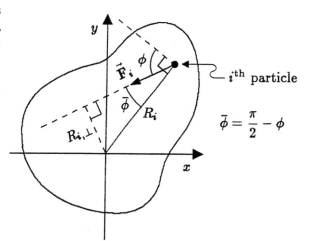

$$\tau_i = \pm |\vec{F}_i| R_{i,\perp} \, ,$$

where $R_{i,\perp} \equiv R_i \cos\phi = R_i \sin\bar{\phi}$ is the component of the displacement vector of the ith particle in the direction perpendicular to the force $\vec{F}_i$. (The $\pm$ sign is included because the factors on the right are by definition nonnegative, while the torque τ_i is negative when the torque is clockwise.)

The formula $\tau_{\text{tot}} = I\alpha$ allows us to calculate the angular acceleration if we know the total torque, but this is still complicated, since the total torque includes contributions from both internal and external forces. This situation is reminiscent of Chapter 5, where we discussed the role of internal and external forces in the translational motion of a system of particles. We found that Newton's third law of motion implied that the internal forces always canceled, so the acceleration of the center of mass of the system could be calculated in terms of the external forces alone. If this were not the case, then a block could accelerate with no external forces acting on it, and conservation of energy would not hold. Now we want to address the analogous question for rotational motion: does Newton's third law imply that the internal torques always cancel? If not, then a rigid body could undergo accelerated rotation with no external forces acting on it, and conservation of energy would have to be abandoned as a physical principle.

To show that internal torques always cancel, it is necessary to assume a form of Newton's third law that is stronger than the version that was postulated by Newton and discussed in Chapter 5. Specifically, we must assume not only that the forces between any two particles are equal in magnitude and opposite in direction, but also that *they are directed along the line joining the two particles*. As can be seen from the diagram on the right, this added assumption implies that the forces between two particles share the same value of $R_{i,\perp}$: $R_{1,\perp} = R_{2,\perp} = h$. Then

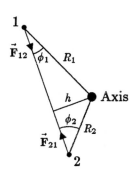

$$|\tau_{12}| = |\vec{F}_{12}| R_{1,\perp} = |\vec{F}_{21}| R_{2,\perp} = |\tau_{21}| \, ,$$

271

and one can see from the diagram that the two torques have opposite signs. Thus, the strengthened form of Newton's third law implies that the internal torques all cancel, just as the internal forces do for translational motion. Conservation of energy therefore remains valid, and angular accelerations can be calculated by including only the external torques:

$$\tau^{ext} = I\alpha .$$

Problems 8E.1, 8E.2, and 8E.6

This result is crucially important, since it allows us to calculate the rotation of a rigid body without any reference to its internal forces.

In Chapter 5 we learned that the total external force applied to a system of particles is equal to the rate of change of its total momentum, so we might ask whether the total external torque could be involved in an analogous relationship. The answer is yes. Since I is constant for a rigid body rotating about a fixed axis, the equation above can be rewritten by defining the **angular momentum** L of the rotating object about the axis by

$$L \equiv I\omega ,$$

giving

$$\tau^{ext} = \frac{dL}{dt} .$$

L is the rotational analogue of the linear momentum, Mv. If there are no external torques, the above formula implies that angular momentum is conserved.

So far, however, we have demonstrated this conservation law only for a rigid body rotating about a fixed axis, in which case it reduces to the statement that $\omega =$ constant. We will see in the next chapter, however, that the principle is much more general: **angular momentum is conserved for any system for which there are no external torques**. The classic example is the (non-rigid) spinning skater who pulls in her arms, thereby reducing her moment of inertia I and causing her angular velocity ω to increase, so that the product $L = I\omega$ is conserved. Like the conservation of energy and momentum, the conservation of angular momentum is, so far as we know, an exact law of nature. Within our experience it has never been seen to fail under any circumstances.*

So far we have considered rotation about a *fixed* axis, such as the rotation of a wheel about a stationary axle. In this case the axle—the supporting shaft about which the wheel is pivoted—coincides with the axis of rotation—the line of points which have zero instantaneous velocity. In many applications, however, one is interested in a rolling wheel, for which the axle is in motion. Such problems combine rotational motion with translational motion. Nonetheless, as long as the motion is two-dimensional in the sense that all particle velocities lie in the xy-plane, these problems can be treated by a minor extension of the methods already developed.

To describe the most general possible two-dimensional motion of a rigid body, we begin by introducing the "center-of-mass axis," the line parallel to the z-axis which passes through the center of mass. In the rolling wheel problem, for example, the center-of-mass axis would lie along the axle of the wheel (assuming that the wheel is symmetric about its axle). We then change our frame of reference by making a time-dependent translation in the x- and y- directions to a frame that follows the center of mass, so that the center-of-mass axis is at all times the z-axis of the new frame of reference. Even though the new frame will in many cases be non-inertial (i.e., it may accelerate), it is still a convenient system to describe the motion. In the new frame the z-axis is by construction a line of fixed points, and hence the z-axis is the axis of rotation. In this frame the problem reduces to the rotation of the rigid body about the z-axis. Returning to the original "laboratory" frame of reference, *the full motion of the rigid body is described by specifying the translational motion of the center of mass and the rotational motion about the center-of-mass axis.*

Beware, however, the requirement that the motion remain two-dimensional is not trivial. For reasons that will be discussed in the next chapter, asymmetric objects will usually wobble, rather than rotate about an axis of fixed orientation. One condition for which such

---

* The strengthened form of Newton's third law, however, which we used to demonstrate the conservation of angular momentum, is more problematic. If interpreted literally as a statement about the forces between two particles, the strengthened form of Newton's third law is not always valid. It holds, however, for all forces between two particles discussed in this book, such as electrostatic and gravitational forces. For contact forces, such as normal forces and friction, the two particles are idealized as being at precisely the same point. In this case the extension to Newton's third law is ill-defined, since no line is defined by two coincident points, but the original form of the third law is sufficient to guarantee that the torques on the two particles are equal and opposite. If one goes beyond the level of this book, however, to consider the forces felt and exerted by electrically charged particles in motion, then the issue becomes more complicated. As discussed in the Supplementary Notes at the end of Chapter 5, in this case even the original form of Newton's third law fails, if one considers only the particles. If one takes into account the momentum and angular momentum carried by the electromagnetic field, however, then both conservation laws are exact, to within the accuracy of the best measurements that have been performed.

stable rotation is possible, however, is when the object is symmetric about an axis parallel to the z-axis—as an idealized wheel usually is.

The equations describing combined translation and rotation in two dimensions are easier to state than they are to demonstrate, so we will begin by stating them. The translational motion of the rigid body is described fully by the methods introduced in Chapter 5, where we learned that the acceleration of the center of mass $\vec{\mathbf{a}}_{cm}$ of any system of particles can be determined from the total external force $\sum \vec{\mathbf{F}}^{ext}$ acting on the system:

$$\sum \vec{\mathbf{F}}^{ext} = M\vec{\mathbf{a}}_{cm} = \frac{d\vec{\mathbf{p}}}{dt} \quad \text{(translational)} .$$

Here M is the mass of the rigid body, and $\vec{\mathbf{p}}$ is its momentum. The rotational motion is described by the equation

$$\sum \tau^{ext} = I_{cm}\alpha = \frac{dL}{dt} \quad \text{(rotational)} ,$$

Problems 8E.8, 9D.6, 10.10

where $\sum \tau^{ext}$ is the total external torque calculated about the center-of-mass axis, I_{cm} is the moment of inertia about the center-of-mass axis, and L describes the angular momentum about this axis. Note that these equations hold even though the axis through the center of mass might be both moving and accelerating.

The easiest way to derive the above equation for the rotational motion is to use a coordinate system that follows the center of mass of the body, so that the center-of-mass axis is the z-axis of the coordinate system. Even though this center-of-mass coordinate system will in many cases be accelerating, it is still the simplest way to describe the rotational motion, which reduces to the problem of rotation about the z-axis. (Note that the axis of rotation is frame-dependent. In the original frame of reference the center of mass of the rigid body is generally moving, so the center-of-mass axis cannot be the axis of rotation.)

To relate the behavior in the center-of-mass frame to that in the original "laboratory" frame, we must be able to convert angles, angular velocities, and angular accelerations between the two frames. The two coordinate frames are related to each other by a time-dependent translation, but happily the orientation of an object does not change under a translation. Thus the quantity θ describing the orientation

Warning — Difficult Material

274

of the object, and the quantities ω and α describing the angular velocity and acceleration of the object, all have the same value in the center-of-mass and laboratory frames:

$$\theta_{cm} = \theta_{lab}; \quad \omega_{cm} = \omega_{lab}; \quad \alpha_{cm} = \alpha_{lab}.$$

The torque is more intricate, since in the center-of-mass frame we must include fictitious forces to compensate for the noninertial nature of the frame, as discussed in Chapter 6. Specifically, to each particle of mass m_i we must assign a fictitious force $\vec{F}_{fict}(t) = -m_i\vec{a}_{cm}(t)$, where $\vec{a}_{cm}(t)$ is the acceleration of the center of mass as measured in the inertial laboratory frame. These fictitious forces are equivalent to a uniform gravitational field with acceleration vector $\vec{g}(t) = -\vec{a}_{cm}(t)$. It is shown in Problem 8E.7 that the total torque about a horizontal axis caused by a uniform gravitational field can be calculated as if all of the force were applied directly to the center of mass. Hence, in the center-of-mass frame the fictitious forces produce no torque about an axis that goes through the center of mass, and hence no torque about the axis of rotation, the z-axis. That is the reason why we chose a coordinate system centered on the center of mass. The torque which appears in the rotational equation of motion can therefore be calculated directly from the real physical forces, such as the force of friction or forces applied by ropes, ignoring the fictitious forces.

To describe a wheel that is rolling without slipping, it is also necessary to understand the relation that such rolling imposes between the angular and linear velocities. In the center-of-mass frame of the wheel, the axle of the wheel is at rest and the edges are moving with a speed $v = R|\omega|$, where R is the radius of the wheel and ω is its angular velocity. (The absolute value sign is necessary because the speed v is by definition positive, but ω may not be.) If the ground is in contact with the wheel and there is no slippage at the interface, then the ground must move at the same speed v. In the rest frame of the ground, therefore, the axle of the wheel must be moving at speed

$$\boxed{v = \pm R|\omega|.}$$

As we saw in Chapter 5, the kinetic energy of an arbitrary system of particles can be conveniently decomposed into contributions from the center-of-mass motion and from the motion about the center of mass:

$$K_{tot} = \frac{1}{2}M_{tot}v_{cm}^2 + \sum_i \frac{1}{2}m_i\left(\vec{v}_i - \vec{v}_{cm}\right)^2.$$

Warning — Difficult Material

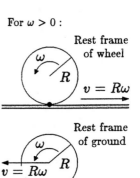

For $\omega > 0$:

Rest frame of wheel

$v = R\omega$

Rest frame of ground

$v = R\omega$

Specializing this relation to the motion of a rigid body, it becomes

$$K_{\text{tot}} = \frac{1}{2} M_{\text{tot}} v_{\text{cm}}^2 + \frac{1}{2} I_{\text{cm}} \omega^2 ,$$

Problems 8E.5, 8E.8, 10.10

rigid body KE rotational kinetic energy i.e. the sum of the *translational* kinetic energy of the body taken as a point mass and the *rotational* kinetic energy about an axis through the center of mass.

Apart from rotational kinetic energy, the new concepts in this chapter (i.e., angular velocity, angular acceleration, torque, and angular momentum) are analogous to *vector* quantities in linear motion, and we shall see in the next chapter that they are indeed vectors. We can treat them as scalars for the special case of rotation about an axis of fixed orientation, just as we can treat force and velocity as scalars when dealing with motion in a straight line. To solve more complicated problems in three dimensions, we will need to treat all of these quantities as vectors, as will be discussed in the next chapter.

To apply the techniques of this chapter, we frequently need to calculate I for the body and axis of interest. In many cases we might know or be able to calculate the moment of inertia about some other axis, so it is useful to know how the moments of inertia about different axes are related. One useful relation is the *parallel-axis theorem*, which relates the moment of inertia I_{cm} about any axis through the center of mass to the moment of inertia $I_\parallel$ about any axis parallel to the first:

$$I_\parallel = I_{\text{cm}} + M d^2 ,$$

Problems 8D.2, 8E.3, and 8E.4

where M is the mass of the object and d is the distance between the two axes. Md^2 is simply the moment of inertia about the $I_\parallel$ axis of a single point particle at the center of mass of the body, so this formula is very similar to the one for the kinetic energy of a system of particles.

Another useful relation is the *perpendicular-axis theorem*, which applies to bodies in the shape of a flat sheet, such as a sheet of paper or a compact disc. If we define a Cartesian coordinate system for which the object lies in the xy-plane, then the moments of inertia about the three axes are related by

$$I_z = I_x + I_y ,$$

Problems 8C.3, 8C.4, and 8C.5

where I_z is the moment of inertia about the z-axis, etc.

TABLE OF STANDARD MOMENTS OF INERTIA

The moment of inertia of any arbitrary rigid body or system of rigid bodies about any axis can always be calculated from the definition, $I = \sum_i m_i R_i^2$, generalizing the sum to an integral if necessary. The integration, however, can be quite complicated, so for convenience the following table contains the moments of inertia of some simple objects (each with mass m) about various axes. More complicated shapes, or moments around different axes, can often be constructed from these using the parallel and perpendicular-axis theorems, along with the principle that the moment of inertia of a complicated system is equal to the sum of the moments of inertia of its parts (all taken about the same axis). In the following table the right-hand column is left as an exercise for you—the examples listed can be constructed from the values in the left-hand column.

Slender uniform rod of length ℓ, axis through center and perpendicular to axis of rod	$\frac{1}{12}m\ell^2$	Slender uniform rod of length ℓ, axis through one end and perpendicular to axis of rod	
Rectangular plate with dimensions $a \times b$, axis along one of the b edges	$\frac{1}{3}ma^2$	Rectangular plate with dimensions $a \times b$, axis through center and perpendicular to plate	
Thin-walled hollow cylinder of radius R, axis along axis of cylinder	mR^2	Thick-walled hollow cylinder of inner radius R_1 and outer R_2, axis along axis of cylinder	
Uniform solid cylinder of radius R, axis along axis of cylinder	$\frac{1}{2}mR^2$		
Thin-walled hollow sphere of radius R, axis through center	$\frac{2}{3}mR^2$		
Solid uniform sphere of radius R, axis through center	$\frac{2}{5}mR^2$		

SUMMARY

* A rigid body is an idealized version of a physical solid object in which the configuration of the body (i.e. the relative positions of its constituent atoms or molecules) is completely fixed. Such a body has only two possible forms of motion: translational motion (like that of a point particle) and rotation.

* Rotational motion in two dimensions is governed by a system of equations closely analogous to those we have already encountered for point-particle motion (Newton's laws and the work-energy theorem). The concepts of velocity, acceleration, mass, force, and momentum are replaced by analogous concepts of angular velocity, angular acceleration, moment of inertia, torque, and angular momentum.

* Angular momentum—defined for two-dimensional motion as the product of the angular velocity and the moment of inertia of the object about the rotation axis—is conserved for any closed system. Like the conservation of energy and momentum, the conservation of angular momentum is believed to be an exact principle of nature, with a validity extending beyond that of classical mechanics.

* Combined translational and rotational motion of a rigid body can also be described straightforwardly, provided that (1) the translation is confined to a plane, (2) the axis of rotation is perpendicular to that plane, and (3) the rotating body is symmetrical about an axis parallel to the axis of rotation. If all three conditions are met, then the motion is two-dimensional. (Two-dimensional motion is actually possible under more general conditions, but their description is beyond the scope of this book.) The acceleration of the center of mass is equal to the total external force divided by the total mass; the angular acceleration is equal to the total external torque about the axis through the center of mass and parallel to the rotation axis, divided by the moment of inertia about this center-of-mass axis.

* Physical concepts introduced in this chapter: rigid body; angular velocity, angular acceleration, rotational kinetic energy, moment of inertia, torque, angular momentum.

* Mathematical concepts introduced in this chapter: none (but you should be sure that you understand the use of radians in measuring angles).

* Equations introduced in this chapter:

Most of the equations in this chapter are most easily remembered in the context of the analogous equations for linear motion in one dimension. These are tabulated on the following page.

Other equations introduced in this chapter:

$$v_r = 0 \; ; \quad v_\perp = R\omega \qquad \text{(velocity of point on rotating body)};$$

$$a_r = -\frac{v^2}{R} = -R\omega^2 \; ; \quad a_\perp = R\alpha \quad \text{(acceleration of point on rotating body)};$$

$$v = \pm R|\omega| \qquad \text{(rolling without slipping)};$$

$$\left. \begin{array}{l} \displaystyle\sum \vec{\mathbf{F}}^{\text{ext}} = M\vec{\mathbf{a}}_{\text{cm}} = \frac{d\vec{\mathbf{p}}}{dt} \\[3mm] \displaystyle\sum \tau^{\text{ext}} = I_{\text{cm}}\alpha = \frac{dL}{dt} \end{array} \right\} \quad \text{(combined translational and rotational motion)};$$

$$K_{\text{tot}} = \tfrac{1}{2}Mv_{\text{cm}}^2 + \tfrac{1}{2}I_{\text{cm}}\omega^2 \qquad \text{(kinetic energy for combined translational and rotational motion)};$$

$$I_{\parallel} = I_{\text{cm}} + Md^2 \qquad \text{(parallel-axis theorem)};$$

$$I_z = I_x + I_y \qquad \text{(perpendicular-axis theorem)}.$$

TRANSLATION (one dimension)		ROTATION (about fixed axis)	
Name	Symbol	Name	Symbol
Position	x	Orientation	θ
Velocity	$v = \dfrac{dx}{dt}$	Angular velocity	$\omega = \dfrac{d\theta}{dt}$
Acceleration	$a = \dfrac{dv}{dt}$	Angular acceleration	$\alpha = \dfrac{d\omega}{dt}$
Mass	$M = \displaystyle\sum_i m_i$	Moment of inertia	$I = \displaystyle\sum_i m_i R_i^2$
Force	F	Torque	$\tau = F_{\perp}R$ $= \pm|\vec{\mathbf{F}}|R_{\perp}$
Force equation	$\displaystyle\sum_i \vec{\mathbf{F}}^{\text{ext}} = M\vec{\mathbf{a}}_{\text{cm}}$	Torque equation	$\displaystyle\sum_i \tau^{\text{ext}} = I\alpha$
Momentum	$p = Mv$	Angular momentum	$L = I\omega$
Kinetic energy	$\tfrac{1}{2}Mv^2$	Kinetic energy	$\tfrac{1}{2}I\omega^2$
Work done	$\vec{\mathbf{F}} \cdot \vec{\Delta \mathbf{r}}$	Work done	$\tau\,\Delta\theta$

PROBLEMS AND QUESTIONS

By the end of this chapter you should be able to answer or solve the types of questions or problems stated below.

Note: throughout this book, in multiple-choice problems, the answers have been rounded off to 2 significant figures, unless otherwise stated.

At the end of the chapter there are answers to all the problems. In addition, for problems with an (H) or (S) after the number, there are respectively hints on how to solve the problems or completely worked-out solutions.

8A **ANGULAR MOTION**

8A.1 At the start of play, a compact disc is spinning at about 700 revolutions per minute; by the end of the disc, one hour later, it has slowed to 200 revolutions per minute. What is its average angular acceleration?

(a) -8.3 rad/s^2; (b) -0.0023 rad/s^2; (c) -0.87 rad/s^2; (d) none of these.

If the angular acceleration is *constant*, what is the total angle through which any point on the CD has turned during the hour? .

(a) 2.7×10^4 rad; (b) 1.7×10^5 rad; (c) 9.7×10^6 rad; (d) none of these.

8A.2 (S) (a) Since the concepts of radial and tangential directions are used so frequently in describing rotational motion, it is sometimes useful to define unit vectors in these directions. These unit vectors are peculiar, however, because their directions depend upon the position of the particle under discussion. For a particle located in the xy-plane at an angle θ counterclockwise from the x-axis, a unit vector in the radial direction can be written as

$$\hat{r}(\theta) = [\cos\theta, \sin\theta, 0] \ .$$

Find the corresponding expression for the unit (counter-clockwise) tangential vector $\hat{u}_\perp(\theta)$.

(b) Show that the derivatives of these unit vectors are given by

$$\frac{d\hat{r}(\theta)}{d\theta} = \hat{u}_\perp(\theta)$$

$$\frac{d\hat{u}_\perp(\theta)}{d\theta} = -\hat{r}(\theta) \ .$$

(c) Use these results to prove the formula given in the *Essentials* for the acceleration of a particle on a rigid body rotating about a fixed axis. Specifically, show that the radial and tangential components of the acceleration are given, respectively, by $a_r = -v^2/R = -R\omega^2$ and $a_\perp = R\alpha$, where ω is the angular velocity, α is the angular acceleration, and R is the distance of the particle from the axis of rotation.

280

8B TORQUE ABOUT AN AXIS

8B.1   The handle of a door is 1 m from its hinged side. You apply a force of 20 N to the door handle, pulling at right angles to the door. What is the torque about the axis through the door hinges?

(a) 20 N; (b) 20 N · m; (c) no net torque; (d) none of these.

8B.2 (H)   Calculate the net torque in each of the following cases about a fixed axis perpendicular to the page and passing through the indicated black dot. (Assume you are looking down on the xy-plane, so counterclockwise torques are positive.)

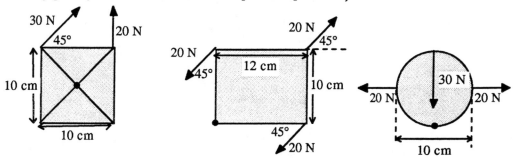

8C MOMENT OF INERTIA

8C.1 (S)   A binary star system consists of two stars, one of mass 2×10^{30} kg and one of mass 3×10^{30} kg, separated by 1.5×10^{14} m. Find the moment of inertia of this system about an axis through its center of mass and perpendicular to the line joining the two stars.

8C.2   A point mass M_A is connected to a point mass M_B by a rod of length ℓ and negligible mass. It is observed that the ratio of the moments of inertia of the system about the two axes AA and BB, which are parallel to each other and perpendicular to the rod, is

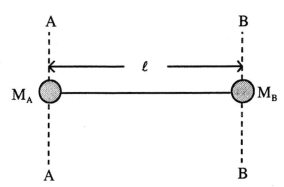

$$\frac{I_{\mathrm{BB}}}{I_{\mathrm{AA}}} = 3 \;.$$

The distance of the center of mass of the system from mass M_A is:

(a) $3\ell/4$; (b) $2\ell/3$; (c) $\ell/2$; (d) $\ell/3$; (e) $\ell/4$; (f) $\ell/9$.

8C.3 (S)   Prove the parallel-axis and perpendicular-axis theorems—i.e. (a) prove that the moment of inertia of a rigid body of mass M about an axis through its center of mass is related to the moment of inertia $I_\|$ about any axis parallel to the first by the formula $I_\| = I_{\mathrm{cm}} + Md^2$, where d is the distance between the two axes; and (b) prove that for a thin flat object in the xy-plane, the moment of inertia about the z-axis is equal to the sum of the moments of inertia about the x- and y-axes.

8C.4 (S) Calculate the moments of inertia of (a) a thin rod about an axis through its center and perpendicular to the rod; (b) a thin flat disk about an axis through its center and perpendicular to its plane; (c) a solid sphere about any diameter. Then deduce the moments of inertia of (d) a thin rod about an axis at one end; (e) a thin flat disk about any diameter; (f) a hollow spherical shell. Assume all the objects are of uniform density and each has mass M.

8C.5 (H) Calculate the moment of inertia of the following shapes about the specified axes (shown by a thick line). In each case assume that the object in question is a thin sheet of mass M. Note that you do *not* need to do any integration to solve this problem (but you do need the table at the end of the *Essentials*).

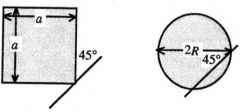

If I apply a torque τ with respect to the specified axis to each of these objects, what will be the angular acceleration in each case?

8D ROTATIONAL KINETIC ENERGY AND ANGULAR MOMENTUM ABOUT AN AXIS

8D.1 The Earth's moment of inertia about its axis of rotation is known to be 8.1×10^{37} kg · m². What is the Earth's rotational kinetic energy as a result of its spinning around its axis? (Neglect the effects of the Earth's orbit around the Sun.)

(a) 2.1×10^{29} J; (b) 4.2×10^{29} J; (c) 3.4×10^{28} J; (d) 4.2×10^{33} J.

8D.2 (H) A ruler of mass m, length ℓ and width w has a hole drilled in it a short distance x from one end and equidistant from both sides. It is anchored on a frictionless air table by a nail driven through the hole and is then set rotating about the nail such that its far end (a distance $\ell - x$ from the hole) is moving with (linear) speed v. Obtain expressions for the rotational kinetic energy K and angular momentum L of the ruler with respect to the axis through the nail. Calculate the values of K and L if the ruler is 35 cm long, 2 cm wide and has a mass of 50 g, the hole is 1 cm from one end, and the other end is moving at 0.2 m/s.

8D.3 Suppose that a long thin rod, of mass M and length ℓ, is suspended horizontally from a stiff wire, with the wire passing through the midpoint of the rod, and the rod is then rotated by an angle θ about the axis formed by the wire. It is found experimentally that a wire twisted in this way exerts a restoring torque $\tau = -K\theta$, where K is a constant, so the rod will undergo simple harmonic motion, forming a *torsion pendulum*. Let θ_m denote the amplitude of the oscillations.

(a) Find the period of the oscillations.

(b) What is (i) the rotational kinetic energy, and (ii) the angular momentum, of the rod at the point when it reaches its maximum angular speed?

8D.3, continued:

(c) If I cut the rod down to three-quarters of its original length and re-hang it, what will the new period be? (Assume that the wire still passes through the center of the reduced rod, and express your answer in terms of the original values of K, M and ℓ.)

8E   ROTATION OF A RIGID BODY ABOUT AN AXIS

8E.1 (S)   A children's playground contains a circular merry-go-round of radius 2 m. One afternoon, three children are sitting on the merry-go-round while three of their friends push its rim to make it revolve. The positions of the children and the forces they apply are shown on the diagram. What is the net torque on the merry-go-round, and what would its acceleration be in the absence of friction, given that the merry-go-round itself is a uniform disk of mass 200 kg and Alfredo, Betty and Chris have masses 30, 40 and 25 kg respectively?

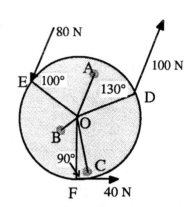

8E.2   Find the torque about the specified axis in each of the following situations, given that the force is 20 N in each case, the rod is 10 cm long, and the fixed axis is perpendicular to the page and passes through the black dot. If the mass of the rod is 0.5 kg, also find the angular acceleration.

OA = 1.5 m, OB = 0.7 m, OC = 1.8 m

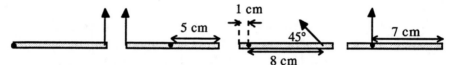

8E.3 (S)   A ceiling fan consists of four blades arranged in a cross. Each blade has mass 2 kg and is one meter long and 10 cm wide, and is connected to the central spindle of the fan by a rod of length 10 cm and negligible mass. The fan rotates at a steady rate of 30 revolutions per minute. What is its kinetic energy and its angular momentum? If it takes 10 s to reach this speed when switched on, what is the average net torque delivered by the motor during this period, and how much work is done?

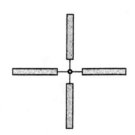

8E.4 (H)   The ruler of problem 8D.2, with length ℓ, width w and mass m, is suspended by a rod passing through the hole x from one end, which thus forms a fixed axis perpendicular to the plane of the ruler. If the ruler is held so that it makes an angle of θ to the vertical and then released, what is the torque acting on it, and what is its angular acceleration? Could such an arrangement be used as a pendulum (i.e. will it undergo simple harmonic motion)?

8E.5 (S)   You are on a camping trip in a rural district. Your water supply comes from a well, and is obtained by hauling up a large bucket using a windlass, i.e. a cylindrical spindle turned by a handle. You have just hauled a full bucket of water, mass 15 kg, the 10

8E.5, continued:

m from the water surface to ground level (at negligible speed) when your hand slips off the windlass handle.

(a) If the windlass is a solid cylinder of mass 20 kg and radius 12 cm, how fast is it spinning when the bucket hits the water? Neglect the mass of the rope and the friction in the bearings of the windlass, take $g = 9.8$ m/s^2, and assume the rope does not slip.

(b) What was the tension in the rope while the bucket was falling, and how long did the fall take?

8E.6 (H) Masses m_1 and m_2 are connected by a light string passing over a pulley as shown. The pulley is a solid uniform disk of mass M and radius R, and the friction between it and the rope is such that when the blocks move the rope turns the pulley without slipping. The friction between the blocks and the slopes is negligible and the rope does not stretch. Find the accelerations of both masses and the angular acceleration of the pulley.

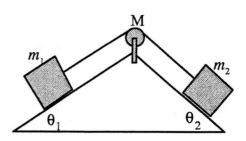

8E.7 (S) (a) A rigid body of unspecified shape is allowed to pivot freely about a horizontal axis through its center of mass. The only force acting is gravity. Show that there is no net torque.

(b) Hence show that the net force of gravity on a rigid body can always be regarded as acting through the center of mass—i.e., the torque it exerts about any horizontal axis is the same as if the total force acted at the center of mass.

8E.8 (S) A rigid body of mass M and having a circular cross-section of radius R rolls without slipping down a slope making an angle θ to the horizontal. The moment of inertia of the body about its central axis of symmetry is kMR^2, where k is a numerical constant.

(a) What is its speed when it has descended through a vertical distance h?

(b) What is the minimum coefficient of static friction required to ensure that it rolls, rather than slides, down the slope?

8E.9 A group of children are playing a game involving rolling an assortment of objects down a slope. The objects include a solid uniform rubber ball, a thin hoop, a solid uniform cylindrical log, a spherical leather soccer ball, essentially all of whose mass is in its leather cover rather than its interior, and a discarded wheel from a toy cart, which has the form of a solid disk of radius R with a central hole of radius $R/2$. All the objects roll without slipping down the slope.

(a) The slope has length ℓ and is at an angle of θ to the horizontal. How long does each object take to reach the bottom? Assume all the objects are small compared to ℓ.

(b) Your little sister is desperate to win this game. Suggest an object that you could make for her which would complete the course faster than any of those currently in play.

8E.5, continued:

8E.10   You are helping out at a local auto mechanic's shop, and he asks you to fetch a truck tire from the store. The tire has a mass of 30 kg, divided equally between its outer tread (which has a diameter of 90 cm) and its sidewalls (which have an inner radius of 30 cm). You roll the tire across the level shop floor at a speed of 1.5 m/s.

(a) From the description, we can model the tire as a thin cylinder of diameter 90 cm and mass 15 kg, and two disks each with outer diameter 90 cm, inner diameter 60 cm, and mass 7.5 kg. Using this model, calculate the work that you did in accelerating the tire from rest to 1.5 m/s.

(b) What impulse did you supply to the tire? If it took you 4 s to reach your final speed, what average torque did you exert?

COMPLETE SOLUTIONS TO PROBLEMS WITH AN (S)

8A.2   (a) *Since the concepts of radial and tangential directions are used so frequently in describing rotational motion, it is sometimes useful to define unit vectors in these directions. These unit vectors are peculiar, however, because their directions depend upon the position of the particle under discussion. For a particle located in the xy-plane at an angle θ counterclockwise from the x-axis, a unit vector in the radial direction can be written as*

$$\hat{r}(\theta) = [\cos\theta, \sin\theta, 0] \ .$$

Find the corresponding expression for the unit (counter-clockwise) tangential vector $\hat{u}_{\perp}(\theta)$.

(b) *Show that the derivatives of these unit vectors are given by*

$$\frac{d\hat{r}(\theta)}{d\theta} = \hat{u}_{\perp}(\theta)$$

$$\frac{d\hat{u}_{\perp}(\theta)}{d\theta} = -\hat{r}(\theta) \ .$$

(c) *Use these results to prove the formula given in the **Essentials** for the acceleration of a particle on a rigid body rotating about a fixed axis. Specifically, show that the radial and tangential components of the acceleration are given, respectively, by $a_r = -v^2/R = -R\omega^2$ and $a_{\perp} = R\alpha$, where ω is the angular velocity, α is the angular acceleration, and R is the distance of the particle from the axis of rotation.*

Conceptualize

In this case the questioner has been helpful, breaking up the problem into relatively small steps. One can view part (c) as being the main question, in which case parts (a) and (b) can be construed as the "Formulate" steps in answering it.

One can seek an expression for $\hat{u}_{\perp}$ with either a geometric approach, by drawing a careful diagram, or with an algebraic approach, by seeking a unit vector which has a vanishing dot product with $\hat{r}$. To distinguish counterclockwise from clockwise, however, it seems that at least a crude diagram is necessary. Here we will use the geometric approach, but we will verify that the answer has the right algebraic properties. By the time we reach parts (b) and (c), each result will follow from the previous results by straightforward calculus, so diagrams will no longer be necessary.

8A.2, continued:

Formulate and Solve (a)

From the diagram it seems obvious that $\theta' = \theta$. One can prove it by first noticing that θ and ϕ are two angles of a right triangle, so ϕ is the complement of θ (i.e., $\phi = 90° - \theta$); then notice that ϕ, θ', and a right angle meet to form a straight angle (180°), so θ' is the complement of ϕ, and hence $\theta' = \theta$. One can then see that the horizontal and vertical components of $\hat{\boldsymbol{u}}_\perp$ are $-\sin\theta$ and $\cos\theta$, so

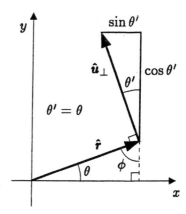

$$\hat{\boldsymbol{u}}_\perp = [-\sin\theta, \cos\theta, 0] .$$

(If you are still having difficulty distinguishing the sine from the cosine, a practical technique is to always draw your angles noticeably smaller than 45°, as was done here. Then the short side of the triangle is always proportional to the sine, and the long side is proportional to the cosine.)

Scrutinize (a)

One can easily check that the expression for $\hat{\boldsymbol{u}}_\perp$ has unit length,

$$\big|[-\sin\theta, \cos\theta, 0]\big|^2 = \sin^2\theta + \cos^2\theta = 1,$$

and that it is perpendicular (i.e., has zero dot product) with $\hat{\boldsymbol{r}}$:

$$\hat{\boldsymbol{u}}_\perp \cdot \hat{\boldsymbol{r}} = [-\sin\theta, \cos\theta, 0] \cdot [\cos\theta, \sin\theta, 0] = -\sin\theta\cos\theta + \cos\theta\sin\theta = 0 .$$

However, these checks do not test whether $\hat{\boldsymbol{u}}_\perp$ is counterclockwise or clockwise. To get that right we need to think about the diagram. If θ is in the first quadrant (i.e., $0 < \theta < \pi/2$), then a counterclockwise vector should have a horizontal component to the left, which means the negative x-direction. Since the first component of our expression for $\hat{\boldsymbol{u}}_\perp$ is negative, we must have this right.

Formulate and Solve (b)

Since we have an explicit component expression for the vectors, we can proceed by differentiating the components:

$$\frac{\mathrm{d}\hat{\boldsymbol{r}}(\theta)}{\mathrm{d}\theta} = \frac{\mathrm{d}}{\mathrm{d}\theta}[\cos\theta, \sin\theta, 0]$$

$$= [-\sin\theta, \cos\theta, 0] = \hat{\boldsymbol{u}}_\perp .$$

Similarly,

$$\frac{\mathrm{d}\hat{\boldsymbol{u}}_\perp(\theta)}{\mathrm{d}\theta} = \frac{\mathrm{d}}{\mathrm{d}\theta}[-\sin\theta, \cos\theta, 0]$$

$$= [-\cos\theta, -\sin\theta, 0] = -\hat{\boldsymbol{r}} .$$

8A.2, continued:

Scrutinize (b)

You may have noticed that in both cases ($\hat{r}$ and $\hat{u}_\perp$), the derivative of the unit vector with respect to θ is perpendicular to the original unit vector. In fact, it can be shown that differentiation of any *unit* vector, with respect to any parameter, always produces a vector that is perpendicular to the original unit vector. To see this, let $\hat{u}(\lambda)$ represent an arbitrary unit vector that depends on some parameter called λ. Since $\hat{u}$ is assumed to be a unit vector for all values of λ, we can write

$$\hat{u}(\lambda) \cdot \hat{u}(\lambda) = 1 \ ,$$

which we can differentiate to find

$$\frac{d}{d\lambda} \{\hat{u}(\lambda) \cdot \hat{u}(\lambda)\} = \frac{d}{d\lambda} 1 \ ,$$

which implies

$$2\hat{u} \cdot \frac{d\hat{u}}{d\lambda} = 0 \ .$$

Thus $\hat{u}$ is perpendicular to $d\hat{u}/d\lambda$.

Formulate (c)

The particle on the rigid body lies at a distance R from the fixed axis of rotation, and we can call its z-coordinate z. We can then describe its position completely by specifying at any time the angle $\theta(t)$ of its x- and y- coordinates in the xy-plane, measured counterclockwise from the x-axis. Specifically, the position vector $\vec{r}(t)$ describing the trajectory of the particle can be written as

$$\vec{r}(t) = [0, 0, z] + R\,\hat{r}\big(\theta(t)\big) \ .$$

Given this expression, we will be able to find the velocity and acceleration by straightforward differentiation.

Solve (c)

To differentiate the expression above, one notices that the only time dependence appears in $\theta(t)$. Using the chain rule for differentiating a function of a function,

$$\vec{v}(t) = \frac{d\vec{r}(t)}{dt} = \frac{d}{dt}\left\{[0, 0, z] + R\,\hat{r}\big(\theta(t)\big)\right\}$$

$$= R\frac{d\hat{r}}{d\theta}\frac{d\theta}{dt} = R\,\hat{u}_\perp(\theta)\,\omega(t) = R\,\omega(t)\,\hat{u}_\perp(\theta) \ .$$

Differentiating again, using the product rule and once more the chain rule,

$$\vec{a}(t) = \frac{d\vec{v}(t)}{dt} = \frac{d}{dt}\{R\,\omega(t)\,\hat{u}_\perp(\theta)\}$$

$$= R\omega\frac{d\hat{u}_\perp(\theta)}{dt} + R\frac{d\omega(t)}{dt}\hat{u}_\perp = R\omega\frac{d\hat{u}_\perp}{d\theta}\frac{d\theta}{dt} + R\alpha\,\hat{u}_\perp = -R\omega^2\,\hat{r} + R\alpha\,\hat{u}_\perp \ .$$

8A.2, continued:

This verifies the final result, except to check that the radial acceleration can also be written as $-v^2/R$. By using $v = |\vec{v}| = R\omega$ from the intermediate result, however, it is easy to see that $-v^2/R = -(R\omega)^2/R = -R\omega^2$.

Scrutinize (c)

The result for the acceleration is reasonable, since we have known for some time that particles in uniform circular motion have an acceleration toward the origin of magnitude v^2/R. The new piece $R\alpha\hat{\boldsymbol{u}}_\perp$ arises when ω is not constant, in which case we would expect a contribution to the acceleration related to the rate of change of the tangential velocity.

Learn

While the results of parts (a) and (b) of this question were used as intermediate steps toward the goal of finding the answer to (c), they are also valuable results in themselves. For example, if we wanted to plot the trajectory of a particle on a rolling wheel, we would probably want to use the vectors $\hat{\boldsymbol{r}}(\theta)$ and $\hat{\boldsymbol{u}}_\perp(\theta)$, and the properties derived here.

8C.1

A binary star system consists of two stars, one of mass 2×10^{30} kg and one of mass 3×10^{30} kg, separated by 1.5×10^{14} m. Find the moment of inertia of this system about an axis through its center of mass and perpendicular to the line joining the two stars.

Conceptualize

We can treat the stars as point masses, since they are small compared to their separation. (The radius of the Sun, for example, is 7×10^8 m.) To solve the problem we must first find the center of mass, and then find the moment of inertia of each star about this axis. Adding these will give us the total moment of inertia. For convenience we can choose an x-axis which goes through both of the stars, and we can even arrange for the origin ($x = 0$) to be located at the center of mass.

Formulate

The position x_{cm} of the center of mass of two bodies, one with mass m_1 at position x_1 and the other with mass m_2 at position x_2, is given by

$$x_{\text{cm}} = \frac{m_1 x_1 + m_2 x_2}{m_1 + m_2} .$$

By choosing the origin to lie at the center of mass, we require the condition

$$m_1 x_1 + m_2 x_2 = 0 .$$

Using ℓ to denote the separation between the stars, the relation above can be combined with

$$\ell = x_2 - x_1$$

to obtain a pair of equations that can be solved for the two unknowns, x_1 and x_2. Since x_1 and x_2 are the distances of the two stars from the axis of rotation, the moment of inertia is then given by

$$I = \sum_{i=1}^{2} m_i x_i^2 = m_1 x_1^2 + m_2 x_2^2 .$$

289

8C.1, continued:

Solve
Solving the pair of equations for x_1 and x_2, one finds

$$x_1 = -\frac{m_2}{m_1 + m_2}\ell \quad \text{and} \quad x_2 = \frac{m_1}{m_1 + m_2}\ell \,.$$

The next step is to insert these expressions into the equation for I and then simplify, with the result

$$I = \frac{m_1 m_2}{m_1 + m_2}\ell^2 \,.$$

Numerically, this gives

$$I = \frac{(2 \times 10^{30} \text{ kg})(3 \times 10^{30} \text{ kg})}{(2 + 3) \times 10^{30} \text{ kg}} \times (1.5 \times 10^{14} \text{ m})^2$$

$$= 2.7 \times 10^{58} \text{ kg} \cdot \text{m}^2 \,.$$

Scrutinize
The dimensions of I are [mass]×[length]^2, as can be seen from its definition. The answer approaches zero as either of the two masses approaches zero, which is a property that we might have foreseen: if one mass vanishes, then the distance of the center of mass from the other mass is zero, and hence the moment of inertia is zero.

Learn
This example is fairly straightforward, but note that *any* calculation of I uses exactly the same principles. The quantity $m_1 m_2/(m_1 + m_2)$ appears so often in problems involving two-body systems that it is given a name: the *reduced mass*.

8C.3 *Prove the parallel-axis and perpendicular-axis theorems—i.e. (a) prove that the moment of inertia of a rigid body of mass M about an axis through its center of mass is related to the moment of inertia $I_\parallel$ about any axis parallel to the first by the formula $I_\parallel = I_{\rm cm} + Md^2$, where d is the distance between the two axes; and (b) prove that for a thin flat object in the xy-plane, the moment of inertia about the z-axis is equal to the sum of the moments of inertia about the x- and y-axes.*

Conceptualize
The moment of inertia of a rigid body about a specified axis is defined as $I = \sum_i m_i R_i^2$, where R_i is the distance of the mass element m_i from the axis. To discuss the parallel axis theorem, we will call the axis through the center of mass $N_{\rm cm}$, and we will call the other axis $N_\parallel$. To prove the theorem, we will need to re-express the distance of the mass element m_i from the $N_\parallel$ axis in terms of its distance from the $N_{\rm cm}$ axis; for the perpendicular-axis theorem, we need the distance from the z-axis in terms of the distances from the x- and y-axes.

Formulate (a)
For the parallel-axis theorem, it is easiest to choose a coordinate system with the origin at the center of mass, and with the z-axis coincident with the axis $N_{\rm cm}$. The moment of inertia about this axis is then given by

$$I_{\rm cm} = \sum_i m_i R_i^2 = \sum_i m_i(x_i^2 + y_i^2) \,.$$

8C.3, continued:

The condition that the center of mass lies at $x_{\text{cm}} = y_{\text{cm}} = 0$ can be expressed as

$$x_{\text{cm}} = \frac{1}{M_{\text{tot}}} \sum_i m_i x_i = 0$$

$$y_{\text{cm}} = \frac{1}{M_{\text{tot}}} \sum_i m_i y_i = 0 .$$

The axis $N_\parallel$ is parallel to the z-axis, so it can be described by its x- and y-coordinates, $x_\parallel$ and $y_\parallel$. Since $N_\parallel$ is a distance d from the center of mass, it follows that

$$x_\parallel^2 + y_\parallel^2 = d^2 .$$

If we let R_i' denote the distance between the mass element m_i and the $N_\parallel$ axis, the moment of inertia about this axis can be written

$$I_\parallel = \sum_i m_i R_i'^2 = \sum_i m_i \left[(x_i - x_\parallel)^2 + (y_i - y_\parallel)^2 \right] .$$

Solve (a)
Expanding the expression above for $I_\parallel$,

$$I_\parallel = \sum_i m_i \left[x_i^2 + y_i^2 - 2x_\parallel x_i - 2y_\parallel y_i + \left(x_\parallel^2 + y_\parallel^2 \right) \right]$$

$$= \sum_i m_i \left(x_i^2 + y_i^2 \right) - 2x_\parallel \sum_i m_i x_i - 2y_\parallel \sum_i m_i y_i + \left(x_\parallel^2 + y_\parallel^2 \right) \sum_i m_i .$$

The first term on the right-hand side is I_{cm}, while the second and third terms vanish due to the center of mass condition written above. The final term can be written as Md^2, so we have the sought-after result:

$$I_\parallel = I_{\text{cm}} + Md^2 .$$

Formulate (b)
The perpendicular-axis theorem is easier to prove. Since the object lies entirely in the xy-plane, the distance of a mass element m_i from the x-axis is $|y_i|$, and the distance from the y-axis is $|x_i|$. The distance of the mass element from the z-axis is $\sqrt{x_i^2 + y_i^2}$.

Solve (b)
Given the distance relationships discussed in the paragraph above, it is straightforward to see that

$$I_z = \sum_i m_i R_i^2 = \sum_i m_i (x_i^2 + y_i^2) = \sum_i m_i x_i^2 + \sum_i m_i y_i^2 = I_y + I_x ,$$

291

8C.3, continued:

which is the desired result.

Scrutinize

Although these proofs were written in terms of a summation over a set of discrete mass elements m_i, they could easily be extended to describe continuous bodies. The sums would then be replaced by integrations, but the proofs would be otherwise unchanged. Since an integral can be defined as the limit of a summation, all the necessary properties of summations are valid for integrals as well.

Learn

These formulas are useful because one often knows the moment of inertia of an object about one axis, but wants to know it about another. In particular, tables of moments of inertia, such as the one at the end of the *Essentials,* cannot possibly list the values of all possible axes. By using the parallel and perpendicular axis theorems, the applicability of such tables can be dramatically increased.

While the parallel and perpendicular axis theorems are very useful, please bear in mind their limitations:

- The perpendicular-axis theorem is only valid for an object in the form of a thin flat sheet, with two of the axes in the plane of the sheet and the third one perpendicular to it. The origin can be anywhere in the plane of the sheet.

- The parallel-axis theorem is only valid if one of the axes passes through the center of mass. Note, however, that as long as you know where the center of mass is, you can use the parallel axis theorem to relate the moments of inertia about any two axes that are parallel to each other. To do this, simply use the parallel axis theorem twice, relating each of the given axes to the axis which is parallel to both and runs through the center of mass.

8C.4   *Calculate the moments of inertia of (a) a thin rod about an axis through its center and perpendicular to the rod; (b) a thin flat disk about an axis through its center and perpendicular to its plane; (c) a solid sphere about any diameter. Then deduce the moments of inertia of (d) a thin rod about an axis at one end; (e) a thin flat disk about any diameter; (f) a hollow spherical shell. Assume all the objects are of uniform density and each has mass M.*

Conceptualize

These are applications of the basic formulas for calculating a moment of inertia. As solid objects are involved, we will first have to consider how to express the sum over discrete masses as an integral over volume—these are not *conceptually* different, but they do require different calculational techniques.

The wording of the question suggests that the last three cases can be solved without an explicit integration. Comparing (d) with (a), we can see that they satisfy the conditions for applying the parallel-axis theorem, while (b) and (e) have the appropriate geometry for the perpendicular-axis theorem. Although it is not immediately clear how to relate (f) and (c), a solid sphere can be built up from a series of concentric hollow shells, so

8C.4, continued:

the moment of inertia of a solid sphere is the sum of the moments of inertia of a series of shells.

Formulate

To convert our sum to an integral, we need to replace the 'mass m_i' at point i by a mass element dm and integrate over the whole mass:

$$I = \int_{\text{body}} R^2 dm \;,$$

where R is the distance of mass element dm from the axis of rotation. For a body of density ρ, dm is simply ρdV, where V is a volume element, so we have

$$I = \int_{\text{body}} \rho R^2 dV \;.$$

The choice of dV depends on the object, as can be seen in the examples.

Solve (a): *Thin rod about perpendicular axis through center:*

This is quite straightforward. We choose the x-axis running down the rod with its origin at the rod's center. Then the volume element we need is just $A dx$, where A is the (small) cross-sectional area of the rod, and we have

$$I = \int_{-\frac{\ell}{2}}^{\frac{\ell}{2}} \rho A x^2 dx \;,$$

where ℓ is the total length of the rod. The mass of the rod is $\rho A \ell$, and we conclude

$$I = \frac{1}{12} M \ell^2 \;.$$

Solve (b): *Thin flat disk about perpendicular axis through center:*

Choose as a volume element the ring of material at a distance between r and $r + dr$ from the center of the disk. The volume of this ring is $dV = 2\pi r z dr$, where z is the thickness of the disk. Our integral is therefore

$$I = 2\pi \rho z \int_0^R r^3 dr \;,$$

where R is the radius of the disk. This is a straightforward integration giving

$$I = \frac{1}{2} \pi \rho z R^4 \;.$$

The total mass M of the disk is $\pi R^2 z \rho$, so we can rewrite this as $I = \frac{1}{2} M R^2$. In fact this holds not just for a thin disk, but for any solid cylinder (we never had to use the fact that z is small). Note that in this case we choose our volume element deliberately

8C.4, continued:

so that we only have to integrate over a single variable r; if we had chosen a simpler volume element (the small piece of disk at coordinates (x, y), say), we would have had to do a much more complicated two-dimensional integral.

Solve (c): *Solid sphere about a diameter:*
Since the moment of inertia is basically a sum, we can break it into pieces, just as we did when calculating centers of mass. Thus we can regard our sphere as a stack of thin disks, each with radius r and moment of inertia $\frac{1}{2}\pi\rho r^4 dz$, where dz is the thickness of each disk. The moment of inertia of the whole sphere is then

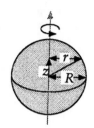

$$I = \int_{-R}^{R} \frac{1}{2}\pi\rho r^4 dz \ .$$

From the diagram, $r^2 = R^2 - z^2$, and thus the integral becomes

$$I = \frac{1}{2}\pi\rho \int_{-R}^{R} (R^4 - 2R^2 z^2 + z^4)dz \ ,$$

which comes to $\frac{8}{15}\pi\rho R^5$. The mass of the sphere is $M = \frac{4}{3}\pi\rho R^3$, so we can write this as $I = \frac{2}{5}MR^2$.

Solve (d): *Rod about one end:*
We want the parallel-axis theorem, since the moment of inertia we have already calculated is the one about the center of mass. It follows that

$$I_{\text{end}} = I_{\text{center}} + M(\ell/2)^2$$

$$= \frac{1}{12}M\ell^2 + \frac{1}{4}M\ell^2$$

$$= \frac{1}{3}M\ell^2 \ .$$

Solve (e): *Thin flat disk about diameter:*
This is an obvious candidate for the perpendicular-axis theorem. If we take a coordinate system with origin at the center of the disk and assume the disk lies in the xy-plane, we have

$$I_z = I_x + I_y \ .$$

We have just calculated I_z, and clearly I_x and I_y are both moments of inertia about a diameter of the disk. They must therefore be equal to each other (there is nothing about our uniform disk to distinguish any diameter from any other diameter) and so

$$I_x = I_y = \frac{1}{2}I_z = \frac{1}{4}MR^2 \ .$$

8C.4, continued:

<u>Solve</u> (f): *Hollow spherical shell about diameter:*
Because moments of inertia add, we can see that the moment of inertia of a sphere of radius $R + dR$ must be equal to the moment of inertia of a sphere of radius R plus that of a hollow spherical shell of radius R and thickness dR. Therefore

$$I_{\text{shell}} = \frac{8}{15}\pi\rho(R + dR)^5 - \frac{8}{15}\pi\rho R^5$$
$$= \frac{8}{15}\pi\rho\, 5R^4 dR \ ,$$

where we have ignored terms involving higher powers of dR (for a thin shell, $dR/R \ll 1$, so $R^3(dR)^2 \ll R^4 dR$ and so on). The mass of the shell is $M = 4\pi\rho R^2 dR$, so we can write the moment of inertia as $I_{\text{shell}} = \frac{2}{3}MR^2$. We could of course have obtained this by direct integration, using rings as volume elements, but the method used above is much easier once we have already done the solid sphere.

<u>Scrutinize</u>
Observe that, as we would expect from dimensional arguments, all the moments of inertia are of the form kMR^2, where k is a dimensionless constant and R is some characteristic length. However, the *values* of k vary quite significantly. For a given torque about the specified axis, which of these objects would have the greatest angular acceleration?

<u>Learn</u>
These examples illustrate the techniques for calculating moments of inertia. See the table at the end of the *Essentials* for a list of moments of inertia for some basic shapes about standard axes. More complicated objects can usually be built up using a combination of these with appropriate application of the parallel-axis and perpendicular-axis theorems.

8E.1   *A children's playground contains a circular merry-go-round of radius 2 m. One afternoon, three children are sitting on the merry-go-round while three of their friends push its rim to make it revolve. The positions of the children and the forces they apply are shown on the diagram. What is the net torque on the merry-go-round, and what would its acceleration be in the absence of friction, given that the merry-go-round itself is a uniform disk of mass 200 kg and Alfredo, Betty and Chris have masses 30, 40 and 25 kg respectively?*

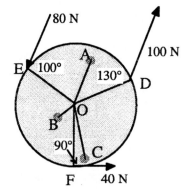

OA = 1.5 m, OB = 0.7 m,
OC = 1.8 m

8E.1, continued:

Conceptualize

There are three separate calculations in this problem. We have to determine the torque applied to the object consisting of merry-go-round plus children; calculate the moment of inertia of that object; and finally combine our results to find the angular acceleration.

The torque calculation is straightforward: we know the forces applied and the points of application, and the relevant axis is vertically through the center of the disk of the merry-go-round.

For the moment of inertia, we will have to add the moments of inertia of the merry-go-round (which is a uniform disk) and the children. We are not told the dimensions of the children, but we saw above that moments of inertia around the center of mass take the form kMR^2, where k is usually less than one. Our children's masses are small compared to the mass of the merry-go-round, and their dimensions are at most comparable to its radius, so it is likely that the effect of each child's orientation is small compared to the overall moment of inertia of the system. Therefore, as a first approximation, we can treat them as point particles. We can come back and reconsider this later, when we have a feel for the numerical values involved.

Formulate

The torque exerted by a force about a specified axis is given by $FR\sin\theta$, where R is the distance between the point at which the force acts and the axis, and θ is the angle between $\vec{F}$ and $\vec{R}$, assuming that both vectors lie in the plane perpendicular to the axis.

The moment of inertia of a uniform disk about an axis through its center is $\frac{1}{2}MR^2$ (see table, or Problem 8C.4). For a point mass m a distance d from the axis, $I = md^2$.

The relation between torque and angular acceleration is $\tau = I\alpha$.

Solve

The torques exerted by our three forces about the central axis are

$$\tau_D = (100 \text{ N}) \times (2 \text{ m}) \times \sin 130° = 153 \text{ N} \cdot \text{m} \; ;$$

$$\tau_E = (80 \text{ N}) \times (2 \text{ m}) \times \sin 100° = 158 \text{ N} \cdot \text{m} \; ;$$

$$\tau_F = (40 \text{ N}) \times (2 \text{ m}) \times \sin 90° = 80 \text{ N} \cdot \text{m} \; .$$

All of these act to produce a counter-clockwise acceleration, so they all have the same sign and the total torque is 390 N · m.

The moment of inertia of the merry-go-round is

$$I_M = \frac{1}{2}MR^2 = (100 \text{ kg}) \times (2 \text{ m})^2 = 400 \text{ kg} \cdot \text{m}^2 \; ,$$

and the children each contribute md^2, i.e. 68, 20 and 81 kg · m² for Alfredo, Betty and Chris respectively. The total moment of inertia is therefore

$$I = 570 \text{ kg} \cdot \text{m}^2 \; .$$

8E.1, continued:

In the absence of friction, the angular acceleration is therefore

$$\alpha = (390 \text{ N} \cdot \text{m})/(570 \text{ kg} \cdot \text{m}^2) = 0.68 \text{ rad/s}^2 \ .$$

Scrutinize

How bad an approximation is it to treat the children as point particles? Let's try a slightly more precise calculation: assume Alfredo is standing upright, and treat him as a uniform cylinder of radius 15 cm. Then his moment of inertia about a vertical axis through his center of mass is $\frac{1}{2}mR^2 = (15 \text{ kg}) \times (0.15 \text{ m})^2 = 0.34 \text{ kg} \cdot \text{m}^2$, and by the parallel-axis theorem we add this to md^2 to get his total moment of inertia about the merry-go-round axis. Clearly it makes a negligible difference! If he is 1.2 m tall and he lies down, treating him as a thin rod gives him a moment of inertia about his center of mass of $\frac{1}{12}m\ell^2 = 3.6 \text{ kg} \cdot \text{m}^2$, which is still only a 5% correction to md^2. We conclude that it is entirely reasonable to treat the children as point particles in this problem.

8E.3

A ceiling fan consists of four blades arranged in a cross. Each blade has mass 2 kg, is one meter long and 10 cm wide, and is connected to the central spindle of the fan by a rod of length 10 cm and negligible mass. The fan rotates at a steady rate of 30 revolutions per minute. What is its kinetic energy and its angular momentum? If it takes 10 s to reach this speed when switched on, what is the average net torque delivered by the motor during this period, and how much work is done?

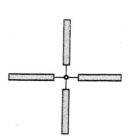

Conceptualize

We know ω, the angular velocity of the fan, and by dividing this by the time the fan takes to spin up we can find the average angular acceleration. To calculate rotational kinetic energy, angular momentum and torque, we also need the moment of inertia of the fan. We have its mass and dimensions, so in principle we can determine I directly by integration, but this looks hard, as the overall shape is quite complicated. Therefore, if possible, we should break the fan down into simpler shapes and use the parallel and/or perpendicular axis theorems to calculate I. The obvious breakdown is to treat each blade as a thin rectangular sheet, rotating about an axis perpendicular to the sheet and located 10 cm from one short side.

Formulate

The moment of inertia of the rectangular plate about an axis through the center of mass, in the plane of the plate, and parallel to the side of length a is $\frac{1}{12}Mb^2$ (both the result and the calculation are identical to problem 8C.4 (a)). The perpendicular-axis theorem says that to get the moment of inertia of the plate about a perpendicular axis through the center we simply add this to the corresponding value for an axis parallel to the b sides, giving $\frac{1}{12}M(a^2 + b^2)$.

This is the basic equation we need to solve this problem. We can apply the parallel-axis theorem to move the axis from the center of mass to the point we want, and then add the four blades together to make the whole fan.

297

8E.3, continued:

Solve

Applying the parallel-axis theorem:

$$I_{\text{blade}} = \frac{1}{12}M(a^2 + b^2) + Md^2 \ ,$$

and putting in the numbers gives us $I_{\text{blade}} = 0.888 \ \text{kg} \cdot \text{m}^2$. This is the moment of inertia for one blade; to find that of the whole fan we just multiply by four to get

$$I = 3.55 \ \text{kg} \cdot \text{m}^2 \ .$$

The angular velocity of the fan is $\omega = 2\pi \times (30 \ \text{rpm})/(60 \ \text{s/min}) = 3.14$ radians per second. Its kinetic energy is therefore $\frac{1}{2}I\omega^2 = 18$ J and its angular momentum $I\omega$ with respect to this axis of rotation is $11 \ \text{kg} \cdot \text{m}^2/\text{s}$.

If the fan takes 10 s to reach its final speed, the average torque dL/dt must be $(11 \ \text{kg} \cdot \text{m}^2/\text{s})/(10 \ \text{s})$, or $1.1 \ \text{N} \cdot \text{m}$. The work done is converted to the fan's kinetic energy, so (neglecting any frictional effects) 18 J of work (or 1.8 W of power) is required.

Scrutinize and Learn

We have cheated slightly in this problem by implicitly assuming that the fan blades are horizontal, whereas in fact they would probably be somewhat tilted to increase the air flow. However, even with these large extended objects the dominant contribution to the moment of inertia was Md^2, which is four times as big as $\frac{1}{12}M(a^2 + b^2)$, so the effect of neglecting the tilt probably isn't too serious.

Note that the dimensions of *torque, moment of inertia* and *angular momentum* differ from the corresponding translational quantities of force, mass and momentum, but rotational kinetic energy is genuinely an energy, with the same dimensions as $\frac{1}{2}mv^2$ or mgh, and can be used directly in energy conservation calculations.

8E.5   *You are on a camping trip in a rural district. Your water supply comes from a well, and is obtained by hauling up a large bucket using a windlass, i.e. a cylindrical spindle turned by a handle. You have just hauled a full bucket of water, mass 15 kg, the 10 m from the water surface to ground level (at negligible speed) when your hand slips off the windlass handle.*

(a)   *If the windlass is a solid cylinder of mass 20 kg and radius 12 cm, how fast is it spinning when the bucket hits the water? Neglect the mass of the rope and the friction in the bearings of the windlass, take $g = 9.8 \ \text{m/s}^2$, and assume the rope does not slip.*

(b)   *What was the tension in the rope while the bucket was falling, and how long did the fall take?*

Conceptualize (a)

The first part of the problem can be solved using energy conservation. Before you let go, the bucket+windlass+rope system had a total energy of mgh—the bucket's gravitational potential energy relative to the level of the water. When the bucket hit the water, it had zero gravitational potential energy and a kinetic energy of $\frac{1}{2}mv^2$, and the spinning

8E.5, continued:

windlass had a kinetic energy of $\frac{1}{2}I\omega^2$. in the absence of friction, the total mechanical energy remains constant, so we can solve this problem if we can relate v and ω.

Formulate (a)
Energy conservation gives

$$mgh = \frac{1}{2}mv^2 + \frac{1}{2}I\omega^2 .$$

We already know that for a solid cylinder rotating about its axis $I = \frac{1}{2}Mr^2$. If the bucket's speed is v, and the rope does not stretch, the speed of any piece of rope must also be v, and if it doesn't slip, the speed of any section of the outer surface of the cylinder must be v as well. We conclude that the angular velocity $\omega = v/r$, where r is the radius of the cylinder.

Solve (a)
The rotational kinetic energy of the windlass is

$$\frac{1}{2}I\omega^2 = \frac{1}{2}(\frac{1}{2}Mr^2)(v/r)^2 = \frac{1}{4}Mv^2 ,$$

so energy conservation implies

$$mgh = \frac{1}{2}mv^2 + \frac{1}{4}Mv^2 = \frac{1}{4}v^2(2m + M) .$$

Now $mgh = (15 \text{ kg}) \times (9.8 \text{ m/s}^2) \times (10m) = 1470$ J, so the velocity of the bucket when it hit the water was $\sqrt{(4 \times 1470 \text{ J})/((2 \times 15 \text{ kg}) + (20 \text{ kg}))} = 11$ m/s, and the angular speed of the windlass was $v/r = 90$ rad/s.

Conceptualize (b)
We can't find the tension in the rope by energy methods—it is an internal force and does no work on the system. Instead we need to consider the forces acting on the bucket and on the windlass. Their force diagrams are shown on the right. There will be three equations in all, two for force and one for torque, and three unknowns: the torque τ, the tension T and the normal force N.

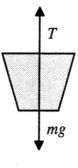
Bucket

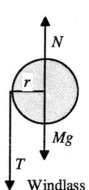
Windlass

Formulate (b)
Taking down and counter-clockwise to be positive for motion and rotation respectively, we find

$$F_{\text{B}} = mg - T$$
$$\tau_{\text{W}} = Tr$$
$$F_{\text{W}} = T + Mg - N ,$$

8E.5, continued:

where B stands for bucket, W for windlass, and N is the normal force exerted on the windlass by its supporting axle. Neither N nor the weight contributes to the torque because both act through the axis of rotation.

Solve (b)

Because the rope doesn't stretch or slip, the angular acceleration $\alpha = a/r$ by the same logic that we used earlier for v and ω. The equations for F_B and τ_W become

$$ma = mg - T$$

$$\tfrac{1}{2}Mra = Tr .$$

From the second of these, $T = \tfrac{1}{2}Ma$, and from the first

$$a = \frac{mg}{(m + \tfrac{1}{2}M)}, \qquad \text{giving} \qquad T = \frac{Mmg}{(2m + M)} .$$

Substituting the numbers gives us $a = 5.9$ m/s^2, $T = 59$ N. The time of fall is given by $h = \tfrac{1}{2}at^2$, which for a 10 m drop gives $t = 1.8$ s.

Scrutinize

We can use the results of part (b) to recheck the speed of our bucket: $v = at = 11$ m/s, in agreement with our earlier result. We can also confirm that our results are of the right general form by looking at extreme cases. If the windlass were very light compared to the bucket $(M \ll m)$, the bucket would essentially be in free fall, and sure enough we find an acceleration of g and a very small tension $T = \tfrac{1}{2}Mg$. If on the other hand the bucket were very light compared to the windlass $(m \ll M)$, its weight would not be sufficient to turn the cylinder and it would simply hang there—and indeed this case gives us $a \sim 0$ and $T = mg$.

8E.7 (a) *A rigid body of unspecified shape is allowed to pivot freely about a horizontal axis through its center of mass. The only force acting is gravity. Show that there is no net torque.*

Conceptualize

To find the total torque, we can use the same approach as we did when proving the parallel-axis theorem in Problem 8C.3—find the torque acting on a small piece of the body at (x_i, y_i), with mass m_i, and then sum over all such small pieces (equivalent to an integral over the body, as in 8C.5).

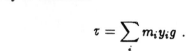

Formulate and Solve

Take the center of mass to be the origin of coordinates, let the z-axis be vertical, and assume the body pivots about the x-axis. Then the torque acting on the element of mass m_i at point i is $m_i g R_i \sin\theta = m_i g y_i$. The total torque on the body is therefore

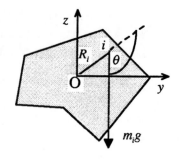

$$\tau = \sum_i m_i y_i g .$$

8E.7, continued:

But $\sum_i m_i y_i = M y_{cm}$, by definition. Since we are considering an axis through the center of mass, y_{cm} is zero, and hence there is no net torque.

Learn
This result explains why you can balance an extended object on a knife-edge if it is arranged so that the knife-edge is located under the center of mass. The term 'center of gravity' is often used as an alternative to 'center of mass' in recognition of this.

(b) *Hence show that the net force of gravity on a rigid body can always be regarded as acting through the center of mass—i.e., the torque it exerts about any horizontal axis is the same as if the total force acted at the center of mass.*

Solve
The conceptualization and formulation of this problem are exactly the same as part (a). The expression for the torque,

$$\tau = \sum_i m_i y_i\, g = M y_{cm}\, g,$$

does not depend on the location of the origin of coordinates.

If we now consider a point mass M at the location of the center of mass, $[x_{cm}, y_{cm}, z_{cm}]$, then, just as for m_i above,

$$\tau_{cm} = Mg R_{cm} \sin\theta = Mg y_{cm}\ .$$

Therefore $\tau = \tau_{cm}$: about any horizontal axis, the torque exerted by gravity on a rigid body is the same as the torque on a point particle having the same mass and located at the position of the rigid body's center of mass.

Learn
This is an extremely useful result which basically states that gravity (or indeed any other force which acts uniformly on every part of an object) can always be regarded as acting at the center of mass. We used this implicitly in a couple of earlier examples.

An important application of this result concerns the "fictitious forces" which have to be introduced when we work in non-inertial reference frames. Since these forces are introduced to compensate for the *frame's* acceleration, they necessarily act like gravity, giving everything in the frame the same acceleration. This theorem therefore holds for them, and we can treat all such forces as acting through the center of mass of any extended object.

8E.8   *A rigid body of mass M and having a circular cross-section of radius R rolls without slipping down a slope making an angle θ to the horizontal. The moment of inertia of the body about its central axis of symmetry is kMR², where k is a numerical constant.*

(a) *What is its speed when it has descended through a vertical distance h?*

(b) *What is the minimum coefficient of static friction required to ensure that it rolls, rather than slides, down the slope?*

8E.8, continued:

Conceptualize (a)
The only forces acting are friction and gravity. Since the body rolls without slipping, friction does no work in this situation (it is always being applied to the contact point between the body and the surface, and if the body rolls without slipping there is no relative motion between the two surfaces at the contact point). Therefore the change in the body's kinetic energy must come from the work done by gravity, Mgh. To determine the speed that this implies, we can decompose the body's motion into translational motion of the center of mass and rotational motion around the center of mass, and then use the condition of rolling without slipping to relate the angular speed ω to the translational speed v_{cm}.

 Formulate (a)
The total kinetic energy of a rigid body of mass M and moment of inertia I is

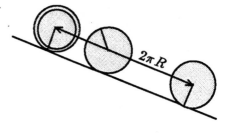

$$K = \tfrac{1}{2}Mv_{\text{cm}}^2 + \tfrac{1}{2}I\omega^2.$$

If the body rolls without slipping, in one complete rotation (2π radians) it covers a linear distance $2\pi R$ (see diagram), and so $v_{\text{cm}} = R\omega$.

 Solve (a)
The work-energy theorem gives

$$Mgh = \tfrac{1}{2}M(R\omega)^2 + \tfrac{1}{2}(kMR^2)\omega^2.$$

Hence

$$Mgh = \tfrac{1}{2}(1+k)MR^2\omega^2,$$

and so

$$\omega = \sqrt{\frac{2gh}{R^2(1+k)}}, \qquad v_{\text{cm}} = \sqrt{\frac{2gh}{1+k}}.$$

 Scrutinize (a)
As is usual with inclined planes, the result does not depend on the mass of the body; it is somewhat more surprising to find that the translational speed doesn't depend on the radius of the body either. It does depend on k, which is to say the shape of the object: balls roll down slopes faster than hoops, for example. If we set $k = 0$, treating the object as a point mass, v_{cm} reduces to the value that we have obtained in earlier problems (e.g. in Chapter 4).

 Conceptualize (b)
To find the coefficient of friction, we need the force diagram for the body. We also need to choose a reference point about which to evaluate the torque: as is often the case, it is convenient to choose the center of mass. As in part (a), we are then treating the motion as translation *of* the center of mass and rotation *about* the center of mass. We

8E.8, continued:

have already determined, in part (a), the relation between these two motions for the condition of rolling without slipping: $v_{cm} = \omega R$.

Formulate (b)

As usual with inclined-plane problems, we define a coordinate system with x pointing down the slope. The components of the net force are

$$F_x = Mg \sin \theta - \mathcal{F}$$

$$F_y = N - Mg \cos \theta$$

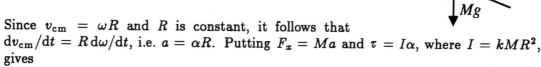

and the net torque about the center of mass is

$$\tau = \mathcal{F} R.$$

Since $v_{cm} = \omega R$ and R is constant, it follows that $dv_{cm}/dt = R\, d\omega/dt$, i.e. $a = \alpha R$. Putting $F_x = Ma$ and $\tau = I\alpha$, where $I = kMR^2$, gives

$$Ma = Mg \sin \theta - \mathcal{F}$$

$$kMRa = \mathcal{F} R.$$

Solve (b)

The torque equation gives $\mathcal{F} = kMa$, and putting this into the force equation we get

$$a = \frac{g \sin \theta}{1+k}, \qquad \mathcal{F} = \frac{kMg \sin \theta}{1+k}.$$

If the object is not slipping, there is no sliding motion between the part of its surface in contact with the slope and the slope itself. Therefore we are dealing with static friction. The minimum value of μ_s for which this is possible is given by

$$\mu_s N = \frac{kMg \sin \theta}{1+k},$$

and since $N = Mg \cos \theta$ (from the fact that $F_y = 0$) we conclude that

$$\mu_s = \frac{k}{1+k} \tan \theta.$$

Scrutinize

The result for μ_s depends, as we would expect, on the shape of the body (and thus the value of k) and the gradient of the slope. Smaller values of k imply that less torque is required to induce the necessary angular acceleration, so we need less friction (since the torque is provided by the frictional force). Steeper gradients increase the net downslope force, hence producing a larger linear acceleration, and thus require a higher angular acceleration to match it. This implies a larger torque, and so more friction.

8E.8, continued:

We can also use our value of a to confirm the energy conservation results for the velocity of the object. Since $v_{\text{cm}} = 0$ at $t = 0$, v_{cm} after traveling a distance $x = h/\sin\theta$ must be given by $v_{\text{cm}}^2 = 2ax = 2gh/(1+k)$, in agreement with part (a).

Learn

Note that the effect of friction on rolling motion is quite different from its effect on sliding motion! One can define a 'coefficient of rolling friction' in analogy to static and kinetic friction, but its interpretation in physical terms is even more complicated than the interpretation of ordinary sliding friction.

Note that we could also solve part (b) using the point of contact as an instantaneous axis of rotation. Only Mg contributes a torque about this point, namely $\tau = MgR\sin\theta$; the parallel-axis theorem gives $I = (k+1)MR^2$, so $\alpha = g\sin\theta/R(1+k)$, and $a = \alpha R$ for the same result.

HINTS FOR PROBLEMS WITH AN (H)
The number of the hint refers to the number of the problem

8B.2 For the square: what is the *perpendicular* distance between the line of action of each force and the black dot? What is the torque produced by each force? Do both torques act in the same direction?

8C.5 Note that both shapes are said to be thin sheets. Are there any theorems you can apply to such objects which relate moments of inertia about different axes?

For the square: what is the moment of inertia about either diagonal? How can you use this to find I about the given axis? (A similar method is used for the disk.)

Still stuck? Study the solutions to problems 8C.3 and 8C.4.

8D.2 What do you have to know to calculate the kinetic energy and angular momentum of an object rotating about an axis?

What is the moment of inertia of the ruler about the given axis? Is there a way to determine this without having to do an integration?

8E.4 Draw a force diagram for the ruler. What force produces a torque about its axis of rotation?

How does the angular acceleration depend on the angular position (i.e. on θ)? What relationship would you expect for simple harmonic motion?

8E.6 Draw free-body diagrams for the pulley and the two masses. Are the tension forces on both sides of the pulley equal in magnitude?

What is the relationship between the angular acceleration of the pulley and the linear acceleration of the two blocks?

If you are still confused, try reviewing the solution to problem 8E.5.

ANSWERS TO HINTS

8B.2 7 cm for 30 N force; 5 cm for 20 N force; -2.1 N·m and 1 N·m respectively, taking counterclockwise to be positive. No.

8C.5 Can use both parallel-axis and perpendicular-axis theorems (former always, latter for thin sheets).

(From perpendicular-axis theorem) $\frac{1}{12}Ma^2$; use parallel-axis theorem.

8D.2 Angular velocity ω and moment of inertia I.

$$\frac{1}{12}m(\ell^2 + w^2) + m(\frac{1}{2}\ell - x)^2$$
$$= m(\frac{1}{3}\ell^2 + \frac{1}{12}w^2 - \ell x + x^2)$$

Use parallel-axis theorem, as above.

8E.4 Gravity

$\alpha = -k\sin\theta$,

$\alpha = -k\theta$, k a positive constant.

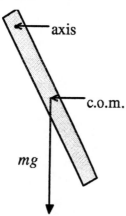

8E.6

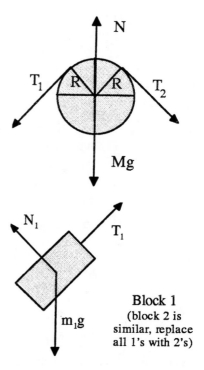

Block 1
(block 2 is similar, replace all 1's with 2's)

No: T_1 for block 1 = T_1 on pulley, and likewise for T_2, but $T_1 \neq T_2$.

$\alpha = a/R$, where a is the linear acceleration of either block (they are equal), and α is the angular acceleration of the pulley.

ANSWERS TO ALL PROBLEMS

8A.1 d; b.

8A.2 See complete solution.

8B.1 b.

8B.2 $\tau = 1.1$ N·m clockwise; zero; zero.

8C.1 See complete solution.

8C.2 e.

8C.3 See complete solution.

8C.4 See complete solution.

8C.5 $\dfrac{7}{12}Ma^2$; $\dfrac{3}{4}MR^2$.

$\dfrac{12\tau}{7Ma^2}$; $\dfrac{4\tau}{3MR^2}$.

8D.1 a.

8D.2 $K = \frac{1}{2}I\omega^2$, $L = I\omega$, where $\omega = v/(\ell - x)$ and $I = m(\frac{1}{3}\ell^2 + \frac{1}{12}w^2 + x^2 - \ell x)$.

$K = 3.3 \times 10^{-4}$ J; $L = 1.1 \times 10^{-3}$ kg $\cdot$ m^2/s.

8D.3 (a) $\pi\ell\sqrt{\dfrac{M}{3K}}$

   (b) Rotational kinetic energy $\frac{1}{2}K\theta_m^2$; angular momentum $\dfrac{1}{2\sqrt{3}}\ell\theta_m\sqrt{MK}$

   (c) $\frac{3}{8}\pi\ell\sqrt{\dfrac{M}{K}}$

8E.1 See complete solution.

8E.2 2 N · m; 1 N · m; 1.1 N · m; 0.

   1200 rad/s^2; 2400 rad/s^2; 930 rad/s^2; 0.

8E.3 See complete solution.

8E.4 $\tau = (\frac{1}{2}\ell - x)mg\sin\theta$; $\alpha = \tau/I$ where I is as given in 8D.2 above.

   Yes (for small angles to vertical).

8E.5 See complete solution.

8E.6 $a = (m_1g\sin\theta_1 - m_2g\sin\theta_2)/(m_1 + m_2 + \frac{1}{2}M)$, and the angular acceleration $\alpha = a/R$.

8E.7 See complete solution.

8E.8 See complete solution.

8E.9 (a) The time taken to roll down the slope is $t = \sqrt{\dfrac{2(1+k^2)\ell}{g\sin\theta}}$, where $k = \dfrac{I}{MR^2}$. The values of k are: uniform rubber ball, $\frac{2}{5}$; hoop, 1; uniform cylindrical log, $\frac{1}{2}$; soccer ball (hollow sphere), $\frac{2}{3}$; wheel (thick cylinder), $\frac{5}{8}$.

(b) You need to minimize the rotational kinetic energy for a given linear speed. An object that can slide without friction would clearly win the race, but since all the objects currently in play roll without slipping, the hope for a frictionless object seems unrealistic. But a wheeled vehicle, say a heavy cart with light wheels, should do fine: the rotational kinetic energy of the wheels is small compared to the kinetic energy of the whole cart. If, however, the rules of the game state that the whole object has to roll, you need something which has most of its mass close to its axis of rotation. An example would be a wheel with a very light rim and spokes, and a heavily ballasted central hub. To see how this works, suppose your wheel consists of a rim with radius R and mass $0.1M$, and a uniform cylindrical hub with radius $0.1R$ and mass $0.9M$ (assume we can neglect the mass of the spokes). Its moment of inertia is $I = (0.1M)R^2 + \frac{1}{2}(0.9M)(0.1R)^2 = 0.1045MR^2$, so $k = 0.1045$, much less than for any of the objects in part (a): your wheel should win comfortably.

8E.10 (a) 63 J; (b) $J = 45$ N·s in the direction of motion; $\tau = 4.4$ N·m.

ESSENTIALS OF INTRODUCTORY CLASSICAL MECHANICS

CHAPTER 9

ROTATION IN THREE DIMENSIONS

OVERVIEW

In the previous chapter we discussed rotations of a rigid body about a fixed axis—that is, the case in which a rigid body rotates about an axis that is fixed in advance by the construction of the physical system. Fixed-axis rotation includes many interesting applications, from pulleys to automobile wheels and airplane propellers. In this chapter, however, we will broaden the discussion to situations for which the rotation axis is not fixed.

To treat such cases, we will introduce the full vector formalism for describing rotational motion. Quantities that were defined as scalars in the previous chapter—such as angular velocity, angular momentum, and torque—will be generalized in this chapter to become vectors. Since the vector formalism is more general than the scalar formalism, most physicists would in fact use the vector formalism even when describing rotation about a fixed axis. If the rotation axis is fixed, each scalar quantity defined in the previous chapter is equal to the component of the corresponding vector quantity along the axis of rotation.

The reader should be prepared for the fact that rotation in three dimensions is a complicated subject. The cause of the complexity lies in the basic geometry. If you translate an object by 1 m in the x-direction and then 2 m in the y-direction, the object ends up at the same place as it would if you performed the operations in the opposite order. Translations commute. However, if you rotate an object by 90° about the x-axis and then 90° about the y-axis, it will **not** end up in the same orientation as it would if you performed the operations in the opposite order. (If you are not convinced, try it.) Rotations do not commute, and therefore one cannot hope to separately describe the rotational motion about the x-, y-, and z-axes.

The ability to describe rotations with no fixed axis has several important practical applications. First, we explore the conditions under which the forces and torques on a given rigid body cancel, so that the body remains in equilibrium. This branch of mechanics, known as *statics*, has obvious relevance to fields such as construction and architecture. We also apply the vector description of rotational motion to the case of planetary orbits, and to the classic example of three-dimensional rotation—the gyroscope.

When you have completed this chapter you should:

> ✔ distinguish between rotation about a fixed axis and rotation for which the axis is free to move;
>
> ✔ understand the vector definitions of angular velocity, angular momentum, and torque;
>
> ✔ be able to do calculations involving equilibrium conditions for simple rigid bodies;
>
> ✔ recognize how conservation of angular momentum can be applied to the motion of point particles;
>
> ✔ be able to do simple calculations involving rotation in three dimensions.

ESSENTIALS

In the previous chapter we studied the motion of rigid bodies moving in a plane, and rotating about an axis perpendicular to that plane. This is clearly not the most general type of rotation — for example, a boat in rough seas can rotate about an axis running from bow to stern, a horizontal axis perpendicular to this (i.e. running across the middle of the boat), or a vertical axis. In aircraft and boats these motions are referred to as roll, pitch and yaw, respectively. In general the motion of the boat will be a combination of these. We can regard rotations about these three perpendicular axes as components of the general rotation of the boat, just as we regard x, y and z as components of its position in space relative to a point.

To discuss rotations in three dimensions with no fixed axis, we will need one new mathematical definition: the vector cross product. Given two vectors $\vec{a}$ and $\vec{b}$, the vector cross product $\vec{a} \times \vec{b}$ is another vector, which can be defined geometrically by specifying its magnitude and direction:

1) $|\vec{a} \times \vec{b}| = |\vec{a}||\vec{b}| \sin\theta$, where θ is the angle between $\vec{a}$ and $\vec{b}$. More precisely θ is defined as the smallest angle by which one vector can be rotated so that it is parallel to the other, so $0 \leq \theta \leq 180°$, and therefore $\sin\theta \geq 0$.

2) The direction of $\vec{a} \times \vec{b}$ is perpendicular to both $\vec{a}$ and $\vec{b}$. The choice between the two opposite directions meeting this description is made by a convention called the right-hand rule: if the knuckles of the right hand are rotated from $\vec{a}$ to $\vec{b}$, the direction in which the thumb points is the direction of the cross product.

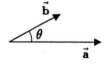

$\vec{a} \times \vec{b}$ is perpendicular to the page, and out of the page.

The cross product can equivalently be defined in terms of the coordinates of the vectors. Writing $\vec{a} = [a_x, a_y, a_z]$ and $\vec{b} = [b_x, b_y, b_z]$, then $\vec{c} \equiv \vec{a} \times \vec{b}$ is given by

$$c_x = a_y b_z - a_z b_y$$
$$c_y = a_z b_x - a_x b_z$$
$$c_z = a_x b_y - a_y b_x \ .$$

Note that the second and third lines can each be obtained from the previous one by a cyclic permutation: $x \rightarrow y$, $y \rightarrow z$, and $z \rightarrow x$. Alternatively, if you are familiar with determinants, the equations above can be written as

$$\vec{a} \times \vec{b} = \begin{vmatrix} \hat{x} & \hat{y} & \hat{z} \\ a_x & a_y & a_z \\ b_x & b_y & b_z \end{vmatrix} ,$$

where $\hat{x}$, $\hat{y}$, and $\hat{z}$ are unit vectors in x, y, and z directions respectively. (If you are not familiar with determinants, just use the previous set of equations.)

There are a number of properties of the cross product that are useful to know:

1) Coordinate independence. This is obvious from the geometric definition, which makes no reference to coordinates, but it is not obvious from the coordinate definition. Nonetheless, if I choose a coordinate system that is rotated relative to yours by any angle about any axis, and we both calculate the cross product $\vec{c} = \vec{a} \times \vec{b}$ using the coordinate definition, our resulting vectors will agree. Since we are using different coordinate systems, my vector components $a_x, a_y, a_z, b_x, b_y, b_z, c_x, c_y$, and c_z will all be different from yours, but if we were to construct our vectors in physical space, as wooden arrows for example, they would line up exactly.

2) Distributive law: $\vec{a} \times (\vec{b} + \vec{c}) = \vec{a} \times \vec{b} + \vec{a} \times \vec{c}$.

3) Anticommutivity: $\vec{a} \times \vec{b} = -\vec{b} \times \vec{a}$.

4) If α is any scalar, then $(\alpha\vec{a}) \times \vec{b} = \alpha(\vec{a} \times \vec{b})$.

Although the definition of the cross product seems at first to be arbitrary (Why $\sin\theta$, and not $\tan\theta$? Why is the cross product perpendicular to the two vectors?), it is in fact highly constrained. If one wants to define a cross product obeying properties (1) and (2) above, it can be shown that the definition is unique, up to a possible redefinition by multiplying the old definition by a constant.

Armed with the new mathematical tool of the cross product, we can now generalize the definitions of each of the three key quantities introduced in the previous chapter: angular velocity, angular momentum, and torque.

If we imagine holding one point of a rigid body fixed, then the most general possible motion it can undergo is by definition a rotation. The purpose of introducing the angular velocity vector is to provide an economical description of this motion. Since the axis of rotation is not fixed, the angular velocity vector should describe not only the speed of the rotation, but also the direction of its axis.

In the previous chapter we discussed rotation about a fixed axis—the z-axis for example—as illustrated at the right. In this case the velocity of any atom in the rigid body is given by

$$|\vec{v}| = R\omega_{\text{axis}} ,$$

313

where R is the distance of the atom from the axis of rotation, and ω_{axis} is the angular velocity about the axis. (We will consistently attach the subscript "axis" to the scalar quantities defined in the previous chapter, to distinguish them from the analogous vector quantities that we are defining in this chapter.) The direction of the velocity is tangential, meaning that it is perpendicular to the radial vector and perpendicular to the axis of rotation. Using the cross product, the magnitude and direction of $\vec{\mathbf{v}}$ can be expressed in one simple formula. To do this, we define the vector $\vec{\omega}$ by

1) $|\vec{\omega}| = \omega_{\text{axis}} =$ rotation rate, measured for example in radians per second.

2) The direction of $\vec{\omega}$ is *along the axis* of the rotation. The choice between the two directions along the axis is made by another right-hand rule convention: if the knuckles of the right hand are curled in the direction of the motion, $\vec{\omega}$ points the same direction as the thumb. Equivalently, if you look at the object along the axis of rotation, $\vec{\omega}$ points toward you if the rotation appears counterclockwise, and away from you if the rotation appears clockwise.

For motion of the rigid body with one point held fixed, the velocity of any atom is then given by

$$\boxed{\vec{\mathbf{v}} = \vec{\omega} \times \vec{\mathbf{r}} \, ,}$$

where $\vec{\mathbf{r}}$ is the displacement vector of the atom, measured from the fixed point. This equation reduces to the formula from the previous chapter when the object rotates about the z-axis, so it is certainly valid in that case. Wherever the axis of rotation points, however, someone can choose it as her z-axis. The formula will then necessarily hold in her coordinate system. Since the cross-product is coordinate independent, the formula must hold in all coordinate systems. This formula compactly describes both the magnitude and direction of $\vec{\mathbf{v}}$, and allows one to describe rotation even when the axis of rotation, and hence $\vec{\omega}$, changes with time. While no atom moves in the direction of $\vec{\omega}$, the velocity of any atom is easily expressed in terms of $\vec{\omega}$ by the formula above.

If a rigid body moves without even one point held fixed, such as a football flying through the air and spinning as it moves, the description is still simple. Choose a reference point P on the body, and define $\vec{\omega}$ as above, in the frame in which P is fixed. (Usually it is most convenient to choose P to be the center of mass.) If $\vec{\mathbf{r}}_P$

314

and $\vec{\mathbf{v}}_P$ are the position and velocity of this reference point, then the velocity of any atom is given by

$$\vec{\mathbf{v}} = \vec{\mathbf{v}}_P + \vec{\omega} \times (\vec{\mathbf{r}} - \vec{\mathbf{r}}_P) \ .$$

Problem 9D.8

As long as one uses only inertial frames of reference, it can be shown that the value of the angular velocity vector $\vec{\omega}$ depends only on which rigid body is being described. It does not depend on the choice of reference point P, the origin of the coordinate system, or even the velocity of the coordinate system.

Another simplifying feature of angular velocity vectors is their additivity. If a gear wheel turns in the engine of a boat, which is itself being tossed about by a turbulent ocean, which in turn is rotating with the Earth about its axis, then it can be shown that the total angular velocity $\vec{\omega}$ of the gear wheel is the vector sum of the angular velocity of the Earth, the angular velocity of the boat relative to the Earth, and the angular velocity of the gear wheel relative to the boat.

To generalize the concept of angular momentum, recall that for rotation about a fixed axis, we defined the angular momentum about the axis as

$$L_{\text{axis}} = I\omega$$
$$= \sum_i m_i R_i^2 \omega$$
$$= \sum_i m_i R_i v_i \ ,$$

where m_i, R_i, and v_i are respectively the mass, the distance from the axis, and the speed of the ith atom. This formula can be generalized to define the vector angular momentum $\vec{\mathbf{L}}$ about the origin by writing

$$\vec{\mathbf{L}} = \sum_i m_i \vec{\mathbf{r}}_i \times \vec{\mathbf{v}}_i \ ,$$

where $\vec{\mathbf{r}}_i$ is the displacement vector of the ith atom, and $\vec{\mathbf{v}}_i$ is its velocity vector. Since $m_i \vec{\mathbf{v}}_i = \vec{\mathbf{p}}_i$, where $\vec{\mathbf{p}}_i$ is the momentum of the ith atom, one usually writes

$$\vec{\mathbf{L}} = \sum_i \vec{\mathbf{r}}_i \times \vec{\mathbf{p}}_i \ .$$

Unlike the angular velocity, the angular momentum usually depends on the choice of the origin, since the displacement vectors $\vec{\mathbf{r}}_i$ are

315

measured from this origin. If the origin is called Q, $\vec{L}$ is called the angular momentum *about the point* Q. However, for the special case in which the total linear momentum of the rigid body $\vec{P}_{\text{tot}} = 0$, $\vec{L}$ has the same value about all points. One can verify that L_{axis} (the scalar angular momentum for rotation about a fixed axis as defined in the previous chapter) is equal to the component of $\vec{L}$ in the direction of the axis, provided that the point about which $\vec{L}$ is calculated lies on the axis about which L_{axis} is calculated.

While $\vec{\omega}$ points along the instantaneous axis of rotation, $\vec{L}$ does not always point in this direction. If the object is symmetric about the axis of rotation, as is often the case in simple problems, then $\vec{L}$ does point along the axis. If the object is asymmetric, however, then $\vec{L}$ need not point along the axis. An example is the obliquely angled dumbbell shown rotating about the vertical axis at the right, for which the direction of $\vec{L}$ is shown. As the object rotates about the vertical axis, the vector $\vec{L}$ turns with it. For such an asymmetric object L_{axis} is equal to the component of $\vec{L}$ along the axis of rotation as always, but L_{axis} is not in this case equal to the magnitude of $\vec{L}$. Because $\vec{L}$ and $\vec{\omega}$ are not always parallel, the concept of a moment of inertia for general three dimensional rotations is quite complicated, and will not be discussed here.

Problems 9B.1, 9D.1, 9D.2

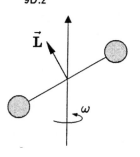

Finally, we wish to find a vector generalization of the definition of torque. Since in the previous chapter τ_{axis} was found to be equal to dL_{axis}/dt, a natural way to proceed is to differentiate our expression for the vector angular momentum $\vec{L}$. The differentiation of the cross product is completely analogous to the differentiation of an ordinary product, as can be verified by using the component definition to express the components of the cross product in terms of ordinary products of functions. Then

Problem 9C.2

Feynman Lectures on Physics, Vol 1, pages 20-1 to 20-4.

$$\frac{d\vec{L}}{dt} = \sum_i \left[\frac{d\vec{r}_i}{dt} \times \vec{p}_i + \vec{r}_i \times \frac{d\vec{p}_i}{dt} \right] \ .$$

But $d\vec{r}_i/dt$ is the velocity $\vec{v}_i$, which is parallel to the momentum $\vec{p}_i$. Since the cross product of two parallel vectors is zero (because $\sin\theta = 0$), the first term vanishes. Using $d\vec{p}_i/dt = \vec{F}_i$, where $\vec{F}_i$ is the total force acting on the ith atom, the second term can be written more simply. Defining the resultant derivative to be the vector torque $\vec{\tau}$, we have

$$\boxed{\vec{\tau} = \frac{d\vec{L}}{dt} = \sum_i \vec{r}_i \times \vec{F}_i \ .}$$

Problem 9D.3

Like the angular momentum $\vec{L}$, the torque $\vec{\tau}$ usually depends on the choice of the origin, since the displacement vectors $\vec{r}_i$ are measured from this origin. If the origin is called Q, $\vec{\tau}$ is called the torque *about the point* Q. However, for the special case in which the total force $\vec{F}_{tot}$ acting on the rigid body is zero, $\vec{\tau}$ has the same value about all points. As with angular momentum, there is a relation between the vector quantity defined here and the scalar quantity defined in the previous chapter. The scalar quantity τ_{axis} defined in the previous chapter is equal to the component of $\vec{\tau}$ in the direction of the axis, provided that the point about which $\vec{\tau}$ is calculated lies on the axis about which τ_{axis} is calculated.

Problem 9C.1

In the previous chapter we found that if the internal forces between any two masses in the system are equal, opposite, and directed along the line joining the two masses, then the internal torques about the fixed axis all cancel. The same result holds for the full vector torque. To see this, let $\vec{\tau}_{ij}$ denote the torque on particle i due to particle j, and let $\vec{F}_{ij}$ denote the force on particle i due to particle j. Then

$$\vec{\tau}_{12} + \vec{\tau}_{21} = \vec{r}_1 \times \vec{F}_{12} + \vec{r}_2 \times \vec{F}_{21} .$$

Using $\vec{F}_{21} = -\vec{F}_{12}$,

$$\vec{\tau}_{12} + \vec{\tau}_{21} = \vec{r}_1 \times \vec{F}_{12} - \vec{r}_2 \times \vec{F}_{12}$$

$$= (\vec{r}_1 - \vec{r}_2) \times \vec{F}_{12} .$$

Finally, using the assumption that $\vec{F}_{12}$ is directed along the line joining the masses, and is therefore parallel to $(\vec{r}_1 - \vec{r}_2)$, we find

$$\vec{\tau}_{12} + \vec{\tau}_{21} = 0 .$$

Thus, the total torque is the same as the total external torque. *If there are no external torques, then the total torque vanishes, and the total angular momentum vector* $\vec{L}$ *is conserved.* Conservation of angular momentum ranks with the conservation of energy and of linear momentum as a basic principle of mechanics; like the other two conservation laws, it remains true even when we include relativity and quantum mechanics.

One application of this vector formalism is the determination of the conditions under which a particular object or structure will *not* move, rather than what will happen if it does move. This branch of mechanics is called *statics*. (The study of motion is *kinematics*, and *dynamics* involves the causes of motion — forces and interactions.)

317

Problems 9A

For point particles we already know that an initially stationary particle will remain so if no net force acts on it. If we extend our consideration to rigid bodies we must also ensure that the object does not rotate, so we must also require that there be no net torque. A possible problem here is that we do not know what reference point to calculate the torque about. Fortunately, in a statics problem the total force acting on the rigid body is always zero, and in that case the vector torque $\vec{\tau}$ is the same for all reference points.

Since many of our problems will involve the uniform acceleration of gravity near the surface of the Earth, it is useful to examine the torque in this case. Since the gravitational force on the ith atom is given by $\vec{F}_i = m_i\vec{g}$, the general formula for the vector torque simplifies as

$$\vec{\tau}_{\text{grav}} = \sum_i \vec{r}_i \times \vec{F}_i$$

$$= \sum_i \vec{r}_i \times m_i\vec{g}$$

$$= \left(\frac{1}{M_{\text{tot}}} \sum_i m_i\vec{r}_i \right) \times M_{\text{tot}}\vec{g}$$

$$= \vec{r}_{\text{cm}} \times \vec{F}_{\text{tot}} \ .$$

Thus, for purposes of calculating the torque, the force associated with a uniform gravitational acceleration can be treated as if the total force were applied at the center of mass.

Notice that our new definitions of angular momentum and torque allow us to apply these concepts to circumstances where we do not seem to have 'rotational motion' in the usual sense. For example, a point particle moving in a straight line has a well-defined position vector $\vec{r}$ (relative to a reference point off to one side of its trajectory), momentum $\vec{p}$ and perhaps some applied force $\vec{F}$. We can therefore assign it an angular momentum $\vec{L}$ and an applied torque $\vec{\tau}$ about this reference point. Further, if the applied torque happens to be zero the angular momentum we calculate will be conserved. This looks very strange at first sight, but it is not really unreasonable—if we consider a planet orbiting a star, we would certainly concede that it is performing rotational motion and should have angular momentum, but at any given instant it simply has a certain velocity and a certain position relative to the star, just as it would have if it were traveling in a straight line.

Since we can have a net force without a net torque, angular momentum may be conserved in situations where linear momentum is changing. An important example of this is a *central force*, in which the force on a particle is always directed toward (or perhaps away from) a specific point P. In such a case $\vec{r}$ (the position vector of the particle relative to P) is parallel to $\vec{F}$, and therefore the torque acting on the particle about P vanishes. The orbits of the planets or comets about the Sun are examples of central force motion, in the approximation that the Sun is stationary in an inertial frame and that the interactions between the planets can be ignored. In such cases the angular momentum about the source P of the force, although not about any other point, is conserved.

Problems 9B.2, 9B.3, 9B.4, and 9B.5

The vector nature of angular momentum is a physical reality, not just a mathematical convenience. This can be most clearly seen in cases where a rotating object behaves in an unexpected way because of the magnitude and direction of its angular momentum vector. One of the most elegant illustrations of this is the precession of gyroscopes, where the action of gravity seems to cause the spinning gyroscope to move sideways instead of downward. This behavior is a direct consequence of the vector nature of torque and angular momentum. The properties of gyroscopes are explored in Problems 9D.4 and 9D.5.

Problems 9D.4 and 9D.5

Finally, we can describe in principle the treatment of combined translational and rotational motion of rigid bodies in three dimensions. As in the two-dimensional case discussed in the previous chapter, combined translational and rotational motion can be treated by separately describing the motion of the center of mass, and the rotation about the center of mass. As we showed in Chapter 5, the translational motion of the center of mass of any system is controlled by the total force acting on the system:

$$\sum \vec{F}^{\text{ext}} = M\vec{a}_{\text{cm}} = \frac{d\vec{p}}{dt} \quad \text{(translational)} ,$$

where M is the mass of the rigid body, $\vec{a}_{\text{cm}}$ is the acceleration of its center of mass, and $\vec{p}$ is its momentum. The rotation of the rigid body about its center of mass is governed by:

$$\sum \vec{\tau}^{\text{ext}} = \frac{d\vec{L}_{\text{cm}}}{dt} \quad \text{(rotational)} ,$$

where $\sum \tau^{\text{ext}}$ is the total external torque calculated about the center of mass, and $\vec{L}_{\text{cm}}$ describes the angular momentum about the center

319

of mass. As in the two-dimensional case, the rotational equation is most easily justified by working in the possibly non-inertial frame in which the center of mass is at rest and at the origin. Since the fictitious forces in such a frame are equivalent to those produced by a uniform gravitational field, the torque caused by the fictitious forces can be calculated as if the entire force acted directly on the center of mass. Thus the torque *about* the center of mass, caused by the fictitious forces, is zero. Only physical torques contribute to the left hand side of the above equation.

In considering combined translation and rotational motion, it is useful to know that the total angular momentum of any system, whether it is rigid or not, can be decomposed in a simple way. The total angular momentum $\vec{L}$ of the system, about any chosen origin, can be written as

$$\vec{L} = \vec{r}_{cm} \times \vec{p}_{tot} + \sum_i \vec{r}_{rel,i} \times m_i \vec{v}_{rel,i} \, ,$$

where $\vec{r}_{rel,i} = \vec{r}_i - \vec{r}_{cm}$ is the position of the ith particle relative to center of mass, and similarly $\vec{v}_{rel,i} = \vec{v}_i - \vec{v}_{cm}$ is the velocity of the ith particle relative to the velocity of the center of mass. The equation can be summarized by saying that the total angular momentum is the angular momentum of the center of mass, plus the angular momentum about the center of mass. Similarly the total torque acting on the system, about any chosen origin, can be decomposed as

$$\vec{\tau} = \vec{r}_{cm} \times \vec{F}_{tot} + \sum_i \vec{r}_{rel,i} \times \vec{F}_i \, ,$$

where $\vec{F}_i$ is the external force acting on the ith particle, and $\vec{F}_{tot}$ is the total external force on the system. Since $\vec{r}_{cm}$ is the only quantity in this formula that depends on the choice of origin, all dependence on the choice of origin disappears if $\vec{F}_{tot} = 0$.

SUMMARY

* To fully describe rotations in three dimensions, the three quantities angular velocity, angular momentum, and torque must be defined as vectors.

* If a rigid body rotates with one point held fixed, then the angular velocity $\vec{\omega}$ is defined to point along the instantaneous axis of rotation, with a magnitude equal to the scalar angular velocity discussed in the previous chapter. The choice of the two directions along the axis is determined by the right-hand rule convention. The velocity of any atom on the rigid body is given by $\vec{v} = \vec{\omega} \times \vec{r}$, where $\vec{r}$ is the displacement of the atom measured from the fixed point.

* The vector angular momentum of a particle about a point P is given by $\vec{L} = \vec{r} \times \vec{p}$, where $\vec{r}$ is the displacement of the particle measured from the point P, and $\vec{p}$ is the momentum.

* The vector torque exerted on a particle about a point P is given by $\vec{\tau} = \vec{r} \times \vec{F}$, where $\vec{r}$ is the displacement of the particle measured from the point P, and $\vec{F}$ is the applied force. The torque is equal to the rate of change of the angular momentum.

* Angular momentum is a conserved quantity: that is, the angular momentum of a system (about any point) does not change in the absence of an external torque.

* An initially stationary rigid body remains in equilibrium if there is no net force and no net torque acting on it. The torque may be calculated about any point.

* Combined translational and rotational motion of a rigid body can be described by separately considering the translational motion of the center of mass, and the rotation of the object about the center of mass.

* Physical concepts introduced in this chapter: angular velocity, angular momentum, and torque as vectors; central forces.

* Mathematical concepts introduced in this chapter: vector (or cross) product.

321

* Equations introduced in this chapter:

$$c_x = a_y b_z - a_z b_y \ ;$$
$$c_y = a_z b_x - a_x b_z \ ; \qquad \text{(vector cross product, component form)};$$
$$c_z = a_x b_y - a_y b_x \ .$$

$$|\vec{c}| = |\vec{a}||\vec{b}|\sin\theta \qquad \text{(magnitude of vector cross product)};$$

$$\vec{v} = \vec{\omega} \times \vec{r} \qquad \text{(velocity of atom in rotating body with a fixed point)};$$

$$\vec{v} = \vec{v}_P + \vec{\omega} \times (\vec{r} - \vec{r}_P) \qquad \text{(velocity of atom in rotating body, general case)};$$

$$\vec{L} = \sum_i \vec{r}_i \times \vec{p}_i \qquad \text{(angular momentum, as vector product)};$$

$$\vec{\tau} = \sum_i \vec{r}_i \times \vec{F}_i \qquad \text{(vector torque, as vector product)};$$

$$\vec{\tau} = \frac{d\vec{L}}{dt} \qquad \text{(torque equation)};$$

$$\left.\begin{aligned} \sum \vec{F}^{\text{ext}} &= M\vec{a}_{\text{cm}} = \frac{d\vec{p}}{dt} \\ \sum \vec{\tau}^{\text{ext}} &= \frac{d\vec{L}_{\text{cm}}}{dt} \end{aligned}\right\} \qquad \text{(combined translational and rotational motion)};$$

$$\vec{L} = \vec{r}_{\text{cm}} \times \vec{p}_{\text{tot}} + \sum_i \vec{r}_{\text{rel},i} \times m_i \vec{v}_{\text{rel},i} \qquad \text{(angular momentum decomposition)};$$

$$\vec{\tau} = \vec{r}_{\text{cm}} \times \vec{F}_{\text{tot}} + \sum_i \vec{r}_{\text{rel},i} \times \vec{F}_i \qquad \text{(torque decomposition)}.$$

PROBLEMS AND QUESTIONS

By the end of this chapter you should be able to answer or solve the types of questions or problems stated below.

Note: throughout the book, in multiple-choice problems, the answers have been rounded off to 2 significant figures, unless otherwise stated.

At the end of the chapter there are answers to all the problems. In addition, for problems with an (H) or (S) after the number, there are respectively hints on how to solve the problems or completely worked-out solutions.

9A   **STATIC EQUILIBRIUM**

9A.1   You're helping a friend move, and the two of you carry a desk out to your truck. The desk is 1.5 m long, and you find that to lift it you have to exert an upward force of 300 N, while your friend only has to apply 200 N. Taking $g = 10$ m/s^2, what is the mass of the desk?

     (a) 25 kg; (b) 30 kg; (c) 50 kg; (d) none of these.

If you're each holding on to a short side of the desk, how far from your end is its center of mass?

     (a) 0.5 m; (b) 0.6 m; (c) 0.9 m; (d) 1 m.

9A.2   A uniform steel girder 10 m long and having a mass of 1500 kg is placed on the flat roof of a building such that part of it sticks out beyond the edge of the roof. As a result of a bet, a 100 kg construction worker walks out and stands at the very end of the beam. What is his maximum possible distance from the edge of the building?

     (a) 5.0 m; (b) 4.7 m; (c) 5.8 m; (d) 4.2 m.

9A.3   A rectangular bin contains three identical cylindrical bottles, each of mass 0.7 kg, stacked horizontally as shown. The two lower bottles do not quite touch. Find all the forces acting on each bottle, assuming frictional effects can be neglected.

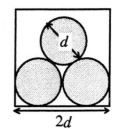

9A.4 (S)   A ball of radius r and mass m is placed against a step of height h. What is the minimum horizontal force F (applied to the center of mass) required to start the ball rolling over the step?

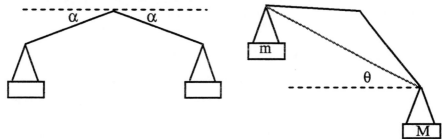

9A.5 (S)   A beam balance consists of two pans suspended from a rod which is bent in the middle as shown. The rod is free to pivot about the bend. If two different masses M and m

9A.5, continued:

$(M > m)$ are placed in the pans, at what angle θ does the balance come to rest? How does its behavior differ from that of a straight rod like a seesaw?

9A.6 (H)   A non-uniform horizontal rod is supported by two massless strings, one making an angle of 30° with the horizontal and one an angle of 45°. The rod is 10 cm long. Where is its center of mass?

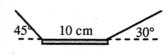

9A.7 (H)   A uniform ladder of mass m and length ℓ rests against a smooth wall. A do-it-yourself enthusiast of mass M stands on the ladder a distance d from the bottom. If the ladder makes an angle θ with the ground, what is the minimum coefficient of friction required between the ladder and the ground in order that the ladder will not slip? Assume that there is negligible friction between the ladder and the wall.

Suppose that the homeowner in question is attempting to do some emergency repairs after her house has been damaged by a storm. Her 3 m ladder is not really long enough for the task, and she has to stand on the top rung, 2.8 m from the base, in order to do the job. Her mass is 70 kg, the mass of the aluminum ladder is negligible, and the angle the ladder makes with the horizontal is 70°. Unfortunately, due to the rain, the coefficient of friction between the ladder and her paved yard is only 0.20. Will she slip? Will the situation be improved if her friend, who has a mass of 90 kg but is afraid of heights, stands on the bottom rung of the ladder, 0.2 meters from the base, while she climbs to the top?

9A.8 (S)   A table consists of a uniform circular top of mass M and radius r, supported by three equally spaced legs of negligible mass situated at the rim of the table. A coffee pot of mass m is located midway between two adjacent legs. Calculate the normal force exerted by the floor on each leg of the table. What if the table had four equally spaced legs?

9A.9 (H)   Three people are carrying a rectangular slab of wood weighing 800 N. The slab is 2.5 m long and 1.5 m wide and of uniform thickness. Two of the people hold the slab at each end of a long side, while the third holds the other long side, 1 m from a corner. Assuming the slab is level and they all lift vertically, find the force exerted by each person. How do these forces depend on the distance between the third carrier and the corner of the slab?

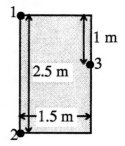

9B   ANGULAR MOMENTUM AND CENTRAL FORCES

9B.1 (S)   A symmetrical rigid body spins about its axis of symmetry. In which direction does its angular momentum vector point? (The body's center of mass is stationary.)

9B.2 (S)   One of the first achievements of the modern scientific method was Johannes Kepler's analysis of Tycho Brahe's observations of planetary positions. Kepler deduced three empirical laws governing planetary motion, from which Newton subsequently developed his law of universal gravitation.

9B.2, continued:

Kepler's second law states that "a line drawn from the Sun to any planet sweeps out equal areas in equal times". Show that this law implies that the angular momentum of the planet due to its orbital motion is constant.

9B.3 (S) Comets, in contrast to planets, follow very elongated elliptical orbits, so that their distance from the Sun varies greatly over the course of the orbit. Suppose that a short-period comet has an orbit whose closest approach to the Sun (or perihelion) is 5×10^{10} m, the furthest point (or aphelion) being 2×10^{12} m. What is its speed at perihelion?

9B.4 (H) Suppose that we wished to dispose of nuclear waste by launching it into space and 'firing it into the Sun'. One simple plan would be to start by putting the rocket into a circular orbit about the Sun at the same radius (and hence the same orbital speed) as the Earth. The rocket would then fire its engines in reverse for a short burst, slowing the rocket just enough so that the resulting orbit would graze the surface of the Sun, causing the rocket to be vaporized. By how much would the speed have to be changed? For comparison, if the rocket fired its engines forward for a short burst, by how much would the speed have to be changed for the rocket to leave the solar system altogether? [The Earth's orbit has a radius of 150 million kilometers and the Sun's radius is about 700 thousand kilometers. The mass of the Sun is 2.0×10^{30} kg, and the value of the gravitational constant G is 6.67×10^{-11} N $\cdot$ m^2/kg^2.]

Challenge Problem:

The method of reaching the Sun described above is far from being the most fuel-efficient. Find a flight plan by which the rocket could reach the Sun with a significantly smaller change in speed required from the engines, and thus with significantly less fuel consumption.

9B.5 On a frictionless table with its surface in the horizontal xy plane, a small object of mass m is attached by a nail to a taut horizontal massless string of length ℓ. Initially the object is at rest and the string lies along the y axis. A second identical object slides on the table with speed v in a direction making an angle θ to the string, as shown. On impact the objects stick together and move off with the string remaining taut.

(a) After impact, what is the magnitude of the angular momentum vector of the two-object system about the nail?

(b) What is the direction of this angular momentum vector?

9C VECTOR TORQUE

9C.1 (H) A particle of mass m at position $[x, y, 0]$ with respect to some point O is acted on by a force $\vec{F}$ given by $[F_x, F_y, 0]$. Using the definition of the torque about an axis given in Chapter 8, namely $\tau_{\text{axis}} = F_\perp R$, where $F_\perp$ is the counterclockwise tangential component of the applied force and R is the radial distance to the axis of rotation, show (without using vector products) that the torque on the particle about the z-axis is

$$\tau_{\text{axis}} = xF_y - yF_x .$$

That is, prove that the scalar torque defined in Chapter 8 is equal to the z-component of the vector torque defined in Chapter 9.

9C.2 (S)   Use the component form of the vector product to verify that $\vec{\tau} = \dfrac{d\vec{L}}{dt}$.

9C.3   Explain, in 100 words or less, the distinction between torque about an *axis* and torque about a *point*.

9D   **MOTION OF A RIGID BODY IN THREE DIMENSIONS**

9D.1 (S)   A uniform rod is fixed to a rotating horizontal turntable so that its lower end is on the axis of the turntable and it makes an angle of 20° to the vertical. (It is thus rotating with uniform angular velocity about an axis passing through one end and inclined at 20° to the direction of the rod.) If the turntable is rotating clockwise as seen from above, what is the direction of the rod's angular velocity vector?

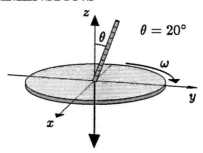

(a) vertically downwards;   (b) down at 20° to the vertical;
(c) up at 20° to the vertical;   (d) vertically upwards.

What is the direction of its angular momentum vector (calculated about its lower end)?

(a) vertically downwards;   (b) down at 20° to the horizontal;
(c) up at 20° to the horizontal;   (d) vertically upwards.

Is there a torque acting on it, and if so in what direction?

(a) yes, vertically;   (b) yes, horizontally;
(c) yes, at 20° to the horizontal;   (d) no.

9D.2 (S)   A conical pendulum consists of a small heavy sphere of mass m attached to a string of length ℓ and negligible mass. The string makes an angle θ with the vertical and the bob describes a circular path with constant speed v.

(a) What is the angular momentum of the bob about a vertical axis through the point of suspension? What torque is exerted about this axis?

(b) What is the angular momentum vector of the bob with respect to the point of suspension itself? What torque is exerted about this point?

9D.3 (H)   A ruler 31 cm long and 2 cm wide is resting on an air table, so there is no frictional force acting. You are asked to apply two 1 N forces to the ruler (in the plane of the air table—no vertical forces allowed!) such that (a) there is a net force on the ruler, but no net torque; (b) there is a net torque, but no net force; (c) there is neither a net force nor a net torque; (d) there is a net torque *and* a net force. In each case, what will the ruler do? (Recall that any two-dimensional motion can be represented as translation

9D.3, continued:

plus rotation about the center of mass, so you can regard the ruler's center of mass as the axis for your torque.)

Suppose you choose to apply your two 1 N forces parallel to one another and perpendicular to the long side of the ruler, one at its midpoint and one at one end. Which of the cases (a)–(d) is this? If you apply these forces for 0.001 s and then let the ruler move freely, what will its final linear and angular velocity be if its mass is 50 g? Make a scale drawing of the ruler's motion by plotting its position and orientation at $t = 0$, 10, 12, 14, 16, 18 and 20 s, defining $t = 0$ as the time the forces were first applied.

9D.4 (S) A gyroscope is a massive rapidly spinning wheel mounted on an axle of negligible mass. If such a device is held with the axle horizontal and supported at one end by a vertical post, what will happen when it is released? Assume the wheel has mass m and moment of inertia I, that it is spinning with angular velocity ω, and that the distance between the wheel and the supported end of the axle is ℓ.

9D.5 (H) A frequent exhibit in science museums is a gyroscope made of a bicycle wheel with a weighted rim and handles along the axle. Visitors to the exhibit take the spinning wheel with its axis horizontal and sit in a chair which is suspended from a frictionless pivot so that it is free to swing or rotate in any direction. They are then instructed to turn the wheel so that its axis is vertical. What happens? Explain what is going on in terms of angular momentum and applied torques.

9D.6 (H) An aircraft lands at a speed v_0. Before it touches down, its wheels are not rotating. Describe in words what happens when the wheels touch the ground. Assuming that each wheel has radius R and moment of inertia I and supports a weight Mg, and that the pilot does not apply reverse thrust until the aircraft is no longer skidding, how fast is the plane moving when it stops skidding?

9D.7 Discuss the relevance of angular momentum in the following examples:

(a) rifles, which have grooved barrels so that the bullet emerges spinning about its long axis, as opposed to smooth-bore guns, whose bullets don't spin;

(b) frisbees;

(c) tail rotors on helicopters;

(d) navigational gyroscopes (mounted on frictionless gimbals, which allow their axes to rotate freely relative to the mounting) in aircraft and satellites;

(e) stabilizing gyroscopes (large flywheels mounted on a fixed axis) on ships.

9D.8 (S) Show that the equation relating the velocity of a point on a rigid body to the body's angular velocity

$$\vec{v} = \vec{v}_P + \vec{\omega} \times (\vec{r} - \vec{r}_P),$$

where P is a reference point on the body, is indeed independent of the choice of reference point P, the origin of the coordinate system, and the velocity of the coordinate system, as stated in the text.

9D.9   A meteoroid in empty space rotates about its center of mass. We choose a coordinate system in which the center of mass is at rest at the origin, and the angular velocity at the time of interest points along the z-axis, so that $\vec{\omega} = [0, 0, \omega_z]$. A small particle, or **chondrule**, of the mineral olivine is embedded in the meteroid at position $\vec{r}_0 = [x_0, 0, z_0]$. The chondrule has mass M. (Note that the chondrule is part of the meteoroid, so its mass and position have been included in the calculation of the meteoroid's center of mass.)

(a) What are the components of the velocity vector $\vec{v}$ of the chondrule?

(b) What is the angular momentum of the chondrule (i) about the z-axis, i.e. the instantaneous axis of rotation; (ii) about the center of mass of the meteoroid?

(c) The overall angular momentum vector of the meteoroid about its center of mass makes an angle θ with the angular velocity vector. Describe in words the motion of the meteoroid as seen by a passing space probe.

COMPLETE SOLUTIONS TO PROBLEMS WITH AN (S)

9A.4   *A ball of radius r and mass m is placed against a step of height h. What is the minimum horizontal force F (applied to the center of mass) required to start the ball rolling over the step?*

Conceptualize

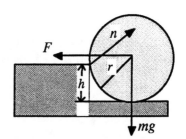

If we consider the case where the ball simply rests on the lower level with no applied force $\vec{F}$, then clearly there will be a force $m\vec{g}$ downwards and a normal force $\vec{N}$ upwards; with no other forces acting, these will be of equal magnitude. As we apply a gradually increasing force $\vec{F}$, the ball will be pulled against the step, which will therefore begin to exert a contact force $\vec{n}$. This has some upward component, so the magnitude of $\vec{N}$ decreases as $\vec{n}$ increases. When the ball eventually starts to roll over the step, it loses contact with the lower level, and $\vec{N}$ is then obviously zero. It follows that the limiting case occurs when the ball is still stationary and in contact with the lower level, but the value of $\vec{N}$ is zero, and the upward component of $\vec{n}$ balances $m\vec{g}$. Increasing $|\vec{F}|$ beyond this will require that $|\vec{n}|$ increase (the ball cannot move horizontally, so the horizontal component of $\vec{n}$ must balance $\vec{F}$) and there will then be a net upward force on the ball to lift it over the step.

Formulate and Solve

In the limiting case the ball is stationary, so there is no net force and no net torque. The force equations involve the unknown magnitude and direction of $\vec{n}$, but if we consider torque *about the point of contact with the step* these are eliminated from the torque equation. This gives

$$\tau = F(r - h) - mgd \ ,$$

where d is the horizontal distance between the center of the ball and the vertical part of the step. Constructing a right-angled triangle between the center of the ball, the point of the step, and the line of $\vec{F}$ gives us

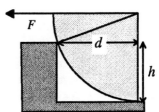

$$d^2 = r^2 - (r - h)^2 = h(2r - h)$$

and so

$$F = mg \frac{\sqrt{h(2r - h)}}{r - h} \ .$$

Scrutinize

The dimensions of our solution are clearly correct, since the term multiplying mg is dimensionless. We can do a further check by considering special situations: if $h \to 0$, $F \to 0$ (no force is required to roll the ball over a nonexistent step!), and if $h \to r$, $F \to \infty$ (if $h = r$ the applied force acts through the point of contact, and hence exerts

9A.4, continued:

no torque about that point, so regardless of its magnitude it cannot cause the ball to roll over the step).

If $h > r$ we get a negative force, which is clearly not a solution (pulling the ball away from the step is not going to work!). Common sense agrees that if our force is actually applied below the level of the step it is never going to succeed in pulling the ball over the top, and if we consider our diagram we see that for such a situation the torque exerted by $\vec{\mathbf{F}}$ is not $F(r - h)$ as we have assumed, because the point of contact between ball and step is no longer the top of the step, but rather the leftmost point of the ball. This is exactly the same as the case $h = r$, and we saw above that $F \to \infty$ in this case.

Learn
Many problems involving limiting cases can be regarded as statics problems, because the limiting case often corresponds to a stationary object with zero net force acting on it. This is frequently the case for friction problems, for example.

Note that in this example a good choice of reference axis for the torques reduced the number of equations we needed from three to one, by eliminating any need to calculate $\vec{\mathbf{n}}$.

9A.5   _A beam balance consists of two pans suspended from a rod which is bent in the middle as shown. The rod is free to pivot about the bend. If two different masses M and m ($M > m$) are placed in the pans, at what angle θ does the balance come to rest? How does its behavior differ from that of a straight rod like a seesaw?_

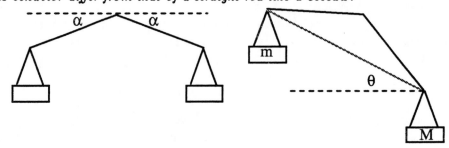

Conceptualize
When the balance is at rest there must be no net force on it (or it would move) and also no net torque (or it would turn). In this case the net force is always zero (a contact force from the pivot is balancing the gravitational force on the pans), so we are only interested in the net torque. The gravitational force always acts through the center of mass, as shown in the _Essentials_, so we can disregard the shape of the pans and simply treat them as point masses.

Formulate
We have three forces acting ($M\vec{\mathbf{g}}$, $m\vec{\mathbf{g}}$, and a contact force from the pivot), but by taking the pivot as the reference axis we can eliminate its contact force from the torque equation. Straightforward trigonometry tells us that the right-hand arm of the balance makes an angle $(\theta + \alpha)$ with the horizontal and the left-hand arm an angle $(\alpha - \theta)$. The torque around the pivot is therefore

$$\tau = Mg\ell\cos(\theta + \alpha) - mg\ell\cos(\alpha - \theta) \ ,$$

9A.5, continued:

writing ℓ for the length of each arm of the balance. Hence for equilibrium

$$M\cos(\theta + \alpha) = m\cos(\alpha - \theta) \ .$$

Solve

To solve this we make use of the trigonometric identity

$$\cos(\alpha \pm \beta) = \cos\alpha\cos\beta \mp \sin\alpha\sin\beta$$

and write

$$(M - m)\cos\theta\cos\alpha = (M + m)\sin\theta\sin\alpha \ ,$$

from which

$$\tan\theta = \frac{1}{\tan\alpha}\left(\frac{M - m}{M + m}\right) \ .$$

A straight rod corresponds to the case $\alpha = 0$, and our condition for equilibrium is then $M\cos\theta = m\cos\theta$. This plainly cannot be met unless $M = m$ or $\theta = 90°$. For unequal masses the balance will therefore tilt until it hangs vertically with M below m (if the design of the pivot allows this). For equal masses *any* value of θ will do—if the balance is held stationary at any angle it will remain so when released. The bent balance, on the other hand, will swing back to the horizontal position if released with equal masses in the pans.

Scrutinize

The equation is clearly dimensionally correct, and in considering the straight rod we have already checked one extreme value. We can also consider $M = m$, in which case we should expect the balance to hang level, as indeed it does ($\tan\theta = 0$). For very large M we would expect the balance to tilt so that the pan containing M hung straight downwards, which requires $\theta = 90° - \alpha$, and this is what our formula gives ($\tan(90° - \phi) = 1/\tan\phi$ for any angle ϕ).

9A.8   *A table consists of a uniform circular top of mass M and radius r, supported by three equally spaced legs of negligible mass situated at the rim of the table. A coffee pot of mass m is located midway between two adjacent legs. Calculate the normal force exerted by the floor on each leg of the table. What if the table had four equally spaced legs?*

Conceptualize

This is again a problem in which the net force and the net torque will be zero. Since the table legs are massless, there must be no net force on them—a net force on a massless object gives infinite acceleration—and so the force that each of them applies to the tabletop is the same as the force that the floor applies to them, and likewise for the force applied to the leg by the tabletop. The coffeepot is small in dimensions compared to the tabletop, so we can treat it as a point mass. All our forces (the weights of the table and coffeepot and the three normal forces) are in the z direction, so we have only one force equation, but we have two components of torque corresponding to rotation about the x-axis and the y-axis respectively.

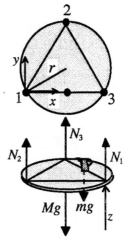

9A.8, continued:

Formulate *Three legs:*
There is no obvious 'best' choice of reference point: we can choose the top of leg 1, which at least removes its normal force from the torque equations. With this choice of coordinate system, our three equations are

$$F_z = N_1 + N_2 + N_3 - (M+m)g$$

$$\tau_y = \frac{\sqrt{3}}{2}rMg + \frac{\sqrt{3}}{2}rmg - \frac{\sqrt{3}}{2}rN_2 - \sqrt{3}\,rN_3$$

$$\tau_x = \frac{1}{2}rMg - \frac{3}{2}rN_2 \ .$$

Solve
The equilibrium conditions for the table are thus

$$(M+m)g = N_1 + N_2 + N_3$$

$$(M+m)g = N_2 + 2N_3$$

$$Mg = 3N_2 \ ,$$

which are easily solved to give

$$N_1 = N_3 = \left(\frac{1}{3}M + \frac{1}{2}m\right)g \ ;$$

$$N_2 = \frac{1}{3}Mg \ .$$

Scrutinize
As we might expect from the symmetry of the situation, the weight of the table is shared equally by all three legs, while the weight of the coffeepot is taken by the two legs between which it sits.

Formulate *Four legs:*
The equations for the four-legged table are very similar:

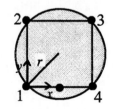

$$F_z = N_1 + N_2 + N_3 + N_4 - (M+m)g$$

$$\tau_y = \frac{1}{\sqrt{2}}rMg + \frac{1}{\sqrt{2}}rmg - \frac{2}{\sqrt{2}}rN_3 - \frac{2}{\sqrt{2}}rN_4$$

$$\tau_x = \frac{1}{\sqrt{2}}rMg - \frac{2}{\sqrt{2}}rN_2 - \frac{2}{\sqrt{2}}rN_3 \ .$$

However, here we have a potential problem—there are still only three equations, but we have added another unknown force. We will not be able to solve this problem completely using only these equations.

332

9A.8, continued:

Solve
If we continue nonetheless, we obtain the equilibrium conditions

$$(M + m)g = N_1 + N_2 + N_3 + N_4$$

$$(M + m)g = 2N_3 + 2N_4$$

$$Mg = 2N_2 + 2N_3 \; ,$$

from which we find

$$N_1 = \left(\frac{1}{2}M + m\right)g - N_4$$

$$N_2 = N_4 - \frac{1}{2}mg$$

$$N_3 = \frac{1}{2}(M + m)g - N_4 \; .$$

This is as far as we can go without making additional assumptions. In this simple case, we can argue that if the floor is uniform the symmetry of the situation implies that $N_1 = N_4$, which gives us the fourth equation we need to deduce that

$$N_1 = \left(\frac{1}{4}M + \frac{1}{2}m\right)g = N_4$$

$$N_2 = \frac{1}{4}Mg = N_3 \; .$$

However, this clearly would not work if the coffeepot had been less symmetrically located, or if we had an uneven floor or legs of slightly different lengths. (For example, a solution with $N_2 = 0$, corresponding to a short leg 2 which does not touch the ground, is perfectly possible.) In such a case we would have to admit that the problem is not completely soluble in terms of rigid bodies. Such problems are called **_underdetermined_** (or sometimes **_indeterminate_**).

Scrutinize
The underdetermined nature of the four-legged table problem is clear to anyone who has ever sat at a table with legs of slightly unequal length (or situated on a slightly uneven floor). Such tables commonly have two more-or-less stable states, each with one leg not touching the ground, and will go from one to the other whenever a small off-center force is applied. This is because such a table is a very good approximation to a rigid body. Less rigid objects do not behave in this way, as discussed below.

Learn
It is apparent from everyday experience that many apparently underdetermined systems do in fact have perfectly well-defined solutions. For example, a car with an asymmetric weight distribution is completely equivalent in rigid-body terms to our four-legged table, but it is obvious that in fact such a car does have a unique stable equilibrium position—if we drove it on to a weighbridge segmented so that the weight on each

9A.8, continued:

wheel was determined separately, we would get a definite value for the downward force on each wheel, and we would expect that answer to remain the same if we repeated the measurement. What happens in this case is that the springs and tires of the car compress until the unequal loadings on the four wheels are balanced by unequal spring forces. We don't know how to deal with this because the car is not now behaving as a completely rigid body—parts of it are deforming and changing their relative positions. Fortunately, most solid objects can be regarded as very-nearly-rigid bodies, and small deformations of the object behave like compression or extension of a spring: a restoring force acts which is proportional to the amount of deformation and directed so as to return the object to its original state. Hence we can solve such problems by combining rigid-body techniques with spring forces, involving some new terminology (introducing the equivalents of the spring constant k for various kinds of deformation) but no new physical principles. Since this book is intended to be introductory, we will not pursue the details of this any further.

9B.1   *A symmetrical rigid body spins about its axis of symmetry. In which direction does its angular momentum vector point? (The body's center of mass is stationary.)*

Conceptualize

We calculate the angular momentum of an extended object by summing (integrating, actually) over its volume. To do this we need to know the momentum of a small mass element as a function of its distance from the axis of rotation (we shall then be able to calculate $\vec{r} \times \vec{p}$ in terms of $\vec{r}$). Therefore the first stage of the solution is to obtain an expression for the linear velocity of such a mass element in terms of the angular velocity of the body. We can then construct its angular momentum, and the wording of the question suggests that the symmetry of the body will lead to a solution.

Formulate

Take the axis about which the body spins to be the z-axis and consider a small element of mass m_i at position vector $[x_i, y_i, z_i]$. After a time Δt it will have position vector $[x_i + \Delta x_i, y_i + \Delta y_i, z_i]$, where we can see from the diagram that

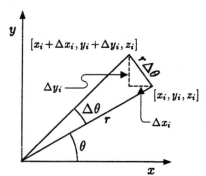

$$\Delta x_i = -r\Delta\theta \sin\theta = -y_i\Delta\theta$$

$$\Delta y_i = +r\Delta\theta \cos\theta = +x_i\Delta\theta \; .$$

Since $\frac{\Delta\theta}{\Delta t} \rightarrow \frac{d\theta}{dt}$ as Δt tends to zero,

$$v_{x,i} = \frac{dx_i}{dt} = -y_i\frac{d\theta}{dt} = -\omega y_i$$

$$v_{y,i} = \frac{dy_i}{dt} = +x_i\frac{d\theta}{dt} = +\omega x_i \; .$$

The angular momentum of this small element of mass about the body's center of mass is therefore

$$\vec{L}_i = \vec{r}_i \times m_i\vec{v}_i = m_i[y_iv_{z,i} - z_iv_{y,i}, \; z_iv_{x,i} - x_iv_{z,i}, \; x_iv_{y,i} - y_iv_{x,i}]$$

$$= m_i\omega[-z_ix_i, -z_iy_i, (x_i^2 + y_i^2)]$$

9B.1, continued:

With this information we can solve the problem.

Solve
The body is symmetrical about its axis of rotation. Therefore there must be an identical element of mass m_i at position vector $[-x_i, -y_i, z_i]$. The angular momentum of this mass element is, by the same logic,

$$\vec{L}_{i'} = m_i \omega [+z_i x_i, +z_i y_i, (x_i^2 + y_i^2)] \ .$$

Adding these two contributions, the x- and y-components cancel out and the net angular momentum points along the z-axis. We can repeat this process for every pair of mirror-image mass elements in the entire body, so our conclusion is that the angular momentum vector of the whole object points along the z-axis, i.e. along the axis of rotation.

Scrutinize
We could actually have deduced the answer to this question without doing any calculation at all. We know our body has an axis of symmetry: that is, there is an axis for which, if the body is rotated about this axis, it will rotate back into itself (i.e. its appearance after this rotation is indistinguishable from its appearance before the rotation). Suppose $\vec{L}$ does *not* point along the axis of symmetry: then after the rotation we have a body which looks the same as before, is rotating in the same way as before (as the body is spinning about its axis of symmetry, our rotation does not change $\vec{\omega}$), and yet has a different angular momentum vector. This is clearly unphysical, and the only way to avoid it is to conclude that $\vec{L}$ *does* point along the axis of symmetry.

Learn
Axes of rotation with the properties of the one in this problem (i.e. they pass through the body's center of mass and the angular momentum vector of the body is along the axis of rotation) are called *principal axes*. It turns out that *any* rigid body, even if not symmetrical, has three mutually perpendicular principal axes (for highly symmetrical objects like spheres there may be more than one possible set of three). This result has interesting consequences. If the angular momentum vector points along the angular velocity vector, no torque is required to keep the object spinning, and consequently once set spinning it will (in the absence of external forces) continue to do so. If, however, it is set spinning about an axis which is not a principal axis, so that the angular momentum does not point along the axis of rotation, a torque is required to keep the body rotating around this axis, because the direction of the angular momentum keeps changing. The result is that a body subject to no net torque (e.g. a projectile) can have stable rotational motion about a time-independent axis only if the axis is a principal axis. If one starts an isolated body spinning with an angular velocity that is not aligned with a principal axis, the direction of the *angular momentum vector* must remain fixed (because no torque is acting, so $\vec{L}$ is constant), and since this is not parallel to the angular *velocity* vector, it follows that the axis of rotation must change with time. The resulting motion is quite similar to the precession of a gyroscope (see problem 9D.4) and is called *torque-free precession*. You can see this effect in the "tumbling" of a thrown football or the wobbling of a badly thrown frisbee.

9B.2 *One of the first achievements of the modern scientific method was Johannes Kepler's analysis of Tycho Brahe's observations of planetary positions. Kepler deduced three empirical laws governing planetary motion, from which Newton subsequently developed his law of universal gravitation.*

Kepler's second law states that "a line drawn from the Sun to any planet sweeps out equal areas in equal times". Show that this law implies that the angular momentum of the planet due to its orbital motion is constant.

Conceptualize

The geometry of the situation is shown in the diagram. As the gravitational force acts along the line of $\vec{r}$, there are only two independent unit vectors in this problem, $\hat{r}$ and $\hat{v}$. These define a plane, and all the motion of the planet will take place in this plane (there is no component of force acting to give it an acceleration out of the plane). This is therefore a two-dimensional problem, and the angular momentum will have only one component, in the direction perpendicular to the orbital plane. To solve the problem we must work out the rate at which the radius vector sweeps out area (the *areal velocity*), and relate this to the angular momentum.

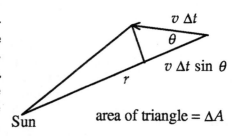

area of triangle $= \Delta A$

Formulate and Solve

Assume that at a given time our planet is a distance r from the Sun and is moving with velocity $\vec{v}$. In a short time interval Δt it moves a distance $v\Delta t$ and the line joining it and the Sun sweeps out a small triangular area $\Delta A = \frac{1}{2}rv\Delta t\sin\theta$, where θ is the angle between $\vec{v}$ and $\vec{r}$. Now the angular momentum of the planet is just $mrv\sin\theta$, where m is the mass of the planet, so

$$\frac{dA}{dt} = \lim_{\Delta t \to 0} \frac{\Delta A}{\Delta t} = \frac{L}{2m}$$

and we conclude that Kepler's second law, $dA/dt =$ constant, implies constant angular momentum (and vice versa).

Scrutinize

We have not used any information about the gravitational force in this derivation *except* the fact that it acts along the line joining the two bodies: it is a *central force*. The equal-area law will in fact hold for *any* central force, since if the force between two objects is directed along the line joining them there is no torque (taking either body as reference point), and thus no change in angular momentum.

Learn

We conclude that Kepler's second law tells us very little about gravity, just that it is a central force. However, Kepler's first and third laws, which describe the shape of planetary orbits and the relation between orbital size and period respectively, are much more restrictive. These laws allowed Newton to deduce the detailed form of the law of gravity.

9B.3 *Comets, in contrast to planets, follow very elongated elliptical orbits, so that their dis-*
tance from the Sun varies greatly over the course of the orbit. Suppose that a short-period
comet has an orbit whose closest approach to the Sun (or perihelion) is 5×10^{10} m, the
furthest point (or aphelion) being 2×10^{12} m. What is its speed at perihelion?

Conceptualize
This problem seems well suited to a conservation-law approach. We have seen in Problem 9B.2 that angular momentum is conserved in planetary orbits, and—since gravity,
a conservative force, is the only force acting—we expect mechanical energy to be conserved as well. The comet's linear momentum is not conserved, because there is a net
force acting on it. As we saw in 9B.2, orbital angular momentum has only one non-zero
component, so we will have two equations, one for energy and one for the z-component
of angular momentum.

Formulate
Recalling from Chapter 4 that the standard expression for gravitational potential energy is $-GMm/r$, where r is the distance
between the two masses M and m and the zero of potential
energy is defined to be infinite separation of the masses, conservation of energy gives

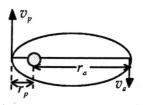

$$v_p^2 - \frac{2GM}{r_p} = v_a^2 - \frac{2GM}{r_a}$$

(where we have divided out the common factor of $m/2$). Since at perihelion and aphelion
the velocity of the comet is at right angles to the line joining it to the Sun, its angular
momentum $L = mvr$ in both cases, so conservation of angular momentum means that

$$v_p r_p = v_a r_a \ .$$

Solve
We use the second equation to eliminate v_a in the first, giving

$$v_p^2 - \frac{2GM}{r_p} = \frac{v_p^2 r_p^2}{r_a^2} - \frac{2GM}{r_a} \ ,$$

i.e.

$$v_p^2 \left(\frac{r_a^2 - r_p^2}{r_a^2} \right) = 2GM \left(\frac{r_a - r_p}{r_a r_p} \right)$$

hence

$$v_p = \sqrt{\frac{2GM r_a}{r_p (r_a + r_p)}} = 72 \text{ km/s} \ .$$

Scrutinize
We can check this equation by setting $r_a = r_p$, i.e. a circular orbit. The equation then
reduces to $v = \sqrt{GM/r}$, which is what we get by considering

$$\frac{GMm}{r^2} = \frac{mv^2}{r} \ .$$

337

9B.3, continued:

The circular orbit speed for $r = r_p$ is 52 km/s, less than the comet's speed at this point. This is as we expect, because the comet is going to move outwards (like a car taking a bend too fast). Conversely, the comet's speed at aphelion is $v_a = v_p r_p / r_a = 1.8$ km/s, less than the circular speed of 8.2 km/s.

Learn

As with most problems where conservation laws can be applied, this is much easier than trying to solve the relevant differential equations. Note that the total energy of the comet is $\frac{1}{2}mv^2 - GMm/r = -GMm/(r_a + r_p)$. The equivalent expression for a circular orbit is $-GMm/2r$ (see problem 6.2), so the radius of the circular orbit with the same total energy as the elliptical orbit is $\frac{1}{2}(r_a + r_p)$, or half the long axis of the ellipse. This quantity appears repeatedly in dynamical calculations of orbital motion and is referred to as the **semi-major axis** of the ellipse.

9C.2   *Use the component form of the vector product to verify that $\vec{\tau} = \dfrac{d\vec{L}}{dt}$.*

Conceptualize

This problem needs little conceptualization, as it is very specific.

Formulate

Torque $\vec{\tau} = \vec{r} \times \vec{F} = \vec{r} \times m\vec{a}$, and angular momentum $\vec{L} = \vec{r} \times \vec{p} = \vec{r} \times m\vec{v}$. We can approach the 'target' equation from either direction, but it is probably simplest to take the component form of $\vec{L}$ and differentiate.

Solve

The component form of the vector product tells us that $L_x = yp_z - zp_y$. Writing this in terms of mass and velocity gives us

$$\frac{dL_x}{dt} = \frac{d}{dt}(myv_z - mzv_y)$$

$$= m\frac{dy}{dt}v_z + my\frac{dv_z}{dt} - m\frac{dz}{dt}v_y - mz\frac{dv_y}{dt}$$

$$= mv_y v_z + y(ma_z) - mv_z v_y - z(ma_y)$$

$$= yF_z - zF_y = \tau_x .$$

The same holds for the y- and z-components, thus verifying the relationship we deduced earlier using vector notation.

Learn

This proof demonstrates that we can always manipulate the vector product by using its coordinate form. Pure vector algebra may be more elegant, but it is never **necessary** to use it.

9D.1   *A uniform rod is fixed to a rotating horizontal turntable so that its lower end is on the axis of the turntable and it makes an angle of 20° to the vertical. (It is thus rotating with uniform angular velocity about an axis passing through one end and inclined at 20° to the direction of the rod.) If the turntable is rotating clockwise as seen from above, what is the direction of the rod's angular velocity vector?*

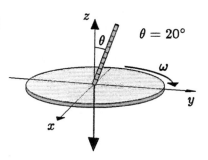

(a) *vertically downwards;*   (b) *down at 20° to the vertical;*
(c) *up at 20° to the vertical;*   (d) *vertically upwards.*

What is the direction of its angular momentum vector (calculated about its lower end)?

(a) *vertically downwards;*   (b) *down at 20° to the horizontal;*
(c) *up at 20° to the horizontal;*   (d) *vertically upwards.*

Is there a torque acting on it, and if so in what direction?

(a) *yes, vertically;*   (b) *yes, horizontally;*
(c) *yes, at 20° to the horizontal;*   (d) *no.*

Conceptualize
The problem asks for the direction of the rod's angular velocity vector, but the motion of the rod is complicated, and a little hard to visualize. However, we are told that the rod is fixed to the turntable, which means that the rod and turntable together form a single rigid body, and therefore must have a common angular velocity. The turntable rotates in the horizontal plane, so the axis is vertical. By definition the vector angular velocity $\vec{\omega}$ points along the axis of rotation, so the only issue will be to use the right-hand rule to determine if it points up or down.

For angular momentum and torque *about a point*, we must use the vector definitions. As we know more about the motion of the rod than we do about the forces acting on it, it makes sense to calculate the angular momentum vector $\vec{L}$ first, and then derive the torque from the rate of change of $\vec{L}$.

Formulate
Assume that at time $t = 0$ the rod is in the yz-plane, and consider a small segment of the rod at a distance r from its lower end. The y-coordinate of this segment is $r \sin \theta$, where $\theta = 20°$, and the x-coordinate is zero. At time t the rod will have rotated through an angle ωt about the vertical (z) axis. Looking from above, we will use our standard convention that angles and angular velocities are taken as positive when counterclockwise, so the clockwise motion in this case implies that $\omega < 0$. The position vector of the segment is then

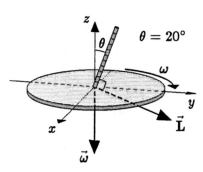

$$\vec{r} = [-\rho \sin \omega t, \, \rho \cos \omega t, \, r \cos \theta] \, ,$$

9D.1, continued:

where $\rho \equiv r \sin \theta$. The velocity of this segment is

$$\vec{v} = \frac{d\vec{r}}{dt} = -\omega\rho[\cos\omega t, \sin\omega t, 0] \,,$$

so its angular momentum is

$$\overrightarrow{\Delta L} = \vec{r} \times (\Delta m\, \vec{v}) = -\omega\rho\,\Delta m\,[-r\cos\theta\sin\omega t,\ r\cos\theta\cos\omega t,\ -\rho]$$

$$= -\omega r^2 \sin\theta\,\Delta m\,[-\cos\theta\sin\omega t,\ \cos\theta\cos\omega t,\ -\sin\theta] \,,$$

where Δm is the mass of the segment, and for the z-component we have used the trigonometric identity $\sin^2\alpha + \cos^2\alpha = 1$. To find the angular momentum for the whole rod, we would integrate this expression along the length of the rod. However, since this problem asks only about directions, we do not need to carry out this integration. From the above expression we see that the direction of $\overrightarrow{\Delta L}$ does not depend on r, so the integration will not affect the direction:

$$\vec{L} \propto -\omega[-\cos\theta\sin\omega t,\ \cos\theta\cos\omega t,\ -\sin\theta] \,,$$

where the proportionality constant is independent of time.

The net torque is the time derivative of $\vec{L}$, so

$$\vec{\tau} = \frac{d\vec{L}}{dt} \propto \omega^2[\cos\theta\ \cos\omega t,\ \cos\theta\ \sin\omega t,\ 0] \,.$$

Solve

The turntable rotates clockwise as viewed from above, so from the definition of $\vec{\omega}$, the angular velocity vector must point downwards, along the negative z-axis. The answer to the first question is *(a)*.

The torque is clearly nonzero, so a torque acts on the rod, but its z-component *is* zero, so it acts horizontally. The answer to the third question is *(b)*.

If we consider time $t = 0$, the angular momentum vector is in the direction $[0, \cos\theta, -\sin\theta]$, where $\theta = 20°$. It clearly points downwards (the z component is negative) at $20°$ to the horizontal. The answer to the second question is *(b)*.

Scrutinize

If you are good at visualizing things in three dimensions, you can work out the direction of the angular momentum vector without resorting to the coordinate form of the cross product. At the time when the rod is in the yz-plane, the instantaneous velocity of any point on the rod is in the positive x-direction, out of the page (since we are dealing with clockwise rotation). The vector $\vec{r}$ is in the plane of the page, pointing $20°$ to the right of the vertical axis. Using the right-hand rule, the vector $\vec{L} \propto \vec{r} \times \vec{v}$ points downward and towards the right, at $20°$ below the horizontal. As the rod rotates, the vertical

9D.1, continued:

component of $\vec{\mathbf{L}}$ remains the same, but the horizontal component sweeps out a circle, remaining constant in magnitude but changing direction: therefore there is no vertical component of torque (L_z remains fixed) but there are x- and y-components (L_x and L_y change with time). Hence the torque acts horizontally.

Learn
Notice that this system has zero angular acceleration ($\vec{\omega}$ is constant), but a nonzero net torque. The simple relation between torque and angular acceleration **_does not hold_** for vector torques, although you can always rely on the scalar relation $\tau_{\text{axis}} = I\alpha_{\text{axis}}$ for cases of rotation about a fixed axis. Recall that the scalar quantity τ_{axis} is not the magnitude of the $\vec{\tau}$, but rather its z-component τ_z, so in this case both sides of the equation $\tau_{\text{axis}} = I\alpha_{\text{axis}}$ are zero.

Why did we not use $\vec{\mathbf{r}} \times \vec{\mathbf{F}}$ to calculate the torque? After all, the unknown contact force exerted by the turntable through the weld at the base of the rod acts through the origin, and therefore contributes no torque—or does it? If we consider the rod when it is stationary, we can see that this would present a problem: there would be nothing to oppose the torque exerted by gravity about the contact point, which has magnitude $\frac{1}{2}MgR\sin\theta$, where M is the total mass of the rod and R is its total length. But this cannot be: the net torque on a stationary object, calculated about any point, must be zero.

The only way out of this impasse is to recognize that the weld is not a geometrical point: it has some small spatial extent. The torque exerted by gravity is cancelled by an upward contact force acting through the near side of the weld (i.e. on the same side of the weld as the body of the rod) together with a downward contact force acting on the far side of the weld. Because they act so close to the origin, each of these forces must be much larger in magnitude than Mg (to satisfy the condition of zero net **_force_**, the difference between them must be Mg upwards). The weld therefore has to withstand forces much larger than the weight of the rod, so the engineering requirements for joints of this kind are much more stringent than one might naïvely expect.

One thorny aspect of this problem is the choice of signs that it forces us to consider: the angular velocity is clockwise, while we conventionally define counterclockwise as positive. Here we took ω to be negative, but we could alternatively have changed our conventions. Changing conventions makes it easier to keep track of which way the turntable is really rotating, but it requires you to rethink the signs that appear in your equations. Either approach requires care. One advantage of becoming accustomed to working with negative values is that one often needs this technique for more complicated problems. If there were two objects rotating about the same axis but in opposite directions, we would certainly not want to use different conventions for each so that both angular velocities would be positive.

9D.2   *A conical pendulum consists of a small heavy sphere of mass m attached to a string of length ℓ and negligible mass. The string makes an angle θ with the vertical and the bob describes a circular path with constant speed v.*

9D.2, continued:

(a) *What is the angular momentum of the bob about a vertical axis through the point of suspension? What torque is exerted about this axis?*

(b) *What is the angular momentum vector of the bob with respect to the point of suspension itself? What torque is exerted about this point?*

Conceptualize

The first part of this problem uses the 'scalar' quantities of torque and angular momentum about an axis. These are evaluated using quantities defined in the plane in which the bob moves. Even without calculation one can see that in this plane the bob behaves as if it were subject to a central force (its acceleration is directed towards the center of the circle in which it moves), and so we predict that the angular momentum will turn out to be constant, and the torque to be zero.

The second part of the problem is three-dimensional, as the suspension point is not in the plane of the bob's motion, and will therefore have to be solved using vector products.

Formulate and Solve (a)

The bob is describing a circle of radius $R = \ell \sin\theta$. Its angular velocity is therefore $\omega = v/R$ and its angular momentum about a vertical axis through the center of the circle is $I\omega = mRv$. This is constant, so there can be no torque about this axis, as we expected from the arguments above.

Formulate (b)

Now consider the situation relative to the point of suspension. Define a coordinate system with the origin at the suspension point and the z-axis vertically upwards. Assume that at time $t = 0$ the bob is in the xz-plane, i.e. its y-coordinate is zero. At time t it has moved through an angle ωt, where ω is its angular velocity about the z-axis, and its position relative to the suspension point is

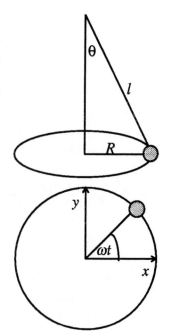

$$x = R\cos\omega t , \quad y = R\sin\omega t , \quad z = -Z ,$$

where $Z = \ell\cos\theta$. Its velocity is

$$\vec{\mathbf{v}} = \left[\frac{dx}{dt}, \frac{dy}{dt}, \frac{dz}{dt}\right]$$

and its momentum $m\mathbf{v}$ is therefore

$$p_x = -\omega mR\sin\omega t , \quad p_y = \omega mR\cos\omega t , \quad p_z = 0 .$$

9D.2, continued:

Solve (b)

Forming the vector product of $\vec{r}$ and $\vec{p}$ gives us the angular momentum

$$L_x = yp_z - zp_y = \omega m R Z \cos \omega t \; ;$$

$$L_y = zp_x - xp_z = \omega m R Z \sin \omega t \; ;$$

$$L_z = xp_y - yp_x = \omega m R^2 (\cos^2 \omega t + \sin^2 \omega t)$$

$$= \omega m R^2 = I\omega \; .$$

Note that this is *not* along the z-axis. It is also not constant, implying the existence of a torque about this point. Differentiating $\vec{L}$ with respect to time gives us $\tau_z = 0$, since L_z is constant, and

$$\tau_x = -\omega^2 m R Z \sin \omega t \; ;$$

$$\tau_y = \omega^2 m R Z \cos \omega t \; ;$$

The magnitude of the total torque is $\omega^2 m R Z$.

Scrutinize

The result of part (b) is, in fact, exactly what we would expect: the centripetal force calculated from the acceleration required for the bob's circular motion is $mv^2/R = m\omega^2 R$, and its line of action is a perpendicular distance Z from the suspension point, so the torque should indeed be $\omega^2 m R Z$.

The results of part (a) and part (b) should be consistent, as they refer to the same situation. We can check this by looking at the z-component of our angular momentum vector—the 'scalar' angular momentum around an axis is simply the component of vector angular momentum parallel to that axis. So the z-component of $\vec{L}$ should be mvR, and indeed it is.

Learn

This example clearly demonstrates the important differences between torque and angular momentum about an *axis*, which are effectively scalar quantities, and torque and angular momentum about a *point*, which are vectors. Although our two calculations are perfectly self-consistent, they represent quite different ways of looking at the situation. In particular, notice that the connection between torque and angular acceleration is no longer apparent for vector torques: our conical pendulum is still moving at constant angular velocity in case (b), but this does not mean that it is not subject to a net torque. The relation between torque and angular *momentum*, however, still holds, and is the more fundamental concept (in a similar way, if we extend our consideration to objects moving near the speed of light, the $\vec{F} = m\vec{a}$ formulation of the second law for linear motion likewise fails, but $\vec{F} = d\vec{p}/dt$ is still relevant).

9D.4 *A gyroscope is a massive rapidly spinning wheel mounted on an axle of negligible mass. If such a device is held with the axle horizontal and supported at one end by a vertical post, what will happen when it is released? Assume the wheel has mass m and moment*

9D.4, continued:

of inertia I, that it is spinning with angular velocity ω, and that the distance between the wheel and the supported end of the axle is ℓ.

Conceptualize

Let us define the x-axis as the initial direction of the axle. Since the gyroscope is symmetric about its axis of rotation, the rapid spin of the gyroscope about its axle will result in an angular momentum along its axis of rotation (see Problem 9B.1), which initially is along the x-axis. We will soon see that the actual motion is slightly more complicated than this, but if the gyroscope is spinning very rapidly, then the angular momentum will be dominated by the contribution from the rotation about the axle, and all other contributions to the angular momentum can be ignored. The forces acting on it are gravity, which acts through the center of mass, and the contact force from the supporting post, which acts at the end of the axle. Since these two points are not coincident, there *must* be a net torque on the gyro.

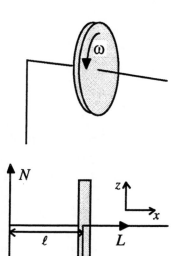

Formulate

It is clearly appropriate to define the torque about the point of support (it's the only point which has any reason to remain fixed), and so only the gravitational force contributes. The net torque is therefore

$$\vec{\tau} = [\ell, 0, 0] \times [0, 0, -mg] = [0, mg\ell, 0] .$$

Solve

In a short time Δt, the angular momentum thus changes by an amount $\Delta L_y = mg\ell\Delta t$, in the y direction. Since this is perpendicular to the angular momentum, the change in the magnitude of the angular momentum would be second order in Δt, and therefore vanishes in the limit of very small Δt. (That is, the rate at which the magnitude of the angular momentum is changing would be

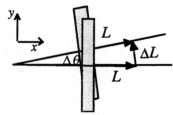

$$\frac{\sqrt{L_x^2 + m^2 g^2 \Delta t^2} - L_x}{\Delta t} ,$$

and this quantity vanishes in the limit $\Delta t \to 0$.) The direction of the angular momentum, however, does change by an amount proportional to Δt:

$$\Delta\theta = \frac{mg\ell\Delta t}{I\omega} .$$

9D.4, continued:

If we use again our assumption that the only relevant contribution to the angular momentum is a vector of magnitude $I\omega$ pointing along the axle of the gyroscope, then the direction of the gyroscope must change by this same angle, $\Delta\theta$. Since the wheel's orientation with respect to its axle is fixed, the entire gyroscope must turn through an angle $\Delta\theta$—hence the gyroscope rotates in the horizontal plane with an angular velocity

$$\Omega = \lim_{\Delta t \to 0} \frac{\Delta\theta}{\Delta t} = \frac{mg\ell}{I\omega} \ .$$

If we consider Ω as a vector, it is oriented along the z direction, since this is the axis about which the axle of the gyroscope is rotating.

Scrutinize and Learn

This phenomenon is called *precession*, and the velocity Ω is the *precessional velocity*. Notice that the faster the gyro is spinning, the more slowly it will precess. The axis of the spin does not have to be horizontal for precession to occur: anything other than absolutely vertical will do (having it horizontal just simplifies the algebra).

Our description is in fact somewhat oversimplified: the development of the precessional motion produces a small angular momentum component in the z-direction which was not originally present. This is illegal because we don't have a torque acting in the z-direction to produce such a component of angular momentum. The result is that the axle of the gyroscope actually ends up pointing slightly below the horizontal (relative to the point of support), so that the spin angular momentum has a small negative z-component to balance that from precession. Before settling down to this steady state, the gyroscope will oscillate for a while about the 'right' position—this superimposes an additional wobble, called *nutation*, on the steady precession. These effects are most clearly seen if the gyro is spinning fairly slowly, so that the precessional velocity (and hence the precessional angular momentum) is larger.

Precessional effects are actually quite common in everyday life, although we do not usually think of them as such—for example, the way in which a spinning coin comes to rest is a consequence of precessional motion.

9D.8   *Show that the equation relating the velocity of a point on a rigid body to the body's angular velocity*

$$\vec{\mathbf{v}} = \vec{\mathbf{v}}_P + \vec{\omega} \times (\vec{\mathbf{r}} - \vec{\mathbf{r}}_P),$$

where P is a reference point on the body, is indeed independent of the choice of reference point P, the origin of the coordinate system, and the velocity of the coordinate system, as stated in the text.

Conceptualize

If the formula is indeed independent of the choice of P, then choosing another point Q should give the same result. We can see if this is so by obtaining expression for the position and velocity *of point P* using Q as origin, and then substituting these for $\vec{\mathbf{r}}_P$ and $\vec{\mathbf{v}}_P$. A similar approach should work for the origin and velocity of the coordinate system.

9D.8, continued:

Formulate and Solve
The velocity of our test point relative to reference point P is

$$\vec{v} - \vec{v}_P = \vec{\omega} \times (\vec{r} - \vec{r}_P).$$

Relative to reference point Q, it is

$$\vec{v} - \vec{v}_Q = \vec{\omega}' \times (\vec{r} - \vec{r}_Q),$$

where, to avoid assuming what we are trying to prove, we have taken the angular velocity vector to be $\vec{\omega}'$. Since this equation holds for any point on the body, it must hold for P:

$$\vec{v}_P - \vec{v}_Q = \vec{\omega}' \times (\vec{r}_P - \vec{r}_Q).$$

Now, subtracting this equation from the previous one gives

$$\vec{v} - \vec{v}_P = \vec{\omega}' \times (\vec{r} - \vec{r}_Q) - \vec{\omega}' \times (\vec{r}_P - \vec{r}_Q)$$
$$= \vec{\omega}' \times (\vec{r} - \vec{r}_Q - \vec{r}_P + \vec{r}_Q)$$
$$= \vec{\omega}' \times (\vec{r} - \vec{r}_P),$$

using the distributive law for cross products.

This formula is identical to the one we started with if and only if $\vec{\omega}' = \vec{\omega}$. Therefore the angular velocity vector is unchanged by the change of reference point.

If we change the origin of the coordinate system, such that the distance from the initial origin O to the new origin O' is $\vec{r}_0$, the position vectors of our test particle and P become $\vec{r} - \vec{r}_0$ and $\vec{r}_P - \vec{r}_0$ respectively. It is clear that $\vec{r} - \vec{r}_P$ is unchanged by this transformation. Similarly, if our new coordinate system has velocity $\vec{v}_0$ relative to our original system, $\vec{v}$ becomes $\vec{v} - \vec{v}_0$, $\vec{v}_P$ becomes $\vec{v}_P - \vec{v}_0$, and $\vec{v} - \vec{v}_P$ is unchanged. Therefore the angular velocity vector is unchanged by changes in the origin or velocity of the coordinate system.

HINTS FOR PROBLEMS WITH AN (H)
The number of the hint refers to the number of the problem

9A.6 Under what conditions will a rigid body be stationary (and nonrotating)? Draw a force diagram for the rod, being careful to draw in all forces at the correct points. What are the equations for the net force and the net torque about some appropriate point?

9A.7 Draw a force diagram, taking care to show all forces acting at the right place. What are the general conditions for a rigid body to be stationary? If you still don't know what to do, review the solution to problems 9A.4 and 9A.5.

9A.9 Can you treat this problem as a rotation about a single axis? How many equations does the condition of zero net *torque* give you? What about zero net *force*? If you're really stuck, look at the solution to problem 9A.8.

9B.4 Try using conservation of energy and conservation of angular momentum. What, in terms of its unknown speed u, is its total energy immediately after the decelerating burst of the engines? What is its angular momentum about the Sun? If at closest approach it just hits the Sun, what then is its total energy and its angular momentum, in terms of its new unknown speed v? You should now be able to solve for u and v.

If you are having difficulty, study the solution to problem 9B.3.

Challenge Problem hint: consider what happens if you start by firing the engines forwards for a short burst.

9C.1 What are the components of $\vec{F}$ in a coordinate system where the x-axis points along $\vec{R} \equiv [x, y, 0]$, and the z-axis is unchanged? What, therefore, is the component of $\vec{F}$ perpendicular to $\vec{R}$?

9D.3 From Chapter 5, what is the expression for the net force on a rigid body (i.e. a system of particles)? Under what circumstances will a net force produce no torque?

9D.5 What quantities are conserved in an isolated system? What is the direction of the angular momentum of the wheel before and after it is turned? What are the possible sources of torques applied (a) to the wheel, (b) to the whole wheel + person + chair system? What are the directions of these torques?

9D.6 Draw a force diagram for the wheel at the instant of touchdown. What force contributes a torque about the axle? What is the net horizontal force?

When the wheels stop sliding, what is the relation between the linear speed of the plane and the angular velocity of the wheels?

ANSWERS TO HINTS

9A.6 No net force and no net torque.

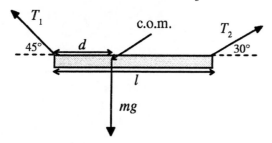

Taking the mass of the rod to be m and other symbols as in the diagram,

$$F_x = T_2 \cos 30° - T_1 \cos 45°;$$

$$F_y = T_2 \sin 30° + T_1 \sin 45° - mg;$$

$$\tau = mgd - T_2 \ell \sin 30°,$$

where the torque is taken about the left-hand end of the rod, the x-axis is along the rod and the y-axis is vertical. (Other suitable points would be the right-hand end of the rod, or its center of mass. These would produce different torque equations.)

9A.7

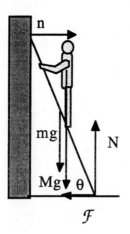

No net force and no net torque.

9A.9 No. The slab is in principle free to rotate in three dimensions (in practice, two, because none of the forces involved acts horizontally, so there is no torque about any vertical axis). Two (about any two mutually perpendicular axes in the plane of the slab—easiest to calculate would be parallel to long and short sides). One (all forces act vertically).

9B.4 At Earth orbit:

$$\tfrac{1}{2}mu^2 - \frac{GMm}{d}$$

$$= m(\tfrac{1}{2}u^2 - 8.9 \times 10^8 \text{ m}^2/\text{s}^2)$$

and $mud = (1.5 \times 10^{11} \text{ m})mu$.

At radius of Sun:

$$\tfrac{1}{2}mv^2 - \frac{GMm}{r}$$

$$= m(\tfrac{1}{2}v^2 - 1.9 \times 10^{11} \text{ m}^2/\text{s}^2)$$

and $mvr = (7 \times 10^8 \text{ m})mv$.

9C.1 $[F_x \cos\theta + F_y \sin\theta,$
$\qquad\qquad F_y \cos\theta - F_x \sin\theta, \; 0]$
where $\cos\theta = x/R$ and $\sin\theta = y/R$;
$(F_y x - F_x y)/R.$

9D.3 $\vec{\mathbf{F}}^{\text{net}} = M\vec{\mathbf{a}}_{\text{cm}}$; if it acts through the axis of rotation (or, equivalently, if several forces produce torques which act in opposite directions and so cancel).

9D.5 Momentum and angular momentum. Along axis of wheel, so horizontal before turning, vertical afterwards.

(a) forces exerted by person holding wheel (any direction);

(b) gravity, if center of mass of system not under suspension point (horizontal).

Torque taken about center of wheel in case (a) and about suspension point in case (b).

9D.6 Diagram at right.

Kinetic friction; $-\mu_k Mg$; $v = R\omega$.

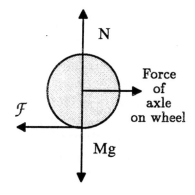

ANSWERS TO ALL PROBLEMS

9A.1 c; b.

9A.2 b.

9A.3 See diagram at right. (Weight of each bottle 7 N; contact forces between bottles 4 N along lines joining bottle centers; horizontal contact forces from walls 2 N; vertical contact forces from base of box 10.5 N. Forces acting on top bottle are shown in gray and vertical contact forces are displaced from their point of action for clarity.)

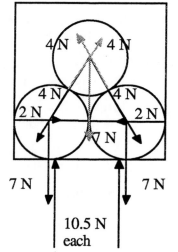

9A.4 See complete solution.

9A.5 See complete solution.

9A.6 3.7 cm from the left-hand (45°) end.

9A.7 $\mu_s = \dfrac{\frac{1}{2}m + Md/\ell}{m + M}\cot\theta$

Yes; yes, minimum required coefficient of friction decreases to 0.16.

9A.8 See complete solution.

9A.9 160, 240 and 400 N respectively;
third person always exerts 400 N, first exerts $160 \cdot (d/1\text{ m})$ N. The second exerts

$$160 \cdot \left(\frac{2.5\text{ m} - d}{1\text{ m}}\right)\text{ N },$$

where d is the distance between the third person and the corner across from number 1.

9B.1 See complete solution.

9B.2 See complete solution.

9B.3 See complete solution.

9B.4 The maximum speed at the Earth's orbit which would lead to a minimum radius (perihelion) inside the Sun is 3 km/s, compared with the Earth's orbital speed of 30 km/s. For comparison, the speed needed to escape from the Solar System altogether starting from the Earth's orbit is 42 km/s. It is thus somewhat more than twice as hard, in terms of required momentum change, to hit the Sun by this method as it is to escape into interstellar space.

Challenge Problem answer: One can first fire the rockets forward, applying an impulse just short of what would be needed to leave the solar system altogether. The maximum radius (aphelion) would then be arbitrarily large, and, conserving angular momentum, the orbital velocity at aphelion would be arbitrarily small. At aphelion the rocket then fires a feeble burst, just canceling this small orbital velocity, and then falls slowly straight into the Sun.

9B.5 (a) $mv\ell\sin\theta$

(b) perpendicularly into plane of page, along $[0, 0, -1]$.

9C.1 Unit vectors along $\vec{\mathbf{R}} = [x, y, 0]$ and perpendicular to $\vec{\mathbf{R}}$ are

$$\hat{\mathbf{R}} = \frac{1}{R}[x, y, 0]$$

and

$$\hat{\mathbf{S}} = \frac{1}{R}[-y, x, 0]$$

respectively.

In terms of these unit vectors the force $\mathbf{F}$ is given by

$$\mathbf{F} = \frac{1}{R}[(xF_x + yF_y)\hat{\mathbf{R}} + (xF_y + yF_x)\hat{\mathbf{S}}] \ .$$

The component of this perpendicular to $\vec{\mathbf{R}}$ is by definition the $\hat{\mathbf{S}}$ term, so the torque is

$$\tau = F_\perp R = xF_y - yF_x$$

as required.

9C.2 See complete solution.

9C.3 An acceptable answer would be:

"Torque about an axis is effectively a scalar quantity, producing clockwise or counterclockwise (negative or positive, respectively) angular acceleration about that axis. Torque about a point is a vector, with no simple relation to angular acceleration (e.g. if an object rotates with constant angular velocity $\vec{\omega}$, the net torque about an axis in the direction of $\vec{\omega}$ must be zero, but the net torque about any point on that axis will not in general be zero). The x-component of the torque vector about a point corresponds to torque about an axis in the x direction, and so on."

9D.1 See complete solution.

9D.2 See complete solution.

9D.3 There are of course infinitely many correct answers to parts (a)–(d)—the diagrams below are just examples!

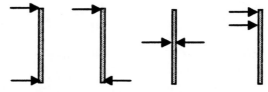

(a) move across table retaining same orientation; (b) rotate around fixed center of mass; (c) remain stationary; (d) move across table with changing orientation.

Case (d)—net force and net torque.

4 cm/s; 0.39 rad/s.

Your scale drawing should have the following features:

distance of center of mass from start: 0, 40, 48, 56, 64, 72, 80 cm;

angle swept through: 0°, 221°, 265°, 309°, 353°, 398°, 442°.

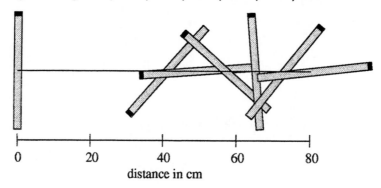

distance in cm

9D.4 See complete solution.

9D.5 Almost certainly, the first thing that happens is that the hapless victim tries to shift the axis to vertical by pushing one end up and the other down. If we define a coordinate system such that z is up and x points along the initial axis of the wheel, we now have a force in the z direction applied at a position on the axis of the wheel (i.e. $\vec{r}$ is in the x direction). This produces a torque in the y direction: the axis of the wheel rotates *sideways*, not vertically. Once our visitor has worked out which direction to push to get the axis to turn vertically, he or she will end up rotating in the opposite direction to the spin of the wheel.

In terms of conservation of angular momentum, we see that there is no external torque on the person + chair + gyro system in the z (vertical) direction. The change in the z-component of the gyro's angular momentum must therefore be balanced by an opposite change in that of the chair + occupant, hence the rotation. The change in the x-component of angular momentum would make the chair rotate around a horizontal axis, but when it does so its center of mass is no longer directly under its suspension point, so gravity provides an external torque. Hence angular momentum in the horizontal direction is not conserved.

In terms of torques, to make the gyro's axis vertical the person has to exert a torque in the z direction, which he/she does by pushing sideways on the axis of the gyro. The force exerted on the gyro is balanced by an equal and opposite force exerted by the gyro on the person (Newton's third law), so the person must develop an opposite angular momentum.

9D.6 $v = \dfrac{M R^2 v_0}{I + M R^2}$.

9D.7 (a) and (b): In both cases, the comparatively large angular momentum of the spinning projectile means that a small accidental torque (e.g. due to a gust of wind) will not produce a significant change in the orientation of the bullet or frisbee. The result is that the projectile maintains the desired attitude (point first, for a bullet; disk horizontal, for a frisbee), minimizing air resistance and thus improving range and accuracy.

(c) When the helicopter pilot changes the speed of the main rotor, one part of the helicopter system (the engine) is exerting an internal torque on another part (the rotor). We would expect the angular momentum of the whole system to remain unchanged by this internal torque, so the main body of the helicopter should start to counter-rotate against the change in the rotor speed. The tail rotor, which is a propeller (i.e. its blades are angled to produce a thrust) can exert a torque to balance that produced by the change in the rotor speed. Even in steady flight, there is an external torque on the helicopter from air friction with the main rotor, tending to reduce the overall angular momentum of the helicopter system; again, this can be counterbalanced by the torque from the tail rotor.

(d) Given the frictionless mount, there can be no net torque on the gyro, which will therefore maintain the same absolute orientation. Checking the orientation of the mount (i.e. the aircraft) relative to the axis of the gyro then gives you the orientation of the craft in that plane.

(e) As in (a) and (b), such a gyroscope stabilizes the orientation of the ship against accidental torques—i.e. it reduces roll and pitch (and hence seasickness among the passengers, or that's the idea).

9D.8 See complete solution.

9D.9 (a) $\vec{v} = [0, \omega_z x_0, 0]$;

(b) $L_z = M\omega_z x_0^2$ about z-axis; $\vec{L} = [-M\omega_z x_0 z_0,\ 0,\ M\omega_z x_0^2]$ about center of mass.

(c) As the meteoroid is in empty space, no external torques act on it, and therefore the orientation (and magnitude) of its angular momentum vector must remain fixed. But if we consider the frame in which the center of mass of the meteoroid is stationary, and require that $\vec{L}$ remain fixed, clearly $\vec{\omega}$ cannot also remain fixed as the meteoroid rotates (either $\vec{L}$ rotates around $\vec{\omega}$, which it can't, or $\vec{\omega}$ rotates around $\vec{L}$). Therefore the cameras on the space probe will see the meteoroid *tumble*: its rotation axis will precess around its angular momentum vector. (This is torque-free precession: see the solution to problem 9B.1.)

ESSENTIALS OF INTRODUCTORY CLASSICAL MECHANICS

CHAPTER 10

MOTION OF A RIGID BODY

OVERVIEW

This chapter contains no new ideas. Instead, we shall take the material covered in chapters 8 and 9 and use it to solve more complicated problems. Notice that in this chapter we shall not divide the problems up into sections dealing with specific topics; instead you will have to decide for yourself which of the physical principles you have learned are relevant to a given problem.

When you have completed this chapter you should:

✔ be able to extract the essential features of a problem and express them in mathematical equations;

✔ be capable of manipulating the equations relevant to a problem to obtain an expression for the required quantity, either symbolically or numerically;

✔ be able to analyze a hypothetical situation in terms of the physics presented in previous units, and explain that analysis clearly in non-mathematical terms.

PROBLEMS AND QUESTIONS

By the end of this chapter you should be able to answer or solve the types of questions or problems stated below.

At the end of the chapter there are answers to all the problems. In addition, for problems with an (H) or (S) after the number, there are respectively hints on how to solve the problems or completely worked-out solutions.

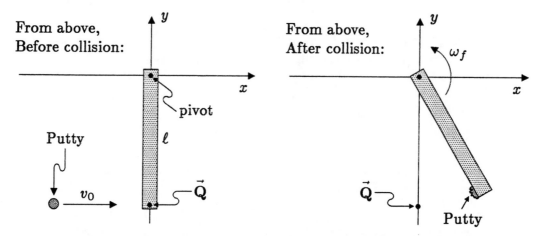

10.1 (S)   On a frictionless horizontal table a slender rigid rod of mass M and length ℓ is attached at one end to a fixed pivot. A nonrotating disk of putty, with mass m, is moving with speed v_0 perpendicular to the line of the rod, and collides with it at point Q, at the opposite end from the pivot. The disk sticks to the end of the rod, so that after the collision they move off together. Assume that the disk is small enough to be treated as a point particle.

(a) Just before the collision, what is the angular momentum of the system of rod plus disk (i) about the the z-axis, (ii) about an axis perpendicular to the page, through the point Q?

(b) Just after the collision, what is the angular velocity of the rod/disk system about the pivot? What is the system's angular momentum about the axis perpendicular to the page and through the point Q? Explain.

(c) Now suppose that the disk is uniform and has a small radius R. It is initially rotating counterclockwise (as seen from above) with an angular speed ω_0 so large that the resulting internal angular momentum cannot be neglected (although R is still negligible compared to ℓ). If the disk's translational speed when it hits the rod is the same as before, what is the final angular velocity about the pivot in this case?

10.2 (H)   Classical mechanics indicates that it is theoretically possible to balance a pencil on its point, but in practice it can't be done. Discuss why this is so by considering the torque acting on the pencil when it is displaced by a small angle from the vertical. Further discuss why, if you attempt this experiment on a very smooth surface, the point of the pencil tends to move in the direction opposite to the direction in which the pencil is toppling.

10.3 (H)   A figure skater executing a spin starts with her arms extended and then brings them in close to her body. What happens to (a) her angular momentum, (b) her angular velocity, (c) her rotational kinetic energy during this procedure? How would the process be affected if she held a weight in each hand? Reconcile these results with the principle of energy conservation.

10.4 (H)   At time $t = 0$, a particle of mass 5 kg is located at position [3, -2, 7] m and moving with velocity [1, 1, -2] m/s. Find its angular momentum about the origin. If it is acted on by a constant force of [0, 3, 0] N, what is the torque on it at $t = 0$, and what will its angular momentum be 10 s later?

10.5   A small disk of mass M is attached to one end of a slender rigid rod of mass M and length ℓ. (The radius of the disk is negligible compared to ℓ.) The assembly is placed on a frictionless horizontal table such that the rod is oriented at an angle θ to one edge of the table, which we define as the x-axis of coordinates, as shown. An impulse $\vec{\mathbf{J}} = [0, J, 0]$ is applied to the midpoint of the rod. What is the subsequent motion of the system, i.e. what is its velocity vector $\vec{\mathbf{v}}$ and its angular velocity $\vec{\omega}$?

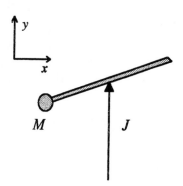

10.6   A cylinder rotates about its horizontal axis of symmetry. It is dropped from a small distance onto a carpet. It does not bounce. Describe, as well as you can, what does happen and why.

10.7 (H)   A car accelerates from rest to 100 km/h in 7.5 s. Its wheels have a radius of 25 cm. What is the average angular acceleration of the wheels relative to their axles? If we can approximate each wheel by a solid cylinder of mass 15 kg, and the mass of the car (without the four wheels) is 1,200 kg, (a) what average net torque must have been applied to each wheel; (b) what average torque must have been applied to each wheel by the axle?

10.8   A car of *total* mass M has four identical wheels, each with a radius R and a moment of inertia about its axle of I. The car is moving with a constant speed v_1 in a straight line on a level road, with the wheels rolling (not skidding). The coefficients of static and kinetic friction between the wheels and the road are μ_s and μ_k respectively. Assume that air drag is negligible and that there is no internal friction within the car (i.e. all wheel bearings etc. are frictionless). The acceleration due to gravity is g.

(a) What is the magnitude of the angular velocity ω of each wheel?

(b) In terms of ω and the given quantities, what is the angular momentum of each wheel about its axle?

(c) What is the net force on the car due to friction?

A deer runs on to the road ahead. The driver brakes suddenly, locking the wheels, so that they stop rotating. The car skids and decelerates until its speed is v_2. During the period when the wheels are locked,

(d) What is the magnitude, a, of the acceleration of the car?

359

(e) In terms of v_1, v_2 and a, what distance does the car travel?

Meanwhile the deer has seen the car and retreated back into the bushes. The driver therefore releases the brakes when the speed of the car has reached v_2.

(f) In no more than 50 words, describe (without formulae or equations) what happens when the brakes are released, and the final motion of the car.

10.9 (H) Two blocks of mass M_1 and M_2 are connected by a light rope running over a pulley of mass m. The rope turns the pulley without slipping. If the coefficient of kinetic friction between the blocks and the slope is μ_k, find the acceleration of the blocks and the tension in each part of the rope. Assume the pulley is a solid uniform disk of radius R, and that M_2 is substantially greater than M_1.

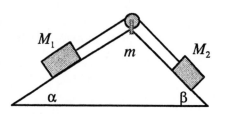

10.10 A yo-yo consists of two solid disks connected by a central spindle. Each disk has mass $M = 20$ g and radius $R = 2.5$ cm; the central spindle has radius $r = 0.5$ cm and negligible mass. The yo-yo has 1 m of string attached; you may assume the string is of negligible mass and thin enough that it does not change the effective diameter of the spindle when it is wound up. If the yo-yo is released from rest, use energy conservation methods to deduce its angular velocity when it reaches the end of the string (assume the string was fully wound at the start and unwinds without slipping). If the string is firmly attached to the yo-yo, what do you expect it to do after reaching the end? What if the last piece of string is tied in a loop around the spindle rather than being firmly attached? Take $g = 10$ m/s^2 and quote your results to two significant figures.

Draw a force diagram for the descending yo-yo, and hence calculate its acceleration. What effect would (a) decreasing the diameter of the central spindle; (b) decreasing the mass of the yo-yo; (c) decreasing the outer radius of the yo-yo have on its acceleration?

10.11 (S) A yo-yo consists of two solid disks, each of mass M and radius R, connected by a central spindle of radius r and negligible mass. A light string is coiled around the central spindle; we shall assume that its thickness is sufficiently small that winding or unwinding it has no effect on the effective radius of the spindle. The yo-yo is placed upright on a flat surface and the string is pulled gently at an angle θ to the horizontal. What happens? Assume that the surface is rough enough that the yo-yo rolls without slipping.

10.12 An anthropologist has discovered a cache of seven pre-Columbian statuettes in the forests of central America. The ceramic statues are approximately cylindrical in shape and all apparently identical, but our hero has reason to believe that one of them is a hollow fake constructed by ingenious drug smugglers. The fake has been ballasted to weigh exactly the same as the genuine articles, and of course our man is unwilling to do anything which might damage the precious artifacts. X-ray machines and similar sophisticated technology not being available in the jungle, use the physics of the last few chapters to suggest non-destructive ways of identifying the not-so-genuine article.

COMPLETE SOLUTIONS TO PROBLEMS WITH AN (S)

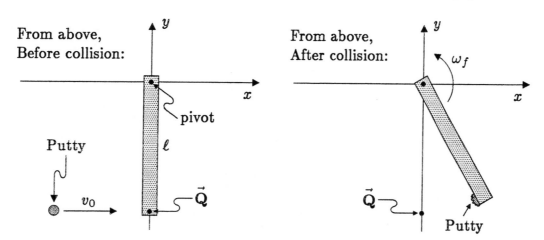

From above,
Before collision:

From above,
After collision:

10.1 *On a frictionless horizontal table a slender rigid rod of mass M and length ℓ is attached at one end to a fixed pivot. A nonrotating disk of putty, with mass m, is moving with speed v_0 perpendicular to the line of the rod, and collides with it at point Q, at the opposite end from the pivot. The disk sticks to the end of the rod, so that after the collision they move off together. Assume that the disk is small enough to be treated as a point particle.*

(a) *Just before the collision, what is the angular momentum of the system of rod plus disk (i) about the the z-axis, (ii) about an axis perpendicular to the page, through the point Q?*

(b) *Just after the collision, what is the angular velocity of the rod/disk system about the pivot? What is the system's angular momentum about the axis perpendicular to the page and through the point Q? Explain.*

Conceptualize

All the motion in this problem takes place in the xy plane, and the question asks only for angular momenta about various axes that are perpendicular to the xy-plane. So we are only concerned with L_z, and can effectively treat angular momentum as a scalar quantity, using the techniques of Chapter 8. The external forces acting are gravity and the normal force from the table (which cancel, since there is no vertical acceleration), and possibly a contact force from the pivot.

Part (a) is straightforward. Initially the rod is stationary, and therefore has no angular momentum about any point, so we need only consider the angular momentum of the putty about the two axes (parallel to the z-axis), through the pivot and through Q.

Part (b) is tricky. During the impact of the putty with the rod, the rod exerts a force on the pivot. By Newton's third law, the pivot exerts an equal and opposite force on the rod. Since we assume the pivot is frictionless, it does not exert a torque on the rod about the pivot. Thus this is a collision problem with an external impulsive force acting on the rod at the pivot during the collision.

As usual in collision problems, we first ask what quantities are conserved.

361

10.1, continued:

The collision is inelastic (the putty sticks to the rod), so energy is not conserved. Because of the impulsive force, angular momentum is also not conserved except about the pivot.

Since angular momentum is conserved about the pivot, we can use this fact to solve for the motion of the rod and putty after the collision. Once we have found the motion of the rod and putty we can calculate their angular momentum about any other point, including Q, using the fact that for any rigid body, the total angular momentum about any point is equal to the angular momentum of the center of mass about that point plus the angular momentum of the body about the center of mass (see p. 320). This will avoid us having to deal with the impulsive force at the pivot.

Formulate and Solve (a)

Just before the collision the position and velocity of the putty are given by $\vec{r}_{\text{putty}} = [0, -\ell, 0]$ and $\vec{v}_0 = [v_0, 0, 0]$ so $\vec{L} = \vec{r}_{\text{putty}} \times m\vec{v}_0 = [0, 0, m\ell v_0]$. So the angular momentum about the z-axis is $L_z = m\ell v_0$. With respect to Q, immediately before the collision $\vec{r}_{\text{putty}} = [0, 0, 0]$, so clearly $\vec{L} = [0, 0, 0]$. The angular momentum about the axis through the point Q is therefore zero.

Formulate (b)

About the pivot the total angular momentum of the system after the collision is

$$L_f = (I_{\text{rod}} + I_{\text{putty}})\,\omega_f,$$

where ω_f is the final angular velocity. Since we concluded that angular momentum about the pivot is conserved, this must be equal to $m\ell v_0$.

We saw in Chapter 8 that the moment of inertia of a slender rod about one end is $\frac{1}{3}M\ell^2$ (see problem 8C.4(d)). Therefore

$$m\ell v_0 = \omega_f \left(\tfrac{1}{3}M\ell^2 + m\ell^2 \right)$$

$$\omega_f = \frac{mv_0}{\left(\tfrac{1}{3}M + m \right)\ell},$$

counterclockwise around the z-axis.

Immediately after the collision, the rod's center of mass has velocity $v = \omega_f \ell/2$, and the angular velocity of the rod about its center of mass is ω_f.

Thus the angular momentum of the center of mass of the rod about an axis through Q and parallel to the z-axis is

$$-Mv\frac{\ell}{2} = -M\omega_f \frac{\ell}{2}\frac{\ell}{2} = -M\omega_f \frac{\ell^2}{4},$$

and the angular momentum of the rod about its center of mass is

$$\frac{1}{12}M\ell^2\omega_f,$$

10.1, continued:

where we have obtained the moment of inertia of a rod about the axis through its center from Chapter 8, p. 277.

Thus the total angular momentum of the rod about Q is

$$-\frac{1}{4}M\ell^2\omega_f + \frac{1}{12}M\ell^2\omega_f = -\frac{1}{6}M\ell^2\omega_f \,,$$

where we have used

$$\vec{L} = \vec{r}_{cm} \times \vec{p}_{tot} + \sum_i \vec{r}_{rel,i} \times m_i\vec{v}_{rel,i}$$

from Chapter 9. The putty still has zero angular momentum about Q, so this is the angular momentum of the system.

Angular momentum about Q clearly is **not** conserved. We noted in the conceptualization that there is a net external force on the system, namely the contact force from the pivot. In the instant after the collision, this force must have a component in the negative x-direction, since this end of the rod remains stationary instead of moving off in the positive x-direction as it would if it were unrestrained. Such a force contributes no torque **about the pivot**, but it clearly **does** contribute a torque about Q. Therefore it is entirely reasonable that angular momentum about Q is not conserved in the collision.

Scrutinize

In (b), our expression for ω_f has dimensions of $1/[\text{time}]$, which is correct for an angular velocity. If m becomes very small, ω_f tends to zero, which is reasonable: a zero-mass lump of putty would obviously not set the rod in motion. If M becomes negligible, $\omega_f = v_0/\ell$: the angular velocity of the putty does not change as a result of the collision. This is also reasonable—the putty is moving in a circle, but its speed has not changed.

Learn

This problem demonstrates that conservation of angular momentum can only be used to analyze the motion of a system **about an appropriate point or axis**. This is because angular momentum depends on $\vec{r}$, and $\vec{r}$ depends on the choice of origin. In particular, angular momentum is conserved when a body moves under the influence of a central force, but only if the angular momentum is calculated with respect to the source of the force. The effects of this can be seen in considering, for example, the effect of Jupiter on the orbit of a comet: if the comet passes close to Jupiter, the ensuing deflection will conserve the comet's angular momentum **with respect to Jupiter**, but it will not conserve the comet's angular momentum with respect to the Sun, and the comet's orbit can be very significantly changed as a result.

10.1 (c) *Now suppose that the disk is uniform and has a small radius R. It is initially rotating counterclockwise (as seen from above) with an angular speed ω_0 so large that the resulting internal angular momentum cannot be neglected (although R is still negligible compared to ℓ). If the disk's translational speed when it hits the rod is the same as before, what is the final angular velocity about the pivot in this case?*

363

10.1, continued:

Conceptualize
The only difference between this problem and part (b) is that the putty's angular momentum now includes a contribution from its own rotation (its *spin angular momentum*, as opposed to its *orbital angular momentum* about the pivot). This is not a serious difficulty, because as we saw earlier the total angular momentum of a rigid body can be expressed as the sum of two parts: its angular momentum about its center of mass, and the angular momentum of its center of mass about the origin. Thus we can simply add the spin angular momentum to the orbital angular momentum we calculated in part (b). Angular momentum is still conserved in the collision: the forces that act to squash the putty against the rod are internal forces in the rod/disk system, and any torques they create must cancel out.

Formulate
As before the angular momentum of a rigid body is given by

$$\vec{L} = \vec{r}_{cm} \times \vec{p}_{tot} + \sum_i \vec{r}_i \times m_i \vec{v}_i,$$

where $\vec{r}_i$ and $\vec{v}_i$ are measured relative to the body's center of mass, and $\vec{r}_{cm}$ is measured relative to the reference point for the angular momentum. For our spinning disk this gives

$$L_z = m v_0 \ell + I_{disk} \omega_0.$$

The moment of inertia of a uniform disk about a perpendicular axis through its center is $\frac{1}{2} m R^2$, so

$$L_z = m \left(v_0 \ell + \frac{1}{2} \omega_0 R^2 \right).$$

Solve
We simply replace $m v_0 \ell$ in our solution for part (b) by this new value of L_z to obtain

$$\omega_f = \frac{m \left(v_0 \ell + \frac{1}{2} \omega_0 R^2 \right)}{\left(\frac{1}{3} M + m \right) \ell^2}.$$

Scrutinize
This obviously reduces to our previous answer if $\omega_0 R^2$ is negligible, which is reassuring. The effect of the disk's spin is to increase the overall angular momentum, since the spin is in the same direction as the post-collision rotation of the rod. We can see how this comes about: as the disk collides with the rod, its lower edge is moving faster than its upper edge ($v_0 + \omega_0 R$ and $v_0 - \omega_0 R$, respectively), and therefore the lower edge imparts a greater impulse to the rod than does the upper edge. The result is that the disk exerts a net torque on the rod, causing the rod to rotate more rapidly than it would have done if the disk were not rotating. We would have seen the opposite effect if the disk had been rotating clockwise rather than counterclockwise.

10.11 *A yo-yo consists of two solid disks, each of mass M and radius R, connected by a central spindle of radius r and negligible mass. A light string is coiled around the central spindle; you may assume that its thickness is sufficiently small that winding or unwinding it has no effect on the effective radius of the spindle. The yo-yo is placed upright on a flat surface and the string is pulled gently at an angle θ to the horizontal. What happens? Assume that the surface is rough enough that the yo-yo rolls without slipping.*

Conceptualize

In principle this set-up contains two distinct problems: what is the net force on the yo-yo (what will its linear acceleration be?) and what is the net *torque* on it about some suitable point (what will its angular acceleration about that point be?)? However, if the yo-yo rolls without slipping, the linear acceleration determines the angular acceleration and vice versa. We can therefore combine the force and torque equations to solve the problem.

Before formulating the torque equations, we must decide on a suitable reference point. There is more than one possible choice, but the most natural approach is probably to consider rotation about the yo-yo's center of mass. If we do this we have effectively split the problem into rotation *about* the center of mass and translational motion *of* the center of mass, with the condition of rolling without slipping to link the two.

Since the question states that the string is pulled *gently*, we can assume that the force applied is not sufficient to lift the yo-yo off the floor, so the vertical component of the net force remains zero throughout. All the forces act, and the yo-yo moves, in the plane of the page, and therefore if we call this the xy-plane only the z-component of torque is non-zero: the vector nature of torque is not going to be important in solving this problem.

Formulate

$\Sigma\int$ There are four forces acting on the yo-yo: the gravitational force $2M\vec{g}$, a normal force $\vec{N}$ from the floor, friction $\vec{\mathcal{F}}$ and the tension T in the string. However, we are only interested in the torque and the horizontal component of the net force. To avoid complicating the force diagram too much we will therefore omit $\vec{N}$ and $2M\vec{g}$, both of which act vertically through the center of mass and therefore contribute neither a torque nor a horizontal component.

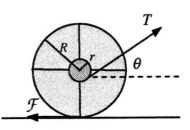

If the yo-yo rolls without slipping, there must be no relative motion at the point of contact with the floor. Therefore the speed of the outer edge of the yo-yo must be $-v$, where v is the speed of the yo-yo's center of mass. This implies $v = \pm\omega R$ and $a = \pm\alpha R$, where the relative sign depends on the directions of translation and rotation we define to be positive. Choosing counterclockwise rotation and rightward translation to be positive selects $v = -\omega R$ and $a = -\alpha R$. With this sign choice the force and torque equations are:

$$F = T\cos\theta - \mathcal{F}$$

$$\tau = Tr - \mathcal{F}R.$$

10.11, continued:

To calculate the acceleration of the yo-yo we use $F = ma$ and $\tau = I\alpha$. The total mass of the yo-yo is obviously $2M$; its moment of inertia about its central axis is MR^2 (since the two solid disks each contribute $\frac{1}{2}MR^2$).

Solve

Setting $F = 2Ma$ and $\tau = MR^2\alpha = -MRa$ gives

$$2Ma = T\cos\theta - \mathcal{F}$$

$$MaR = -Tr + \mathcal{F}R,$$

and hence (dividing the second equation by R and adding it to the first)

$$a = \frac{T}{3M}\left(\cos\theta - \frac{r}{R}\right).$$

This is positive for $\cos\theta > r/R$ (yo-yo will roll to the right) and negative for $\cos\theta < r/R$ (yo-yo will roll to the left). If $\cos\theta = r/R$, the torque and the horizontal force are both zero and the yo-yo won't roll at all. If you pull hard enough, either the vertical component of the tension will exceed the weight of the yo-yo (in which case the yo-yo will lift off the ground), or the horizontal component of tension will exceed the maximum static friction force (in which case it will skid, rather than roll, to the right). Analysis of the two limiting cases (zero normal force, i.e. $T\sin\theta = 2Mg$, and $\mathcal{F} = \mu_s N$) shows that, regardless of μ_s, the limit for skidding occurs at a lower tension than the limit for lifting: the yo-yo skids before it lifts.

Scrutinize and Learn

Note that these solutions are only valid if the yo-yo rolls without slipping, since we used the relation between a and α to solve the equations. If the yo-yo rolls and slips, we have nothing to tie the torque and force equations together, and thus cannot solve the problem without more information (e.g. the value of μ_k). We can determine the minimum value of μ_s needed to ensure that the yo-yo does roll without slipping by substituting our derived value for a back into the equations to determine $\mathcal{F}$, and then setting this equal to $\mu_s N$.

What is the significance of r/R as a value of $\cos\theta$? We can see this most easily by looking at the yo-yo's motion in an unconventional way. Because the yo-yo does not slip, the point of contact between the yo-yo and the ground has zero velocity when it starts to move. We can therefore look at this initial instant of motion as a rotation of the yo-yo about this point of contact. (The point of contact forms an instantaneous axis of rotation for the yo-yo.) If we use this view-point, then the moment of inertia of the yo-yo is (by the parallel-axis theorem) $3MR^2$, and only the tension in the string contributes a torque (friction, the normal force and gravity all act through the point of contact and thus produce no torque). The torque produced is Tx, where x is the perpendicular distance between the line of action of the tension and the point of contact. From the diagram, $\cos\theta = (r + x)/R$, and thus the net torque

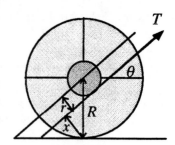

10.11, continued:

is $T(R\cos\theta - r)$. Dividing by the appropriate moment of inertia gives us the same angular acceleration as we had using the more obvious choice of axis through the center of the yo-yo, but this time the significance of r/R is clear—this is the value of $\cos\theta$ for which $x = 0$, i.e. the line of action of the tension passes through the point of contact, and therefore contributes no torque. There is then zero net torque around this axis, and the yo-yo cannot roll. Looking a little more carefully, you can also see that the sign of the torque around this axis changes for $\theta > r/R$, because the line of action of the tension will pass to the right rather than the left of the point of contact.

Working with an instantaneous axis of rotation is somewhat like choosing a different coordinate system or reference frame in a translational-motion context. It is never *necessary* to work this way in order to solve a problem, but it may *simplify* the solution or make the underlying physical principles more apparent.

HINTS FOR PROBLEMS WITH AN (H)
The number of the hint refers to the number of the problem

10.2 Draw a force diagram for the pencil at a small angle to the vertical. What are the forces acting? Which contributes a torque about the pencil point, and in what direction does that torque act?

What is happening to the *linear* momentum of the pencil as it topples? What force must act to cause this?

10.3 Is the skater an isolated system? What quantities are conserved for isolated systems?

Does the skater exert any net force or torque on herself? Does she do any work?

If you are still puzzled, look back at problem 4D.1.

10.4 This problem is clearly an exercise in the use of vectors in three dimensions. What do we need to know to calculate the torque exerted on and angular momentum of a particle about a specified point?

What is the momentum of the particle at $t = 10$ s? What is its position then?

(Use the coordinate form of the vector product to calculate $\vec{r} \times \vec{p}$ and $\vec{r} \times \vec{F}$ in this problem.)

10.7 (a) How is the angular acceleration of the wheels related to the linear acceleration of the car?

(b) Draw a force diagram for one wheel.

(c) What average force does the road surface apply to the car if the magnitude of its average acceleration is a? What torque about the wheel axis does this force apply to the wheels?

10.9 If you are having trouble with this problem, first look back at problem 8E.6, a very similar setup without the complication of friction. The same approach applies:

Draw free-body diagrams for the pulley and each mass. Does the tension in the two parts of the rope (on either side of the pulley) have to be the same? What quantity is the same for the two masses and the rim of the pulley?

How is the angular acceleration of the pulley related to the linear acceleration of the blocks?

ANSWERS TO HINTS

10.2 Gravity and friction; gravity; away from the equilibrium position.

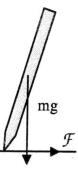

The pencil gains both vertical and horizontal linear momentum; gravity produces vertical component; horizontal component must come from friction.

10.3 Yes, there is no net external force or torque on her (her center of mass is on her axis of rotation). Linear and angular momentum.

No, (by the Third Law, she cannot exert a net force on herself; in pulling her arms in she exerts a force parallel to the line joining her arms to the axis, so there is no torque).

Yes, (in pulling in her arms, she exerts a force on her hands and forearms, which undergo a non-zero displacement in the direction of the force).

10.4 The vectors representing (a) the position of the particle relative to the point in question; (b) the force on the particle and (c) the particle's linear momentum.

$[5, 35, -10]$ kg · m/s;
$[13, 38, -13]$ m.

10.7 (a) $a = r\alpha$.

(b)

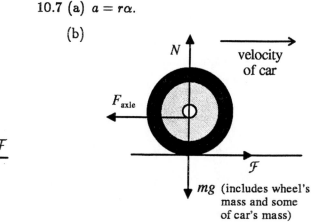

(c) Ma; a total of Mar, where M is the mass of the car and r is the radius of the wheels.

10.9

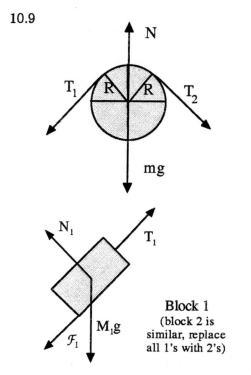

Block 1
(block 2 is similar, replace all 1's with 2's)

No: T_1 for block $1 = T_1$ on pulley, and likewise for T_2, but $T_1 \neq T_2$.

$\alpha = a/R$, where a is the linear acceleration of either block (they are equal), and α is the angular acceleration of the pulley.

ANSWERS TO ALL PROBLEMS

10.1 See complete solution.

10.2 Any small displacement from vertical produces a torque which tends to increase the displacement; if point does not move, center of mass of pencil gains net horizontal momentum, which implies a net horizontal force—the only such force acting is friction.

10.3 (a) unchanged; (b) increased; (c) increased; increase of angular velocity and K.E. would be greater; work done by skater's arms in moving weights.

10.4 $[-15, 65, 25]$ kg $\cdot$ m^2/s; $[-21, 0, 9]$ N $\cdot$ m; $[75, 65, 265]$ kg $\cdot$ m^2/s.

10.5 $\vec{v} = \left[0, \dfrac{J}{2M}, 0 \right]$; $\omega = \dfrac{6J}{5M\ell} \cos\theta$ ($\vec{\omega}$ in positive z direction).

As soon as the cylinder touches the carpet, a horizontal frictional force will act to oppose the relative motion between the carpet and the cylinder. This will have two effects: first, it will obviously tend to slow down the rotation (it produces a net torque acting in the direction opposite to the direction of rotation); secondly, as it is the only horizontal force acting, it will produce a horizontal acceleration of the center of mass of the cylinder. Initially, the frictional force will be kinetic friction, which has a constant magnitude of $\mu_k N$, so the cylinder will have a uniform horizontal acceleration and a constant (negative) angular acceleration: it will skid sideways with steadily increasing velocity, while continuing to rotate at a steadily decreasing rate. Eventually, however, the condition for rolling without slipping must be met (we started with $v = 0$ and $\omega > 0$, so $v < \omega R$: v is increasing and ω is decreasing, so at some point we must have $v = \omega R$). At that moment there is no relative motion between the carpet and the part of the cylinder in contact with it, so the frictional force goes to zero and there is no net force on the cylinder. It should then continue to roll at constant speed indefinitely. In practice, there are additional drag forces we have not considered (air resistance, deformation of the carpet pile, etc.), so the cylinder will slow down and finally stop.

10.7 15 rad/s^2; (a) 6.9 N·m; (b) 300 N·m

10.8 (a) $\omega = v_1/R$

   (b) $L = I\omega$

   (c) Zero

   (d) $g\mu_k$

   (e) $\left(v_1^2 - v_2^2 \right)/2a$

   (f) Kinetic friction continues to decelerate the car while simultaneously increasing the angular velocity of the wheels. Eventually the condition for rolling without slipping is met, friction drops to zero, and the car continues at constant speed (if the driver does not accelerate).

10.9 $a = g \dfrac{M_2 \sin\beta - M_1 \sin\alpha - \mu_k (M_2 \cos\beta + M_1 \cos\alpha)}{M_1 + M_2 + \frac{1}{2}m}$;

   $T_1 = M_1 (a + g(\sin\alpha + \mu_k \cos\alpha))$;

$T_2 = M_2(g(\sin\beta - \mu_k \cos\beta) - a)$, where a is given above.

10.10 $\sqrt{2gh/\left(r^2 + \frac{1}{2}R^2\right)} = 240$ rad/s, where $h = 1$ m is the length of the string;

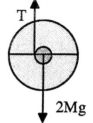

climb back up string to previous height; continue to spin, slowing due to friction between loop of string and surface of spindle (or climb back up, if friction sufficient to prevent slipping).

$$a = \frac{2r^2 g}{2r^2 + R^2} = 0.74 \text{ m/s}^2.$$

(a) decrease; (b) none; (c) increase.

10.11 See complete solution.

10.12 Although the fake statue has been ballasted to give the same total mass as the genuine objects, it is most unlikely that the *distribution* of mass within the statue is the same. Our hero can check this in a number of ways:

- find the position of the center of mass of each statue (by balancing it on something, or hanging it from a rope and adjusting the rope position until it hangs horizontally);

- measure the moment of inertia of the statue about one end, by suspending the statue by that end from a short rope and measuring the period of small oscillations, as in Problem 8E.4;

- measure the moment of inertia about a short axis through the center of mass, by suspending the statue horizontally by a rope (or a pair of ropes) around its middle and measuring the period of small oscillations produced by twisting the ropes (this is a torsion pendulum, as in problem 8D.3: the torque produced by the twisted ropes is proportional to $-\Delta\theta$, where $\Delta\theta$ is the angle of twist);

- measure the moment of inertia about the long axis of the statue, by rolling it down an inclined plane and measuring its velocity, as in Problem 8E.8. (He would, of course, package the statue in a light but well-padded cylindrical barrel before attempting this!)

ESSENTIALS OF INTRODUCTORY CLASSICAL MECHANICS

CHAPTER 11

KINETIC THEORY AND THE IDEAL GAS

OVERVIEW

The rigid bodies discussed in the last two chapters can be thought of as 'ideal solids': they have a fixed shape and the application of external forces just moves or rotates the entire object. Though idealized, this provides quite a good description of real solid objects subjected to small external forces. It is clearly quite inadequate to describe liquids and gases, which have no fixed shape and will therefore respond to external and internal forces in different ways. In this chapter we look at the other extreme by considering an ideal gas: a system of identical, independently-moving, non-interacting particles. This model is in fact a very good description of many real gases. We describe the bulk properties of such a gas by a statistical approach, looking at the cumulative effect of many individual particles. This approach, known as *kinetic theory*, introduces the new physical concepts of *pressure*, *heat* and *temperature*. Using Newton's laws, we can define the temperature of a gas in terms of the motion of its molecules, thus relating it to the internal energy of the gas. By using the ideal-gas model we can see how work done on or by a gas can result in a change of the internal energy, and hence the temperature, of the gas.

Some topics, such as the relation between the pressure of an ideal gas and its translational kinetic energy, can be treated very thoroughly with the techniques that we have learned. Other topics, however, such as the precise definition of temperature or the thermal excitation of the vibrations and rotations of molecules, are beyond the level of this book. Since these topics are very important, we will nonetheless discuss them at a qualitative level.

When you have completed this chapter you should:

- ✔ recognize that kinetic theory uses statistical principles to calculate the bulk properties of systems of many particles from the average behavior of individual particles;

- ✔ understand the concept of pressure, and be able to relate it to the momentum change of a gas particle colliding with the walls of a container;

- ✔ know how to define the temperature of a gas in terms of the kinetic energy of its constituent particles, and recognize the distinction between temperature and heat;

- ✔ be able to calculate the work done when an ideal gas changes its volume.

ESSENTIALS

In everyday experience, we say that a substance is gaseous if it changes shape and volume according to its surroundings. For example, if a certain mass of gas is enclosed in a box and we then suddenly expand the volume of the box by moving out one of the sides, we expect that the gas will expand to fill the newly enlarged container uniformly, whereas we would not expect a liquid or a solid to behave this way. This experience indicates that the constituent atoms of the gas are moving (so that they can move into the empty space created by enlarging the box), and furthermore that the motion is randomly directed (because we don't find that the behavior of the gas depends on the direction in which we expand the box). Also, the atoms move further apart when the gas expands, so they cannot be confined to deep potential energy minima as is the case with solids. We may conclude that the attractive part of the interatomic forces in a gas is quite weak compared to those acting in a solid.

These experimental properties of gases suggest that a suitable idealized model for a gas would be one in which the interatomic or intermolecular forces are completely negligible. This would be the case if

- the average distance between gas atoms or molecules is very large compared to the size of an individual atom or molecule;

- molecules interact with each other only when they collide;

- collisions between molecules, or between a molecule and the wall of the container, are both rare (i.e. the time spent in collisions is negligible compared to the time spent between collisions) and perfectly elastic.

We further assume that the motions of the gas molecules are randomly directed: that is, if we choose a reference frame in which the center of mass of the gas sample is not moving, the velocity vectors of individual gas molecules have no preferred orientation. It is possible to visualize conditions in which that would not be so (for example, if all our molecules were originally moving exactly perpendicular to one face of a perfectly reflecting cubical box, and there were no collisions between molecules). However, as long as we do allow rare elastic collisions between molecules, it seems reasonable that over a sufficiently long time the velocities of individual molecules should become randomly oriented, even if the container housing the gas is asymmetric in shape. An actual proof of this statement is well beyond the scope of this book, but we shall assume that it is true. The motion of a single particle in the gas will be very complex, but we do not observe it: our experimental measurements are the cumulative result of the action of large numbers of particles, and will thus depend only on the *average* behavior of a particle.

376

This idealized model is referred to as an *ideal gas*. We would expect that it is likely to be a good approximation to a *low-density* gas.

The observed properties of an ideal gas are bulk properties—any sample of gas we study consists of a very large number of particles whose motions are not individually measured. This is a very different type of system from those we have studied so far, and we will need to develop a new set of concepts to deal with it. We can do this by considering the average behavior of a particle of the gas over time. For simplicity, we will normally assume that the gas is homogeneous and monatomic, i.e. its particles are single atoms, not molecules, and only one kind of atom is present.

As a route to developing the new concepts needed to describe the properties of a gas, we start by investigating an aspect of its behavior which is clearly relevant to classical mechanics: the force exerted by the gas on the walls of its container. To do this, consider a closed box of volume V containing N gas atoms. The total mass of gas in the box is Nm (where m is the mass of one atom), and its density is Nm/V. It's also sometimes useful to think of the *number density*, i.e. the number of atoms per unit volume; this is obviously $n = N/V$. Changing the volume of the box will change the density and the number density, but not the mass, since no atoms are removed from or added to the box.

If the atoms of the gas are all moving randomly around, clearly in any given time interval Δt some of them will collide with the walls of the box. We assume the collisions are elastic, so any particle which does collide will be reflected back with the magnitude of its momentum unchanged, but the sign of the component perpendicular to the wall reversed. Each collision therefore transfers momentum $2mv_x$ to the wall, where x is the direction perpendicular to the wall.

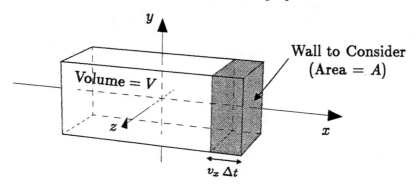

Suppose the box contains just one particle, whose velocity has an x-component of *magnitude* v_x, i.e. at any given time its value is $+v_x$ or $-v_x$ with equal probability. If this particle is to collide with the wall in a specified time interval, then at the start of that interval it must be within a perpendicular distance $v_x \Delta t$ of the wall (otherwise it won't reach the wall before the end of the time interval). If it could be anywhere in the box, the probability of its being within this distance is $A v_x \Delta t / V$, where A is the area of the wall. If its motion is random, then half the time it spends in this part of the box it will actually be moving away from the wall, so in fact the chance of its colliding with the wall in the specified time is

$$A v_x \Delta t / 2V .$$

Therefore, if we consider many time intervals Δt, the average momentum transferred to the wall by this single molecule is the probability that it collides with the wall at all in a particular time interval, times the momentum that it transfers if it does collide:

$$\Delta p = 2 m v_x \frac{A v_x \Delta t}{2V} = \frac{m A \Delta t}{V} v_x^2 .$$

Problem 11A.4.

The average force exerted on the wall is given by $F = \Delta p / \Delta t$, so this means that our particle exerts an average force

$$F = \frac{mA}{V} v_x^2 .$$

For a box containing N particles, the total force applied to the wall is the sum of the averages for individual particles:

$$F = \frac{mA}{V} \sum_i v_{x,i}^2 .$$

The sum of all $v_{x,i}^2$ is just N times the average $v_{x,i}^2$, by the definition of 'average', so we conclude that

$$F = \frac{NmA}{V} \left\langle v_x^2 \right\rangle .$$

[Putting a quantity in triangular brackets denotes the average of the quantity for all the particles in the system.]

The factor $\left\langle v_x^2 \right\rangle$ in the above equation can be simplified by noticing that the total speed of each particle is given by $v^2 = v_x^2 + v_y^2 + v_z^2$, and that the randomness of the velocities implies that there is no distinction on average between the x-, y-, and z-directions. It follows that $\left\langle v_x^2 \right\rangle = \left\langle v_y^2 \right\rangle = \left\langle v_z^2 \right\rangle = \frac{1}{3} \left\langle v^2 \right\rangle$, and therefore

$$F = \frac{2}{3} \frac{NA}{V} \left\langle \frac{1}{2} m v^2 \right\rangle .$$

The ideal gas exerts a force on the wall which is proportional to the area of the wall and the average kinetic energy of an atom of the gas.

This means that the force per area, F/A, is a bulk property of the gas: it depends only on the number density of the gas and the average kinetic energy of its particles. We call this property the **pressure**, P, of the gas. The direction of the force exerted on any wall is, from our derivation, always perpendicular to the wall, so we define pressure as a scalar quantity; its units are N/m^2, or pascals ($1 \, Pa = 1 \, N/m^2$).

Using the definition of P, we can write the above equation in the form

Problems 11A.1, 11A.4, and 11B

$$PV = \frac{2}{3}N\left\langle \frac{1}{2}mv^2 \right\rangle .$$

This equation closely resembles an equation derived from experimental measurements on real gases in the 17th and 18th centuries, namely

$$PV = \mathcal{N}RT ,$$

where $\mathcal{N}$ is related to N and R is a numerical constant. We are therefore encouraged to conclude that (i) our idealized model does indeed describe real gases to some level of accuracy and (ii) *the average kinetic energy of particles in a gas is a measure of its temperature*. We define the scale of temperature in SI units by

$$\left\langle \frac{1}{2}mv^2 \right\rangle = \frac{3}{2}kT ,$$

where T is measured in *kelvin* (K), and k is *Boltzmann's constant*. The scale of T is set, and the value of k determined, by defining the temperature of the *triple point* of water to be exactly 273.16 K. The triple point of a substance is the unique combination of pressure and temperature at which the solid, liquid and gas phases all exist together in equilibrium: its value as a defining point is that it automatically specifies the pressure at which the measurement is made. From the above equation, we see that 0 K, *absolute zero*, corresponds to zero kinetic energy of the gas particles. Absolute zero is thus a physically meaningful concept, unlike the arbitrary zeros of the Centigrade and Fahrenheit scales.

With the scale set in this way, $k = 1.38 \times 10^{-23}$ J/K, and the size of the kelvin is the same as the size of a degree Centigrade (both the Centigrade, or Celsius, scale and the Fahrenheit scale were, of course, in use long before the formal definition of the kelvin). Boltzmann's constant can be thought of as a unit conversion: we could in principle measure temperature in joules, and have $k = 1$.

This definition of temperature is called the *kinetic temperature*. Our earlier definition of an ideal gas ensures that the potential energy associated with intermolecular forces is negligible compared to the kinetic energy of the molecules, so if the gas forms a closed system, with no energy transfer in or out, it will have constant kinetic temperature.

Kinetic temperature is a fairly recent concept. There is an older, logically independent, definition of temperature, the *thermodynamic temperature*, first formalized by Lord Kelvin, which does not rely on the molecular picture of gases. If two closed systems have each been left undisturbed until they settle into a steady state (this is called 'reaching *thermal equilibrium*'), and are then placed in contact so that energy can flow between them, they are said to be at the same thermodynamic temperature if there is, in fact, no net energy flow. If energy does flow, it flows from the system at higher temperature to the system at lower temperature. The thermodynamic temperature *scale* relates the temperature ratio of the two systems to the heat exchanged with them by an idealized *heat engine*.

Problem 11D.7

To show that these definitions are consistent, which they must be if our concept of temperature is to make scientific sense, we need to demonstrate that if two gases in contact are in thermal equilibrium, with no net energy transfer, their molecules have the same average kinetic energy. This sounds intuitively plausible, and it is in fact true, but a rigorous mathematical proof is beyond the scope of this book. We would also need to show that the scales are consistent, i.e. that an increase of 10% in the average kinetic energy corresponds to an increase of 10% in the thermodynamic temperature: this is done by showing that the kinetic temperature has the same relation to the exchanged heat as does the thermodynamic temperature.

The equivalence of the kinetic and thermodynamic definitions of temperature implies that if we mix two different gases in a box, one gas having molecular mass m_1 and the other m_2, and let the box stand until equilibrium is reached, we will have

Problems 11A.2 and 11B.4

$$\left\langle \frac{1}{2}m_1v_1^2 \right\rangle = \left\langle \frac{1}{2}m_2v_2^2 \right\rangle \ .$$

Giving the temperature of an ideal gas is equivalent to stating the average kinetic energy of its component molecules (measured in the reference frame of the center of mass of the gas).

We can now restate our relation between pressure and volume using the kinetic temperature:

Problems 11C

$$\boxed{PV = NkT \ .}$$

This is called the *ideal gas law*. Note that there is *no* dependence here on the mass of the atoms making up the gas. Given the same conditions, N atoms of helium occupy the same space and exert the same pressure as N atoms of xenon, although xenon has a mass 33 times greater than helium. The xenon atoms hit the walls $\sqrt{33}$ times less often than the helium atoms would, but impart $\sqrt{33}$ times more momentum on each impact.

Because a single atom is such a small object, for macroscopic applications it is convenient to work in larger units, which would correspond to large numbers of atoms. For historical reasons, the large number used is the number of atoms contained in 0.012 kg of carbon 12, ^{12}C: this is called *Avogadro's number*, after the nineteenth-century Italian scientist who first suggested that equal volumes of different gases at the same temperature and pressure contain equal numbers of molecules. One *mole* of a substance is the amount of that substance that contains Avogadro's number of elementary entities (atoms, molecules, ions, etc.). The mass of a mole therefore depends on the mass of the individual atom or molecule. Atomic and molecular masses are measured in *atomic mass units* (symbol u); 1 u is defined such that an atom of ^{12}C has a mass of exactly 12 u. The mole (abbreviated 'mol') is the SI base unit of "amount of substance". Quantities defined in terms of moles are dimensionally different from similar quantities defined in terms of mass.

In units of moles, the ideal gas law is written

$$PV = \mathcal{N}RT$$

where $\mathcal{N}$ is the number of moles and the gas constant R is 8.31 J/mol·K (joules per mole per kelvin). This is the experimental law that we quoted above. In physical applications one tends to work in terms of atoms and k, but moles and R are widely used in chemistry. Avogadro's number is experimentally measured to be $N_A = 6.02 \times 10^{23}$; from the definitions above we see that $R = N_A k$.

The translational kinetic energy of gas molecules, relative to the center of mass of the gas sample as a whole, is clearly energy internal to the gas-sample system. If a gas has a complicated molecular structure (e.g. methane, CH_4), energy can also be stored in vibrations or rotations of individual molecules. The total energy, both kinetic and potential, stored in these various internal motions is called the *internal energy* of the gas and is given the symbol U. The *principle of equipartition* states that the internal energy of the gas is divided equally amongst the available degrees of freedom (i.e. possible directions of motion). Each mode of rotation within the gas molecule will on average contribute $\frac{1}{2}kT$ to the internal energy, just like each of the three components of the molecule's overall velocity, while each mode of vibration will contribute $\frac{1}{2}kT$ from its kinetic energy and $\frac{1}{2}kT$ from its associated potential energy, making kT in all.

Problem 11D.6

Changing the temperature of an ideal gas therefore implies changing its internal energy. This can obviously be done by doing work on the gas. It can also be done, through transfer of kinetic energy in intermolecular collisions, by placing the gas in contact with a substance at higher temperature. Energy transferred by this second route is called *heat*. Heat and temperature are not equivalent concepts, as can be seen by considering the energy change corresponding to a given temperature change:

- Temperature measures the average *translational kinetic energy* of the gas particles. If two gases have different numbers of degrees of freedom, e.g. if one consists of single atoms and the other of diatomic molecules, the change in energy per gas particle required for a given temperature change is higher for the gas with more degrees of freedom, because of the principle of equipartition.

Problem 11D.6

- Since heat measures the *total* energy transferred rather than the average per molecule, the amount of heat corresponding to a given temperature change depends on the number of degree of freedom—it will be higher for a gas of diatomic molecules than for a monatomic gas—*and* on the mass involved: less energy is required to heat a cupful of water than is needed for a gallon.

If a mass M of some substance is heated, the resulting temperature change will be

$$\Delta T = \frac{Q}{Mc},$$

where Q is the heat supplied and c is a constant called the *specific heat capacity* of the substance, measured in $J/kg \cdot K$. For gases, it is often useful to consider the number of moles of the gas instead of its mass, and the resulting ratio $Q/N\Delta T$ is called the *molar heat capacity*, measured in $J/mol \cdot K$. From the discussion above, we expect the specific heat capacity of a gas to depend on its molecular structure, with more complicated molecules having higher specific heats. In addition, the specific heat capacity depends on the conditions under which we heat the gas: if we maintain a constant volume, all the energy we supply will go into raising the temperature, whereas if we allow the gas to expand (for instance by pushing a piston or inflating a balloon) we must also take into account the work done by the gas pressure in the expansion.

Conservation of energy implies that the total change ΔU in internal energy U of the gas is equal to the total energy supplied to it (or removed from it) as work W and as heat Q:

Problems 11D.1 and 11D.2

$$\Delta U = Q + W \qquad \text{(if work } W \text{ is done } \textbf{\textit{on}} \text{ the gas) or}$$

$$\boxed{\Delta U = Q - W \qquad \text{(if work } W \text{ is done } \textbf{\textit{by}} \text{ the gas).}}$$

The first choice of sign seems more logical, but the second one is the standard convention.

(This is a basic principle of the branch of physics known as thermodynamics, and is usually called the *first law of thermodynamics*. However, it is really a specific application of energy conservation rather than an independent law.)

We have previously argued that 'non-conservation' of energy in inelastic collisions and the action of dissipative forces is due to changes in the internal energy of the bodies in question. In the case of gases we are now in a position to test this, because we have a way to measure the internal energy of a gas—for a monatomic gas with no additional degrees of freedom, we can deduce the internal energy from the temperature.

Problem 11D.4

Suppose we have a gas in a box which has a frictionless piston closing one side. The gas exerts a force PA on the piston, where A is the area of the piston, and by Newton's third law the piston exerts a force $-PA$ on the gas. If the pressure of the gas pushes the piston out by a distance Δx, the work done by the gas on the piston (which is minus the work done by the piston on the gas) is

Problems 11D.1 through 11D.5.

$$\Delta W = F \, \Delta x = PA \, \Delta x .$$

But $A \, \Delta x$ is just the change in the volume of the box, so in fact

$$\boxed{\Delta W = P \, \Delta V.}$$

Thus if a gas initially has pressure P_i and volume V_i, and undergoes some process leading to a final state with pressure and volume (P_f, V_f), *we can calculate the work done by the gas by integrating $P\mathrm{d}V$ from V_i to V_f*, i.e. by measuring the area under the curve that the process traces out on a plot of P against V. Note that the value of this integral will depend on the exact path traced by the pressure and volume of the gas during the process.

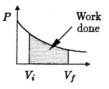

This path dependence of the integral is the principle on which internal-combustion engines, refrigerators, etc. operate: *by changing the conditions under which a gas expands and contracts, we can return to the initial pressure and volume by a different route and have done some net work during the process.* (Of course, energy conservation requires that this is 'paid for' in energy supplied, for example, by burning gasoline.)

Problems 11D.3, 11D.7

The relations between internal energy, heat, and work are at the heart of *thermodynamics*. Thermodynamics is an important field with many practical applications, notably the study of the efficiency of energy generation (i.e. the proportion of the total energy of a given system which can be transformed into work).

How useful in practical applications is the concept of an ideal gas? The answer turns out to be "extremely useful"—most 'everyday' gases, such as air, methane, or carbon dioxide, are very good approximations to an ideal gas. This is in contrast to the situation in the next chapter, where the 'ideal liquid' that we shall consider is *not* a very good approximation to real liquids.

SUMMARY

* The *ideal gas* model consists of free, non-interacting particles which move randomly and may undergo elastic collisions with each other or with other objects in the vicinity. This model is a very good approximation to many real gases at room temperature and atmospheric pressure.

* Gases exert a force on any surrounding wall which is directed perpendicular to the wall and is proportional to its area. The force exerted divided by the area is called the *pressure* of the gas.

* The pressure exerted by an ideal gas is proportional to the average kinetic energy of its constituent particles and to the number of particles present, and inversely proportional to the volume in which the gas is contained.

* The *temperature* of an ideal gas is the average translational kinetic energy of its constituents (times a numerical conversion factor). Temperature is defined relative to an *absolute zero*, at which the average kinetic energy of the atoms of an ideal gas would be zero, and is measured in *kelvin*.

* The *internal energy* of a gas is the mechanical energy, both kinetic and potential, stored in the motions of the individual molecules of the gas. This includes both translational kinetic energy of whole molecules and rotational and vibrational energy within a molecule.

* The temperature of an object can be increased by supplying energy, either by doing work on the object or by placing it in contact with something at a higher temperature. The energy transferred in the second case is called *heat*. The *specific heat capacity* of a substance, in $J/kg \cdot K$, is the heat required to raise the temperature of 1 kg of the substance by 1 K; the *molar heat capacity* of a gas is the heat required to raise the temperature of one mole (Avogadro's number of molecules) of the gas by 1 K. The values of specific and molar heat capacity for a given gas depend on the conditions under which the gas is heated; for different gases they depend on the complexity of the gas molecule, i.e. the number of degrees of freedom for motion within a single molecule.

* Physical concepts introduced in this chapter: pressure, heat, temperature, internal energy (of a gas); Avogadro's Number, mole; specific heat capacity, molar heat capacity.

* Mathematical concepts introduced in this chapter: notation $\langle x \rangle$ for 'average value of x'.

* Equations introduced in this chapter:

$$PV = \frac{2}{3} N \left\langle \frac{1}{2} mv^2 \right\rangle \quad \text{(pressure of an ideal gas)};$$

$$\left\langle \frac{1}{2} mv^2 \right\rangle = \frac{3}{2} kT \quad \text{(definition of kinetic temperature)};$$

$$PV = NkT = \mathcal{N}RT \quad \text{(ideal-gas law)};$$

$$\Delta U = Q - W \quad \text{(first law of thermodynamics)};$$

$$\Delta W = P \Delta V \quad \text{(work done by expanding gas)}.$$

* Useful constants:

$$R = 8.3 \text{ J/mol} \cdot \text{K} \qquad \text{(gas constant);}$$

$$k = 1.38 \times 10^{-23} \text{ J/K} \qquad \text{(Boltzmann's constant);}$$

$$N_A = 6.02 \times 10^{23} \text{ molecules/mole} \qquad \text{(Avogadro's number);}$$

$$1 \text{ u} = 1.66 \times 10^{-27} \text{ kg} \qquad \text{(atomic mass unit).}$$

* Temperature scales:

$$T(\text{K}) = T(^\circ\text{C}) + 273.15 \text{ K} \qquad \text{(Centigrade to Kelvin);}$$

$$T(^\circ\text{F}) = 32^\circ\text{F} + \tfrac{9}{5} T(^\circ\text{C}) \qquad \text{(Centigrade to Fahrenheit);}$$

$$T(^\circ\text{C}) = \tfrac{5}{9}\left(T(^\circ\text{F}) - 32^\circ\text{F}\right) \qquad \text{(Fahrenheit to Centigrade).}$$

The triple point of water corresponds to 273.16 K, or 0.01°C, by definition.

PROBLEMS AND QUESTIONS

By the end of this chapter you should be able to answer or solve the types of questions or problems stated below.

Note: throughout this book, in multiple-choice problems, the answers have been rounded off to 2 significant figures, unless otherwise stated.

At the end of the chapter there are answers to all the problems. In addition, for problems with an (H) or (S) after the number, there are respectively hints on how to solve the problems or completely worked-out solutions.

11A FUNDAMENTAL CONCEPTS (THE IDEAL GAS)

11A.1   A strong wind has a velocity of 80 km/h. Compare this with the typical speed of an air molecule at 290 K. What do we mean by 'wind velocity', and why is the effect of a wind so different from that of still air?

11A.2 (H)   Small dust particles suspended in air seem to dance randomly about, a phenomenon called *Brownian motion*. Explain why this occurs. Why is Brownian motion only perceptible for small particles?

11A.3   Give briefly, in your own words, the microscopic description of a gas and, in the context of your description, explain the origin and meaning of the term "pressure of a gas".

11A.4   In this chapter we have introduced the new concepts of the *pressure* and (kinetic) *temperature* of a large quantity of an ideal gas. What are the measurable properties of a single atom or molecule of that gas which correspond to the bulk properties of pressure and temperature?

Suppose that the pressure and temperature of a quantity of ideal gas are accurately known. Are the corresponding properties of the individual atoms also accurately known? If not, what is known about them?

11B KINETIC THEORY

11B.1   Air is a mixture of oxygen molecules with a mass of 32 u ($1u = 1.66 \times 10^{-27}$ kg) and nitrogen molecules with a mass of 28 u. What is the ratio of the speed of a typical oxygen molecule to that of a typical nitrogen molecule?

(a) 1.07; (b) 0.94; (c) 0.88; (d) 1.00.

11B.2 (S)   What is the typical speed of (a) a helium atom, (b) a nitrogen molecule, at 300 K? Helium has a mass of 4 u, N_2 a mass of 28 u; $1u = 1.66 \times 10^{-27}$ kg.

11B.3 (H)   At what temperature would (a) the average kinetic energy and (b) the rms speed of a hydrogen molecule (mass 2 u) be equal to that of an oxygen molecule (mass 32 u) at 300 K?

11B.4 Air contains a small proportion (about 1% of the total number of molecules) of argon, a monatomic gas with an atomic mass of 40 u (1 u = 1.66×10^{-27} kg). What is the average kinetic energy of the argon atoms in a room at a typical room temperature of 68°F (20°C)? What is the typical speed of an argon atom at this temperature? What is the total number of argon atoms in a room of size 2.5 m × 3 m × 5 m, and what pressure do they exert on the walls of the room? (Atmospheric pressure is 1.01×10^5 Pa.)

11B.5 (S) According to quantum physics, a light wave is actually composed of particles, called *photons*. While a complete understanding of photons involves both quantum physics and relativity, the pressure exerted by photons inside a perfectly reflecting box can be calculated using the same method we employed for the ideal gas. The differences are that photons always move at the speed of light, which is denoted by c (i.e. $|\vec{\mathbf{v}}| = c$), and the momentum $\vec{\mathbf{p}}$ of a photon is not $m\vec{\mathbf{v}}$, but

$$\vec{\mathbf{p}} = \frac{E}{c^2}\vec{\mathbf{v}},$$

where E is the energy of the photon.

Using this information, calculate the pressure exerted by a 'gas' of N photons confined inside a rectangular box of volume V. Assume the walls of the box are perfectly reflecting, so that a photon-wall interaction is an elastic collision.

11C THE IDEAL GAS LAW

11C.1 A closed box containing air at 72°F is placed in a refrigerator so that its temperature decreases to 36°F. If the original pressure of the air in the box was 10^5 Pa, what is its pressure at the new temperature?

(a) 5.0×10^4 Pa; (b) 2.0×10^5 Pa; (c) 9.3×10^4 Pa; (d) 1.1×10^5 Pa.

11C.2 Atmospheric pressure is about 10^5 Pa, and a typical room temperature might be 300 K. Approximately how many molecules are there in an air-filled room of dimensions 3 meters by 3 meters by 4 meters?

(a) 8.7×10^{26}; (b) 2.6×10^{29}; (c) 2.4×10^{25}.

11C.3 (H) A chemistry laboratory buys supplies of pure gases in pressurized cylinders with a volume of 10 liters (0.01 m³), and later returns the cylinders for refilling. To avoid accidentally sending out empty cylinders, the supply company keeps a record of the masses of its cylinders when 'empty', and weighs each one before sending it back out. When full, the cylinders have a pressure of 2.0×10^7 Pa, when 'empty', they contain the same gas, but at a pressure of 1.0×10^5 Pa (one atmosphere). The weighing is done at room temperature (22°C). What is the mass difference between a full and an empty cylinder of hydrogen (molecular mass 2 u)?

11C.4   A pressure cooker is a pan whose lid can be tightly sealed to prevent gas from escaping. If an empty (but sealed) pressure cooker were inadvertently left on a hot stove, what would be the force on the lid due to air pressure when the air inside the cooker had been heated to 120°C? Assume that the temperature of the room outside is 20°C and that the pressure cooker is 30 cm in diameter. Atmospheric pressure is 1.01×10^5 Pa.

If the pressure relief valve on the lid is now opened, allowing hot air to escape until the pressure inside is reduced to atmospheric, and the pot is then sealed again and removed from the stove, what is the net force on the lid due to air pressure when the contents have cooled back to 20°C?

11C.5 (H)   Air is approximately 80% nitrogen and 20% oxygen by mass (i.e. 1 kg of air contains 800 g of nitrogen and 200 g of oxygen). What is the ratio of the number of nitrogen molecules to the number of oxygen molecules? Estimate the density (in kg/m^3) of air at 20°C and 10^5 Pa. By how much does this change if the air is at 0°C and the same pressure? A molecule of nitrogen has a mass of 28 u, oxygen 32 u.

11C.6 (S)   If the atmosphere of a planet is all at the same temperature T and consists of a gas whose molecules have mass m, how does the density of the atmosphere vary with height above the ground? Assume that the atmosphere does not extend far enough from the planet for g to change significantly.

11D   INTERNAL ENERGY AND WORK DONE BY IDEAL GAS

11D.1 (H)   Explain, on both a microscopic and macroscopic level, why a bicycle pump gets hot when you use it. Does the temperature it reaches depend on the speed at which you pump?

 Note for problems 11D.2–11D.5: a monatomic ideal gas such as helium has no internal molecular degrees of freedom. Hence the internal energy of the gas is entirely stored in the translational kinetic energy of the atoms.

11D.2 (H)   A monatomic ideal gas, originally at a pressure P_i, volume V_i and temperature T_i, expands to three times its initial volume. Calculate the final pressure and temperature if this expansion takes place (a) isothermally (i.e. at constant temperature); (b) isobarically (at constant pressure). In each case, how much heat is supplied to the gas and how much work is done by the gas during the expansion?

11D.3 (H) (a)   A standard tool in thermodynamics is a plot of pressure as a function of volume (i.e. a plot with P as the y-axis and V as the x-axis). On such a PV plot, draw lines representing each of the expansion processes you calculated in problem 11D.2. What is the graphical representation of the work done during each expansion?

(b)   A *cycle* on a PV plot is a closed loop, i.e. a series of expansions and compressions which eventually brings the gas back to its starting point. What is the *net* change in the internal energy of an ideal gas after it has completed such a cycle? Is it possible that a net amount of *work* has been done during the cycle? If so, draw a cycle in which a net amount of work is done. Explain how this satisfies energy conservation.

11D.3, continued:

(c) Use the PV plot you drew in part (a) to construct a cycle in which a gas expands isobarically to three times its initial volume, is then allowed to cool at constant volume back to its original temperature, and finally is compressed isothermally back to its original volume. How much net work is done by the gas during this cycle?

11D.4 (S) Obtain expressions for the molar heat capacities of a monatomic ideal gas at constant volume and at constant pressure, and hence show that their ratio is 5/3.

 We saw in the *Essentials* that the conditions under which a gas is heated affect its measured heat capacity. These two extremes (heating without change of volume, which implies an increase in pressure, and conversely heating at constant pressure, which requires expansion) are the standard ways to quote specific or molar heat capacities: the corresponding values are labeled C_V and C_P respectively.

11D.5 (H) If the volume of a sealed vessel filled with helium at atmospheric pressure (1.01×10^5 Pa) and room temperature (295 K) is 0.5 m^3, calculate the internal energy of the helium gas at 295 K and at 77 K. Hence calculate the heat transferred from the vessel during the cooling process. What is the molar heat capacity of helium at constant volume?

 The following problem demonstrates how the number of atoms in each molecule of a polyatomic gas affects the heat capacity of that gas. This material is quite difficult—consider it a challenge problem.

11D.6 (S) The **principle of equipartition** states that internal energy is equally shared amongst the available degrees of freedom, i.e. $\left\langle \frac{1}{2}mv_x^2 \right\rangle = \left\langle \frac{1}{2}mv_y^2 \right\rangle = \left\langle \frac{1}{2}mv_z^2 \right\rangle = \frac{1}{2}kT$ for a monatomic gas, and each internal degree of freedom for a polyatomic gas also contributes $\frac{1}{2}kT$. What effect will this have on the molar heat capacities of polyatomic ideal gases? For a diatomic molecule, what do you expect the ratio of heat capacities to be (a) if only rotational internal motion occurs, and (b) if vibration also contributes?

11D.7 (S) An *adiabatic* expansion or contraction is one in which $Q = 0$, i.e. no heat is transferred to or from the gas.

(a) Show that this implies that $P_i V_i^\gamma = P_f V_f^\gamma$, where i denotes the initial state, f the final state, and $\gamma = C_P/C_V$ is the ratio of specific heat capacities.

(b) Suppose that $\mathcal{N}$ moles of an ideal gas expand isothermally from (P_a, V_a) to (P_b, V_b), and then adiabatically from (P_b, V_b) to (P_c, V_c). The gas is then compressed isothermally from (P_c, V_c) to (P_d, V_d), and finally compressed adiabatically back to its starting point. How much heat is (i) supplied to, (ii) lost by, the gas during this cycle? What is the *efficiency* of the cycle, where efficiency is defined as the work done divided by the heat supplied?

COMPLETE SOLUTIONS TO PROBLEMS WITH AN (S)

11B.2   *What is the typical speed of (a) a helium atom, (b) a nitrogen molecule, at* 300 K? *Helium has a mass of* 4 u, N_2 *a mass of* 28 u; 1 u = 1.66×10^{-27} kg.

Conceptualize
The kinetic temperature of an ideal gas is defined in terms of the average kinetic energy of its constituent atoms or molecules. Therefore we can calculate the average kinetic energy of a gas atom/molecule corresponding to a temperature of 300 K. This gives us the average value of v^2, and the square root of this will presumably represent a 'typical' speed.

Formulate and Solve
The average kinetic energy of the molecules of an ideal gas is $\langle \frac{1}{2}mv^2 \rangle = \frac{3}{2}kT$. Thus any ideal gas at 300 K has an average molecular kinetic energy of 6.2×10^{-21} J. Dividing by $\frac{1}{2}m$ gives $\langle v^2 \rangle = 1.9 \times 10^6 \, \text{m}^2/\text{s}^2$ for helium and $2.7 \times 10^5 \, \text{m}^2/\text{s}^2$ for nitrogen. A typical speed would be the square root of this, so 1.4 km/s for helium and 520 m/s for nitrogen.

Scrutinize and Learn
These speeds are high by everyday standards, though much less than the speed of light (we are still safely in the realm of classical mechanics). However, the velocities of individual gas molecules will be randomly oriented in space, so the speed of the center of mass of a volume of gas remains essentially zero.

The square root of $\langle v^2 \rangle$ is called the ***root-mean-square*** or ***rms*** speed. It is ***not*** equal to the average speed, $\langle v \rangle$: for example, two point masses with speeds 2.0 and 6.0 m/s have average speed 4.0 m/s, but rms speed 4.5 m/s—and their average *velocity* depends on the directions in which they are moving. Both $\langle v \rangle$ and the rms speed represent 'typical' speeds, but the rms speed is more useful for problems in more than one dimension, since $\langle v^2 \rangle$ is easier to express in component form than $\langle v \rangle$.

11B.5   *According to quantum physics, a light wave is actually composed of particles, called* **photons**. *While a complete understanding of photons involves both quantum physics and relativity, the pressure exerted by photons inside a perfectly reflecting box can be calculated using the same method we employed for the ideal gas. The differences are that photons always move at the speed of light, which is denoted by c (i.e.* $|\vec{v}| = c$), *and the momentum* $\vec{p}$ *of a photon is not* $m\vec{v}$, *but*

$$\vec{p} = \frac{E}{c^2}\vec{v},$$

where E is the energy of the photon.

Using this information, calculate the pressure exerted by a 'gas' of N photons confined inside a rectangular box of volume V. Assume the walls of the box are perfectly reflecting, so that a photon-wall interaction is an elastic collision.

Conceptualize
Our basic premise is that photons behave like the particles of an ideal gas: they move randomly around the box and undergo elastic collisions with the walls. We can therefore use the same line of attack that we used to calculate the pressure of an ideal gas in the

11B.5, continued:

Essentials. We consider one wall of the rectangular box and define the x-axis so that it is perpendicular to our chosen wall. We then calculate the average momentum transferred to the wall in a time interval Δt by a single photon of energy E, and finally sum over all N photons to obtain the total force.

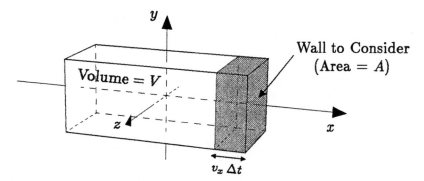

Formulate

Let the wall in question have area A as shown, and consider a photon reflected off the wall. The effect of the reflection is to reverse the sign of the x-component of the photon's velocity, while leaving its magnitude unchanged; the y- and z-components are unaffected. If the magnitude of the x-component is v_x, the photon's velocity changes by $\Delta v_x = -2v_x$ in the collision, so its momentum change is

$$\Delta p_x = -2\frac{E}{c^2}v_x,$$

and, by conservation of momentum, the momentum transferred to the wall is $-\Delta p_x$.

To determine the average force exerted by the photon on the wall, we need to calculate the momentum transferred per unit time, since $\vec{F} = d\vec{p}/dt$. This means that we have to find the probability that the photon collides with the wall in a given time interval Δt. The average momentum transferred in a time Δt is then the probability of a collision times the momentum transferred if a collision does occur, and the force is $\langle\vec{p}\rangle/\Delta t$.

Solve

For the photon to collide with our chosen wall in a given time interval Δt, its x-velocity must be positive (otherwise it is moving away from the wall). If it moves randomly, there is a 50% probability that this will be so. Given that it is moving in the right direction, it must be close enough to the wall to reach it in the specified time: that is, when we start the clock it must be not more than $v_x\Delta t$ away from the wall, in the shaded volume in the diagram. If it could be anywhere in volume V, the probability that it is within the shaded volume is

$$\frac{Av_x\Delta t}{V}.$$

The average momentum transferred to the wall is therefore

$$\langle p\rangle = \frac{1}{2} \times \frac{Av_x\Delta t}{V} \times 2v_x\frac{E}{c^2}$$

11B.5, continued:

and the average force exerted on the wall is

$$\langle F \rangle = \frac{EA}{c^2 V} v_x^2.$$

For N photons we need to sum over the individual photons. Since all photons travel at the speed of light c, we know

$$c^2 = v_x^2 + v_y^2 + v_z^2,$$

and if the photons are moving randomly they will (by definition of "random") have no preferred direction, so

$$\langle v_x^2 \rangle = \langle v_y^2 \rangle = \langle v_z^2 \rangle = \tfrac{1}{3} c^2.$$

The pressure exerted by our N photons is the total force per unit area:

$$P = \frac{F}{A} = \frac{1}{3} \frac{N \langle E \rangle}{V}.$$

Scrutinize

If we compare this expression with the ideal gas pressure

$$P_{\text{gas}} = \frac{2}{3} \frac{N \langle K \rangle}{V},$$

where $K = \frac{1}{2} m v^2$, we see that the two are extremely similar, as we might expect since we derived them in the same way. However, the difference between E and K is very significant when we take into account Einstein's famous equation $E = mc^2$. For the ideal gas, most of the energy is actually locked up in the mass of the gas particles, so the pressure is quite a small effect; for the massless photons, the pressure is related to the *total* energy E, and is therefore a much larger effect in relative terms. In absolute terms, however, it is very small under normal everyday conditions, and therefore we do not think of light as exerting a pressure (whereas we do recognize in everyday life the pressures exerted by gases and liquids).

Learn

The term $N \langle E \rangle / V$ is simply the total energy per unit volume, or *energy density*, associated with the light (or other electromagnetic radiation, such as radio waves or X-rays) in our box. As discussed above, the energy density associated with light is very small under typical experimental conditions, but this is emphatically not true in more exotic locations. Radiation pressure plays a significant role in the evolution of stars, and probably also in the processes which power quasars and other active galaxies. In addition, cosmologistsbelieve that for the first 10,000 to 100,000 years of the history of the universe, its mass density was not dominated by matter as we know it, but by radiation. During this period the pressure—equal to one-third of the energy density—was enormous. This huge pressure prevented matter from clumping under the influence of gravity. The process of galaxy formation, therefore, could not begin until the universe

11B.5, continued:

had cooled enough to lower the radiation energy density to the point where gravity could win out over radiation pressure.

11C.6 *If the atmosphere of a planet is all at the same temperature T and consists of a gas whose molecules have mass m, how does the density of the atmosphere vary with height above the ground? Assume that the atmosphere does not extend far enough from the planet for g to change significantly.*

Conceptualize

It seems reasonable to assume that the planet's atmosphere is basically stable, that is, it is not condensing onto the ground or leaking away into space. If that is the case, there must be no net force acting on a typical small volume element of atmosphere at some height h above the planet's surface. The individual forces acting on this small volume element are

- $g\Delta m$ downwards, where $\Delta m = \rho_h dV = \rho_h A\Delta h$;

- $P(h) \cdot A$ upwards;

- $P(h + \Delta h) \cdot A$ downwards;

- various horizontal pressure forces.

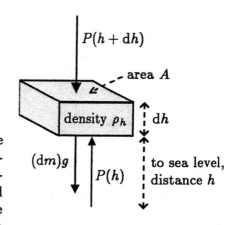

The symmetry of the situation implies that the horizontal pressure forces all cancel. The vertical pressure forces, however, must not cancel, since they must contribute a net upward force to balance $g\Delta m$. If the atmosphere is an ideal gas, then $P = nkT$, where n is the number density. We are told T does not vary with height, so the only way to have pressure decreasing with height is to have n decrease with height: $\Delta P = kT\Delta n$.

Formulate

The net force on our small volume element is

$$P(h + \Delta h) \cdot A - P(h) \cdot A = -\rho_h A g\Delta h,$$

or, writing $P = nkT$ and $\rho_h = nm$, where m is the average mass of one molecule of atmosphere,

$$\frac{dn}{dh} = \lim_{\Delta h \to 0} \frac{\Delta n}{\Delta h} = -\frac{nmg}{kT}.$$

Solve

If we rearrange this slightly we have

$$\frac{dn}{n} = -\frac{mg}{kT}dh,$$

11C.6, continued:

which we can integrate from zero, or ground level, to height H to give

$$\ln n_H - \ln n_0 = -\frac{mgH}{kT}$$

or

$$n_H = n_0 \exp\left(-\frac{mgH}{kT}\right),$$

where n_0 is the number density at ground level. (The mass density has the same form, since $\rho_H = n_H m$.) The density of the atmosphere decreases exponentially with height: at $H = kT/mg$ it has decreased to 37% of its value at ground level, at twice that height to 14%, and so on. For the Earth, taking nitrogen gas at 290 K to be representative of the atmosphere, $kT/mg \simeq 9$ km.

Scrutinize

The value we obtain for the Earth seems reasonable: it explains why commercial airplanes flying at about 10 km have to be pressurized, and why climbers of high mountains often use oxygen masks. We have, however, cheated somewhat: our coordinate system implicitly assumes that the Earth is flat. If you are confident of your calculus, you might like to investigate the surprising results of trying to do this calculation for an isothermal atmosphere about a spherical planet. Further, the isothermal approximation is not a very good one—anyone who has climbed a mountain will be aware that the Earth's atmosphere is not at all isothermal! Despite these approximations, the actual numerical value for the scale height of the atmosphere is not too bad.

Learn

Taking this result together with that from problem 11B.2, we can also understand why the Earth has an atmosphere of nitrogen and oxygen, the Moon has no atmosphere at all, and Jupiter has an atmosphere of hydrogen and helium. Although the speed of a typical helium atom is not high enough to escape from Earth's gravity, gas atoms actually have a wide range of speeds about this typical value, and helium (having smaller m) also extends out to greater heights than heavier elements. A helium atom which happens to be moving fast is therefore quite likely to escape from the atmosphere before a collision with another atom slows it down, and over the five billion years of Earth's history we have lost any gaseous hydrogen and helium we originally possessed. The Moon, with only one-sixth of Earth's surface gravity, is unable to retain any gaseous atmosphere at all, whereas Jupiter, with both a higher gravity and a lower temperature, keeps even the least massive gases.

Notice that the form of the exponential is $-(\text{potential energy})/kT$. This turns out not to be a special coincidence for height, but instead a very general feature of gas distributions. Potential energy and kinetic energy are very closely related, so it is not too surprising to find that the distribution of molecular speeds follows a similar law: the probability of finding a molecule with speed in the range v to $v + \Delta v$ does indeed include a factor of $\exp\left(-\frac{1}{2}mv^2/kT\right)\Delta v$. The full formula, including normalization, is the *Maxwell-Boltzmann distribution*,

$$f(v)\mathrm{d}v = 4\pi\left(\frac{m}{2\pi kT}\right)^{3/2} v^2 e^{-\frac{1}{2}mv^2/kT}\mathrm{d}v.$$

11C.6, continued:

The significance of this formula is that it tells us the *spread* of molecular speeds about the average we deduce from the temperature. This is important when one considers, for example, the evaporation of a liquid (fast molecules escape as vapor) or—as above—the loss of light gases from a planetary atmosphere.

11D.4 *Obtain expressions for the molar heat capacities of a monatomic ideal gas at constant volume and at constant pressure, and hence show that their ratio is 5/3.*

Conceptualize

For a monatomic ideal gas, the internal energy U is just the total kinetic energy $N\left\langle \frac{1}{2}mv^2 \right\rangle = \frac{3}{2}NkT$. If we heat the gas at constant volume, no work is done by the gas, and therefore all the energy we transfer to the gas just increases its internal energy. Therefore the amount of energy needed to raise the temperature of one mole of gas by an amount ΔT under these conditions is simply $C_V \Delta T = \frac{3}{2}N_A k\left((T + \Delta T) - T\right)$, where N_A is Avogadro's number.

In the case of constant pressure, the change in internal energy for a given temperature change ΔT must be the same, $C_V \Delta T$, because the kinetic temperature of a gas depends *only* on the kinetic energy of its constituent particles, and not on the volume they happen to be occupying. However, to maintain constant pressure while changing the temperature the volume occupied by the gas must change, and so the gas must do work—e.g. in pushing out a piston, as in the *Essentials*. Conservation of energy implies that additional energy must be supplied to the gas to allow it to do this work, and therefore the molar heat capacity at constant pressure, C_P, must be greater than C_V.

Formulate

We have already seen that the work done by the gas for a change of volume ΔV is $P\Delta V$. To raise the temperature of a mole of gas by ΔT at constant pressure P, the total energy that must be supplied to the gas is therefore

$$\Delta Q = P\Delta V + C_V \Delta T.$$

(Denoting the heat transferred by Q is standard notation, because the obvious abbreviation, H, unfortunately has a technical meaning in thermodynamics.)

Solve

The molar heat capacity at constant volume is

$$C_V = \frac{dU}{dT} = \lim_{\Delta T \to 0} \frac{\Delta U}{\Delta T} = \frac{3}{2}N_A k.$$

Since $N_A k = R$ by definition, this implies $C_V = \frac{3}{2}R$. Numerically this comes to 12.47 J/mol·K.

The molar heat capacity at constant pressure is

$$C_P = \frac{dQ}{dT} = \lim_{\Delta T \to 0} \frac{\Delta Q}{\Delta T} = P\frac{dV}{dT} + C_V.$$

11D.4, continued:

What is dV/dT? From the ideal-gas law,

$$V = \frac{RT}{P}$$

for one mole of gas, and both R and P are constant if the heating is done at constant pressure. Hence

$$\frac{dV}{dT} = \frac{R}{P},$$

and so

$$C_P = R + C_V = \tfrac{5}{2}R,$$

which comes to 20.79 J/mol·K. The ratio of molar heats is

$$\frac{C_P}{C_V} = \frac{\tfrac{5}{2}R}{\tfrac{3}{2}R} = \frac{5}{3}.$$

Scrutinize

We have assumed here that the energy transferred to the gas goes *either* into increasing the kinetic energy of its constituent particles *or* doing work on its surroundings. This is reasonable for the *monatomic ideal gas* specified in the question.

The dimensions of C_V and C_P must be [energy]/[temperature]·[mole], since they both represent the amount of energy needed to raise the temperature of one mole of the gas by 1 K. From the equation $PV = \mathcal{N}RT$ we see that the dimensions of R are [force] × [length]/([temperature] × [$\mathcal{N}$]). As $\mathcal{N}$ is measured in moles, this is consistent. Note that the units of the *specific* heat capacity, which is the energy required to raise the temperature of *one kilogram* of material through 1 K, are slightly different: J/kg·K, rather than J/mol·K. The specific heat capacity, not the molar heat capacity, is the quantity normally tabulated in data books, since in practical applications the amount of material is more likely to be given in kilograms than in moles. The ratio of specific heats is of course equal to the ratio of molar heats.

Learn

For ideal gases which are not monatomic, the ratio of molar heats (or specific heats) depends on the structure of the molecule (see Problem 11D.6). This ratio also arises in other contexts in thermodynamics—for example, in describing the path followed on the PV plot by a mass of gas expanding or contracting without exchanging heat with its surroundings. For this reason, the ratio of specific heats is given its own symbol: $C_P/C_V \equiv \gamma$.

11D.6   *The **principle of equipartition** states that internal energy is equally shared amongst the available degrees of freedom, i.e. $\left\langle \tfrac{1}{2}mv_x^2 \right\rangle = \left\langle \tfrac{1}{2}mv_y^2 \right\rangle = \left\langle \tfrac{1}{2}mv_z^2 \right\rangle = \tfrac{1}{2}kT$ for a monatomic gas, and each internal degree of freedom for a polyatomic gas also contributes $\tfrac{1}{2}kT$. What effect will this have on the molar heat capacities of polyatomic ideal gases?*

11D.6, continued:

For a diatomic molecule, what do you expect the ratio of heat capacities to be (a) if only rotational internal motion occurs and (b) if vibration also contributes?

Conceptualize and Formulate

The kinetic temperature of a gas is defined in terms of the translational kinetic energy of its constituent molecules. Internal kinetic or potential energy plays no part in this definition. Therefore, to raise the temperature of a mole of a polyatomic ideal gas from T to $T + \Delta T$, we still have to increase $\langle \frac{1}{2}mv^2 \rangle$ by an amount $\frac{3}{2}k\Delta T$. The principle of equipartition states that this implies raising the energy stored in all the other degrees of freedom by $\frac{1}{2}k\Delta T$ each. This implies that the molar heat capacity at constant volume will increase to $\frac{1}{2}fR$, where f is the total number of degrees of freedom (including the three for translational kinetic energy).

The calculation in Problem 11D.4 which gave $C_P = C_V + R$ was not in any way dependent on the actual value of C_V. Therefore it still holds for our polyatomic gas, which must have $C_P = R + C_V = (1 + \frac{1}{2}f)R$. The ratio of molar heats is then

$$\gamma = \frac{C_P}{C_V} = \frac{1 + \frac{1}{2}f}{\frac{1}{2}f} = \frac{2}{f} + 1.$$

Solve

To solve this problem for a diatomic molecule, we therefore have to count the number of degrees of freedom—the number of coordinates required to specify the motion of one molecule. We already know that three degrees of freedom are taken up by the three independent directions of translational motion, i.e. the three coordinates needed to specify the velocity vector of the molecule's center of mass.

What about rotational motion? We can consider a diatomic molecule as two point particles connected by a spring (representing the interatomic force binding the molecule together). If we put the origin of coordinates at the molecule's center of mass and the x-axis runs along the line joining the two atoms, the molecule can

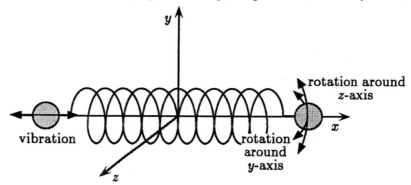

rotate about the y- or z-axis or some combination of these, so the angular motion has two components. (Rotation about the x-axis is meaningless if we assume the atoms are

11D.6, continued:

point particles.) Adding these to the three components of the velocity of the molecule's center of mass, we have $f = 5$, and so we would predict $\gamma = 1.4$.

Vibration adds only one degree of freedom, because the molecule has only one possible way to vibrate. Hence we must add another $\frac{1}{2}kT$ for the average *kinetic* energy of vibration of the molecule. However, if we think of the atoms as being connected by a spring, there is also *potential* energy associated with this vibration, and we can work out from our knowledge of simple harmonic motion that the average potential energy is equal to the average kinetic energy. (It is reasonably obvious that this must be so, since the total energy in the oscillation varies from all kinetic, when the spring is at its natural length, to all potential at the points of greatest compression or extension, and back again.) We must account for this in our sum, so effectively $f = 7$ and the expected ratio is 1.286.

Scrutinize and Learn

Writing the ideal-gas law in terms of internal energy rather than temperature gives us

$$PV = \frac{2}{f}U = (\gamma - 1)U.$$

This expression allows us to calculate the internal energy, and to count the number of degrees of freedom, from the *measured* ratio of molar heats. We can therefore check our understanding of kinetic theory by measuring this ratio for a variety of different diatomic gases. The results are surprising: for most diatomic molecules the ratio of specific heats comes out close to 1.4 (see any standard data book). This suggests that the bond between the molecules is more like a rigid rod than a spring, and vibration is not possible. However, this explanation cannot be right, because (i) some heavy diatomic gases, such as iodine, have molar heat ratios close to 1.3 and (ii) the ratio of molar heats for diatomic gases varies with temperature, approaching 1.286 as the temperature gets very high, even for those gases which have ratios of 1.4 at room temperature.

This is a real failure of our model, since there is nothing in our calculation which suggests a temperature dependence. In the 19th century, when the kinetic theory of gases was first developed, this disagreement was not understood (it is not that these gases are not ideal, because they obey the ideal-gas law very well; they just have the 'wrong' value of γ!). We now know that it occurs because at these small distances and energies it is necessary to apply the rules of quantum mechanics. Under these rules, a diatomic molecule may not actually be able to 'use' all its potential degrees of freedom at low energy, and therefore our calculation represents the high-energy (or high temperature) limit of the specific heat ratio, which will be different at lower temperatures.

11D.7   *An adiabatic expansion or contraction is one in which $Q = 0$, i.e. no heat is transferred to or from the gas.*

(a) *Show that this implies that $P_iV_i^\gamma = P_fV_f^\gamma$, where i denotes the initial state, f the final state, and $\gamma = C_P/C_V$ is the ratio of specific heat capacities.*

11D.7, continued:

Conceptualize

If $Q = 0$, then the work done by the gas must be equal to the change in its internal energy. We can express both of these in terms of P, V, and T, and then use the ideal gas law to eliminate T. This will leave a relation between P and V.

Because the work done depends on the specific path taken on the PV plot, it will be best to start by considering *small* changes of pressure and volume. We can then integrate to find the result for large changes.

Formulate

For the case $Q = 0$, the first law of thermodynamics reduces to $\Delta U = -\Delta W$, where we use ΔW to denote a *small* amount of work. We know that $\Delta W = P\Delta V$, and the definition of the molar heat capacity tells us that $\Delta U = \mathcal{N} C_V \Delta T$. (When heating at constant volume, no work is done, and so C_V relates the heat supplied directly to the change in internal energy of the gas.) Thus,

$$\mathcal{N} C_V \Delta T = -P\Delta V.$$

This equation describes a small adiabatic change of volume in an ideal gas. To solve the problem, we need to express ΔT in terms of P, V, ΔP and ΔV.

Solve

The ideal gas law is $\mathcal{N} RT = PV$. If we differentiate this with respect to some variable, say time, then the product rule for differentiation gives

$$\frac{d}{dt}(\mathcal{N} RT) = \mathcal{N} R\frac{dT}{dt} = P\frac{dV}{dt} + V\frac{dP}{dt}.$$

This gives us the *differential form* of the ideal gas law:

$$\mathcal{N} R\Delta T = P\Delta V + V\Delta P.$$

Using this, we can substitute for ΔT in our adiabatic volume change:

$$\frac{C_V}{R}(P\Delta V + V\Delta P) = -P\Delta V$$

$$\implies (C_V + R)P\Delta V = -C_V V\Delta P.$$

But we saw in Problem 11D.4 that $C_V + R = C_P$, so this equation reduces to

$$C_P \frac{\Delta V}{V} = -C_V \frac{\Delta P}{P}.$$

We can now integrate this equation from the initial state (P_i, V_i) to the final state (P_f, V_f):

$$\gamma \int_{V_i}^{V_f} \frac{dV}{V} = -\int_{P_i}^{P_f} \frac{dP}{P}$$

$$\implies \gamma \ln \frac{V_f}{V_i} = -\ln \frac{P_f}{P_i},$$

11D.7, continued:

where $\gamma = C_P/C_V$ as in Problem 11D.4. Taking antilogs, using the fact that $\ln(x^a) = a \ln x$, we have

$$P_i V_i^\gamma = P_f V_f^\gamma$$

as required.

Scrutinize

The dimensions of the equation are OK: in particular, γ, being a ratio of two quantities with the same units, is dimensionless (it would be meaningless to speak of "x to the power of $(y$ joules)", for example). We can use the ideal gas law to eliminate P, giving $T_i V_i^{\gamma-1} = T_f V_f^{\gamma-1}$, and since $\gamma > 1$ this correctly implies that T must decrease if V increases (as no heat is supplied from outside, the work done by the gas in expanding must come from a loss of internal energy, i.e. a reduction in temperature).

Learn

Adiabatic expansion and compression is a useful idealization in describing *rapid* changes in volume, when there is no time for significant heat exchange with the surroundings. An example would be the motion of the piston in an automobile engine: both the compression stroke and the power stroke are approximately adiabatic.

(b) *Suppose that N moles of an ideal gas expand isothermally from (P_a, V_a) to (P_b, V_b), and then adiabatically from (P_b, V_b) to (P_c, V_c). The gas is then compressed isothermally from (P_c, V_c) to (P_d, V_d), and finally compressed adiabatically back to its starting point. How much heat is (i) supplied to, (ii) lost by, the gas during this cycle? What is the efficiency of the cycle, where efficiency is defined as the work done divided by the heat supplied?*

Conceptualize

By definition, no heat is lost by or supplied to the gas in the adiabatic legs of the cycle, so when calculating the heat supplied we need consider only the isothermal legs $a \rightarrow b$ and $c \rightarrow d$. The gas does positive work in expanding from a to b, and as its internal energy does not change (the expansion is isothermal) heat must be supplied to balance this work: conversely, the gas does negative work, and loses heat, during the isothermal compression from c to d. Since the gas winds up back at its starting point, its internal energy does not change over a complete cycle, and so, by the first law of thermodynamics, the work done during the cycle must be the difference between the heat **supplied** in the ab leg and the heat **lost** during the cd leg. Thus we do not need to calculate the work done during the adiabatic stages. We will, however, have to use the adiabatic legs to work out the relationship between the temperatures of the two isothermal stages.

Formulate

Since $PV = NRT$ and T is constant, the work done during an isothermal expansion or compression is

$$W = \int_{V_i}^{V_f} P \, dV = NRT \int_{V_i}^{V_f} \frac{dV}{V} = NRT \ln \frac{V_f}{V_i}.$$

11D.7, continued:

As we saw in part (a), the relation between temperature and volume for an adiabatic expansion or compression is

$$T_i V_i^{\gamma-1} = T_f V_f^{\gamma-1}.$$

This is all we need to solve the problem.

Solve
The heat supplied during stage ab is

$$Q_S = N R T_H \ln \frac{V_b}{V_a},$$

where T_H is the temperature of the gas during this expansion (the subscript H indicates that it is **higher** than the temperature during the cd compression). Likewise, the heat lost in stage cd is

$$Q_L = -N R T_L \ln \frac{V_c}{V_d}.$$

From stage bc we know that

$$\left(\frac{V_c}{V_b}\right)^{\gamma-1} = \frac{T_H}{T_L},$$

and likewise from da

$$\left(\frac{V_d}{V_a}\right)^{\gamma-1} = \frac{T_H}{T_L}.$$

Comparing these, we see that

$$\frac{V_c}{V_b} = \frac{V_d}{V_a}$$

$$\implies \frac{V_c}{V_d} = \frac{V_b}{V_a}.$$

From the first law of thermodynamics, we know that over this cycle $Q = W$, i.e. $Q_S + Q_L = W$. Hence the efficiency is given by

$$\epsilon = \frac{W}{Q_S} = 1 + \frac{Q_L}{Q_S}$$

$$= 1 - \frac{T_L}{T_H}.$$

Scrutinize
The efficiency is dimensionless, as it should be, and lies in the range 0 to 1 (or 0% to 100%), as energy conservation dictates that it must. Note that 100% efficiency can only be attained if $T_L = 0$, which is never true in practice—this cycle cannot transform **all** the energy supplied to it into useful work.

11D.7, continued:

Learn
The cycle we have analyzed here was first studied by the nineteenth-century French engineer N.L. Sadi Carnot, and is called the *Carnot cycle* in his honor. It can be shown that *for a given T_L and T_H, no engine can convert heat to work more efficiently than the Carnot cycle*. An engine using the Carnot cycle is not in fact practical, but it is possible to approximate real engines by different cycles on the PV plot and calculate their maximum efficiencies: for example, the operation of an automobile engine is approximately described by the *Otto cycle*, which consists of an adiabatic compression (the compression stroke of the piston), heating at constant volume (the ignition of gasoline by the spark), adiabatic expansion (the piston power stroke), and cooling at constant volume (the exhaust). The efficiency of the Otto cycle turns out to be $1 - (V_{\min}/V_{\max})^{\gamma-1}$, which means that high auto engine efficiencies require a high *compression ratio* $(V_{\max}/V_{\min})$. Real engines always have lower efficiencies than their idealized counterparts on the PV plot, owing to the effects of friction, turbulence, etc.

The statement that for a Carnot cycle (or other ideal reversible engine) working between temperatures T_H and T_L, the ratio of heat lost to heat supplied

$$\frac{|Q_L|}{|Q_S|} = \frac{T_L}{T_H}$$

was used by Lord Kelvin to *define* the thermodynamic temperature scale. The fact that we have derived it using our kinetic temperature scale shows that the two are equivalent. Historically, this is not surprising: although the two definitions are logically independent, in practice they are both rigorous formulations of the empirical ideal-gas temperature scale, which states that the temperature of an ideal gas at constant volume is proportional to its pressure.

HINTS FOR PROBLEMS WITH AN (H)
The number of the hint refers to the number of the problem

11A.2 If instead of small dust particles in the air you had a small admixture of a different gas, what would the average kinetic energy of a molecule of this gas be? Does this depend on the mass of the molecule?

11B.3 How does the average kinetic energy at a given temperature depend on mass and on temperature? If you are having trouble with this problem, study the solution to problem 11B.2

11C.3 How many molecules of gas does a cylinder contain when full? When 'empty'?

11C.5 How many molecules of mass m are there in a total mass M of a given gas?

What is the total number of molecules (of any kind) per unit volume of air at the given pressure and temperature?

11D.1 If the compression is *rapid*, there is no time for air to escape through the delivery valve of the pump or for the compressed gas to cool. Under these circumstances, what will happen to the internal energy of the air in the pump? Where does the energy come from?

11D.2 What is the internal energy of N molecules of a monatomic gas?

What is the work done by the gas as a result of a small change of volume ΔV? If the pressure is *constant*, can you integrate this over a large volume change?

How is the change in internal energy related to the heat supplied and the work done?

11D.3 (a) What is the expression for work done in terms of pressure and change in volume? What is the graphical equivalent of this?

(b) Can the temperature of the ideal gas be different if it has returned to the same point on the *PV* plot? Can the path it traces out on its return be different from the path it followed originally?

11D.5 What is the change in internal energy of the gas as a result of the temperature change? Has any work been done on or by the gas?

What is the definition of molar heat capacity? How many moles of gas are there in the vessel?

ANSWERS TO HINTS

11A.2 Same as the air molecules; no.

11B.3 Independent of mass; proportional to temperature.

11C.3 4.92×10^{25}; 2.46×10^{23}.

11C.5 M/m; 2.47×10^{25} m^{-3}.

11D.1 It will increase. You did work on the piston of the pump, which in turn did work on the gas.

11D.2 $\frac{3}{2}NkT$; $\Delta W = P\Delta V$;

$W = P(V_f - V_i)$ where f and i are final and initial values.

Change in internal energy of gas = heat supplied to gas minus work done by gas.

11D.3 (a) $W = \int_{start}^{end} PdV$; the integral is the area under the graph.

(b) No; yes.

11D.5 -56 kJ; no.

Heat transferred per mole of gas for a temperature change of 1 K; 20.6 moles.

ANSWERS TO ALL PROBLEMS

11A.1 Typical speed about 500 m/s (1800 km/h).

Wind velocity represents a net velocity of large quantities of air, whereas net velocity of a large quantity of still air is zero (individual velocities have random orientation). Wind can therefore exert a net force on large objects, whereas pressure exerts no *net* force on any object large enough for random fluctuations to average out.

11A.2 The motion of the dust particles is caused by their collisions with randomly moving air molecules. For large particles the characteristic kinetic energy for room temperature corresponds to an unmeasurably small speed.

11A.3 All answers to this question should, of course, be different! A reasonable response would be:

"A gas consists of an extremely large number of small particles (usually atoms or molecules) moving randomly about with some distribution of speeds. The interparticle forces are very small (zero, for an ideal gas), and all collisions are elastic. Each collision of a gas particle with a container wall or other object will impart an impulse to the object struck: the time averaged sum of all these small impulses, divided by the area of the object, is the pressure exerted by the gas."

11A.4 Change of momentum per unit time; translational kinetic energy. No; the average over all the atoms or molecules in the sample.

11B.1 b

11B.2 See complete solution.

11B.3 (a) 300 K; (b) 19 K (if hydrogen were still an ideal gas at this low temperature!).

11B.4 6.1×10^{-21} J; 430 m/s; 9.4×10^{24}; 1.0×10^{3} Pa.

11B.5 See complete solution.

11C.1 c

11C.2 a

11C.3 0.16 kg

11C.4 2.4 kN upwards; 1.8 kN downwards.

11C.5 4.57:1; 1.18 kg/m^{3}; by a factor of 1.07, to 1.27 kg/m^{3}.

11C.6 See complete solution.

11D.1 The piston of the pump does work in compressing the gas, which increases its internal energy—microscopically, each gas molecule bouncing off the moving piston rebounds with a slightly higher speed. The average kinetic energy of a gas molecule increases and therefore so does its temperature. On the return stroke, fresh air is drawn in from outside the pump, so when the piston returns to its initial position the gas in the pump has not returned to its initial temperature—unlike a pendulum, this is not a closed, isolated system. Yes, both because the piston does more work if you apply more force in moving it, and because given time the gas will exchange heat with its surroundings.

11D.2 (a) $P_f = P_i/3$, $T_f = T_i$, $Q = (\ln 3)P_iV_i$,; $W = (\ln 3)P_iV_i$.

(b) $P_f = P_i$, $T_f = 3T_i$, $Q = 5P_iV_i$, $W = 2P_iV_i$.

11D.3 (a)

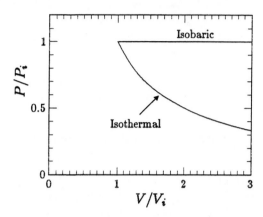

Work done in each case is area under curve.

(b) Zero; yes; any cycle where the line representing the *expansion* phase is higher than the line representing the *compression* phase.

Some of the heat supplied during the cycle has been converted to work.

(c) 0.9 P_iV_i

11D.4 See complete solution.

11D.5 12.5 J/mol·K.

11D.6 See complete solution.

11D.7 See complete solution.

ESSENTIALS OF INTRODUCTORY CLASSICAL MECHANICS

CHAPTER 12

FLUID MECHANICS

OVERVIEW

In real substances, the ideal-gas assumption of non-interacting molecules is never completely accurate. There is always some force acting between molecules. Under some conditions of pressure and temperature the intermolecular forces are strong enough to keep the molecules packed closely together, so that the substance no longer expands to fill its container completely: the gas has become a *liquid*. In this chapter we shall investigate the behavior of liquids, using a combination of Newton's laws and some of the concepts we developed in our study of gases.

When you have completed this chapter you should:

✔ recognize the similarities and differences between liquids and gases;

✔ be able to calculate the pressure in a liquid under different conditions;

✔ understand the phenomenon of buoyancy and Archimedes' principle;

✔ know how to use Bernoulli's equation to solve problems involving fluid flow, and understand its derivation in terms of energy conservation for the moving fluid;

✔ know what is meant by surface tension, and have a qualitative understanding of its origin in terms of intermolecular forces;

✔ have a qualitative understanding of the properties of real liquids.

ESSENTIALS

We saw in the last chapter that in an ideal gas intermolecular forces are assumed to be negligible. However, if we imagine cooling a real gas (so that its constituent molecules are moving more slowly) or compressing it (so that they are closer together) we will reach a state where the intermolecular forces are *not* negligible. In these circumstances the gas will diverge from the behavior expected of an ideal gas; if we continue the process it will eventually condense into a *liquid*. (We call the gas, liquid and solid states of a substance *phases*, and the sudden change from one to another is a *phase transition*.) The molecular interpretation of the gas-liquid phase transition is that the magnitude of the potential energy of the molecules due to the forces between them is comparable to their kinetic energy, so that they have a strong tendency to position themselves in the minimum of potential energy, at separations of r_0 (see diagram at right).

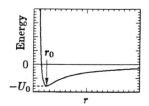

What are the characteristics of a liquid? Because the intermolecular separation is essentially fixed, the density must be nearly constant regardless of external conditions, and thus the volume occupied by a given mass of liquid is fixed. Unlike a gas, a liquid does not expand to fill its container. On the other hand, the molecules of the liquid are still free to move randomly, and so the *shape* of the liquid is not fixed (this is the basic difference between liquids and solids). Since the rise in intermolecular potential energy with decreasing separation below r_0 is not quite vertical, it is in fact possible to compress real liquids slightly; they also (like solids) expand or contract slightly with changing temperature. However, these changes are so small compared to those we found in the case of an ideal gas that it is reasonable to idealize liquids as having absolutely fixed density (such an ideal liquid is called *incompressible*) and no sensitivity to temperature. Because the intermolecular forces are important, the motion of molecules in a liquid is much more complicated to calculate than the ideal gas: we cannot construct a simple kinetic theory of liquids. Instead we use Newton's laws to analyse behavior of liquids *in bulk*. Much of this analysis is also applicable to gases, and it is therefore given the name *fluid mechanics* (a fluid is either a liquid or a gas — literally something that flows).

Our analysis will obviously use the standard concepts of mass, volume and density. In addition, the concept of pressure that we developed in the ideal-gas model is still applicable (the molecules in a liquid, though subject to intermolecular forces, are still moving and can collide with walls and other molecules). We do not have an equivalent of the ideal-gas law to calculate the pressure or temperature directly, but we can use Newton's laws to determine how the pressure within a liquid varies with position.

410

Consider a small volume element ΔV of liquid within a larger sample. If the liquid is in stable equilibrium, no net force must act on this small volume element. We know there is a downward force on it: its weight $\Delta mg = \rho g \Delta V$, where Δm is the mass of our small element and ρ is its density (so $\Delta m = \rho \Delta V$). This must be balanced by a difference between the pressure from below (acting upwards) and the pressure from above (acting down) to give zero net force, i.e.

$$\rho g\, \Delta V - PA + (P + \Delta P)A = 0 \ ,$$

where A is the horizontal cross-section of our volume element, i.e.

$$\Delta V = A\, \Delta y \ ,$$

taking the y-axis to be vertical. Dividing the equation by ΔV yields, in the limit of small Δy,

$$\frac{\mathrm{d}P}{\mathrm{d}y} = -\rho g \ .$$

This is valid for any fluid, even if the density depends on the pressure as in a gas. For a liquid ρ is a constant, so we can integrate this equation very easily to get

$$\boxed{P_2 - P_1 = -\rho g(y_2 - y_1)}$$

for the difference in pressure between two different vertical coordinates within the liquid. The obvious choice of reference point is the surface of the liquid, which we can define to be $y = 0$; the pressure at any depth h below the surface is then

$$P = P_0 + \rho g h$$

Problems 12A.

(note that a positive h corresponds to a negative y, and thus to a higher pressure). We see that the pressure depends only on the pressure at the surface and the depth below the surface — as in the case of a gas, it does not depend on the shape of the container. Our analysis deals directly only with the vertical pressures, but since we expect the motion of molecules in liquids to be randomly oriented our molecular understanding of pressure tells us that the pressure in other directions will also be given by this equation.

This equation is simpler than the corresponding relation for gases, because the density in this case is a constant; in a gas, the density increases with increasing depth.

The same argument can be applied to understanding the phenomenon of **buoyancy**. If we have a mass m of liquid (of arbitrary shape), its weight is $m\vec{g}$ acting through its center of mass. If it is contained within a larger sample of the same liquid, the net force on it due to pressure from the surrounding liquid must be $-m\vec{g}$ through the center of mass, assuming the whole system is in equilibrium. If we then replace this mass of liquid by another body of the same shape, the net force from pressure remains the same (since the surrounding liquid is unaffected). The object therefore feels an upward *buoyant force* of magnitude mg and a *net* force $(M - m)\vec{g}$, where M is its own mass.

This result is known as Archimedes' principle. It is valid for gases as well as liquids, since it does not require constant density.

As we saw in Chapter 9, the weight $M\vec{g}$ acts through the center of mass of the body. Since the buoyant force $-m\vec{g}$ balances the weight of the original mass of liquid, it acts as if through *the liquid's* center of mass, which is referred to as the *center of buoyancy* of the immersed object. Since the center of mass and the center of buoyancy do not in general coincide, the buoyant force may exert a net torque about the object's center of mass.

Problem 13.3

If $M > m$ obviously the net force is downward, and the object sinks. If $M < m$ there is a net upward force and the object will rise towards the surface of the liquid. Once it breaks the surface the upward force on it changes, because only part of its volume is surrounded by liquid: the net force is thus $(M - \rho V)\vec{g}$, where ρ is the density of the liquid and V is the volume of the submerged part of the object. Equilibrium is reached when

Problems 12B.

$$M = \rho V \ ,$$

i.e. the mass of the object is equal to the mass of liquid corresponding to the submerged part of its volume. We call this the amount of liquid *displaced* by the floating object. [The mass of a ship is often quoted in terms of its *displacement*, i.e. the mass of water it displaces when afloat.]

So far we have considered static liquids. This approach ignores an obvious feature of fluids: as the name implies, they flow. Fluid flow is actually a very complicated phenomenon and extremely difficult to calculate for real situations (hence the use of wind tunnels to *measure* fluid flow around complex shapes such as auto bodies and airplanes), but we can use basic conservation principles to deduce results which are useful in simple situations.

The simple situations we shall consider involve steady flow of an *ideal liquid*. Steady flow means that the flow pattern is constant over time: a small element of liquid that is initially at some point (x, y, z) will always follow the same subsequent path. (The paths followed by such small elements of liquid are called *flow lines*; the curves defined by the direction of the liquid's velocity at any point are called *streamlines*. For steady flow these concepts are interchangeable, since the path of an element of liquid is clearly determined by the direction of its velocity.) An ideal liquid is incompressible and has no internal friction, so the motion of a small element is not affected by that of neighboring elements.

In steady flow, flow lines do not cross, because an element of liquid at a given point has a unique, well-defined velocity which in turn defines a unique flow line: we cannot have a point with two possible flow lines. Therefore we can define a *flow tube* as a bundle of neighboring flow lines, and any liquid element which is inside this flow tube at any given time will stay inside it. Given that we have a steady flow, it follows that the mass of liquid *entering* any section of the tube in a time interval Δt must be equal to the amount *leaving* the section in the same interval.

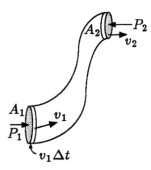

Consider a narrow flow tube, so that the velocity and pressure of the fluid do not vary across it. If the cross-sectional area of the tube where the fluid enters is A_1 and its speed at that point is v_1, the mass of fluid entering the tube in a time interval Δt is $\rho A_1 v_1 \, \Delta t$, and the mass leaving is similarly $\rho A_2 v_2 \, \Delta t$. Equating these gives us the *equation of continuity*

Problems 12C.1 and 12C.2.

$$\boxed{A_2 v_2 = A_1 v_1 \, .}$$

Since $Av \, \Delta t$ is just the volume of the small cylinder of fluid which moves past a specific point on the flow tube in time Δt, we can also express this as the *volume flow rate*

$$\frac{dV}{dt} = Av = \text{constant} \, .$$

The *mass flow rate*, dm/dt, is given by $\rho \, dV/dt$.

If we now consider the work done on the fluid in this section of the tube during time Δt, we observe that the work done by the external pressure P_1 is

$$P_1 A_1 v_1 \, \Delta t \, ,$$

since $P_1 A_1$ is the force and $v_1 \Delta t$ is the distance through which it acts. Similarly, the work done by external pressure P_2 is

$$-P_2 A_2 v_2 \, \Delta t \, .$$

(the minus sign enters because this pressure is directed opposite to the direction of motion). The net work done by pressure inside the section of tube is zero, by Newton's third law—only external forces contribute. Hence the total work done is

$$P_1 A_1 v_1 \,\Delta t - P_2 A_2 v_2 \,\Delta t = (P_1 - P_2)\,\Delta V \ .$$

The kinetic energy of the water in the volume $A_1 v_1 \,\Delta t$ is

$$\frac{1}{2}(\rho A_1 v_1 \,\Delta t)v_1^2 = \frac{1}{2}\rho v_1^2 \,\Delta V \ ,$$

and likewise for volume $A_2 v_2 \Delta t$, so the change in kinetic energy of the fluid originally inside our section of flow tube is

$$\Delta K = \frac{1}{2}\rho\,\Delta V\left(v_2^2 - v_1^2\right) \ ,$$

(The middle of the section is full of fluid in both cases, so clearly we need only consider the difference between the two small volumes at the ends.)

The change in *potential* energy is clearly

$$\Delta U = \rho g\,\Delta V\left(y_2 - y_1\right) \ ,$$

where y_1, y_2 are the heights of each end of the tube. Assuming the internal energy of an ideal fluid is constant (part of the same assumption that fluid is incompressible and at constant temperature) we can apply conservation of energy $\Delta W = \Delta K + \Delta U$, and obtain

$$P_1 - P_2 = \frac{1}{2}\rho\left(v_2^2 - v_1^2\right) + \rho g(y_2 - y_1) \ .$$

This is *Bernoulli's equation*. It is often convenient to rearrange it into the form

Problems 12C.3 through 12C.8.

$$\boxed{\, P_1 + \frac{1}{2}\rho v_1^2 + \rho g y_1 = P_2 + \frac{1}{2}\rho v_2^2 + \rho g y_2 \,}$$

i.e. the sum of the pressure, the kinetic energy per unit volume, and the potential energy per unit volume is the same at any point in the flow. If the liquid is *stationary*, this equation reduces to the equation for the variation of pressure with depth for a static liquid, as it must for consistency.

Problem 12C.6.

We derived this equation for an incompressible fluid in steady flow, but it can also be used for gases provided the pressure differences involved are not too large. It has many important practical applications, some obvious (calculating and measuring the flow speed of fluid in a pipe, for instance) and some less so (one can explain, albeit in a somewhat oversimplified fashion, why an airplane wing provides lift, and why the direction of spin affects the trajectory of the ball in games such as golf, tennis and baseball). Bernoulli's equation does not work if the flow is *turbulent* rather than steady—white-water rapids on a river, for example. In turbulent flow the flow patterns are constantly changing and our assumptions about well-defined flow lines break down. Fluid flow in a given situation is usually steady, or *laminar*, at low speeds but becomes turbulent (often very suddenly) above a certain critical speed. The study of turbulent flow is an application of chaos theory and far beyond the scope of this book.

Our derivation also ignored frictional effects. We know that real fluids—particularly liquids—are composed of molecules which exert forces on one another, so it is not surprising that frictional effects are actually important in many cases. In particular, because of friction, an object moving through a fluid is generally surrounded by a thin *boundary layer* of fluid which is almost at rest relative to the object; in laminar flow there is a smooth transition from this boundary layer to the steady flow of the fluid as a whole. This effect is significant in many applications of Bernoulli's equation: for example, the fact that the trajectory of a spinning ball curves is due to the difference in air speed on the two sides of the ball resulting from the formation of a boundary layer.

The property of a liquid which measures its internal friction is its *viscosity*, a quantity related to the force necessary to maintain a given flow rate relative to a stationary wall. A fluid with a high viscosity, molasses for example, has a high resistance to flow; gases, which flow much more readily than liquids, have low viscosity.

So far we have concentrated on the behavior of a volume element *within* the liquid. What happens when we consider a volume element at the surface?

We can make some predictions about this from the molecular picture. A molecule at the surface of the liquid is in an asymmetric situation—it has molecules below it and on either side, but not above it (of course the air or other gas above the liquid consists of molecules, but their number density is much less than within the liquid).

It is therefore subject to a net force tending to pull it back into the body of the liquid; alternatively, it has a positive potential energy relative to a typical molecule within the liquid. Our model therefore predicts that the equilibrium state for a sample of liquid is the one which minimizes its surface area. (Zero potential energy would actually require zero surface, but this is clearly impractical!) Any change in the surface area produces a change in the associated potential energy, and therefore results in a net force (recall from Chapter 4 that a conservative force can be expressed as $-dU/dx$). We conclude that there should be a force associated with the surface of a liquid which acts to reduce the surface area. This is indeed the case: the effect is known as *surface tension*. Surface tension causes liquids to behave rather as though their surfaces were covered by a thin stretched membrane: to increase the surface area one has to stretch the membrane, and this requires energy, as for example in blowing up a balloon.

More precisely, the surface tension γ of a liquid is defined as the ratio of the net surface force to the length along which the force acts:

$$\boxed{\gamma = \frac{F}{\ell}}\ .$$

(Note that this definition of γ has nothing whatsoever to do with the ratio of specific heats—the fact that they have the same standard symbol is an unfortunate coincidence.)

Surface tension is thus a force per unit length, with SI unit N/m. The molecular picture tells us that it is actually more helpful to picture it as an energy per unit area (you can easily check that this has the same units)

Problems 12D.

$$\boxed{\gamma = \frac{U}{A}}\ .$$

To check that the two pictures are self-consistent, consider a thin film of liquid (e.g. a soap bubble) held in a wire frame with one movable side. We expand the frame by an area ΔA by moving our wire a distance Δx. The work done by the wire is $F\Delta x$, where F is the force we exerted to move it; if the wire has length ℓ, the area of the soap bubble has increased by $2\Delta A = 2\ell\Delta x$ (the factor of 2 allows for the two surfaces of the film). The increase in energy associated with this increase in surface area must, by energy conservation, equal the work done by the wire, so

$$\gamma = \frac{\Delta U}{\Delta A} = \frac{F}{2\ell}.$$

416

The force we exerted on each of the two surfaces is, by symmetry, $\frac{1}{2}F$, so the first definition of γ also gives $F/2\ell$: the two definitions are consistent.

The phase transition between the gas and liquid states also involves the intermolecular potential energy: we noted that in the liquid state the separation between molecules corresponds to the minimum potential energy, whereas in a gas under the same external conditions of pressure and temperature the separation is much larger. Therefore in going from liquid to gas the molecules gain potential energy, which has to be supplied from outside as heat, whereas in condensing from gas to liquid the molecules lose potential energy, which is released to the surroundings as heat. The amount of heat lost or gained per kilogram is called the *latent heat of vaporization* of the substance. (The equivalent quantity for the liquid-solid phase transition is the *latent heat of fusion*.)

Both surface tension and latent heat therefore depend on the intermolecular potential energy. This interpretation of two experimentally measurable quantities was used in the mid-19th century to provide one of the earliest estimates of the actual size of molecules. The results obtained are accurate to about a factor of 5, which is astonishing given that we are using macroscopic quantities to measure sizes of the order of 10^{-10} m. This illustrates how even very simple and idealized models can provide important information about real physical quantities.

Problem 13.11.

417

SUMMARY

* The molecules of a substance in the liquid state are strongly constrained to intermolecular separations corresponding to the minimum potential energy of the intermolecular forces. Within this limitation, the molecules can still move randomly.

* An ideal liquid therefore has a fixed density (since molecules are at fixed separation), but is free to assume any shape (since molecules can move randomly). Changes of volume with pressure or temperature do occur in real liquids, but are very small compared to the equivalent changes in gases, and can be neglected in an idealized model.

* The pressure in a liquid is the same in all directions, as with gases, and at rest depends only on the surface pressure and the depth below the surface. For an ideal incompressible liquid, the pressure increases linearly with depth.

* A fluid exerts a *buoyant force* on a body immersed in it which is equal in magnitude and opposite in direction to the weight of the fluid displaced by the body (*Archimedes' Principle*). For purposes of calculating the torque, the buoyant force can be treated as if it acts directly on the center of mass of the displaced liquid, which is called the *center of buoyancy*.

* In steady flow of an incompressible fluid the volume flow rate is constant; the speed of flow is therefore inversely proportional to the cross-sectional area of the flow tube.

* Conservation of energy implies that the sum of the pressure, the kinetic energy per unit volume and the potential energy per unit volume is the same at any point in the steady flow of an incompressible fluid (*Bernoulli's theorem*).

* The molecules at the surface of a liquid have greater potential energy than the molecules within the liquid volume. A force known as *surface tension* therefore acts to resist any attempt to increase the surface area of a given mass of liquid.

* Condensation of a gas to the liquid state releases energy (known as *latent heat*) since the potential energy of the molecules decreases. The transition from one state to another is called a phase transition.

* Physical concepts introduced in this chapter: liquid; buoyancy; phase transition; latent heat; surface tension.

* Mathematical concepts introduced in this chapter: none.

* Equations introduced in this chapter:

$$P_2 - P_1 = -\rho g(y_2 - y_1)$$ (Pressure in a liquid as a function of height, for a stationary liquid);

$$A_2 v_2 = A_1 v_1$$ (equation of continuity for steady flow);

$$P + \frac{1}{2}\rho v^2 + \rho g y = \text{constant}$$ (Bernoulli's equation);

$$\gamma = \frac{F}{\ell} = \frac{U}{A}$$ (surface tension).

PROBLEMS AND QUESTIONS

By the end of this chapter you should be able to answer or solve the types of questions or problems stated below.

Note: throughout the book, in multiple-choice problems, the answers have been rounded off to 2 significant figures, unless otherwise stated.

At the end of the chapter there are answers to all the problems. In addition, for problems with an (H) or (S) after the number, there are respectively hints on how to solve the problems or completely worked-out solutions.

12A   PRESSURE AND ITS VARIATION WITH HEIGHT

12A.1 A large glass tank in an aquarium is filled with seawater (density 1030 kg/m³) to a depth of 5 m. The top of the tank is open to the air. How much pressure should the glass used to construct the tank be able to withstand if the tank is not to crack at the base? (Take g to be 9.8 m/s² and atmospheric pressure to be 1.01×10^5 Pa.)

(a) 1.5×10^5 Pa; (b) 5.0×10^4 Pa; (c) 2.5×10^5 Pa; (d) 1.0×10^5 Pa.

12A.2 (S) A U-shaped tube of constant cross-sectional area A is filled with a liquid of density ρ. One end of the tube is open to the atmosphere, while the other side is connected to a vessel containing gas at some unknown pressure P. Calculate the unknown pressure in terms of the difference in level between the liquid on the two sides of the U.

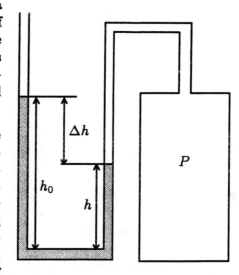

12A.3 (H) Some types of pump ('suction' pumps) operate by producing a reduced pressure in the area towards which you want the fluid to flow. A landscape gardener wishing to create an artificial waterfall plans to use such a device to pump water from a lake to the head of her waterfall, from where it will cascade decoratively back into the lake. What is the absolute maximum possible height of fall she can achieve using a pump of this type (neglecting viscosity and similar effects)? How would you go about pumping water up to greater heights (e.g. to service the restrooms on the observation deck of the John Hancock tower)? (Take atmospheric pressure to be 1.01×10^5 Pa; the density of fresh water is 1000 kg/m³.)

12A.4 (S) An auto mechanic is using a hydraulic jack to lift a car off the ground in order to fit new tires. If the car has a mass of 1500 kg and the mechanic applies a force of 300 N to the jack, what ratio of piston areas will be required? If the car is to be lifted 20 cm, how far must the piston at the mechanic's end move, and how much work is done, assuming that both ends of the

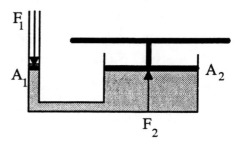

12A.4, continued:

jack—the car's and the mechanic's—are at the same height? (Take $g = 10$ m/s^2; the diagram shows a schematic drawing of the jack.)

12A.5 (S) Three flasks each contain (when full) one liter of water. One has straight sides and a circular base of area A; one has inward-sloping sides and a base of area $2A$, and the last has outward-sloping sides and a base of area $A/2$. The flasks are shaped so that when they are full the level of the water above the base is the same in each case, namely h. Calculate the force on the base of each container due to the water pressure. Explain qualitatively why the shape of the container does not affect the reading on a weigh-scale.

12A.6 (H) You are designing a diving vessel to serve as an underwater laboratory at a depth of 500 m. Assuming that seawater is completely incompressible, what pressure do the walls of your vessel have to withstand if it is (a) completely sealed, with its internal air maintained at atmospheric pressure; (b) provided with an exit underneath which is open to the ocean, with the inside air maintained at the pressure required to prevent flooding of the vessel? Given that human beings cannot tolerate rapid decreases in pressure, under what circumstances would you prefer a design of type (a) rather than type (b) and vice versa? (The density of sea-water is 1030 kg/m^3; take $g = 9.8$ m/s^2.)

12B BUOYANCY AND ARCHIMEDES' PRINCIPLE

12B.1 A cylindrical glass vase is 15 cm in diameter and 15 cm high. You notice while washing it that when empty it floats so that its rim is 4 cm above the surface of the water. What is its mass?

(a) 1.9 g; (b) 1.9 N; (c) 19 N; (d) none of these.

12B.2 (S) Water is unusual in that its solid phase—ice—is less dense than its liquid phase. In fact ice has a density of 920 kg/m^3. To analyze the old proverb, how much of an iceberg really is under water? (Assume seawater, which has a density of 1030 kg/m^3. By how much does your answer change if you assume fresh water?)

12B.3 (S) (a) A hydrometer is basically a calibrated float, resembling a standard liquid-in-glass thermometer in shape, weighted at the bottom so it always floats in the same orientation. If the stem of such a hydrometer has a cross-sectional area of 0.5cm^2, the total volume of the float is 15 cm^3, and in fresh water with a density of 1000 kg/m^3 4.0 cm of the stem is above water level, how much of the stem will be exposed if the hydrometer floats in seawater with a density of 1030 kg/m^3? The hydrometer is then placed in a sample of unknown liquid where it floats with 2.0 cm of stem exposed: what is the density of this liquid?

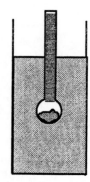

(b) A beaker containing one liter of water is placed on a scale and found to weigh 12 N (this of course includes the weight of the beaker). A cubical

block of wood 8 cm on a side is suspended from a spring balance and lowered into the water. The density of the wood is 700 kg/m^3. How far is the base of the cube below the surface of the water, and what is the reading on the scale, when the reading on the spring balance is 2.5 N? Take $g = 9.8$ m/s^2.

12B.4, continued:

12B.4 (H) A beaker contains a thick layer of oil, of density 650 kg/m^3, floating on water (density 1000 kg/m^3). A cubical block of wood of density 750 kg/m^3 and with dimensions $10 \times 10 \times 10$ cm^3 is lowered very gently into the beaker, taking care not to disturb the layers of liquid, until it is completely submerged. At what position relative to the interface between oil and water does the block come to rest? If the beaker has a circular cross-section of diameter 20 cm and the oil layer was 10 cm deep before the block was inserted, what is the pressure on the upper and lower surfaces of the block when it is in equilibrium?

12C   FLUIDS IN STEADY FLOW: BERNOULLI'S LAW

12C.1 A pipe in a factory has a diameter of 10 cm and carries water flowing at a speed of 5.0 m/s. At one point on its route it has to pass behind a large piece of equipment, and here the pipe has been squashed from its original circular cross-section to a rectangle of dimensions 14 cm by 1.7 cm. What is the speed of the water in this region? Assume that the pipe runs at the same height above sea-level throughout its route, and that the flow of the water is laminar.

(a) 5.0 m/s; (b) 16.5 m/s; (c) 1.5 m/s; (d) none of these.

12C.2 (S) A water faucet turned on at a very low rate will produce a smooth laminar stream of water whose initial diameter is equal to the diameter d of the faucet. What is the diameter of the water stream when it has fallen through a height h? Assume that the water leaves the faucet with speed v, and that surface tension is sufficient to maintain the water in a single steady stream.

12C.3 (H) The diagram shows a Venturi meter installed in a water main. If the water in the pipe is flowing at 5×10^{-3} m^3/s (volume flow rate), what is (a) the speed of flow in each section of pipe; (b) the difference in the water level in the two tubes? The pipe has a circular cross-section at all points.

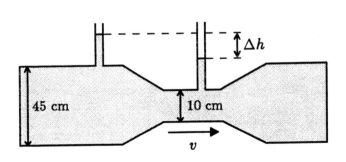

12C.4 Many spray devices, e.g. perfume atomizers, some insecticide sprays, etc., are designed along the lines of the diagram at right. Treating air as an incompressible fluid, explain how these devices work. If the height of the spray tube above the level of the fluid is h, at what speed v must the spray be expelled if it is to contain liquid? Assume that the bottle is vented, so that the air inside it is at atmospheric pressure.

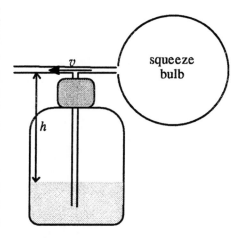

Most practical versions of this design have a constriction in the spray tube where the vertical tube joins it, so that the diameter of this part of the spray is smaller. What is the advantage of this arrangement?

12C.5 (S) Two flat sheets of metal are suspended so that they hang parallel, separated by a short distance d. We then arrange, e.g. by using a blow dryer with a suitably shaped nozzle, to blow a stream of air between the plates. What happens?

12C.6 (H) If an incompressible fluid flows past the object shown in the diagram in the direction indicated by the arrow, what happens? Do any pressure differences develop, and if so what is the direction of the net force which results? Assume that the fluid flow is laminar. (Take the diagram to be a side view of a long object oriented perpendicular to the plane of the page.)

Discuss how your conclusions relate to the shape of aircraft wings.

12C.7 Due to frictional effects, the velocity of air in an air jet from a blower is highest in the center of the jet. What will happen to a ping-pong ball placed in the center of such a jet if the airstream is directed vertically upwards, and why?

12D   SURFACE TENSION

12D.1 (H) The various types of small insects which can 'walk on water' tend to have feet which are covered with an oily or waxy substance to which water does not readily adhere. How does this help them to avoid sinking into the water? What would happen if they instead had feet covered with a substance with a strong affinity for water?

12D.2 (S) In terms of the surface tension γ of the liquid, what is the pressure difference between the liquid inside a liquid drop and the surrounding gas? What is the corresponding result for the difference in air pressure inside and outside a soap bubble?

12D.3 (H) What is the difference between the pressure inside and outside a soap bubble of diameter 5 cm in air at atmospheric pressure? What will happen if the bubble drifts into an area where, due to local wind conditions, the pressure is 5 Pa less than it was where the bubble was originally formed, although the temperature is the same? (Atmospheric pressure: 101.3 kPa; surface tension of soap solution: 25 mN/m.)

12D.4 In 100 words or less, explain the origin of surface tension.

COMPLETE SOLUTIONS TO PROBLEMS WITH AN (S)

12A.2   *A U-shaped tube of constant cross-sectional area A is filled with a liquid of density ρ. One end of the tube is open to the atmosphere, while the other side is connected to a vessel containing gas at some unknown pressure P. Calculate the unknown pressure in terms of the difference in level between the liquid on the two sides of the U.*

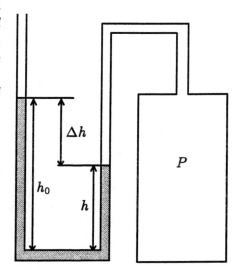

Conceptualize
We assume that the liquid is incompressible and that the system is in a steady state. If this is so, there must be no net force on any part of the liquid (it is not moving). In particular, the downward pressure of the liquid at the base of the left-hand vertical tube must equal the upward pressure of the liquid in the horizontal section, and likewise for the right-hand vertical tube. Since the pressure at both ends of the horizontal section must be the same, it follows that the pressures at the bases of the two vertical tubes must also be equal. Because the liquid is not flowing, we can use the static pressure-height relationship to calculate these pressures.

Formulate and Solve
Thus,

$$P_0 + \rho g h_0 = P + \rho g h,$$

$$\text{i.e.} \quad P - P_0 = -\rho g(h - h_0).$$

Scrutinize
If both ends of the tube were open, we would expect $h = h_0$, and indeed the equation gives this result for $P = P_0$. Everyday experience (e.g., sucking on a straw) says that the height should be greater on the side with lower pressure, and the minus sign in the equation ensures that this is so. The special case where $P = 0$ is discussed below.

Learn
The tube can be thought of as a pressure gauge measuring the **difference** between the unknown pressure P and atmospheric pressure. In general pressure gauges do indeed measure pressure differences, usually with respect to atmospheric pressure, and this has resulted in the definition of the **gauge pressure** as $P - P_{\text{amb}}$, where P is the pressure in question and P_{amb} is the reference pressure of the gauge (the ambient pressure; usually local atmospheric pressure), in contrast to the **absolute pressure** P. Many pressures we encounter in everyday life (e.g. tire pressures) are gauge pressures rather than absolute pressures.

A special case is where $P = 0$, i.e. the right-hand side of the tube is evacuated. In this case our gauge has become a **barometer**, measuring atmospheric pressure:

$$P_0 = \rho g \Delta h.$$

12A.2, continued:

For mercury, with a density of 13.6×10^3 kg/m^3, the value of Δh corresponding to standard atmospheric pressure is 760 mm, or 29.9 inches. Atmospheric pressures are often quoted in terms of the equivalent Δh for mercury, in mm Hg (or inches of mercury, as in TV weather forecasts). Mercury is conventionally used in such barometers and pressure gauges (*manometers*) because it is by far the densest room-temperature liquid: using a less dense liquid would require an impractically large tube (a water barometer, for example, would have a height of over thirty feet).

12A.4   *An auto mechanic is using a hydraulic jack to lift a car off the ground in order to fit new tires. If the car has a mass of 1500 kg and the mechanic applies a force of 300 N to the jack, what ratio of piston areas will be required? If the car is to be lifted 20 cm, how far must the piston at the mechanic's end move, and how much work is done, assuming that both ends of the jack— the car's and the mechanic's—are at the same height. (Take $g = 10$ m/s^2; the diagram shows a schematic drawing of the jack.)*

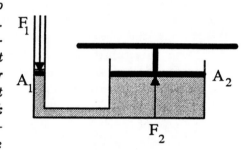

Conceptualize

We assume that the liquid is incompressible and that it is not flowing (or is flowing at negligible speed). We can therefore apply the static pressure-height relationship, which states that if the height difference between the two sides is negligible, the pressures must be equal. Since pressure is force per unit area, it follows that the ratio of forces, F_1/F_2, will give the ratio of areas, A_1/A_2.

To calculate the work done we need the dot product of force and displacement. The displacement on the right-hand side is known; we can calculate the displacement on the left-hand side from the ratio of areas, since the total volume of liquid in the system is assumed to be constant.

Formulate

The surface pressure at the left-hand end is $P_1 = F_1/A_1$, (by Newton's Third Law, the pressure of the piston on the water is equal to the pressure of the water on the piston) and at the right-hand end it is $P_2 = F_2/A_2$. Since $P_1 = P_2$, the ratio of forces is given by the ratio of areas:

$$\frac{F_2}{F_1} = \frac{A_2}{A_1}.$$

For the work done, we note that if the piston A_2 moves a distance Δh_2, the right-hand end of the jack needs an additional volume of liquid $A_2 \Delta h_2$. This must come from depressing the left-hand piston a distance Δh_1, which decreases the volume of the left-hand end by $A_1 \Delta h_1$. The total volume of liquid is constant, since this is a sealed system and we assume an ideal incompressible liquid, so $A_2 \Delta h_2 = A_1 \Delta h_1$, giving

$$\frac{\Delta h_1}{\Delta h_2} = \frac{A_2}{A_1}.$$

12A.4, continued:

Solve

To solve the problem we simply put in the numbers. We have $F_1 = 300$ N and want $F_2 = 15000$ N (mg, where m is the mass of the car), so we need $A_2/A_1 = 50$. It follows that $\Delta h_1 = 50 \times \Delta h_2$: to move the large piston by 20 cm we must move the small piston 10 m! The work done is $F_1 \Delta h_1 = F_2 \Delta h_2 = 3.0$ kJ.

Scrutinize

Note that the same amount of work is done on both sides, as we expect from energy conservation. The hydraulic jack is very like the block and tackle of Problem 7.7: it is a device to enable you to do the same amount of work by applying a smaller force over a longer distance.

Learn

Obviously a hydraulic jack 10 m long is not very practical! This difficulty arises because we assumed the working fluid was a fixed amount of incompressible liquid. In fact we could instead use a compressible gas—air, for instance. This is less efficient, since some of the work goes into compressing and heating the gas instead of lifting the car, but it has the great advantage that with an appropriate system of valves it is possible to do the lift by repeated short strokes of the small piston, drawing in more air with each return, rather than one long stroke.

12A.5   *Three flasks each contain (when full) one liter of water. One has straight sides and a circular base of area A; one has inward-sloping sides and a base of area 2A, and the last has outward-sloping sides and a base of area A/2. The flasks are shaped so that when they are full the level of the water above the base is the same in each case, namely h. Calculate the force on the base of each container due to the water pressure. Explain qualitatively why the shape of the container does not affect the reading on a weigh-scale.*

Conceptualize

Since the water is not flowing, we are again entitled to use the static pressure-height relationship. The surface pressure and the water depth are the same for all three flasks, so it follows that the pressure on the base is also the same in all cases. Since pressure is force per unit area, the downward *force* exerted by the water on the base of the container is proportional to the base area, so it will be different for each container.

The readings on the scale will nonetheless be the same in each case because this is not the *net* force acting.   There is also a pressure on the *sides* of the con-

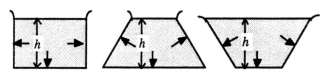

tainer: the resulting force is purely horizontal for the flask with straight sides, but it has a net upward component for the flask with inward-sloping sides and a net downward component for the third flask.

12A.5, continued:

Formulate and Solve

The pressure at depth h is $P = P_0 + \rho g h$ for all three containers, where ρ is the density of water. If the flasks were suspended in air, the net pressure would be $\rho g h$, since there would be an inward pressure P_0 from the surrounding air. This gives the net pressure force on the base of each container as $\rho g h A$, $2\rho g h A$ and $\rho g h A/2$, respectively. In each case, however, the *net* downward force, taking into account the pressure forces on the sides of the container, is equal to the weight of the water, and so the scale readings will be the same.

Scrutinize

Although we have presented a qualitative argument that the forces on the sides of the container act to counterbalance the effect of the different base areas, we have not in fact shown quantitatively that the cancellation is exact, nor can we do so without more information about the slopes of the sides of the containers. However, we know that the quantitative calculation will work, because this principle of balancing pressure forces against the weight of the liquid is exactly what we used to derive the pressure-height relationship in the *Essentials*.

12B.2   *Water is unusual in that its solid phase—ice—is less dense than its liquid phase. In fact ice has a density of* 920 kg/m^3. *To analyze the old proverb, how much of an iceberg really is under water? (Assume seawater, which has a density of* 1030 kg/m^3. *By how much does your answer change if you assume fresh water?)*

Conceptualize

Archimedes' principle tells us that the iceberg is in equilibrium when it is floating at a level such that it displaces an amount of water equal to its own mass. The mass of water displaced is $\rho_{\text{water}} V_{\text{sub}}$, where V_{sub} is the volume of berg submerged, and the total mass of the iceberg is $\rho_{\text{ice}} V_{\text{tot}}$, where V_{tot} is the total volume. Equating these will give us the ratio $V_{\text{sub}}/V_{\text{tot}}$.

Formulate and Solve

If $\rho_{\text{water}} V_{\text{sub}} = \rho_{\text{ice}} V_{\text{tot}}$, it follows that

$$\frac{V_{\text{sub}}}{V_{tot}} = \frac{\rho_{\text{ice}}}{\rho_{\text{water}}} = \frac{920 \text{ kg/m}^3}{1030 \text{ kg/m}^3} = 0.89.$$

(Almost) nine-tenths of an iceberg really is under water! If we consider fresh water, 92% of the berg is submerged. (Note that icebergs are frozen *fresh* water, so we don't have to worry about whether the density of frozen seawater is different).

Scrutinize and Learn

This calculation agrees well with our intuitive idea of how things float: the less dense the object, the higher it floats—e.g. balsa wood versus teak, or a heavily laden cargo ship versus an empty one. Note that we can calculate the mass of a floating object by measuring the amount of water it displaces: this is how ships' masses are measured, and indeed they are often quoted as "so many tons *displacement*".

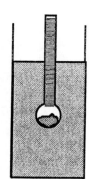

12B.3 (a) *A hydrometer is basically a calibrated float, resembling a standard liquid-in-glass thermometer in shape, weighted at the bottom so it always floats in the same orientation. If the stem of such a hydrometer has a cross-sectional area of 0.5 cm², the total volume of the float is 15 cm³, and in fresh water with a density of 1000 kg/m³ 4.0 cm of the stem is above water level, how much of the stem will be exposed if the hydrometer floats in seawater with a density of 1030 kg/m³? The hydrometer is then placed in a sample of unknown liquid where it floats with 2.0 cm of stem exposed: what is the density of this liquid?*

Conceptualize

The situation is essentially the same as Problem 12B.2, except that here we are looking for the volume exposed rather than the volume submerged. Since we know the cross-sectional area of the hydrometer tube, calculating the exposed volume will determine the length of tube exposed.

Formulate

The basic equation is the same one we derived in the solution to problem 12B.2:

$$\frac{V_{\text{sub}}}{V_{\text{tot}}} = \frac{\rho_h}{\rho_{\text{liquid}}},$$

where ρ_h is the overall density of the hydrometer. We could calculate this from the information we have, but we don't need to: we can simply take this equation for water and divide it by the same equation for the liquid we want to measure (the seawater, or our unknown sample):

$$\frac{V_{\text{sub}}^{\text{water}}}{V_{\text{sub}}^{\text{liquid}}} = \frac{\rho_{\text{liquid}}}{\rho_{\text{water}}}.$$

Solve

The submerged volume for water is

$$(15.0 \text{ cm}^3) - (0.5 \text{ cm}^2 \times 4.0 \text{ cm}) = 13.0 \text{ cm}^3.$$

We conclude that the submerged volume for seawater must be

$$(13.0 \text{ cm}^3)/1.03 = 12.6 \text{ cm}^3,$$

leaving $(2.4 \text{ cm}^3)/(0.5 \text{ cm}^2) = 4.8$ cm of stem exposed. The submerged volume for the unknown liquid is

$$(15.0 \text{ cm}^3) - (0.5 \text{ cm}^2 \times 2.0 \text{ cm}) = 14.0 \text{ cm}^3,$$

so its density is $(1000 \text{ kg/m}^3) \times (13 \text{ cm}^3)/(14 \text{ cm}^3) = 930 \text{ kg/m}^3.$

Scrutinize

As we expect, the denser the liquid, the higher the hydrometer floats, and the more of its stem is exposed. Note, however, that a density change of only 3% produced a change in hydrometer reading of 20%. This is because we measure the exposed volume,

12B.3, continued:

which for a suitable ballasting of the hydrometer can be made a rather small fraction of the total volume. As a result hydrometers are a very useful tool for making quick measurements of fairly small differences in liquid density. This has a variety of practical applications, e.g. strength of car battery acid, alcohol content of beer, etc.

(b) *A beaker containing one liter of water is placed on a scale and found to weigh* 12 N *(this of course includes the weight of the beaker). A cubical block of wood* 8 cm *on a side is suspended from a spring balance and lowered into the water. The density of the wood is* 700 kg/m³. *How far is the base of the cube below the surface of the water, and what is the reading on the scale, when the reading on the spring balance is* 2.5 N? *Take* $g = 9.8$ m/s².

Conceptualize
The force diagram for the system is shown below. The spring balance reading is the tension T in the spring, while the scale reading is the normal force N exerted by the pan of the scale on the beaker and its contents. Gravity exerts a downward force Mg on the beaker-plus-water system, where M is the combined mass of beaker and water, and mg on the block of wood, where m is its mass. Neglecting ambient pressure, which is the same in all directions and will therefore cancel, these are the only external forces acting on the whole beaker-plus-water-plus-wood system, and so if the block and beaker are both stationary it follows that $N + T = (M + m)g$. This will solve the second part of the problem.

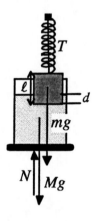

For the first part, we recall that the net pressure force on a partially or wholly submerged body is $-m_W g$, where m_W is the mass of the displaced water. The downward force on the block of wood is mg, so for zero net force the tension in the spring balance must be the difference between these, $T = (m - m_W)g$.

Formulate
The mass of water displaced is $m_W = \rho V_{sub}$, where ρ is the density of water (1000 kg/m³) and $V_{sub} = \ell^2 d$ is the submerged volume of the cube (writing ℓ for the side of the cube and d for the depth to which it is submerged). The cube's mass is $m = \rho' V_{tot}$, where ρ' is 700 kg/m³ and V_{tot} is the total volume of the cube. The tension in the spring balance is therefore

$$T = (m - m_W)g = \rho'\ell^3 g - \rho\ell^2 dg = (\rho'\ell - \rho d)\ell^2 g.$$

Solve
If we put in the numbers we find that

$$d = \frac{1}{\rho}\left(\rho'\ell - \frac{T}{g\ell^2}\right)$$

$$= \frac{1}{1000 \text{ kg/m}^3}\left((700 \text{ kg/m}^3) \times (0.08 \text{ m}) - \frac{2.5 \text{ N}}{(9.8 \text{ m/s}^2) \times (0.08 \text{ m})^2}\right)$$

$$= 0.016 \text{ m, or } 1.6 \text{ cm.}$$

12B.3, continued:

The mass of the whole block of wood is $\rho' V_{\text{tot}} = 0.36$ kg, so

$$N = (M + m)g - T = (12 \text{ N}) + (0.36 \text{ kg} \times 9.8 \text{ m/s}^2) - (2.5 \text{ N}) = 13 \text{ N}.$$

 Scrutinize
The spring balance tension should be zero when the block is floating on the water. Our equation says that this will happen when $\rho' \ell = \rho d$. This corresponds exactly to the relation $\rho'/\rho = V_{\text{sub}}/V_{\text{tot}}$ that we used in part (a).

Learn
If we had used a metal block, with $\rho' > \rho$, the logic of this problem would be unaltered. If we then completely submerge the block, such that $d = \ell$, the tension in the spring balance is $(\rho' - \rho)V_{\text{tot}}g$, and we can determine V_{tot} by measuring the rise in the level of the water. Thus this set-up can serve to determine the density of an object of unknown composition, provided that said object is denser than water. This, legend has it, was Archimedes' own application of Archimedes' Principle: he had been asked by the king of Sicily to determine whether a particular crown was made of pure gold or of a less dense gold/silver alloy.

12C.2   *A water faucet turned on at a very low rate will produce a smooth laminar stream of water whose initial diameter is equal to the diameter d of the faucet. What is the diameter of the water stream when it has fallen through a height h? Assume that the water leaves the faucet with speed v, and that surface tension is sufficient to maintain the water in a single steady stream.*

 Conceptualize
If the water falls in a steady stream, the volume flow rate must be constant, i.e. the volume of water leaving the faucet in one second must equal the volume disappearing down the drain in the same time interval. Once the water has left the faucet it is in free fall, so (assuming air resistance can be neglected) its speed v_h after descending a distance h is given by energy conservation:

$$\tfrac{1}{2}v_h^2 = \tfrac{1}{2}v^2 + gh$$

(i.e. the gain in kinetic energy is equal to the loss of potential energy; we have canceled a common factor of m, the mass of our volume element of water). To maintain the same volume flow rate, this increase in linear speed will have to be balanced by a decrease in the cross-sectional area of the stream.

 Formulate and Solve
Assuming the stream of water has a circular cross-section, its cross-sectional area will be $\pi d^2/4$, where d is its diameter. Then the equation of continuity gives for the diameter d_h of the stream after falling through distance h

$$\tfrac{1}{4}\pi d_h^2 v_h = \tfrac{1}{4}\pi d^2 v,$$

12C.2, continued:

i.e., using the above equation for v_h,

$$d_h = d \left(1 + \frac{2gh}{v^2} \right)^{-\frac{1}{4}}.$$

Scrutinize

This equation appears to make sense, in that the change in diameter is less for smaller heights or higher initial velocities. It is, at first sight, somewhat worrying that it does not work for initial $v = 0$ (surely we are entitled to have our water start from rest?), but on second thought we can see that the volume flow rate is meaningless if the liquid is not moving—the stream of water never actually emerges from the faucet.

Learn

It is possible to observe this effect with a real faucet, but the experiment only works for low flow rates. At higher flow rates the stream becomes turbulent, and the analysis of this chapter no longer applies. Turbulent flow is very common in real situations, but extremely difficult to analyze. The study of turbulence is one of the areas of application of chaos theory.

12C.5 *Two flat sheets of metal are suspended so that they hang parallel, separated by a short distance d. We then arrange, e.g. by using a blow dryer with a suitably shaped nozzle, to blow a stream of air between the plates. What happens?*

Conceptualize

Although we are considering a gas here, the velocities involved are small enough that we can still apply Bernoulli's equation. If we consider a flow tube which goes between the two plates and then out to the atmosphere, it's clear that at a sufficiently large distance from the plates we will have atmospheric pressure and zero velocity (meaning here zero net velocity of a volume element,

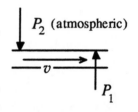

of course, not zero molecular velocity), whereas in the region between the plates we have a non-zero velocity and therefore, according to Bernoulli's equation, a lower pressure.

Formulate

Using a point between the plates as point 1, and for point 2 our distant point where the pressure is ambient and the velocity zero, Bernoulli's equation gives

$$P_1 + \tfrac{1}{2}\rho v^2 = P_2.$$

Solve

The pressure between the plates is less than atmospheric pressure, by an amount proportional to v^2. Since the plates still have atmospheric pressure acting on them on their outer sides, they will be subject to a net inward force and will move together.

Scrutinize

This rather counterintuitive result can be easily demonstrated by holding two sheets of paper a short distance apart and blowing between them. As in Problem 12C.2, it is best to blow slowly, so that the flow remains laminar (and so that the air is not significantly compressed).

12D.2   *In terms of the surface tension γ of the liquid, what is the pressure difference between the liquid inside a liquid drop and the surrounding gas? What is the corresponding result for the difference in air pressure inside and outside a soap bubble?*

Conceptualize

To avoid having to worry about curved surfaces, let's initially think about half a drop, say a hemispherical blob of liquid on a thin membrane. If the difference between the pressure in the liquid and atmospheric pressure is ΔP, then the net force on the membrane is $\Delta P \pi r^2$, where r is the radius of the drop. Putting two half-drops together to form a spherical drop, we conclude that each half of the drop exerts a net force $\Delta P \pi r^2$ on the other half. Why do the two halves not fly apart? The answer is that surface forces counteract this force. Each half of the drop will pull on the other half of the drop, at the surface along the junction between the two halves, with a force $2\pi r\gamma$ (surface tension force per unit length, γ, times the circumference of $2\pi r$).

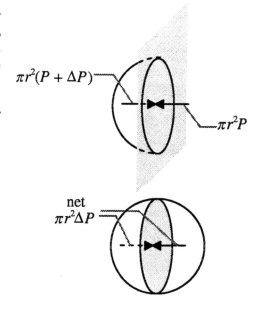

$\pi r^2(P + \Delta P)$

$\pi r^2 P$

net
$\pi r^2 \Delta P$

Formulate and Solve

Since the drop is in equilibrium, outward pressure force and the inward surface tension force must balance, i.e.

$$\Delta P \pi r^2 = 2\pi r\gamma$$

or

$$\Delta P = \frac{2\gamma}{r}.$$

In the case of a bubble, there are two surfaces at approximately the same radius (since the thickness of the bubble is negligible compared to its diameter), so the force from surface tension is doubled. Hence there is twice as large a pressure difference.

Scrutinize and Learn

For typical surface tensions these pressure differences are very small: for example soap solution has a surface tension of about 25 mN/m, so a soap bubble 2.5 cm in radius would have an internal pressure 4 Pa higher than the ambient pressure—a difference of 0.004%! Notice that the larger the bubble, the smaller the pressure difference required to maintain it (though the total *force* being exerted is greater, since the pressure difference acts over a larger surface area).

The energy-per-unit-area picture of surface tension can help when considering the *stability* of bubbles and droplets. If a droplet is not spherical, its surface area is higher (for a given volume) than a spherical drop, and therefore the energy stored in its surface tension is larger: this is why liquid drops tend to be spherical (unless some external force is acting).

HINTS FOR PROBLEMS WITH AN (H)

The number of the hint refers to the number of the problem

12A.3 What is the maximum possible pressure difference that can be achieved between the surface of the lake and the other end of the suction pump?

If you're stuck, study the solution to problem 12A.2.

12A.6 What is the pressure outside the vessel? How does this compare with the internal pressure in the two cases?

12B.4 Draw a force diagram for the block. What are the buoyant forces from the oil and the water? Check that the total buoyant force is equal to the force due to the difference in the pressures on the top and bottom of the block—why should this be so?

12C.3 How does the speed of flow relate to the volume flow rate?

What is the relation between the pressures at the water surface in the two tubes?

12C.6 How does the path length of a streamline deflected by the object compare with one flowing just underneath it and hence undisturbed? What does this imply for the speed of the fluid in the two cases?

12D.1 Draw the surface in the two cases. In which direction is the net force from surface tension?

12D.3 Is the pressure inside a soap bubble equal to the pressure outside? If not, how is it that the bubble can be in equilibrium? (If you're not sure, review the solution to problem 12D.2.)

Taking the air in the bubble to be an ideal gas, can you find an equation for the outside pressure in terms of the radius of the bubble?

Now differentiate this equation to find the relation between a small change ΔP in this pressure and the resulting small change in the radius of the bubble.

ANSWERS TO HINTS

12A.3 101 kPa, which corresponds to atmospheric pressure at the bottom and zero at the top.

12A.6 5.05×10^6 Pa, compared to 10^5 Pa in case (a) and 5.05×10^6 Pa in case (b).

12B.4 $\rho_{\text{water}} V_1 g$, where V_1 is the volume of the cube under water, and $\rho_{\text{oil}}(V - V_1)g$, where V is the total volume of the cube.

(Water buoyancy shown displaced for clarity)

Buoyant force *is* simply total upward pressure force, and as sides of block are vertical the only vertical pressure forces are those on top and bottom.

12C.3 $\dfrac{dV}{dt} = Av$, i.e. volume flow rate = speed of flow times cross-sectional area of pipe.

Both are equal to the ambient pressure.

12C.6 Longer; faster.

12D.1 See answer to problem.

12D.3 No, inside is greater. Surface tension provides force opposing expansion of bubble.

$$P = \frac{3P_0 V_0}{4\pi r^3} - \frac{4\gamma}{r},$$

where r is the radius and P_0, V_0 the starting inside pressure and volume of the bubble. (The first term is the pressure inside the bubble, using $PV = NkT$; the second is the difference between this and the outside pressure.) The second term turns out to have a negligible effect (i.e. we can really regard the pressures inside and outside the bubble as equal). To find the small change in radius resulting from a small change in pressure, differentiate this and put $V_0 = \frac{4}{3}\pi r^3$ to get

$$\frac{\Delta r}{r} \approx -\frac{\Delta P}{3P}.$$

12D.4 An acceptable answer would be:

"The molecules making up a liquid exert attractive forces on their neighbors. A molecule at the surface, which has many more neighbors in the dense liquid below it than in the gas above it, therefore feels a net inward force. The sum of all such forces acts to minimize the liquid's surface area—this is surface tension."

ANSWERS TO ALL PROBLEMS

12A.1 b

12A.2 See complete solution.

12A.3 10.3 m; use overpressure at the bottom of the vertical section instead of reduced pressure at the top, and/or have holding tanks at various levels and pump in stages.

12A.4 See complete solution.

12A.5 See complete solution.

12A.6 5.05×10^6 Pa; zero.

First design preferable if the vessel makes frequent return trips to the surface and no-one leaves it while it is submerged. Second is better if vessel is to serve as a base for divers and will seldom return to the surface.

12B.1 d

12B.2 See complete solution.

12B.3 See complete solution.

12B.4 The base of the block is 2.9 cm below the interface.

To two significant figures, 320 and 1100 Pa above atmospheric, respectively. (To three significant figures, 325 and 1060 Pa above atmospheric.)

12C.1 c

12C.2 See complete solution.

12C.3 0.031 m/s (wide section); 0.637 m/s (narrow section); 2.1 cm.

12C.4 Applying Bernoulli's equation, we find that the pressure inside the tube (where the air is moving) is less than that outside the tube (where the air is stationary). The liquid in the bottle will therefore rise in the vertical tube to a height h, where $\rho_{\text{liquid}}gh = \frac{1}{2}\rho_{\text{air}}v^2$. If the design of the spray ensures that this value of h is greater than the actual height of the spray tube above the liquid level, liquid will enter the stream of moving air and be sprayed out.

$$v = \sqrt{\frac{2gh\rho_{\text{liquid}}}{\rho_{\text{air}}}}.$$

A constriction in the tube increases the speed of the airstream at that point, as can be calculated using the equation of continuity.

12C.5 See complete solution.

12C.6 The streamlines deflected upwards by the object are more crowded than those which pass below it undisturbed, and therefore the speed of the fluid above is higher. This results in a lower pressure above the object, and therefore a net upward force.

This object is approximately the same shape as the cross-section of an airplane wing, and thus the same arguments apply if air can be considered incompressible. (In this case the

434

airfoil moves through stationary air, as seen from the ground, but if we consider the reference frame of the airplane we have a stationary object and a moving fluid. If the airplane is moving at a steady speed the results in the two frames must be equivalent, so we are allowed to do this.)

In reality, the lift of an airplane wing is much more complicated than this, because turbulent flow plays an important role.

12C.7 The ping-pong ball remains in the center of the airstream rather than falling out (even if the air is not directed vertically), because the lower velocities on each side lead to a net pressure difference pushing the ball towards the center.

12D.1 Because the water does not wet the insect's legs, the surface curves *down* where the insect's leg presses on it. Hence the net surface tension (acting to minimize surface area) is upwards and supports the insect. If water did wet the leg, the surface would curve upwards, and the surface tension would act to pull the insect under.

Non-wetting   Wetting

12D.2 See complete solution.

12D.3 4 Pa.

It expands, because the decrease in external pressure creates a net outward force.

The radius of the bubble will increase by an undetectable 4.1×10^{-5} cm. The pressure in the bubble decreases as it expands because there is a fixed mass of air inside, so the bubble is not (as one might think) unstable against small pressure changes.

ESSENTIALS OF INTRODUCTORY CLASSICAL MECHANICS

REVIEW

OVERVIEW

This chapter contains no new ideas. Instead, we shall take what we have learned in this book and use it to solve more complicated problems. Notice that in this chapter we shall not divide the problems up into sections dealing with specific topics; instead you will have to decide for yourself which of the physical principles you have learned are relevant to a given problem. Most of the problems will concentrate on the material of the last two chapters, but some problems included here relate to earlier material. Since this is the last chapter of the book we also include a Summary reviewing what we have covered and explaining how it fits into the wider context of physical science.

When you have completed this chapter you should:

> ✔ be able to extract the essential features of a problem and express them in mathematical equations;
>
> ✔ be capable of manipulating the equations relevant to a problem to obtain an expression for the required quantity, either symbolically or numerically;
>
> ✔ be able to analyse a hypothetical situation in terms of the physics presented in previous chapters, and explain that analysis clearly in non-mathematical terms;
>
> ✔ see how classical mechanics fits into the general structure of scientific knowledge.

SUMMARY

WHAT HAVE WE ACHIEVED?

We have now completed our introduction to classical mechanics. At this point it may be useful to look back over the semester as a whole and see what we have achieved in this book and how the knowledge we have gained relates to the rest of physics and wider fields of science.

We began by studying the motion of a simple point particle—an idealized, simplified object which is easy to describe and manipulate mathematically and avoids the complications of real-world effects such as friction, internal energy, etc. We saw how to analyze and predict the motion of a point particle by means of Newton's laws and introduced the concepts of position, time, force, mass and energy as measurable quantities whose mathematical interrelations allow us to describe and predict the behavior of the particle.

We then extended our picture to systems of point particles, first simple two-particle systems and then those involving many particles. We found that the motion of a system of particles could be decomposed into an overall motion of the whole system, which obeyed the same laws as point particles, and internal motions of components of the system relative to the system center of mass. The first result indicates how our simple point-particle dynamics can be applied to real objects, while the second underlies such apparently unrelated concepts as rotation and temperature.

A system of many particles is described in exact classical mechanics by a large system of simultaneous differential equations, which very rapidly becomes impossible to handle analytically. However, there are many special cases in which the exact analytical approach is not necessary. We considered the case where all the components of a system have fixed relative positions (a rigid body, or idealized solid) and, at the opposite extreme, the case where the components of the system have completely random and uncorrelated motion (the kinetic theory of an ideal gas; also, with slightly different conditions, fluid mechanics and idealized liquids). The results of analyses of this type are not *complete* solutions to the motion of the system, but they are often complete predictions of the *observable* behavior of the system, and they have many extremely important practical applications.

We developed our theoretical structure of classical mechanics on a remarkably small foundation: the fact that mathematics can be used to describe natural phenomena, a few basic rules (Newton's Laws and the conservation of energy, momentum and angular momentum) and some fundamental concepts (position, time, mass, energy, the four fundamental forces of gravity, electromagnetism and the short-range strong and weak interactions). These building blocks, especially the conservation laws which are deeply rooted in the most basic properties of the universe, underpin the whole theoretical structure of physical science, although they appear in a particularly clear and straightforward way in classical mechanics. It is an amazing demonstration of the essential simplicity of our universe that so many disparate experimental findings and observations can be interpreted with such a small number of initial assumptions.

One should, however, stress that in concentrating on the logical construction of this mathematical structure we have seriously misrepresented its historical development. Physics, like all science, is based on observation, and in fact this structure began as a collection of independent experimental results, observations and partial theories which were only gradually unified into the elegant logical structure we have erected. Archimedes' Principle, for example, predates Newton's laws (from which we derived it) by more than 1500 years, and the ideal-gas law was first deduced from experiment and only subsequently understood in terms of kinetic theory.

We could increase the number of practical applications of our techniques by making some small improvements to our idealizations:

- Solids are not perfectly rigid, but deform and break if subjected to large forces. We have already modeled this behavior for the particular case of a spring, and we could improve our description of solids by introducing analogues of $F = -k\Delta x$ for the various types of deformation possible.

- Our discussion of ideal liquids neglected frictional forces, which are important for many liquids (compare water and treacle). This can be remedied by introducing the concept of *viscosity*.

- Finally, the ideal gas model is actually an excellent description of most common gases, but it can be improved by allowing for the finite size of the gas molecules and the existence of weak intermolecular forces. The resulting *van der Waals equation* can be used for gases near their liquefaction point, such as gasoline vapor at room temperature.

Although these extensions of our models would improve, in some cases dramatically, our description of real objects, they would *not* introduce any new principles or concepts.

There are some physical systems which are described by the laws of mechanics we have developed here, but for which neither exact analytical solutions nor helpful idealized models exist. An example is the gravitational interactions of the members of the Solar System. Although the gravitational interactions of stars and planets are very simple, there is in fact no general exact analytical solution to even the second-simplest possible problem, namely the motion of three gravitationally interacting point particles, so a computational approach using numerical integration is the only hope. A common difficulty with such systems is that the result after a long period of numerical simulation may turn out to be extremely sensitive to the initial conditions (e.g. giving one planet an initial velocity of 10.0000000001 km/s rather than just 10 km/s may produce a completely different outcome after the numerical equivalent of 100 million years). This sensitivity is also common in numerical problems in fluid dynamics, the most familiar example being the inaccuracy of long-term weather forecasts. The behavior of such systems is generally extremely complicated; when graphed it looks random and disorganized, even though in fact it may be governed by very simple deterministic laws like those of gravity or fluid mechanics. Systems of this kind are common and important, but have long been neglected by physicists because there was no simple way to handle them mathematically. In recent years they have been attracting a great deal of interest from theoretical physicists and applied mathematicians, and the branch of science known as *chaos theory* has developed as a result.

WHERE DO WE GO FROM HERE?

Many features of classical mechanics are extremely typical of the scientific approach to understanding natural phenomena.

- The laws of mechanics are firmly based on *observation and experiment*.

441

- We start with *simple situations* and make use of *idealized models* to extract the essential features of a phenomenon.

- We develop *predictive theories* which are then *tested* by more experimentation and/or observation.

Although the content and formalism of other branches of science may be very different from classical mechanics, you will see this underlying structure everywhere, from designing clinical trials in medicine to developing high temperature superconductors in solid-state physics.

Because the idea of objects in motion underlies so much of physical science, classical mechanics also forms a jumping-off point for many other areas of physics. Some, such as the study of periodic motion (waves and oscillations) resulting from small displacements from equilibrium, are alternative ways of studying the behavior of matter in bulk, while others, such as the study of material properties, make use of the molecular picture we developed in studying kinetic theory (although we neglected interactions between atoms, whereas such interactions are fundamental to understanding the physical and chemical properties of matter). We looked at the Newtonian theory of gravity, which is the first and simplest of the theories describing the fundamental forces. Soon you may study the far richer field of electricity and magnetism, the phenomena associated with the electromagnetic fundamental force.

We can also extend the core topic of our subject—mechanics itself. Classical mechanics has a wide field of applications, from the expansion of gases to the trajectories of space probes, but it does fail in the domains of the very large (where the geometry of spacetime may differ from our simple assumptions), the very small (where quantum phenomena are important) and the very fast (where our assumptions about the absolute flow of time break down). Studying mechanics in these conditions is like studying a pendulum which has a large amplitude (so that one cannot take $\sin \theta \approx \theta$): we must throw out our approximations and develop more exact theories. The more exact theories developed to date are relativity, which describes motion on very large scales and involving very high velocities, and quantum theory, which applies to very small scales.

The existence of these more precise theories does not imply that classical mechanics is wrong, any more than the analysis of a pendulum swinging with a small amplitude is wrong because we can also analyze the large amplitude case. If we use velocities and distances which are in the appropriate range, the mathematics of the more exact theories reduces, to a very high degree of accuracy, to that of classical mechanics. On a very large scale, we are once again using an idealized model—our theory is an approximation, but one which in its proper context gives results which are virtually indistinguishable from more exact calculations.

Furthermore, even relativity and quantum mechanics are *not* complete and finished descriptions of nature. Our current state of knowledge does not connect quantum mechanics (the theory of the very small) with General Relativity (the theory of the very large, especially gravity and the structure of spacetime), essentially because we do not understand the quantum mechanical structure of the fundamental force of gravity. Recent developments in *superstring theory*, an exotic desciption of the elementary matter and force particles in terms of vibrating multidimensional strings, offer the prospect of describing quantum mechanics and gravity in a consistent framework, but as yet the mathematics of this field is not sufficiently well understood to make quantitative calculations and predictions possible. Physics is not simply a fixed body of knowledge, but a dynamic and evolving subject which will surely continue to grow and develop for many years to come.

PROBLEMS AND QUESTIONS

By the end of this chapter you should be able to answer or solve the types of questions or problems stated below.

At the end of the chapter there are answers to all the problems. In addition, for problems with an (H) or (S) after the number, there are respectively hints on how to solve the problems or completely worked-out solutions.

13.1 (H)   Liquid water has a density of 1000 kg/m³ and a molecular weight of 18 u (1 u = 1.66×10^{-27} kg). How many molecules are there in one liter (1000 cm³) of liquid water? What average spacing does this imply between the centers of adjacent molecules? Repeat this calculation for an ideal gas at 10^5 Pa and 300 K. Discuss your answers in terms of the assumptions we made in constructing the ideal-gas model.

(Atoms and small molecules have diameters of the order of 10^{-10} or 10^{-9} m.)

13.2 (H)   The diagram on the right shows a *Cartesian diver*. The large bottle is covered by a rubber sheet, so you can increase the surface pressure on the water by pushing down on the sheet. If at a certain pressure P the diver (i.e. the small bottle with the air bubble in it) is stationary, what will happen if you push down harder on the rubber sheet, and why?

13.3 (S)   A uniform cuboidal block of wood, of dimensions $a \times b \times c$ where $a \gg b \gg c$, is dropped into a lake. In which orientation will it float, and why?

13.4 (S)   A quantity of liquid of density ρ is contained in a U shaped tube of constant cross-section A. Initially one end of the tube is closed and the liquid in that end stands higher by an amount $2h$ than the liquid in the other end. The closed end of the tube is now opened so that the pressures at both ends are equal. What is the subsequent motion of the liquid in the tube?

13.5   A large open tank is filled with water to a height h. There is a small leak in the tank a distance d below the water surface. Calculate the speed at which the water emerges from this hole, and hence the distance from the tank at which it hits the ground, x. For a given height h, what is the value of d for which x is maximized? Neglect viscosity and air resistance and assume laminar flow.

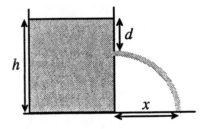

13.6   A thin uniform wooden rod of mass M and length ℓ hangs vertically from one end on a frictionless pivot. A bullet of mass m is shot horizontally with speed v_i into the other end of the rod; it passes through and emerges with a lower speed v_f, but with no change of direction. The amount of mass lost by the rod due to splintering by the bullet is negligible.

(a) Derive an expression for the angular speed of the rod immediately after the bullet emerges from it.

13.6, continued:

(b) In terms of the given quantities, what is the maximum angle $\theta_{\max}$ that the rod makes with the vertical?

(c) Describe the subsequent motion of the rod.

13.7 (H)   You have a canoe made of aluminum (density 2700 kg/m^3) designed so that when empty it floats in water with its sides extending 20 cm above water and 30 cm below water. If it were possible to take the floating canoe and gradually increase the value of g from 9.8 m/s^2 to an infinitely large value, what would happen to the canoe as g increased, and why? Assume water and aluminum are both incompressible, i.e. the increase in g does not affect the density of either substance. [Note for science-fiction buffs: this problem was inspired by an episode in Hal Clement's classic novel *Mission of Gravity*.]

13.8 (H)   A mass M is initially stationary on a horizontal frictionless air table. Firmly attached to the mass is a tube of gas (of negligible mass) sealed with a cork of mass m as shown. The height of the cork above the table is h and it is initially located a distance L from the edge of the block.

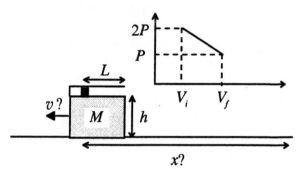

The experimenter now heats the gas inside the tube. The inner edges of the tube have some static friction, such that the cork does not blow off until the pressure inside the tube is double the ambient pressure, but negligible kinetic friction. As the cork travels along the tube the pressure of the gas behind it decreases linearly as shown in the inset PV plot, reaching ambient pressure just as the cork exits the tube.

(a) With what speed is the block traveling immediately after the cork leaves the tube?

(b) Relative to its starting position, where is the block when the cork leaves the tube?

(c) Relative to *its* starting position, how far away does the cork land?

13.9   Hailstones falling with speed v at an angle θ to the vertical collide elastically with a vertical wall. If the density of the hail (in kg of hailstones per cubic meter of air) is ρ, calculate the pressure exerted on the wall.

13.10   Discuss, in as much detail as possible, the aerodynamics of a frisbee, particularly the application of Bernoulli's equation to the airflow over, under and around the frisbee in flight. You should assume that the airflow is essentially laminar and that the speeds involved are small enough that air behaves as an incompressible fluid. You should *not* assume that there is no friction between the air and the frisbee.

If you are right-handed, you normally throw a frisbee so that it spins clock-wise as seen from above. Compare the trajectory and spin of a frisbee thrown normally, with the same initial velocity, by a left-handed person. Explain.

13.11 (S)   Mercury has a surface tension of 465 mN/m, a latent heat of vaporization of 272 kJ/kg, and a density of 13.6×10^3 kg/m³. Using only these data, estimate the size and mass of an atom of mercury.

13.12 (H)   If the pressure of water in the mains is 4.0×10^5 Pa, i.e. four times atmospheric pressure, what is (i) the speed, (ii) the volume flow rate, of water emerging from a fire hose with a nozzle diameter of 6.5 cm? Assume the diameter of the mains pipe is much larger than that of the fire hose, that the nozzle of the hose is 2 m above the level of the mains, and that viscosity and frictional effects can be neglected. What will happen to the speed and flow rate if the firefighter climbs 10 m up a ladder to fight a fire on the third floor, so that the nozzle is now 12 m above mains level? What is the maximum height to which any water can be delivered; does it matter if the firefighter climbs a ladder with the hose, or simply stands on the ground and directs the stream of water upwards?

   A little experimentation with a garden hose will convince you that the results you obtain in doing this problem are wrong—the experimental results don't agree with theoretical predictions. Since Bernoulli's equation follows directly from energy conservation, it must surely be correct (energy conservation is probably the single most trusted axiom in physics): we conclude that one of the assumptions we used in applying Bernoulli's equation to this problem must be unjustified. The trouble turns out to be that viscosity (a dissipative force) is *not* negligible in this situation: in fact it is the dominant effect. When viscous forces are important internal energy increases in the fluid and Bernoulli's equation is not valid. We should have used Poiseuille's law (which is beyond the scope of this book) to calculate the flow rate.

13.13   A cylindrical container of length L is full to the brim with a liquid which has mass density ρ. It is placed on a weigh-scale (which measures the downward force on the pan of the scale), and the scale reading is W. A light ball (which would float on the liquid if allowed to do so) of volume V and mass m is pushed gently down and held beneath the surface of the liquid with a rigid rod of negligible volume, as shown.

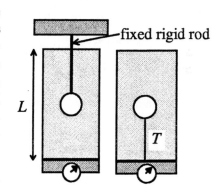

(a) What is the mass M of liquid which overflowed while the ball was being pushed into the container?

(b) What is the reading on the scale when the ball is fully immersed?

(c) If instead of being pushed down by a rod the ball is held in place by a fine string attached to the bottom of the container, what is the tension T in the string?

(d) In part (c), what is the reading on the scale?

13.14   A child is playing with a motorized toy airplane of mass M. The plane is attached to a string of length ℓ and is currently flying in horizontal circles directly above the child's hand, such that the string makes an angle θ to the vertical. The engine supplies a power P, and the plane flies at constant speed v. The direction of its motion is

445

counterclockwise as seen from above, and its wings remain horizontal as it flies (it does not bank). Neither the motor nor the aerodynamic forces (the forces exerted on the plane by the air around it) contribute any net horizontal force perpendicular to the plane's direction of motion.

(a) Why is the engine necessary?

(b) Draw a force diagram for the plane, explaining the origin of all your forces.

(c) What is the tension in the string?

(d) What is the angular velocity vector of the plane?

(e) What is the angular momentum vector of the plane about the child's hand (considered as a stationary point anchoring the string)?

(f) About the same point, what torque acts on the plane?

(g) What force is responsible for this torque?

(h) An airliner in a holding pattern would bank as it flew in horizontal circles. Why?

13.15 (H) A level conveyor belt moves with constant speed u. At time $t = 0$, a bowling ball is placed on the conveyor belt. The bowling ball is a uniform sphere of mass M and radius R, and at $t = 0$ it has zero linear and angular velocity, $v(0) = 0$ and $\omega(0) = 0$. The coefficient of kinetic friction between the ball and the conveyor is μ_k, and the coefficient of static friction is μ_s, with $\mu_k < \mu_s$.

(a) At $t = 0$, what is the total force $\vec{F}$ acting on the ball, and what is the total torque acting on the ball about its center? Assume that the conveyor is moving in the positive x direction, and that the y-axis points vertically upward.

(b) The ball will slip for some period after it is placed on the conveyor belt. What is its angular velocity $\omega(t)$ during this period of slipping?

(c) After a time t_1, the bowling ball stops slipping. Determine t_1. What is the (linear) velocity of the center of the ball at this point?

(d) What is the total work done by the force of friction on the bowling ball between $t = 0$ and $t = t_1$?

COMPLETE SOLUTIONS TO PROBLEMS WITH AN (S)

13.3   *A uniform cuboidal block of wood, of dimensions $a \times b \times c$ where $a \gg b \gg c$, is dropped into a lake. In which orientation will it float, and why?*

Conceptualize

In order for the wood to be stable, the following conditions must hold:

- there is no net *force* on the wood (this simply sets the depth at which it floats, i.e. the proportion of its volume not submerged);

- there is no net *torque* on the wood;

- if the wood is tilted slightly from its present position, the torque that results tends to *reduce* the amount of tilt.

The first two conditions produce equilibrium, while the third ensures that the equilibrium is stable.

The second condition implies that the center of mass of the wood (which is at the geometrical center of the block, since the wood is uniform) lies on the same vertical line as the center of mass of the displaced water. (Remember that the buoyant force acts through the same point as the weight of the water, *not* the block.) We can see from the symmetry of the situation that this means the block must float with one of its sides parallel to the water surface. (If this is not clear, look at the diagram, where the black blob represents the block's center of mass and the open circle the center of mass of the displaced water. When the block is tilted, more water is displaced on the side where it is lower, so the center of mass of the water is off to one side.)

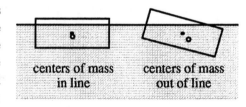

centers of mass in line   centers of mass out of line

To deal with the stability question in the most general case requires some slightly tedious geometry to calculate the position of the center of mass of the displaced water. However, if the sides of the block are very different in length, we can see what happens diagrammatically. If the block floats with a long side vertical, the submerged volume is dominated by a region of rectangular cross-section whose center of mass is clearly to the *left* (as drawn) of the block's center of mass. The remaining small submerged region, of triangular cross-section, has its center of mass to the right of the block's, but its mass is much smaller. The overall torque is clockwise, increasing the tilt: this position is not stable.

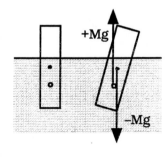

447

13.3, continued:

If, on the other hand, the block floats with a short side vertical, the center of mass of the exposed triangular section is clearly to the left of the block center of mass, and so the center of mass of the displaced water must be to the right. (If the block were very light, we would have a submerged triangle, whose center of mass would likewise be to the right of that of the block.) In either case, the resulting torque reduces the tilt, and the position is stable.

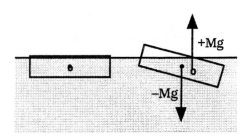

Solve

We therefore conclude that our block will float so that the longest sides are parallel to the water surface. For a more symmetrical block the situation would be less clear, and we would have to do a full calculation of the water's center of mass to determine if a position with long side vertical was stable against *small* displacements. (For a large angle of tilt, a block with unequal sides will always settle with the shortest sides vertical, but the other positions could still be stable against small tilts. As an analogy, consider a cereal box: in its normal upright orientation, it is stable against small nudges, but if you drop it from a height it will come to rest on its side.)

Learn

The question of stability is an important one for boats, particularly large cargo vessels. Since a ship is continuously being subjected to tilting forces from wave and wind action, it is vital that the load distribution in the vessel be adjusted to ensure stability. A particular problem is cargo shifting: if the ship develops a sideways list and the cargo is inadequately secured, it will tend to slide towards the low side of the ship, moving the ship's center of mass that way and increasing the probability that the net torque will be in the wrong direction. For this reason cargo holds are subdivided by bulkheads, and ships carry ballast to lower their center of mass. The problem is especially acute for car ferries, which tend to have large unobstructed car decks full of unsecured cars.

13.4   *A quantity of liquid of density ρ is contained in a U shaped tube of constant cross-section A. Initially one end of the tube is closed and the liquid in that end stands higher by an amount 2h than the liquid in the other end. The closed end of the tube is now opened so that the pressures at both ends are equal. What is the subsequent motion of the liquid in the tube?*

Conceptualize

There are two possible approaches to this problem:

- When the tube is opened, the surface pressures are equalized. Since the height of the liquid is greater in the previously closed arm, the pressure at the base of this arm will be greater than that at the base of the other arm, by Pascal's law, and therefore there will be a net force. We can use this to set up the equations of motion using Newton's laws.

13.4, continued:

- When the tube is opened, the 'extra' liquid in the previously sealed arm clearly has positive gravitational potential energy compared to the equilibrium position where both columns of liquid have equal height. We can differentiate this to find the force.

The energy approach seems cleaner, because we don't have to worry about the exact shape of the base of the tube.

Formulate

When the tube is first unsealed, the level of liquid in the previously closed arm is $+h$, and the level in the other arm $-h$, compared to the equilibrium state where both levels are equal. The extra mass of liquid in the closed tube is $2Ah\rho$. Taking $-h$ as the reference level for the gravitational potential energy, it has

$$U(h) = (2Ah\rho)gh = 2A\rho gh^2,$$

since its center of mass is at $y = 0$ (where y is the vertical coordinate).

At equilibrium, this 'extra' liquid is distributed equally between the two arms. Its potential energy relative to $-h$ is now

$$U_0 = 2(Ah\rho)g(\tfrac{1}{2}h = A\rho gh^2,$$

since each arm contributes a mass $Ah\rho$ of liquid whose center of mass is $h/2$ above the reference level.

The potential energy of the initial configuration compared to the equilibrium position is thus

$$U(h) - U_0 = A\rho gh^2.$$

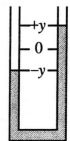

Solve

To see how the motion develops, consider a time t when the right-hand column is at height $+y$ compared to the equilibrium position (where both columns have the same height) and the left-hand column is at height $-y$. The potential energy of the liquid at this point, relative to equilibrium, is $U(y) - U_0 = A\rho gy^2$. Differentiating, we have

$$F = M\frac{d^2y}{dt^2} = -2A\rho gy.$$

If H is the total length of liquid in the whole tube, the total mass $M = AH\rho$, and so we have the differential equation

$$\frac{d^2y}{dt^2} = -\frac{2g}{H}y.$$

449

13.4, continued:

This is the equation for simple harmonic motion, which we first met in Chapter 2. Our boundary conditions in this case are that the top of the right-hand column was at coordinate $+h$ at time $t = 0$, so the solution is

$$y = h \cos \sqrt{\frac{2g}{H}}\, t$$

(and the top of the left-hand column is always at position $-y$, since the total length is constant). This assumes that our liquid has zero viscosity; in practice, friction between the liquid and the tube would gradually reduce the amplitude of the oscillations.

Scrutinize

$\sqrt{2g/H}$ clearly has the appropriate dimensions of $1/[\text{time}]$, and the whole solution is highly analogous to the simple pendulum, although in this case there is no requirement that h be small. By considering the net force at the lowest point in the tube, we can check the solution using the Pascal's law approach: the pressure difference between the bases of the right and left columns is $\rho g(2y)$, so the net force acting on mass $M = \rho AH$ is $-2\rho gyA$ (with a minus sign because the force acts to reduce y), giving an acceleration of $-2gy/H$ as above. The advantage of the energy approach is that we do not have to worry about the possible effects of contact forces where the tube bends.

13.11   *Mercury has a surface tension of 465 mN/m, a latent heat of vaporization of 272 kJ/kg, and a density of 13.6×10^3 kg/m^3. Using only these data, estimate the size and mass of an atom of mercury.*

Conceptualize

To do this problem, we need to find some relationship between the surface tension— the force which acts to minimize surface area—and the latent heat of vaporization— the energy required to transform unit mass of the substance from the liquid phase to the gaseous phase. To see what this relationship might be, we have to consider the origins of surface tension and the latent heat.

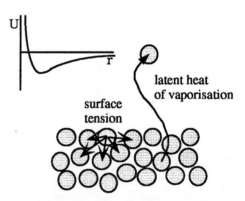

Surface tension arises because the constituent atoms or molecules of a liquid interact with one another via intermolecular forces: a schematic diagram of the relevant potential energy is shown in the diagram. An atom at the surface is in an asymmetric position, and a net force will act to pull it in towards the body of the liquid: it has a higher potential energy than an atom in the interior of the liquid.

The latent heat of vaporization is the energy one has to supply to move all the atoms or molecules away from the minimum of the intermolecular potential energy, out to $r \approx \infty$. Both surface tension and latent heat are therefore related to the intermolecular potential energy. If we express γ as energy divided by area,

$$\gamma = U/A \,,$$

450

13.11, continued:

and the latent heat of vaporization as energy divided by mass,

$$L_v = U/M \ ,$$

we might reasonably hope that in each case U is essentially the average intermolecular potential energy.

Formulate
To quantify this argument, consider a spherical particle with diameter d. Its surface area is πd^2 and its mass is $\frac{1}{6}\pi d^3 \rho$, where ρ is its density. If we substitute these for A and M in the above equations, we have

$$U = \gamma A = \gamma \pi d^2$$

$$U = L_v M = \frac{1}{6} L_v \pi d^3 \rho$$

which gives

$$d = \frac{6\gamma}{\rho L_v}.$$

Solve
For mercury, we conclude that

$$d = \frac{6\gamma}{\rho L_v} = \frac{6 \times (0.465 \text{ N/m})}{(13.6 \times 10^3 \text{ kg/m}^3) \times (2.72 \times 10^5 \text{ J/kg})} = 7.5 \times 10^{-10} \text{ m} \ .$$

For the atomic mass, we use $M = \frac{1}{6}\pi \rho d^3$, giving

$$M = \left(\frac{\pi}{6}\right) \times (13.6 \times 10^3 \text{ kg/m}^3) \times (7.5 \times 10^{-10} \text{ m})^3 = 3.1 \times 10^{-24} \text{kg} \ .$$

Scrutinize
We can see from dimensional arguments that if there *is* any way to obtain the size of an atom from surface tension, latent heat and density, the only suitable combination is $\gamma/\rho L_v$, since it is the only combination with dimensions of length. The numerical factor cannot be deduced dimensionally, and in fact slightly different ways of formulating the relationship between L_v and γ give different numerical coefficients in d, which can change our estimate for m by up to a factor of 10. From modern tables, the atomic mass of mercury is 200.6 u $= 3.33 \times 10^{-25}$ kg. Our estimate is within a factor of 10 of this, which may seem unimpressive, but recall that we are using numbers derived from macroscopic measurements involving grams or kilograms of fluid to derive properties of single molecules!

Learn
This method of estimating molecular sizes was first used by Waterston in 1858. The accuracy of our results for mercury is fairly typical (for instance, using textbook data

451

13.11, continued:

for water gives the molecular mass within a factor of 5, and for ethanol within a factor of about 10). The most interesting feature of this technique is that the phenomena that provide our numbers (the force exerted by the surface of the liquid, and the heat required to vaporize it) are apparently unrelated until we interpret them in terms of the molecular model. Under the circumstances, the fact that our estimates are anywhere near the right value is remarkable, and provides a strong indication that our model of the molecular structure of a liquid is reasonable.

There is a somewhat more direct method of estimating molecular sizes using macroscopic measurements, which can be most easily applied to oily fluids which float on water. If a small volume V of such a substance is poured onto the surface of a large pool of water, it will form a roughly circular slick of radius r. Assuming that the slick is one molecule thick, the length d of one molecule is simply $d = V/(\pi r^2)$.

HINTS FOR PROBLEMS WITH AN (H)
The number of the hint refers to the number of the problem

13.1 If you imagine a substance in which each molecule lies at the center of a small cube of side d, what is the average distance between molecules, and how many molecules are there in a cube of side 1 meter? How are these two quantities related?

13.2 If the pressure at the surface of the water is increased, what happens to the pressure on the air in the bubble? What then happens to the volume of the bubble?

13.7 What is the condition for the canoe to float stably? Does this depend on g?

What about the net pressure on the sides of the canoe?

13.8 How much work is done by the gas in expanding?

What happens to the center of mass of the block-cork system?

13.12 Is the speed of the water the same if it is contained within a hose? Is the volume flow rate the same?

13.15 (c) What is the condition for the ball to roll without slipping?

(d) What is the total kinetic energy of the ball at time t_1?

ANSWERS TO HINTS

13.1 d; $1/d^3$; spacing is cube root of one over number density.

13.2 Pressure increases; volume decreases.

13.7 $M = \rho V$, mass of canoe equals density of water times volume displaced; no (except insofar as increased gravity may tend to slightly increase the mass of air within the canoe).

Net pressure $= \rho g d$, where d is depth of bottom of canoe below water surface; this does depend on g.

13.8 $\frac{1}{2}P(V_f - V_i)$; it remains stationary until cork leaves tube, then drops slightly (no external forces acting except gravity).

13.12 Yes; no.

13.15 (c) $R\omega(t) + v(t) = u$.

(d) $\frac{1}{2}Mv^2(t_1) + \frac{1}{2}I\omega^2(t_1) = \frac{1}{2}Mv^2(t_1) + \frac{1}{5}MR^2\omega^2(t_1)$.

ANSWERS TO ALL PROBLEMS

13.1 3.35×10^{25}; $\approx 3 \times 10^{-10}$ m;

2.4×10^{22}; $\approx 3.5 \times 10^{-9}$ m.

In liquid water the molecules are almost in contact, so surely the inter-molecular forces cannot be neglected; in an ideal gas they are separated by perhaps ten times their size, so there is some reason to expect that forces between them are small (note: this suggests that big molecules containing ten or more atoms are unlikely to behave like ideal gases under typical conditions of pressure and temperature).

13.2 The diver sinks, because the increased pressure compresses the air bubble inside it, reducing the volume it occupies and thus increasing the overall density of the diver.

13.3 See complete solution.

13.4 See complete solution.

13.5 $v = \sqrt{2gd}$; $x = 2\sqrt{d(h-d)}$; $d = h/2$.

13.6 (a) $\omega = \dfrac{3m(v_i - v_f)}{M\ell}$

(b) $\sqrt{\dfrac{6m^2(v_i - v_f)^2}{M^2 g \ell}}$

(c) It will oscillate back and forth in simple harmonic motion.

13.7 The canoe will continue to float undisturbed until some critical point, at which it will suddenly collapse. The reason is that the relative densities of canoe and water don't change (except for a slight effect caused by increase in air density), but the net pressure on the sides of the canoe increases, as the water pressure is proportional to g. Eventually the sides of the canoe will begin to bend inwards: this reduces the volume of the canoe, increasing its relative density and causing it to sink slightly, which in turn further increases the net pressure. The result is a sudden catastrophic collapse.

13.8 (a) $\sqrt{\dfrac{2K}{M + M^2/m}}$, where $K = \frac{1}{2}P(V_f - V_i)$.

(b) $\dfrac{L}{1 + \frac{M}{m}}$

(c) $\dfrac{L}{1 + \frac{m}{M}} + 2\sqrt{\dfrac{hK}{gm(1 + \frac{m}{M})}}$.

13.9 $2\rho v^2 \sin^2 \theta$.

13.10 The path of the air deflected over the frisbee is longer than that of the undisturbed air passing underneath, so the air over the frisbee has a higher speed, and thus (by Bernoulli) a lower pressure. Hence there is a net upward force, so the frisbee will remain airborne longer than it would in the absence of this effect. Friction between the frisbee and the surrounding

13.10, continued:

air tends to drag the streamlines around the frisbee in the direction of its spin, producing a difference in pressure between the two sides of the frisbee and hence causing its path to curve sideways. The spin also provides stability due to angular momentum effects (Chapter 9).

Your frisbee tends to curve to the right as you look at it, your friend's curves left.

13.11 See complete solution.

13.12 24 m/s; 79 liters/s; speed reduces to 19 m/s, volume flow to 63 liters/s; 31 m above the level of the mains; yes: the maximum height and the speed of the water at any height will be the same in both cases, but the volume flow rate is higher if the fireman stands on the ground. This is because the equation of continuity forces the volume flow rate to be lower if the water is confined within the hose, whereas once it leaves the hose it can spread out over a wider area as it slows down.

13.13 (a) $V\rho$;   (b) W;   (c) $(M - m)g$;   (d) $W - Mg + mg$.

13.14 (a) The motor supplies the forward force needed to counteract the backward force due to air drag.

(b) Forward force F_E from engine (more specifically, the engine supplies a torque which turns the propellor, and the motion of the propellor creates aerodynamic forces which act on the plane). Backward force F_D from air drag, related to the velocity of the plane relative to the air around it (probably of form $-kv^2\hat{v}$). Mg is weight of plane, T is tension in string, and L is lift, created by the Bernoulli effect acting mainly on the plane's wings, as in Problem 12C.6: the wing cross-section is shaped so that the air traveling over the top has a longer path, and must therefore move more quickly, than the air beneath. (It would be reasonable to draw two lift forces, one on each wing, but there is no way to separate out the individual contributions in this problem.)

(c) $T = \dfrac{Mv^2}{\ell \sin \theta}$.

(d) $\vec{\omega} = \left[0, 0, \dfrac{v}{\ell \sin \theta}\right]$ in a coordinate system where z points directly upwards.

(e) $\vec{L} = M\ell v[-\cos\theta\cos\omega t, -\cos\theta\sin\omega t, \sin\theta]$, where $\omega = |\vec{\omega}|$.

(f) $\vec{\tau} = \dfrac{Mv^2}{\sin\theta}[\cos\theta\sin\omega t, -\cos\theta\cos\omega t, 0]$.

(g) The lift (more precisely, the difference between lift and weight).

(h) The lift acts perpendicular to the wing surfaces, so by banking the plane, the pilot can arrange to give the lift an inward component which supplies the centripetal force needed to maintain circular motion.

13.15 (a) $\vec{F} = [\mu_k Mg, 0, 0]$; $\vec{\tau} = [0, 0, \mu_k MgR]$. (As the axis of rotation of the bowling ball has a fixed orientation, always parallel to the z-axis, we will use the 'scalar' definitions of angular quantities in answers to the remainder of this problem. With the given coordinate system, these correspond to the z-components of the vector equivalents; the x- and y- components are zero.)

(b) $\omega(t) = \dfrac{5\tau t}{2MR^2} = \dfrac{5\mu_k g}{2R}t.$

(c) $t_1 = \dfrac{2u}{7\mu_k g}$; $v = \frac{2}{7}u$ in the positive x direction.

(d) $W = \frac{1}{7}Mu^2.$

(This should be evaluated using the work-energy theorem. Although it is also possible to use force times distance, one has to be particularly careful, for two reasons: first, since the ball is turning as it skids, the point on the surface of the ball to which the force is applied is constantly changing; secondly, the part of the ball which is in contact with the conveyor belt does not have the same velocity as the center of the ball. One must use a calculus-based approach: in an infinitesimal time Δt, the work done $\Delta W = F\Delta x$, where Δx is the displacement of the atoms to which the force is applied. The power $P = \Delta W/\Delta t = Fv_c$, where $v_c = \Delta x/\Delta t$ is the velocity of the atoms at the contact point, $v_c(t) = v(t) + R\omega(t)$. One can then integrate $P\,dt$ from $t = 0$ to $t = t_1$ to find the work done. Applying the work-energy theorem is much more straightforward—another example of the advantages of conservation-law approaches to problem solving.)

MASSACHUSETTS INSTITUTE OF TECHNOLOGY
Department of Physics

Physics 8.01

Fall 1997

FINAL EXAMINATION
Monday, December 15, 1997
(Reformatted to Remove Blank Spaces)

FAMILY (LAST) NAME

GIVEN (FIRST) NAME

STUDENT ID NUMBER

Your class (check one) $\Longrightarrow$

Instructions:
1. SHOW ALL WORK. All work is to be done in this booklet. Extra blank pages are provided.
2. This is a closed book test.
3. <u>CALCULATORS</u>, BOOKS, and NOTES are NOT ALLOWED.
4. Do all SEVEN (7) problems.
5. Print your name on each page of this booklet.
6. Exams will be collected 5 minutes before the hour.

Problem	Maximum	Score	Grader
1	10		
2	10		
3	15		
4	15		
5	17		
6	15		
7	18		
TOTAL	100		

Cl. 1	MW 1:00	R. Remillard	
Cl. 2	MW 2:00	R. Remillard	
Cl. 3	MW 1:00	A. Kerman	
Cl. 4	MW 2:00	A. Kerman	
Cl. 5	TR 2:00	W. Busza	
Cl. 6	TR 3:00	W. Busza	
Cl. 7	TR 9:00	S. Nahn	
Cl. 8	TR 10:00	S. Nahn	
Cl. 9	TR 2:00	E. Lomon	
Cl. 10	TR 3:00	E. Lomon	
Cl. 11	MW 12:00	I. Pless	
Cl. 12	MW 1:00	I. Pless	
Cl. 13	TR 10:00	R. Hulsizer	
Cl. 14	TR 11:00	R. Hulsizer	
Cl. 15	MW 2:00	H. Gao	
Cl. 16	MW 3:00	H. Gao	
Cl. 17	MW 3:00	M. Feld	
Cl. 18	MW 4:00	M. Feld	
Cl. 19	TR 9:00	L. Royden	
Cl. 20	TR 10:00	L. Royden	
Cl. 21	TR 10:00	W. Smith	
Cl. 22	TR 11:00	W. Smith	
Cl. 23	TR 10:00	R. Aggarwal	
Cl. 24	TR 11:00	R. Aggarwal	
Cl. 25	TR 2:00	P. Haridas	
Cl. 26	TR 3:00	P. Haridas	

MASSACHUSETTS INSTITUTE OF TECHNOLOGY
Department of Physics

Physics 8.01

Fall 1997

FINAL EXAMINATION ERRATA
Monday, December 15, 1997

1) The exam as printed is too long!

The following parts are therefore ***deleted*** from the exam:

Problem 3(e)	*@3 points*
Problem 4(e)	*@3 points*
Problem 5(d)	*@6 points*
Problem 6(d)	*@3 points*
Total:	*15 points*

The maximum score on the exam, after the deletions, is therefore 85. The scores will be multiplied by 100/85 before they are averaged with the other components to compute your final course grade.

Recommendation: Put X's over the deleted problems before you start.

Do not waste time on the deleted parts, because they will **not** be graded.

2) Clarification for Problem 5(c):

Recall that v_0 is the orbital speed of the shuttle before the cannon is fired.

3) Clarification for Problem 7(d):

You may express your answer in terms of any of the quantities m, v_0, h, R, and I, where I is the moment of inertia of the disk about the pivoted axis. Please leave your answer in terms of I, whether or not you evaluated it in part (b). Consider this a challenge problem, so don't feel frustrated if you can't get it.

FORMULA SHEETS: A five page "formula sheet" was handed out as part of this examination. It is available on the 8.01 website at

http://web.mit.edu/8.01/www/gen97/fif1l97.html.

Problem 1 (*10 points*):

This problem is based on Problem 3 of the Unit 7 Quiz of this term.

A rocket-propelled railroad flatcar begins at rest at time $t = 0$, and then accelerates along a straight track with a speed given by

$$v(t) = b\,t^2$$

where b is a constant, for $0 < t < t_2$. Then the acceleration ends, and the flatcar continues at a constant speed of $v_f = bt_2^2$, as shown on the graph below. A coin is initially at rest on the floor of the flatcar. At $t = t_1$ the coin begins to slip, and it stops slipping at $t = t_3$. You may assume that $0 < t_1 < t_2 < t_3$, as shown in the graph. Gravity acts downward with an acceleration of magnitude g.

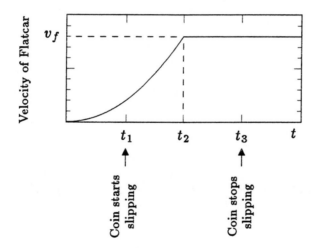

a) (*5 points*) What is the coefficient of static friction μ_s between the coin and the floor?

b) (*5 points*) What is the coefficient of kinetic friction μ_k between the coin and the floor? (Hint: Note that between $t = t_1$ and $t = t_3$, the coin has a constant acceleration. Can you find this acceleration from some or all of the quantities b, t_1, t_2, t_3, and v_f?)

Problem 2 (*10 points*):

This problem is based on Problem 6.3 of the Study Guide.

An Eskimo child of mass M is using her parents' hemispherical igloo as a slide. She starts off from rest at the top and slides down under the influence of gravity. The surface of the igloo is effectively frictionless.

a) (*2 points, no partial credit*) What is her potential energy at point P (see diagram)? Define the potential energy so that it is zero when the child is on the ground. (Note the sphere has radius r, and that a straight line between P and O, the center of the sphere of which the igloo is a part, makes an angle θ with the vertical.)

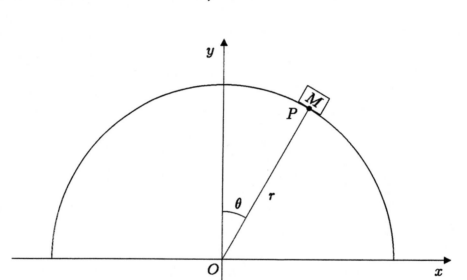

b) (*3 points*) On the diagram above, indicate (and clearly label) the forces acting on her at point P.

c) (*5 points*) Does she remain in contact with the igloo all the way to the ground? If not, at what angle θ does she lose contact?

Problem 3 (*15 points*):

This problem is based on Problem 13.13 of the Study Guide.

A cylindrical container of length L is full to the brim with a liquid which has mass density ρ. It is placed on a weigh-scale (which measures the downward force on the pan of the scale), and the scale reading is W. A light ball (which would float on the liquid if allowed to do so) of volume V and mass m is pushed gently down and held beneath the surface of the liquid with a rigid rod of negligible volume, as shown.

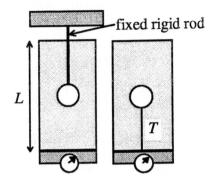

In each of the following parts, you can express your answer in terms of the given variables and/or the answers to the previous parts, whether or not you have correctly answered the previous parts.

a) (*3 points, no partial credit*) What is the mass M of liquid which overflowed while the ball was being pushed into the container?

b) (*3 points, no partial credit*) What is the reading R_1 on the scale when the ball is fully immersed?

c) (*3 points, no partial credit*) If instead of being pushed down by a rod the ball is held in place by a fine string attached to the bottom of the container, what is the tension T in the string?

d) (*3 points, no partial credit*) In part (c), what is the reading R_2 on the scale?

e) (*3 points, no partial credit*) If the string is cut, what will be the initial acceleration a of the ball? Assume that viscosity effects are negligible.

Problem 4 (*15 points*):

a) (*3 points, no partial credit*) A ball is thrown straight upward with an initial speed v_0. Denoting the magnitude of the acceleration of gravity as g, and neglecting friction, what will be the maximum height h that the ball will reach?

b) (*3 points*) A ball of mass M and velocity $\vec{v}_1 = [v_M, 0, 0]$ collides with a ball of mass m and velocity $\vec{v}_2 = [0, 0, v_m]$. The two stick together. Ignoring friction, what is the speed of the combined mass after the collision?

c) (*3 points, no partial credit*) A block of mass m slides down a frictionless hill, starting at a height h and finishing at height zero. Let g be the magnitude of the acceleration of gravity. What is the kinetic energy of the block at the bottom of the hill?

d) (*3 points, no partial credit*) A ball of radius R and mass m rolls without slipping down a hill, starting at a height h and finishing at height zero. Again let g be the magnitude of the acceleration of gravity. Neglecting all friction besides the force needed to keep the ball from slipping, what is the kinetic energy of the ball at the bottom of the hill?

e) (*3 points*) A compressed spring of negligible mass, which provides a fixed but un-calibrated force, is placed in contact with an <u>unknown</u> mass labeled A. When the spring is released, so that it pushes on the block, the initial acceleration of the block is measured to have magnitude a_A. In an identical experiment with the same spring compressed by the same amount, a block labeled B is found to have an initial acceleration of magnitude a_B. If the two blocks are glued together (neglect the mass of the glue) and the identical experiment is carried out with the pair, what will be the magnitude of the initial acceleration?

Problem 5 (*17 points*):

A space shuttle is in a circular orbit of radius R about the Earth. The shuttle and its contents have mass M, and the Earth has mass M_E.

a) (*3 points*) In the frame of the Earth, which you may treat as an inertial frame, what is the orbital speed v_0 of the shuttle? You may express your answer in terms of any of the quantities R, M, M_E, and G (Newton's constant), and you may assume that $M \ll M_E$.

b) (*4 points*) What is the gravitational potential energy of the shuttle, relative to the potential energy it would have at infinite distance from the Earth? Again you may express your answer in terms of any of the quantities R, M, M_E, and G (Newton's constant).

c) (*4 points*) A cannon on the shuttle fires a probe of mass m in the direction opposite to the shuttle's velocity. After the firing, the probe has a speed Δv relative to the shuttle, where $\Delta v < v_0$. What is the speed v_1 of the probe, relative to the Earth, immediately after the firing? You may assume that no other mass is ejected in the firing of the probe. Do not assume, however, that m is negligible compared to M. You may express your answer in terms of any of the quantities R, m, M, M_E, G, v_0, and Δv.

d) (*6 points*) After being fired from the cannon, the probe will follow an elliptical orbit. Assume that it remains far enough from the Earth so that friction with the atmosphere can be ignored. Write two equations which could be solved to determine r_p and v_p, the radius and speed of the orbit at perigee, the nearest point to the center of the Earth. **Do not attempt to solve these equations.** Note that r_p is to be measured from the center of the Earth. You may express your answer in terms of any of the quantities v_1, R, m, M_E, and G.

Problem 6 (*15 points*):

A piston chamber of volume V_0 is filled with an ideal monatomic gas at temperature T_0 and pressure P_0. Denote Boltzmann's constant by k, and Avogadro's number by N_A.

a) (*2 points, no partial credit*) In terms of the given quantities, what is the number N of atoms of the gas present in the chamber?

b) (*2 points, no partial credit*) What is the number $\mathcal{N}$ of moles of the gas present in the chamber?

c) (*2 points, no partial credit*) The gas is allowed to expand, so the volume increases by an amount ΔV. The gas is heated while it expands by just the right amount to keep it at constant pressure P_0. How much work ΔW does the gas do during this expansion?

d) (*3 points*) By what amount ΔU does the internal energy change during this expansion? Define ΔU so that a positive value denotes an increase in internal energy.

e) (*6 points*) Starting again from the initial values of $V = V_0$, $T = T_0$, and $P = P_0$, the gas is allowed to expand without the addition or emission of any heat. As the gas expands the values of T and P can both be measured as a function of V. Find an expression for $\dfrac{dP}{dV}$ that depends on no variables other than P and V.

Problem 7 (*18 points*):

A uniform disk of mass M and radius R i~
ented in a vertical plane. The y axis is vertical, ~
the x axis is horizontal. The disk is pivoted abo~
the origin of the coordinate system, with the center
of the disk hanging a distance h below the pivot, as
shown. The disk is free to rotate without friction
about the pivot in the x-y plane. The magnitude
of the acceleration of gravity is g, directed in the
negative y direction.

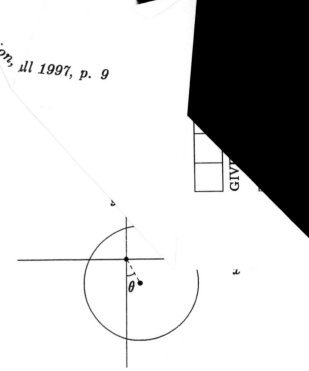

a) (*4 points*) If the disk is rotated by an angle θ from its equilibrium position, as shown,
what is the magnitude of the torque about the
pivot? (In this part, do not assume that the
angle θ is necessarily small.)

b) (*4 points*) What is the moment of inertia I of the disk about the pivoted axis?

c) (*4 points*) If the disk is allowed to oscillate about its equilibrium position, what
will be the period of small oscillations? Your answer may be written in terms of I,
whether or not you answered the previous part.

d) (*6 points*) A ball of putty of mass m collides
with the disk from the right, hitting it at the
point $[R, -h, 0]$, as shown. At the moment
just before the impact, the ball of putty has a
velocity $\vec{v} = [-v_0, 0, 0]$, and the disk is at rest.
If the putty sticks to the side of the disk, what
will be its velocity vector $\vec{v}_f$ immediately after
the collision?

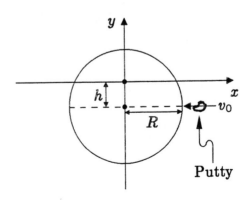

Fall 1997

XAMINATION SOLUTIONS
Monday, December 15, 1997

...) NAME

...N (FIRST) NAME

STUDENT ID NUMBER

Your class (check one) $\Longrightarrow$

Instructions:
1. SHOW ALL WORK. All work is to be done in this booklet. Extra blank pages are provided.
2. This is a closed book test.
3. <u>CALCULATORS</u>, BOOKS, and NOTES are NOT ALLOWED.
4. Do all SEVEN (7) problems.
5. Print your name on each page of this booklet.
6. Exams will be collected 5 minutes before the hour.

Problem	Maximum	Score	Grader
1	10		
2	10		
3	12		
4	12		
5	11		
6	12		
7	18		
TOTAL	85		

Cl. 1	MW 1:00	R. Remillard	
Cl. 2	MW 2:00	R. Remillard	
Cl. 3	MW 1:00	A. Kerman	
Cl. 4	MW 2:00	A. Kerman	
Cl. 5	TR 2:00	W. Busza	
Cl. 6	TR 3:00	W. Busza	
Cl. 7	TR 9:00	S. Nahn	
Cl. 8	TR 10:00	S. Nahn	
Cl. 9	TR 2:00	E. Lomon	
Cl. 10	TR 3:00	E. Lomon	
Cl. 11	MW 12:00	I. Pless	
Cl. 12	MW 1:00	I. Pless	
Cl. 13	TR 10:00	R. Hulsizer	
Cl. 14	TR 11:00	R. Hulsizer	
Cl. 15	MW 2:00	H. Gao	
Cl. 16	MW 3:00	H. Gao	
Cl. 17	MW 3:00	M. Feld	
Cl. 18	MW 4:00	M. Feld	
Cl. 19	TR 9:00	L. Royden	
Cl. 20	TR 10:00	L. Royden	
Cl. 21	TR 10:00	W. Smith	
Cl. 22	TR 11:00	W. Smith	
Cl. 23	TR 10:00	R. Aggarwal	
Cl. 24	TR 11:00	R. Aggarwal	
Cl. 25	TR 2:00	P. Haridas	
Cl. 26	TR 3:00	P. Haridas	

MASSACHUSETTS INSTITUTE OF TECHNOLOGY
Department of Physics

Physics 8.01   Fall 1997

FINAL EXAMINATION ERRATA
Monday, December 15, 1997

1) The exam as printed is too long!

The following parts are therefore ***deleted*** from the exam:

Problem 3(e)	*@3 points*
Problem 4(e)	*@3 points*
Problem 5(d)	*@6 points*
Problem 6(d)	*@3 points*
Total:	*15 points*

The maximum score on the exam, after the deletions, is therefore 85. The scores will be multiplied by 100/85 before they are averaged with the other components to compute your final course grade.

Recommendation: Put X's over the deleted problems before you start.

Do not waste time on the deleted parts, because they will **not** be graded.

2) Clarification for Problem 5(c):

Recall that v_0 is the orbital speed of the shuttle before the cannon is fired.

3) Clarification for Problem 7(d):

You may express your answer in terms of any of the quantities m, v_0, h, R, and I, where I is the moment of inertia of the disk about the pivoted axis. Please leave your answer in terms of I, whether or not you evaluated it in part (b). Consider this a challenge problem, so don't feel frustrated if you can't get it.

469

FORMULA SHEETS: A five page "formula sheet" was handed out as part of this examination. It is available on the 8.01 website at
http://web.mit.edu/8.01/www/gen97/fif1l97.html.

Problem 1 (*10 points*):

This problem is based on Problem 3 of the Unit 7 Quiz of this term.

A rocket-propelled railroad flatcar begins at rest at time $t = 0$, and then accelerates along a straight track with a speed given by

$$v(t) = b\,t^2$$

where b is a constant, for $0 < t < t_2$. Then the acceleration ends, and the flatcar continues at a constant speed of $v_f = bt_2^2$, as shown on the graph below. A coin is initially at rest on the floor of the flatcar. At $t = t_1$ the coin begins to slip, and it stops slipping at $t = t_3$. You may assume that $0 < t_1 < t_2 < t_3$, as shown in the graph. Gravity acts downward with an acceleration of magnitude g.

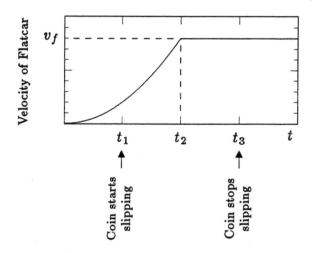

a) (*5 points*) What is the coefficient of static friction μ_s between the coin and the floor?

b) (*5 points*) What is the coefficient of kinetic friction μ_k between the coin and the floor? (*Hint: Note that between $t = t_1$ and $t = t_3$, the coin has a constant acceleration. Can you find this acceleration from some or all of the quantities b, t_1, t_2, t_3, and v_f?*)

Solution:

(a) As the flatcar begins to accelerate, the coin is held at a fixed position relative to the car by static friction. The coefficient of static friction can be computed from the time at which it starts to slip, t_1, which is when static friction has reached its maximal force. The acceleration along the track during the period $0 \leq t \leq t_2$ is given by

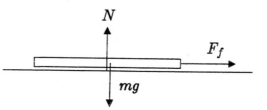

$$a = \frac{dv}{dt} = \frac{d}{dt}bt^2 = 2bt .$$

It slips when

$$ma = \mu_s N ,$$

where m is the mass of the coin and $N = mg$ is the normal force. So

$$m(2bt_1) = \mu_s mg \quad \implies \quad \boxed{\mu_s = \frac{2bt_1}{g} .}$$

(b) As the hint suggests, the coefficient of kinetic friction is found from acceleration during the time interval $t_1 < t < t_3$, while the coin is slipping. The acceleration along the track is given by

$$a = \frac{F_f}{m} = \frac{\mu_k mg}{m} = \mu_k g .$$

Knowing that the acceleration is constant, we can express its value in terms of the initial and final velocities:

$$a = \frac{v(t_3) - v(t_1)}{t_3 - t_1} = \frac{b\left(t_2^2 - t_1^2\right)}{t_3 - t_1} .$$

Equating the two expressions for a,

$$\boxed{\mu_k = \frac{b\left(t_2^2 - t_1^2\right)}{(t_3 - t_1)g} ,}$$

or equivalently

$$\boxed{\mu_k = \frac{v_f - bt_1^2}{(t_3 - t_1)g} .}$$

Problem 2 (*10 points*):

This problem is based on Problem 6.3 of the Study Guide.

An Eskimo child of mass M is using her parents' hemispherical igloo as a slide. She starts off from rest at the top and slides down under the influence of gravity. The surface of the igloo is effectively frictionless.

a) (*2 points, no partial credit*) What is her potential energy at point P (see diagram)? Define the potential energy so that it is zero when the child is on the ground. (Note the sphere has radius r, and that a straight line between P and O, the center of the sphere of which the igloo is a part, makes an angle θ with the vertical.)

Solution: *In general*

$$U = Mgh ,$$

where h is the height above the zero of potential, which in this case is the ground. Since

$$h = r \cos \theta ,$$

we have

$$\boxed{U = Mgr \cos \theta .}$$

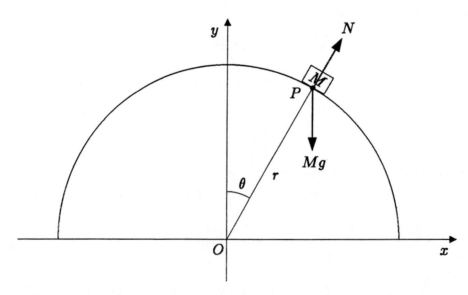

b) (*3 points*) On the diagram above, indicate (and clearly label) the forces acting on her at point P.

c) (*5 points*) Does she remain in contact with the igloo all the way to the ground? If not, at what angle θ does she lose contact?

Solution: *She will remain in contact as long as the normal force is positive, but she will lose contact if it ever falls to zero. To find the normal force, balance forces in the radial direction. To know the radial acceleration, we must know v, which can be found by energy conservation:*

$$Mgr\cos\theta + \frac{1}{2}Mv^2 = Mgr \quad \Longrightarrow \quad v^2 = 2gr(1-\cos\theta) \ .$$

The radial component of the $\vec{\mathbf{F}} = M\vec{\mathbf{a}}$ *equation reads:*

$$N - Mg\cos\theta = -M\frac{v^2}{r} \ ,$$

so

$$N = Mg\cos\theta - 2Mg(1-\cos\theta)$$
$$= Mg(3\cos\theta - 2) \ .$$

So $N = 0$ *when* $3\cos\theta - 2 = 0$, *at which point the child would lose contact. Finally,*

$$\boxed{\textit{Child loses contact at } \theta = \cos^{-1}\left(\frac{2}{3}\right) \ .}$$

Problem 3 (*12 points, after deletion*):

This problem is based on Problem 13.13 of the Study Guide.

A cylindrical container of length L is full to the brim with a liquid which has mass density ρ. It is placed on a weigh-scale (which measures the downward force on the pan of the scale), and the scale reading is W. A light ball (which would float on the liquid if allowed to do so) of volume V and mass m is pushed gently down and held beneath the surface of the liquid with a rigid rod of negligible volume, as shown.

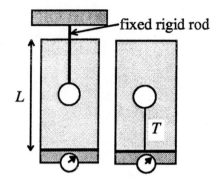

In each of the following parts, you can express your answer in terms of the given variables and/or the answers to the previous parts, whether or not you have correctly answered the previous parts.

a) (*3 points, no partial credit*) What is the mass M of liquid which overflowed while the ball was being pushed into the container?

> *Solution: The displaced volume is V and the density of the liquid is ρ, so the displaced mass is*

$$\boxed{M = \rho V} \; .$$

b) (*3 points, no partial credit*) What is the reading R_1 on the scale when the ball is fully immersed?

> *Solution: The ball experiences a buoyant force upward with magnitude equal to the weight of the displaced liquid, $F_B = \rho V g$. By Newton's third law, the ball must exert a force on the liquid of equal magnitude, acting downward. Since the weight of liquid on the scale has been reduced from its initial value by $\rho V g$, the reading is*

$$R_1 = W - \rho V g + F_B = \boxed{W} \; .$$

c) (*3 points, no partial credit*) If instead of being pushed down by a rod the ball is held in place by a fine string attached to the bottom of the container, what is the tension T in the string?

> **Solution:**
>
> *The vertical component of the net force acting on the ball must be zero, so*
>
> $$F_B - mg - T = 0 \ .$$
>
> *But $F_B = \rho V g$, so*
>
> $$\boxed{T = \rho V g - mg = (\rho V - m)g \ .}$$

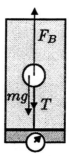

d) (*3 points, no partial credit*) In part (c), what is the reading R_2 on the scale?

> **Solution:** *There are no forces acting on the items on the scale other than the usual forces of gravity and the normal force of the scale acting upward. So, the scale simply weighs the items. The weight started as W, was reduced by the weight of the displaced liquid $\rho V g$, and increased by the weight of the ball mg:*
>
> $$\boxed{\therefore R_2 = W - \rho V g + mg \ .}$$

e) (*3 points, no partial credit*) If the string is cut, what will be the initial acceleration a of the ball? Assume that viscosity effects are negligible.

$$\boxed{\text{DELETED FROM EXAM}}$$

Problem 4 (*12 points, after deletion*):

a) (*3 points, no partial credit*) A ball is thrown straight upward with an initial speed v_0. Denoting the magnitude of the acceleration of gravity as g, and neglecting friction, what will be the maximum height h that the ball will reach?

Solution: By conservation of energy,

$$\frac{1}{2}mv_0^2 = mgh \ ,$$

where m is the mass of the ball. So

$$\boxed{h = \frac{v_0^2}{2g} \ .}$$

b) (*3 points*) A ball of mass M and velocity $\vec{v}_1 = [v_M, 0, 0]$ collides with a ball of mass m and velocity $\vec{v}_2 = [0, 0, v_m]$. The two stick together. Ignoring friction, what is the speed of the combined mass after the collision?

Solution: By conservation of momentum,

$$\vec{P}_f = \vec{p}_1 + \vec{p}_2 = [Mv_M, 0, mv_m] = (M+m)\vec{v}_f \ .$$

So

$$\vec{v}_f = \frac{[Mv_M, 0, mv_m]}{M+m} \ ,$$

and

$$\boxed{|\vec{v}_f| = \frac{\sqrt{M^2 v_M^2 + m^2 v_m^2}}{M+m} \ .}$$

c) (*3 points, no partial credit*) A block of mass m slides down a frictionless hill, starting at a height h and finishing at height zero. Let g be the magnitude of the acceleration of gravity. What is the kinetic energy of the block at the bottom of the hill?

Solution: Conservation of energy implies $\boxed{E_{k,f} = mgh}$.

d) (*3 points, no partial credit*) A ball of radius R and mass m rolls without slipping down a hill, starting at a height h and finishing at height zero. Again let g be the magnitude of the acceleration of gravity. Neglecting all friction besides the force needed to keep the ball from slipping, what is the kinetic energy of the ball at the bottom of the hill?

> **Solution:** *Again, conservation of energy implies* $\boxed{E_{k,f} = mgh}$. [The energy will be divided between translational and rotational kinetic energy, but the total kinetic energy must equal the original potential energy.]

e) (*3 points*) A compressed spring of negligible mass, which provides a fixed but un-calibrated force, is placed in contact with an <u>unknown</u> mass labeled A. When the spring is released, so that it pushes on the block, the initial acceleration of the block is measured to have magnitude a_A. In an identical experiment with the same spring compressed by the same amount, a block labeled B is found to have an initial acceleration of magnitude a_B. If the two blocks are glued together (neglect the mass of the glue) and the identical experiment is carried out with the pair, what will be the magnitude of the initial acceleration?

$$\boxed{\text{DELETED FROM EXAM}}$$

477

Problem 5 (*11 points, after deletion*):

A space shuttle is in a circular orbit of radius R about the Earth. The shuttle and its contents have mass M, and the Earth has mass M_E.

a) (*3 points*) In the frame of the Earth, which you may treat as an inertial frame, what is the orbital speed v_0 of the shuttle? You may express your answer in terms of any of the quantities R, M, M_E, and G (Newton's constant), and you may assume that $M \ll M_E$.

> **Solution:**
>
> *Writing the radial component of $\vec{\mathbf{F}} = m\vec{\mathbf{a}}$,*
>
> $$F_r = -\frac{GMM_E}{R^2} = -\frac{Mv_0^2}{R} \ ,$$
>
> *which implies that*
>
> $$v_0^2 = \frac{GM_E}{R} \quad \Longrightarrow \quad \boxed{v_0 = \sqrt{\frac{GM_E}{R}} \ .}$$

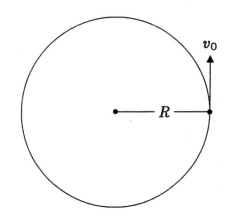

b) (*4 points*) What is the gravitational potential energy of the shuttle, relative to the potential energy it would have at infinite distance from the Earth? Again you may express your answer in terms of any of the quantities R, M, M_E, and G (Newton's constant).

> **Solution:** *In general, for point masses or spherical bodies,*
>
> $$U_{\text{grav}} = -\frac{GM_1M_2}{R} \ .$$
>
> *So, in this case*
>
> $$U_{\text{grav}} = -\frac{GMM_E}{R} - \left[-\frac{GMM_E}{\infty} \right] = \boxed{-\frac{GMM_E}{R} \ .}$$

c) (*4 points*) A cannon on the shuttle fires a probe of mass m in the direction opposite to the shuttle's velocity. After the firing, the probe has a speed Δv relative to the shuttle, where $\Delta v < v_0$. What is the speed v_1 of the probe, relative to the Earth, immediately after the firing? You may assume that no other mass is ejected in the firing of the probe. Do not assume, however, that m is negligible compared to M. You may express your answer in terms of any of the quantities R, m, M, M_E, G, v_0, and Δv.

Solution:

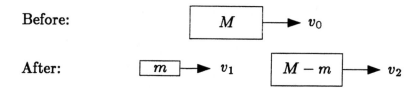

Conservation of momentum implies that

$$mv_1 + (M - m)v_2 = Mv_0 . \tag{1}$$

The condition that the relative speed is Δv implies that

$$v_2 - v_1 = \Delta v . \tag{2}$$

Thus we have two equations and two unknowns (v_1 and v_2), so the problem is reduced to algebra. From (2),

$$v_2 = \Delta v + v_1 .$$

Substituting into (1),

$$mv_1 + (M - m)(\Delta v + v_1) = Mv_0 .$$

$$\therefore Mv_1 + (M - m)\Delta v = Mv_0$$

$$\boxed{\therefore v_1 = v_0 - \frac{(M - m)\Delta v}{M} .}$$

d) (*6 points*) After being fired from the cannon, the probe will follow an elliptical orbit. Assume that it remains far enough from the Earth so that friction with the atmosphere can be ignored. Write two equations which could be solved to determine r_p and v_p, the radius and speed of the orbit at perigee, the nearest point to the center of the Earth. **Do not attempt to solve these equations.** Note that r_p is to be measured from the center of the Earth. You may express your answer in terms of any of the quantities v_1, R, m, M_E, and G.

$$\boxed{\text{DELETED FROM EXAM}}$$

Problem 6 (*12 points, after deletion*):

A piston chamber of volume V_0 is filled with an ideal monatomic gas at temperature T_0 and pressure P_0. Denote Boltzmann's constant by k, and Avogadro's number by N_A.

a) (*2 points, no partial credit*) In terms of the given quantities, what is the number N of atoms of the gas present in the chamber?

    Solution:

$$PV = NkT \implies \boxed{N = \frac{P_0 V_0}{kT_0}} .$$

b) (*2 points, no partial credit*) What is the number $\mathcal{N}$ of moles of the gas present in the chamber?

    Solution:

$$\mathcal{N} = \frac{N}{N_A} \implies \boxed{\mathcal{N} = \frac{P_0 V_0}{N_A k T_0}}$$

    or equivalently

$$PV = \mathcal{N} RT \implies \boxed{\mathcal{N} = \frac{P_0 V_0}{RT_0}} .$$

c) (*2 points, no partial credit*) The gas is allowed to expand, so the volume increases by an amount ΔV. The gas is heated while it expands by just the right amount to keep it at constant pressure P_0. How much work ΔW does the gas do during this expansion?

    Solution: In general $dW = P \, dV$, so if the pressure is constant we have

$$\boxed{\Delta W = P_0 \, \Delta V} .$$

d) (*3 points*) By what amount ΔU does the internal energy change during this expansion? Define ΔU so that a positive value denotes an increase in internal energy.

$$\boxed{\text{DELETED FROM EXAM}}$$

480

e) (*6 points*) Starting again from the initial values of $V = V_0$, $T = T_0$, and $P = P_0$, the gas is allowed to expand without the addition or emission of any heat. As the gas expands the values of T and P can both be measured as a function of V. Find an expression for $\dfrac{dP}{dV}$ that depends on no variables other than P and V.

Solution: *From the first law of thermodynamics,*

$$dU = dQ - P\,dV \ ,$$

but in this case we are told that no heat is transferred, so $dQ = 0$. It follows that

$$dU = -P\,dV, \ or \ \frac{dU}{dV} = -P \ .$$

For an ideal monatomic gas, we also know that

$$U = N\left\langle \frac{1}{2}mv^2 \right\rangle = \frac{3}{2}PV \ .$$

Differentiating this expression gives

$$\frac{dU}{dV} = \frac{3}{2}P + \frac{3}{2}V\frac{dP}{dV} \ .$$

Equating the two expressions for $\dfrac{dU}{dV}$,

$$\frac{3}{2}P + \frac{3}{2}V\frac{dP}{dV} = -P \ ,$$

so

$$\frac{3}{2}V\frac{dP}{dV} = -\frac{5}{2}P \ ,$$

and

$$\boxed{\frac{dP}{dV} = -\frac{5}{3}\frac{P}{V} \ .}$$

Problem 7 (*18 points*):

A uniform disk of mass M and radius R is oriented in a vertical plane. The y axis is vertical, and the x axis is horizontal. The disk is pivoted about the origin of the coordinate system, with the center of the disk hanging a distance h below the pivot, as shown. The disk is free to rotate without friction about the pivot in the x-y plane. The magnitude of the acceleration of gravity is g, directed in the negative y direction.

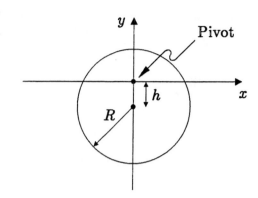

a) (*4 points*) If the disk is rotated by an angle θ from its equilibrium position, as shown, what is the magnitude of the torque about the pivot? (In this part, do not assume that the angle θ is necessarily small.)

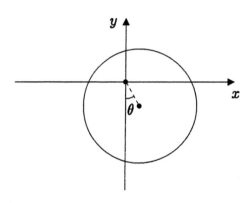

Solution:

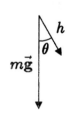

In general,

$$\vec{\tau} = \vec{r} \times \vec{F} .$$

In this case the force is gravity, Mg downward, which can be taken to act on the center of mass. From the diagram,

$$\boxed{|\vec{\tau}| = Mgh\sin\theta ,}$$

where by right-hand rule $\boxed{\text{the direction is into the page.}}$ *Expressed alternatively in components,*

$$\boxed{\vec{\tau} = [0, 0, -Mgh\sin\theta] .}$$

482

b) (*4 points*) What is the moment of inertia I of the disk about the pivoted axis?

> **Solution:** *This problem can be answered by using the parallel axis theorem. The moment of inertia of a uniform disk about its central axis is given in the table at the start of the exam as*
>
> $$I_{\text{cm}} = \frac{1}{2} M R^2 \ .$$
>
> *By the parallel axis theorem, the moment of inertia about a parallel axis separated by a distance h from the central axis is given by*
>
> $$I = I_{\text{cm}} + M h^2 \ ,$$

so

$$\boxed{I = M \left(\frac{1}{2} R^2 + h^2 \right) \ .}$$

c) (*4 points*) If the disk is allowed to oscillate about its equilibrium position, what will be the period of small oscillations? Your answer may be written in terms of I, whether or not you answered the previous part.

> **Solution:** *The disk is pivoted about the z axis, so the equation of motion is*
>
> $$I\alpha = \tau_z = -Mgh \sin\theta \ .$$

To discuss small oscillations, we approximate $\sin\theta \approx \theta$, *so*

$$\alpha = \frac{d^2\theta}{dt^2} = -\frac{Mgh}{I}\theta \ .$$

To put this into the standard form we define

$$\omega^2 \equiv \frac{Mgh}{I} \ , \quad so \quad \frac{d^2\theta}{dt^2} = -\omega^2\theta \ .$$

As listed in the Formula Sheet, this equation has the solution $\theta = A\sin\omega t$, *where A is any constant. The sine function has a period of* 2π, *so* θ *will go through one full cycle in a time T, where* $\omega T = 2\pi$. *So*

$$T = \frac{2\pi}{\omega} = \boxed{2\pi\sqrt{\frac{I}{Mgh}} \ .}$$

d) (*6 points*) A ball of putty of mass m collides with the disk from the right, hitting it at the point $[R, -h, 0]$, as shown. At the moment just before the impact, the ball of putty has a velocity $\vec{v} = [-v_0, 0, 0]$, and the disk is at rest. If the putty sticks to the side of the disk, what will be its velocity vector $\vec{v}_f$ immediately after the collision?

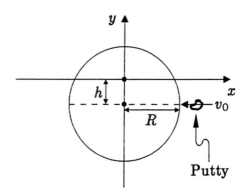

Solution: *The collision is inelastic, so mechanical energy is not conserved. The pivot will exert a force to prevent the axis of rotation of the disk from moving, so momentum is also not conserved. But nothing in the problem can exert a torque about the axis of rotation, so angular momentum about the axis is conserved.*

The angular momentum of the putty is given by $\vec{L} = \vec{r} \times \vec{p}$, where $\vec{r}$ is the displacement vector from the origin (the point about which the angular momentum is to be computed), and $\vec{p}$ is the momentum. Right-hand rule shows that the direction is into the page. $|\vec{L}| = pr\sin\theta = pr^{\perp}$, where $r^{\perp} = r\sin\theta$ is the component of $\vec{r}$ in the direction perpendicular to $\vec{p}$. $r^{\perp}$ can be described as the length of a line which extends from the point about which the torque is calculated to the line along which the object is moving, intersecting the line at a right angle. In this case, that line has length $r^{\perp} = h$, so

$$\vec{L} = [0, 0, -mv_0 h] \ .$$

After the collision the putty and disk will move together. Since the putty is at a distance $\sqrt{h^2 + R^2}$ from the origin, the total moment of inertia will be

$$I_{\text{tot}} = I + m(h^2 + R^2) \ .$$

Conservation of angular momentum implies that the angular velocity just after the collision, ω_f, can be found from

$$L_z = I_{\text{tot}}\omega_f = -mv_0 h \quad \Longrightarrow \quad \omega_f = -\frac{mv_0 h}{I + m(h^2 + R^2)} \ .$$

The velocity of the putty can be found from

$$\vec{v}_f = \vec{\omega}_f \times \vec{r} = \left[0, 0, -\frac{mv_0 h}{I + m(h^2 + R^2)}\right] \times [R, -h, 0] \ .$$

Using the component definition of the cross product from the Formula Sheet, one has finally,

$$\boxed{\vec{v}_f = -\frac{mv_0 h}{I + m(h^2 + R^2)}[h, R, 0] \ .}$$

Department of Physics

FINAL EXAMINATION
FORMULA SHEET
Monday, December 18, 2000

$\frac{1}{2}mv^2 + U(x) = \text{constant}$ (energy conservation)

$W = K_f - K_i$ (work-energy theorem)

$U = \frac{1}{2}kx^2$ (potential energy for spring force)

$U = mgh$ (gravitational potential energy, near Earth)

$U = -\dfrac{GMm}{r}$ (gravitational potential energy, spherical bodies)

1 Dimension	3 Dimensions	Description
$W = F\Delta x$	$W = \vec{F}\cdot\Delta\vec{r}$	Work done by a constant force $\vec{F}$
$W = \int F(x)\,dx$	$W = \int_{\vec{r}_1}^{\vec{r}_2}\vec{F}\cdot d\vec{r}$	Work done by a varying force $\vec{F}$
$U(x_p) = U_0 - \int_{x_0}^{x_p} F\,dx$	$U(\vec{r}_p) = U_0 - \int_{\vec{r}_0}^{\vec{r}_p}\vec{F}\cdot d\vec{r}$	Potential energy derived from force $\vec{F}$
$F = -\dfrac{dU}{dx}$	$\vec{F} = \left[-\dfrac{\partial U}{\partial x}, \dfrac{\partial U}{\partial y}, \dfrac{\partial U}{\partial z}\right]$	Force derived from potential energy

Equations introduced in Chapter 5:

$\vec{F}_{AB} = -\vec{F}_{BA}$ (Newton's third law);

$\vec{p} = m\vec{v}$ (momentum);

$\dfrac{d\vec{P}_{tot}}{dt} = 0$ (conservation of momentum in absence of external force);

$\vec{F} = \dfrac{d\vec{p}}{dt}$ (Newton's second law in terms of momentum);

$\vec{r}_{cm} = \dfrac{1}{M_{tot}}\sum_i m_i\vec{r}_i$ (position of center of mass);

$\vec{v}_{cm} = \dfrac{d\vec{r}_{cm}}{dt} = \dfrac{1}{M_{tot}}\sum_i m_i\vec{v}_i$ (velocity of center of mass);

$\vec{F}_{tot}^{ext} = M_{tot}\vec{a}_{cm} = \dfrac{d\vec{P}_{tot}}{dt}$ (acceleration of a system of particles);

$\vec{P}_{tot} = \sum_i m_i\vec{v}_i = M_{tot}\vec{v}_{cm}$ (momentum of a system of particles);

$K_{tot} = \dfrac{1}{2}M_{tot}v_{cm}^2 + \sum_i \dfrac{1}{2}m_i(\vec{v}_i - \vec{v}_{cm})^2$ (K.E. of a system of particles);

$\vec{J} = \int_{t_1}^{t_2}\vec{F}\,dt = \int_{t_1}^{t_2}\dfrac{d\vec{p}}{dt}\,dt = \vec{p}_2 - \vec{p}_1$ (impulse-momentum theorem).

Equations introduced in Chapter 1:

$\vec{v} = \dfrac{d\vec{r}}{dt}$; $\quad \vec{a} = \dfrac{d\vec{v}}{dt} = \dfrac{d^2\vec{r}}{dt^2}$; $\quad \vec{r}(t_1) = \vec{r}_0 + \int_0^{t_1}\vec{v}\,dt$; $\quad \vec{v}(t_1) = \vec{v}_0 + \int_0^{t_1}\vec{a}\,dt$.

For *constant* acceleration $\vec{a}$, if $\vec{r} = \vec{r}_0$ and $\vec{v} = \vec{v}_0$ at time $t=0$, then

$$\vec{v}(t) = \vec{v}_0 + \vec{a}t$$
$$\vec{r}(t) = \vec{r}_0 + \vec{v}_0 t + \frac{1}{2}\vec{a}t^2.$$

For one-dimensional motion with constant acceleration a:

$$v^2 = v_0^2 + 2a(x - x_0).$$

For circular motion at constant speed v:

$$a = \frac{v^2}{r},$$

where r is the radius of the circle, and the acceleration is directed towards the center of the circle.

If an object has position $\vec{r}$ and velocity $\vec{v}$, its position and velocity relative to an observer with position $\vec{r}_0$ and velocity $\vec{v}_0$ are given respectively by

$$\vec{r}' = \vec{r} - \vec{r}_0, \qquad \vec{v}' = \vec{v} - \vec{v}_0.$$

Average velocity and acceleration are given by

$$\vec{v}_{average} = \frac{\Delta\vec{r}}{\Delta t}, \qquad \vec{a}_{average} = \frac{\Delta\vec{v}}{\Delta t}.$$

Equations introduced in Chapter 2:

$\vec{F} = m\vec{a}$ (Newton's second law);

$\vec{F} = -\dfrac{GMm}{r^2}\hat{r}$ (the gravitational force between two particles);

$\vec{F} = \dfrac{1}{4\pi\epsilon_0}\dfrac{Qq}{r^2}\hat{r}$ (the electrostatic force between two particles);

$F_x = -kx$ (Hooke's law);

$\dfrac{d^2x}{dt^2} = -\omega^2 x$ (for a particle near a point of stable equilibrium; equation leads to simple harmonic motion);

$x = A\sin\omega t$ (a solution to the above equation; any solution can be written this way if we choose $t=0$ when $x=0$);

$\omega = 2\pi f$ (relation between angular frequency and frequency);

$T = \dfrac{1}{f} = \dfrac{2\pi}{\omega}$ (period of an oscillator).

Equations introduced in Chapter 4:

$\vec{a}\cdot\vec{b} = |\vec{a}||\vec{b}|\cos\theta$ (scalar (or dot) product of two vectors)

$\phantom{\vec{a}\cdot\vec{b}} = a_x b_x + a_y b_y + a_z b_z$

$\frac{1}{2}mv^2 + mgh = \frac{1}{2}mv_0^2$ (kinetic & potential energy for projectile)

485

Slender uniform rod of length ℓ, axis through center and perpendicular to axis of rod	$\frac{1}{12}m\ell^2$
Rectangular plate with dimensions $a \times b$, axis along one of the b edges	$\frac{1}{3}ma^2$
Thin-walled hollow cylinder of radius R, axis along axis of cylinder	mR^2
Uniform solid cylinder of radius R, axis along axis of cylinder	$\frac{1}{2}mR^2$
Thin-walled hollow sphere of radius R, axis through center	$\frac{2}{3}mR^2$
Solid uniform sphere of radius R, axis through center	$\frac{2}{5}mR^2$

Equations introduced in Chapter 9:

$c_x = a_y b_z - a_z b_y$;
$c_y = a_z b_x - a_x b_z$;
$c_z = a_x b_y - a_y b_x$.   (vector cross product, component form);

$|\vec{c}| = |\vec{a}||\vec{b}|\sin\theta$ (magnitude of vector cross product);

$\vec{v} = \vec{\omega} \times \vec{r}$ (velocity of atom in rotating body with a fixed point);

$\vec{v} = \vec{v}_P + \vec{\omega} \times (\vec{r} - \vec{r}_P)$ (velocity of atom in rotating body, general case);

$\vec{L} = \sum_i \vec{r}_i \times \vec{p}_i$ (angular momentum, as vector product);

$\vec{\tau} = \sum_i \vec{r}_i \times \vec{F}_i$ (vector torque, as vector product);

$\vec{\tau} = \dfrac{d\vec{L}}{dt}$ (torque equation);

$\left. \begin{array}{l} \sum \vec{F}^{ext} = M\vec{a}_{cm} = \dfrac{d\vec{p}}{dt} \\[6pt] \sum \vec{\tau}^{ext} = \dfrac{d\vec{L}_{cm}}{dt} \end{array} \right\}$ (combined translational and rotational motion);

$\vec{L} = \vec{r}_{cm} \times \vec{p}_{tot} + \sum_i \vec{r}_{rel,i} \times m_i \vec{v}_{rel,i}$ (angular momentum decomposition);

$\vec{\tau} = \vec{r}_{cm} \times \vec{F}_{tot} + \sum_i \vec{r}_{rel,i} \times \vec{F}_i$ (torque decomposition).

Equations introduced in Chapter 6:

$|\vec{F}_k| = \mu_k|\vec{N}|$;   (kinetic friction);

$|\vec{F}_s| \le \mu_s|\vec{N}|$;   (static friction);

$\vec{F}_{fict} = -m\vec{a}(t)$ (fictitious force in linearly accelerating frame).

Equations introduced in Chapter 8:

Most of the equations in this chapter are most easily remembered in the context of the analogous equations for linear motion in one dimension:

TRANSLATION (one dimension)		ROTATION (about fixed axis)	
Name	Symbol	Name	Symbol
Position	x	Orientation	θ
Velocity	$v = \dfrac{dx}{dt}$	Angular velocity	$\omega = \dfrac{d\theta}{dt}$
Acceleration	$a = \dfrac{dv}{dt}$	Angular acceleration	$\alpha = \dfrac{d\omega}{dt}$
Mass	$M = \sum_i m_i$	Moment of inertia	$I = \sum_i m_i R_i^2$
Force	F	Torque	$\tau = F_\perp R$ $= \pm|\vec{F}|R_\perp$
Force equation	$\sum_i \vec{F}^{ext} = M\vec{a}_{cm}$	Torque equation	$\sum_i \tau^{ext} = I\alpha$
Momentum	$p = Mv$	Angular momentum	$L = I\omega$
Kinetic energy	$\frac{1}{2}Mv^2$	Kinetic energy	$\frac{1}{2}I\omega^2$
Work done	$\vec{F}\cdot\vec{\Delta r}$	Work done	$\tau\,\Delta\theta$

Other equations introduced in this chapter:

$v_r = 0$; $v_\perp = R\omega$ (velocity of point on rotating body);

$a_r = -\dfrac{v^2}{R} = -R\omega^2$; $a_\perp = R\alpha$ (acceleration of point on rotating body);

$v = \pm R|\omega|$ (rolling without slipping);

$\left. \begin{array}{l} \sum \vec{F}^{ext} = M\vec{a}_{cm} = \dfrac{d\vec{p}}{dt} \\[6pt] \sum \tau^{ext} = I_{cm}\alpha = \dfrac{dL}{dt} \end{array} \right\}$ (combined translational and rotational motion);

$K_{tot} = \frac{1}{2}Mv_{cm}^2 + \frac{1}{2}I_{cm}\omega^2$ (kinetic energy for combined translational and rotational motion);

$I_\parallel = I_{cm} + Md^2$ (parallel-axis theorem);

$I_z = I_x + I_y$ (perpendicular-axis theorem).

Equations introduced in Chapter 11:

$$PV = \frac{2}{3}N\left\langle \frac{1}{2}mv^2 \right\rangle \quad \text{(pressure of an ideal gas);}$$

$$\left\langle \frac{1}{2}mv^2 \right\rangle = \frac{3}{2}kT \quad \text{(definition of kinetic temperature);}$$

$$PV = NkT = NRT \quad \text{(ideal-gas law);}$$

$$\Delta U = Q - W \quad \text{(first law of thermodynamics);}$$

$$\Delta W = P\Delta V \quad \text{(work done by expanding gas).}$$

* Useful constants:

$$R = 8.3 \text{ J/mol} \cdot \text{K} \qquad \text{(gas constant);}$$

$$k = 1.38 \times 10^{-23} \text{ J/K} \qquad \text{(Boltzmann's constant);}$$

$$N_A = 6.02 \times 10^{23} \text{ molecules/mole} \quad \text{(Avogadro's number);}$$

$$1 \text{ u} = 1.66 \times 10^{-27} \text{ kg} \qquad \text{(atomic mass unit).}$$

* Temperature scales:

$$T(\text{K}) = T(°\text{C}) + 273.15 \text{ K} \quad \text{(Centigrade to Kelvin)}$$

$$T(°\text{F}) = 32°\text{F} + \frac{9}{5}T(°\text{C}) \quad \text{(Centigrade to Fahrenheit)}$$

$$T(°\text{C}) = \frac{5}{9}(T(°\text{F}) - 32°\text{F}) \quad \text{(Fahrenheit to Centigrade)}$$

The triple point of water corresponds to 273.16 K, or 0.01°C, by definition.

Equations introduced in Chapter 12:

$$P_2 - P_1 = -\rho g(y_2 - y_1) \quad \text{[Pascal's Law: pressure in a liquid as a function of height, for a stationary liquid);}$$

$$A_2 v_2 = A_1 v_1 \quad \text{(equation of continuity for steady flow);}$$

$$P + \frac{1}{2}\rho v^2 + \rho g y = \text{constant} \quad \text{(Bernoulli's equation);}$$

$$\gamma = \frac{F}{\ell} = \frac{U}{A} \quad \text{(surface tension).}$$

Physics 8.01   Fall 2000

FINAL EXAM
MONDAY, December 18, 2000

FAMILY (Last) NAME

GIVEN (First) NAME

Student ID Number

Your Recitation (check one) →

Instructions:

1. SHOW ALL WORK. All work must be done in this booklet. Extra blank pages are provided.
2. This is a closed book exam.
3. CALCULATORS, BOOKS, and NOTES are NOT ALLOWED.
4. Do all TEN (10) problems.

Yellow Formula Sheets for this exam will be handed out separately.

Problem	Maximum	Score	Grader
1	10		
2	10		
3	10		
4	10		
5	10		
6	10		
7	10		
8	10		
9	10		
10	10		
TOTAL	100		

R01	MW 1:00	W. Bertozzi	
R02	MW 2:00	W. Bertozzi	
R03	MW 3:00	W. Bertozzi	
R12	TR 1:00	A. Bolton	
R18	TR 9:00	B. Burke	
R19	TR 10:00	B. Burke	
R20	TR 11:00	B. Burke	
R21	TR 2:00	M. Evans	
R22	TR 3:00	M. Evans	
R06	MW 2:00	M. Feld	
R07	MW 3:00	M. Feld	
R08	MW 4:00	M. Feld	
R16	TR 11:00	D. Fernie	
R15	TR 10:00	A. Guth	
R23	TR 11:00	J. Hager	
R24	TR 12:00	J. Hager	
R09	MW 1:00	P. Joss	
R10	MW 2:00	P. Joss	
R11	MW 3:00	P. Joss	
R26(M)	TR 3:00	McBride/Bove	
R17	TR 12:00	TA- Ribeiro	
R13	TR 2:00	J. Shelton	
R14	TR 3:00	J. Shelton	
R04	MW 1:00	G. Stephans	
R05	MW 2:00	G. Stephans	

488

Problem 1 (10 points, no partial credit)

At a location where the acceleration due to gravity is 10 m/s^2, a 2 kg ball is dropped from rest in vacuum at $t = 0$. On the scale below, indicate the vertical position of the ball at one second intervals after the ball is released (i.e., at $t = 1$s, 2s, 3s, ...) until it falls off of the scale.

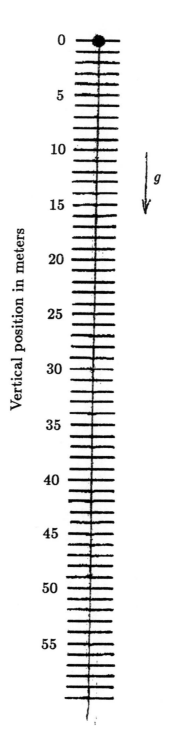

Problem 2 (10 points)

You are walking on a horizontal road. At some instant of time you accelerate forward. Your acceleration has magnitude a. Your mass is M.

a) In words, state what forces are acting on you and which force causes the acceleration.

b) What is the magnitude of that force?

Problem 3 (10 points)

The diagram shows a Venturi meter installed in a water main. The pipe has a circular cross section at all points, with diameter D_1 in the first segment and D_2 in the second segment, with $D_2 < D_1$. The mass density of the water is ρ, and the acceleration of gravity is g ($g > 0$). If the water in the pipe is flowing at volume flow rate R (measured, for example, in m^3/s), what is:

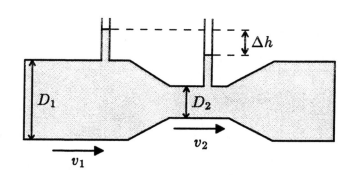

a) the speed of flow v_1 in the first section of pipe (of diameter D_1), and the speed of flow v_2 in the second section of pipe (of diameter D_2)?

b) the difference in the water level Δh in the two tubes?

Problem 4 (10 points)

A monatomic ideal gas, originally at a pressure P, volume V and temperature T, is compressed to one half of its initial volume.

A) If the compression is isothermal (i.e., at constant temperature)

   a) The final pressure is:

      i) P ii) $2P$ iii) $3P$ iv) $4P$ v) $5P$

      vi) $P/2$ vii) $P/3$ viii) $P/4$ ix) $P/5$

   b) The work done **by the gas** during the compression is:

      i) $-PV \ln 2$ ii) $PV \ln 2$ iii) $-\frac{P}{V} \ln 2$ iv) $\frac{P}{V} \ln 2$ v) $-2PV$

      vi) $2PV$ vii) $-2\frac{PV}{T}$ viii) $2\frac{PV}{T}$ ix) $-\frac{PV}{2T}$

      ix) $\frac{PV}{2T}$

B) If the compression is isobaric (i.e., at constant pressure)

   a) The final temperature is:

      i) $T/2$ ii) $2T$ iii) $T/4$ iv) $4T$ v) $T \ln 2$

      vi) $T/\ln 2$ vii) $T \ln 4$ viii) $T/\ln 4$

   b) The amount of heat supplied **to the gas** during the compression is :

      i) $-\frac{1}{4}PV$ ii) $\frac{1}{4}PV$ iii) $-\frac{1}{2}PV$ iv) $\frac{1}{2}PV$ v) $-\frac{3}{4}PV$

      vi) $\frac{3}{4}PV$ vii) $-\frac{5}{4}PV$ viii) $\frac{5}{4}PV$ ix) $-\frac{11}{4}PV$

      ix) $\frac{11}{4}PV$

Problem 5 (10 points)

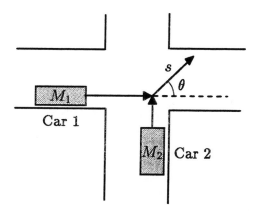

Two cars collide at an intersection. They remain locked together after the collision and travel a distance s, at an angle θ to car 1's original direction. Car 1 has mass M_1 and car 2 has mass M_2. The accident happened in conditions when the coefficient of kinetic friction between rubber and the road is μ_k. What were the speeds of the two cars immediately before the collision?

You may assume that the acceleration due to gravity is g, and that the force of the collision causes the wheels of the cars to immediately lock, so that the rotation of wheels can be ignored.

Problem 6 (10 points)

A uniform plank of wood with mass M and length ℓ rests against the top of a free standing wall which has height h and a frictionless top. The plank makes an angle θ with the horizontal.

a) On the picture on the right, draw a free body diagram for the plank.

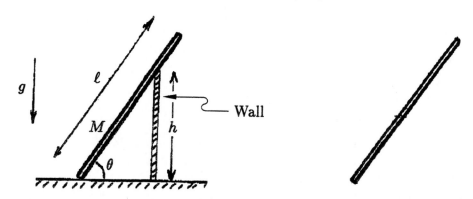

b) In the boxes below, write a complete set of independent equations which when solved give the minimum value of θ for which the plank will not slip. Express your equations in terms of only M, ℓ, h, g, and μ_s, the coefficient of static friction between the plank and the floor. Do not solve the equations.

Note: The number of equations you write could depend on how you have defined your variables, so some correct answers will not fill all boxes.

Problem 7 (10 points)

A ball is placed on a vertical massless spring which obeys Hooke's Law and which initially has its natural uncompressed length. It is observed that at first the ball makes vertical simple harmonic oscillations with period T.

After a very large number of oscillations the ball comes to rest because of air resistance and losses in the spring. What is the final compression of the spring in terms of *only* T and g.

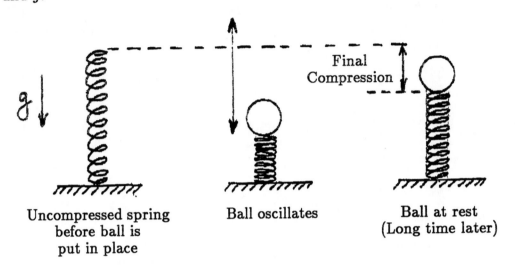

Uncompressed spring
before ball is
put in place

Ball oscillates

Ball at rest
(Long time later)

Problem 8 (10 points)

You have been given a nugget which you are told is a mixture of gold and zinc. You want to find out how much gold you have been given. Being an MIT student you make the following observations:

1. You put a cup partly full of water on an electronic (weight) scale and observe that it reads M_1, meaning that the force on the scale is equivalent to the gravitational force of a mass M_1.

2. You attach the nugget to a very thin stiff piece of wire and hold the nugget in the water fully submerged but not touching the bottom of the cup. The water does not overflow. You observe that the scale now reads M_2.

3. You remove the wire and drop the nugget into the cup. No water is spilled. The scale now reads M_3.

4. In a reference book you find that gold has a density ρ_{Au}, zinc ρ_{Zn}, and water ρ_{H_2O}.

Using these observations determine

   a) the volume of the nugget

   b) the mass of the nugget

   c) the mass of the gold in the nugget.

Problem 9 (10 points)

A uniform disk of mass M_1 and radius R is pivoted on a frictionless horizontal axle through its center.

a) A small mass M_2 is attached to the disk at radius $R/2$, at the same height as the axle. If this system is released from rest:

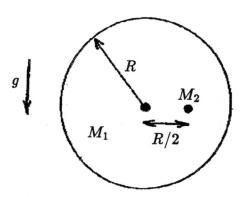

    i) What is the angular acceleration of the disk immediately after it is released?

    ii) What will be the magnitude of the maximum angular velocity that the disk will reach?

b) Now consider the situation if the mass M_2 is a disk of radius $R/2$ located with its center at the same place where M_2 is located in part (a). For this case, find the angular acceleration immediately after the system is released from rest.

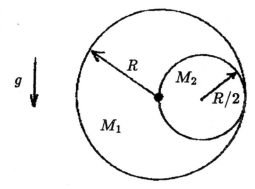

Problem 10 (10 points)

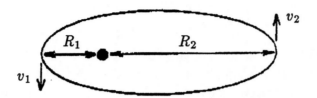

A satellite follows an elliptical orbit. Its closest approach to the earth is R_1, at which point it has speed v_1, and the furthest point is R_2, at which point it has speed v_2. Both distances are measured from the center of the earth. At the surface of the earth the acceleration due to gravity is g and the earth's radius is R.

What is the magnitude of v_1 in terms of **only** R_1, R_2, R and g?

MASSACHUSETTS INSTITUTE OF TECHNOLOGY

Department of Physics

Physics 8.01   Fall 2000

FINAL EXAM SOLUTIONS
MONDAY, December 18, 2000

FAMILY (Last) NAME

GIVEN (First) NAME

Solutions written by Alan Guth

Student ID Number

Your Recitation (check one) →

Instructions:

1. SHOW ALL WORK. All work must be done in this booklet. Extra blank pages are provided.
2. This is a closed book exam.
3. CALCULATORS, BOOKS, and NOTES are NOT ALLOWED.
4. Do all TEN (10) problems.

New Formula Sheets for this exam will be handed out separately.

Problem	Maximum	Score	Grader
1	10		
2	10		
3	10		
4	10		
5	10		
6	10		
7	10		
8	10		
9	10		
10	10		
TOTAL	100		

R01	MW 1:00	W. Bertozzi	
R02	MW 2:00	W. Bertozzi	
R03	MW 3:00	W. Bertozzi	
R12	TR 1:00	A. Bolton	
R18	TR 9:00	B. Burke	
R19	TR 10:00	B. Burke	
R20	TR 11:00	B. Burke	
R21	TR 2:00	M. Evans	
R22	TR 3:00	M. Evans	
R06	MW 2:00	M. Feld	
R07	MW 3:00	M. Feld	
R08	MW 4:00	M. Feld	
R16	TR 11:00	D. Fernie	
R15	TR 10:00	A. Guth	
R23	TR 11:00	J. Hager	
R24	TR 12:00	J. Hager	
R09	MW 1:00	P. Joss	
R10	MW 2:00	P. Joss	
R11	MW 3:00	P. Joss	
R26(M)	TR 3:00	McBride/Bove	
R17	TR 12:00	TA- Ribeiro	
R13	TR 2:00	J. Shelton	
R14	TR 3:00	J. Shelton	
R04	MW 1:00	G. Stephans	
R05	MW 2:00	G. Stephans	

499

Note: this exam included a 6-page formula sheet, which can be downloaded separately.

Problem 1 (10 points, no partial credit)

At a location where the acceleration due to gravity is 10 m/s^2, a 2 kg ball is dropped from rest in vacuum at $t = 0$. On the scale below, indicate the vertical position of the ball at one second intervals after the ball is released (i.e., at $t = 1$ s, 2 s, 3 s, ...) until it falls off of the scale.

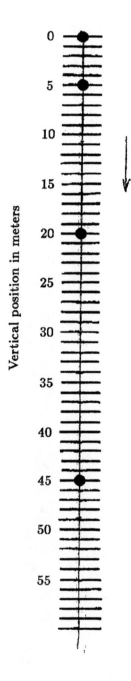

$$s = \tfrac{1}{2}gt^2 = 5\,\mathrm{m}\,(t/\mathrm{s})^2$$

t	s
1 s	5 m
2 s	20 m
3 s	45 m
4 s	80 m

Problem 2 (10 points)

You are walking on a horizontal road. At some instant of time you accelerate forward. Your acceleration has magnitude a. Your mass is M.

a) In words, state what forces are acting on you and which force causes the acceleration.

b) What is the magnitude of that force?

Solution:

a) The forces are that of gravity acting downward, the normal force of the road acting upward, and the force of friction acting forward. It is the force of friction that causes the acceleration.

b) Since $\vec{F} = M\vec{a}$, the magnitude of the frictional force must be

$$\left| \vec{F}_{friction} \right| = Ma \ .$$

Problem 3 (10 points)

The diagram shows a Venturi meter installed in a water main. The pipe has a circular cross section at all points, with diameter D_1 in the first segment and D_2 in the second segment, with $D_2 < D_1$. The mass density of the water is ρ, and the acceleration of gravity is g ($g > 0$). If the water in the pipe is flowing at volume flow rate R (measured, for example, in m^3/s), what is:

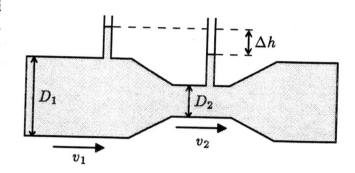

a) the speed of flow v_1 in the first section of pipe (of diameter D_1), and the speed of flow v_2 in the second section of pipe (of diameter D_2)?

b) the difference in the water level Δh in the two tubes?

Solution:

a) The volume flow rate R is constant throughout the pipe and is given by the product of the cross sectional area A of the pipe and the speed of the flow v. Hence

$$v_1 = \frac{R}{A_1} = \boxed{\frac{4R}{\pi D_1^2}} \, , \quad v_2 = \boxed{\frac{4R}{\pi D_2^2}} \, .$$

b) First, we use Bernoulli's equation to relate the pressures P_1 and P_2 at the center of the pipe in the regions of large and small cross sections

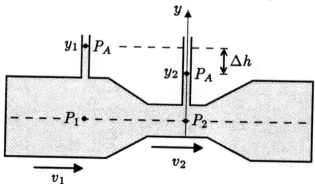

$$P_1 + \frac{1}{2}\rho v_1^2 = P_2 + \frac{1}{2}\rho v_2^2 \implies P_1 - P_2 = \frac{1}{2}\rho\left(v_2^2 - v_1^2\right) \ .$$

We have defined the vertical y-coordinate to be zero at the center of the pipe. Now we use Pascal's law to relate the pressures P_1 and P_2 to the pressure P_A at the heights y_1 and y_2 of the water levels in the two tubes. Since the two tubes are in contact with the surrounding air, the pressure at the top of either column of liquid is just the ambient air pressure P_A. We find

$$P_1 = P_A + \rho g y_1, \ P_2 = P_A + \rho g y_2 \implies$$

$$\Delta h = y_1 - y_2 = \frac{P_1 - P_2}{\rho g} = \frac{v_2^2 - v_1^2}{2g} = \boxed{\frac{8R^2}{\pi^2 g}\left(\frac{1}{D_2^4} - \frac{1}{D_1^4}\right)} \ .$$

Note on subtle point: In this problem one has to be careful about where to apply Bernoulli's equation, and where to use Pascal's law. The correct solution uses Bernoulli's equation to find the pressure differences along the flow line through the center of the pipe, but Pascal's law must be used to find how the pressure varies with height.

Along the y-axis, for example, Pascal's law says that the pressure should vary according to

$$P(y) = P_2 - \rho g y \ ,$$

where ρ is the density of water and g is the acceleration of gravity. Note that Bernoulli's equation would give a different result, since it would imply that

$$P(y) + \frac{1}{2}\rho v^2(y) + \rho g y \underset{\substack{\text{(If Bernoulli's eq}\\\text{were valid)}}}{=} P_2 + \frac{1}{2}\rho v_2^2 \ .$$

The two equations agree when $v(y) = v_2$, a relation which holds inside the horizontal pipe but not in the vertical pipes (where $v \approx 0$).

To understand which equation is valid, we need to examine the behavior of the water where its velocity v changes, at the interface of the horizontal and vertical pipes. While the actual flow of water at such an interface can be complicated, for our purposes we can approximate the change in the water velocity as happening discontinuously along a horizontal line:

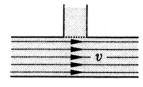

Recall that the derivation of Bernoulli's equation showed that the Bernoulli quantity is constant along flow lines. Since there are no flow lines that cross the dotted line along the velocity discontinuity, we can see that there is no reason to believe that the Bernoulli quantity has the same value on both sides. Pascal's equation, on the other hand, was derived by examining the forces on the water in the vertical direction. Since the vertical acceleration of the water is zero both above and below the dotted line, the derivation of Pascal's equation remains valid. The pressure varies continuously across the dotted line, while the velocity and the Bernoulli quantity undergo a jump at the dotted line.

Note, however, that Bernoulli's equation does describe the pressure variation along the flow lines of a pipe, even when those flow lines are vertical. In that case the derivation of Pascal's equation can break down, since the vertically flowing liquid can undergo acceleration in the vertical direction, if the pipe changes diameter.

Problem 4 (10 points)

A monatomic ideal gas, originally at a pressure P, volume V and temperature T, is compressed to one half of its initial volume.

A) If the compression is isothermal (i.e., at constant temperature)

 a) The final pressure is:

   i) P ii) $2P$ iii) $3P$ iv) $4P$ v) $5P$

   vi) $P/2$ vii) $P/3$ viii) $P/4$ ix) $P/5$

 b) The work done **by the gas** during the compression is:

   i) $-PV \ln 2$ ii) $PV \ln 2$ iii) $-\frac{P}{V} \ln 2$ iv) $\frac{P}{V} \ln 2$ v) $-2PV$

   vi) $2PV$ vii) $-2\frac{PV}{T}$ viii) $2\frac{PV}{T}$ ix) $-\frac{PV}{2T}$

   ix) $\frac{PV}{2T}$

B) If the compression is isobaric (i.e., at constant pressure)

 a) The final temperature is:

   i) $T/2$ ii) $2T$ iii) $T/4$ iv) $4T$ v) $T \ln 2$

   vi) $T/\ln 2$ vii) $T \ln 4$ viii) $T/\ln 4$

 b) The amount of heat supplied **to the gas** during the compression is:

   i) $-\frac{1}{4}PV$ ii) $\frac{1}{4}PV$ iii) $-\frac{1}{2}PV$ iv) $\frac{1}{2}PV$ v) $-\frac{3}{4}PV$

   vi) $\frac{3}{4}PV$ vii) $-\frac{5}{4}PV$ viii) $\frac{5}{4}PV$ ix) $-\frac{11}{4}PV$

   ix) $\frac{11}{4}PV$

Solution:

A) a) Since $PV = NkT$, *constant temperature implies that* $P \propto 1/V$. *So if* V *is halved,* P *is doubled. The correct answer is* $\boxed{(ii)\ 2P.}$

 b) Since the pressure is changing, we must integrate to find the total work done:

$$W = \int P \, dV \ .$$

Since $P \propto 1/V$, we can write $P = P_0(V_0/V)$, where P_0 and V_0 denote the original pressure and volume. So

$$W = P_0 V_0 \int_{V_0}^{\frac{1}{2}V_0} \frac{dV}{V} = P_0 V_0 \left[\ln\left(\frac{1}{2}V_0\right) - \ln V_0 \right] = -P_0 V_0 \ln 2 \; .$$

Since the problem called the initial values of pressure and volume P and V, respectively, the right answer is $\boxed{(i) \; -PV \ln 2.}$

B) a) For isobaric expansion (constant pressure), $PV = NkT$ implies that $T \propto V$. So, if the volume is halved, then the temperature must be halved, and the correct answer is $\boxed{(i) \; T/2.}$

b) First we must calculate the work done by the gas. Since the pressure is constant, this is simply

$$W = P \, \Delta V = -\frac{1}{2}PV \; .$$

Next we must calculate the change in the internal energy of the gas. For a monatomic ideal gas, the internal energy is given by

$$U = N \left\langle \frac{1}{2}mv^2 \right\rangle = \frac{3}{2}NkT = \frac{3}{2}PV \; .$$

During the compression the temperature falls by a factor of 2, so the internal energy also falls by a factor of 2, and therefore

$$\Delta U = -\frac{3}{4}NkT = -\frac{3}{4}PV \; .$$

By conservation of energy,
$$\Delta U = Q - W \; ,$$

so the heat Q supplied to the gas is given by

$$Q = \Delta U + W = -\frac{5}{4}PV \; .$$

The correct answer is therefore $\boxed{(vii) \; -\frac{5}{4}PV.}$

506

Problem 5 (10 points)

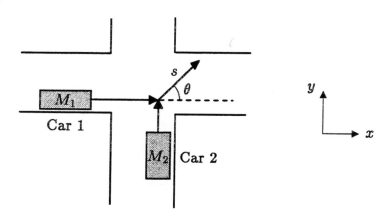

Two cars collide at an intersection. They remain locked together after the collision and travel a distance s, at an angle θ to car 1's original direction. Car 1 has mass M_1 and car 2 has mass M_2. The accident happened in conditions when the coefficient of kinetic friction between rubber and the road is μ_k. What were the speeds of the two cars immediately before the collision?

You may assume that the acceleration due to gravity is g, and that the force of the collision causes the wheels of the cars to immediately lock, so that the rotation of wheels can be ignored.

Solution: *We treat the sequence of events as an instantaneous collision followed by a period of skidding. During the skidding phase, the only horizontal force acting is that of kinetic friction, which has a magnitude $F_f = \mu_k(M_1 + M_2)g$. This force directly opposes the motion, so the work done by friction is $W = \vec{\mathbf{F}} \cdot \vec{\mathbf{r}} = -\mu_k(M_1 + M_2)gs$. By the work-energy theorem this must equal the change in the kinetic energy of the wreckage. Since the final kinetic energy is zero, the kinetic energy at the start of the skidding phase must be $E_k = \mu_k(M_1 + M_2)gs$. Thus the speed at the start of the skidding phase is given by*

$$\frac{1}{2}(M_1 + M_2)v_s^2 = \mu_k(M_1 + M_2)gs \quad \Longrightarrow \quad v_s = \sqrt{2\mu_k g s} \ .$$

This is the speed of the wreckage just after the collision.

The collision is inelastic, since the cars stick together, so kinetic energy is not conserved. Momentum is conserved, however, as long as there are no external forces. (Note that the downward force of gravity is canceled by the upward normal force, but the force of friction can act horizontally during the collision. We use the approximation, however, that the collision happens during a very short length of time, so the change in momentum due to friction during the collision is negligible.) If we adopt a coordinate system as shown above, conservation of momentum can be written as

$$M_1 v_1 = (M_1 + M_2) v_s \cos\theta \qquad (x\text{-component})$$

$$M_2 v_2 = (M_1 + M_2) v_s \sin\theta \qquad (y\text{-component}) \ ,$$

where v_1 and v_2 are the speeds of the two cars, respectively, before the collision. Thus

$$\boxed{v_1 = \frac{M_1 + M_2}{M_1} \sqrt{2\mu_k g s} \, \cos\theta \ ,}$$

and

$$\boxed{v_2 = \frac{M_1 + M_2}{M_2} \sqrt{2\mu_k g s} \, \sin\theta \ .}$$

Problem 6 (10 points)

A uniform plank of wood with mass M and length ℓ rests against the top of a free standing wall which has height h and a frictionless top. The plank makes an angle θ with the horizontal.

a) On the picture on the right, draw a free body diagram for the plank.

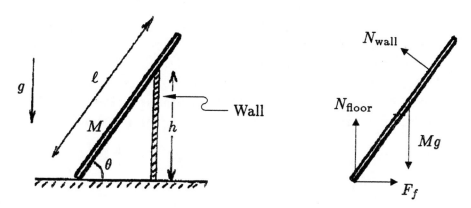

b) In the boxes below, write a complete set of independent equations which when solved give the minimum value of θ for which the plank will not slip, in terms of only M, ℓ, h, g, and μ_s, the coefficient of static friction between the plank and the floor. Do not solve the equations.

F_x: $F_f - N_{\text{wall}} \sin \theta = 0$

F_y: $N_{\text{floor}} - Mg + N_{\text{wall}} \cos \theta = 0$

τ (about contact with floor): $-Mg\dfrac{\ell}{2} \cos \theta + \dfrac{N_{\text{wall}} h}{\sin \theta} = 0$

About to slip: $F_f = \mu_s N_{\text{floor}}$

Note: The number of equations you write could depend on how you have defined your variables, so some correct answers will not fill all boxes.

Alternatively, you could have calculated the torque about different points:

About center of plank: $-N_{\text{floor}}\dfrac{\ell}{2} \cos \theta + F_f \dfrac{\ell}{2} \sin \theta + N_{\text{wall}}\left(\dfrac{h}{\sin \theta} - \dfrac{\ell}{2}\right) = 0$

About contact with wall: $F_f h - \dfrac{N_f h}{\tan \theta} + Mg\left(\dfrac{h}{\tan \theta} - \dfrac{\ell}{2} \cos \theta\right) = 0$

509

Extension of solution: You were not asked to solve these equations, but now that the exam is over you might be interested in trying. After the unknowns N_{wall}, N_{floor}, and F_f are eliminated, one is left with one equation to determine θ:

$$\sin\theta\,\cos\theta(\sin\theta + \mu_s\cos\theta) = \frac{2\mu_s h}{\ell}\,.$$

If one solves this equation numerically, one finds that, depending on μ_s and the ratio h/ℓ, it might have zero, one, or two solutions in the allowed range, where the allowed range extends from the case where the tip of the plank makes contact with the wall $(\theta = \sin^{-1}(h/\ell))$ to the case where the plank is vertical $(\theta = \pi/2)$. You might want to think about how the number of solutions is related to the description of the circumstances under which the plank will or will not slip.

Problem 7 (10 points)

A ball is placed on a vertical massless spring which obeys Hooke's Law and which initially has its natural uncompressed length. It is observed that at first the ball makes vertical simple harmonic oscillations with period T.

After a very large number of oscillations the ball comes to rest because of air resistance and losses in the spring. What is the final compression of the spring in terms of **only** T and g.

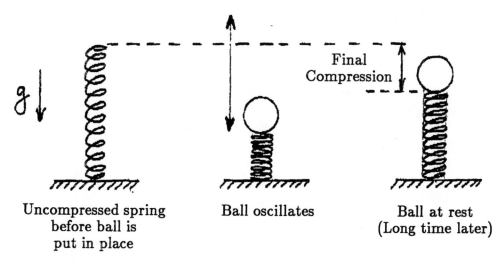

Uncompressed spring
before ball is
put in place

Ball oscillates

Ball at rest
(Long time later)

Solution: *The first step is to relate the period T to the spring constant k. Let y equal the vertical coordinate of the wall, with $y = 0$ the position for which the spring is at its uncompressed length. Then*

$$M\frac{d^2y}{dt^2} = -ky - Mg \; ,$$

where M is the mass of the ball. The equilibrium point is where the force vanishes, so

$$-ky_{eq} - Mg = 0 \quad \Longrightarrow \quad y_{eq} = -\frac{Mg}{k} \; .$$

The differential equation simplifies if we define a new coordinate $\tilde{y}$ which measures the vertical displacement relative to the equilibrium point:

$$\tilde{y} \equiv y - y_{eq} \; .$$

Since y_{eq} is independent of time,

$$\frac{d^2\tilde{y}}{dt^2} = \frac{d^2y}{dt^2} \; ,$$

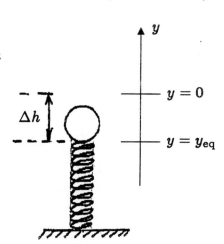

511

so

$$M\frac{\mathrm{d}^2\tilde{y}}{\mathrm{d}t^2} = -k\tilde{y} \ .$$

This equation can be cast into the standard simple-harmonic-motion form by writing

$$\frac{\mathrm{d}^2\tilde{y}}{\mathrm{d}t^2} = -\omega^2\tilde{y} \ ,$$

where $\omega = \sqrt{k/M}$. A solution to this differential equation can be written as

$$\tilde{y}(t) = A\sin\omega t \ ,$$

where A is a constant. The period T is the time it takes for the argument of the sine function to change by 2π, so

$$T = \frac{2\pi}{\omega} = 2\pi\sqrt{\frac{M}{k}} \ .$$

The amount of compression Δh is equal to $-y_{\mathrm{eq}}$, so

$$\Delta h = \frac{Mg}{k} = \boxed{g\left(\frac{T}{2\pi}\right)^2} \ .$$

Problem 8 (10 points)

You have been given a nugget which you are told is a mixture of gold and zinc. You want to find out how much gold you have been given. Being an MIT student you make the following observations:

1. You put a cup partly full of water on an electronic (weight) scale and observe that it reads M_1, meaning that the force on the scale is equivalent to the gravitational force of a mass M_1.

2. You attach the nugget to a very thin stiff piece of wire and hold the nugget in the water fully submerged but not touching the bottom of the cup. The water does not overflow. You observe that the scale now reads M_2.

3. You remove the wire and drop the nugget into the cup. No water is spilled. The scale now reads M_3.

4. In a reference book you find that gold has a density ρ_{Au}, zinc ρ_{Zn}, and water ρ_{H_2O}.

Using these observations determine

    a) the volume of the nugget

    b) the mass of the nugget

    c) the mass of the gold in the nugget.

Solution:

a) the volume of the nugget: This can be determined by comparing the results of observations 1 and 2. From observation 1, we know that the mass of the beaker plus the water in it is M_1. When observation 2 is made, the forces acting on the beaker-plus-water system are:

1) The force of gravity $M_1 g$ downward.

2) The bouyant force F_b downward that the nugget exerts on the water. By Newton's 3rd law this is equal in magnitude to the bouyant force that the water exerts on the nugget, which by Archimedes' law is equal to $\rho_{H_2O} V g$, where V is the volume of the nugget.

3) The normal force of the scale acting upward on the beaker. Since the scale reads M_2, this normal force is $M_2 g$.

Since the system is in equilibrium the total force must be zero, so

$$-M_1 g - \rho_{H_2O} V g + M_2 g = 0 \quad \Longrightarrow \quad \boxed{V = \frac{M_2 - M_1}{\rho_{H_2O}}}.$$

513

b) *the mass of the nugget:* *This can be determined by comparing the results of observations 3 and 1. The extra mass when the nugget is added to the scale is just the mass of the nugget, so*

$$M_{\text{nugget}} = M_3 - M_1 \ .$$

c) *the mass of the gold in the nugget:* *By knowing the mass and volume of the nugget, and the relevant densities, the mass of gold can be found. We need to assume that when metals are mixed the resulting volume is equal to the sum of the original volumes, which is certainly an accurate assumption. If we let* M_{Au} *and* M_{Zn} *denote the mass of gold and zinc in the nugget, respectively, then*

$$M_{\text{Au}} + M_{\text{Zn}} = M_{\text{nugget}} = M_3 - M_1 \ .$$

The volume of gold and zinc are then given by $M_{\text{Au}}/\rho_{\text{Au}}$ *and* $M_{\text{Zn}}/\rho_{\text{Zn}}$*, respectively, so we can write*

$$\frac{M_{\text{Au}}}{\rho_{\text{Au}}} + \frac{M_{\text{Zn}}}{\rho_{\text{Zn}}} = V = \frac{(M_2 - M_1)}{\rho_{\text{H}_2\text{O}}} \ .$$

The two equations above can then be solved for the two unknowns (M_{Au} *and* M_{Zn}*). After some algebra, one finds*

$$M_{\text{Au}} = \frac{\rho_{\text{Au}}\rho_{\text{Zn}}}{\rho_{\text{Au}} - \rho_{\text{Zn}}} \left[\frac{(M_3 - M_1)}{\rho_{\text{Zn}}} - \frac{(M_2 - M_1)}{\rho_{\text{H}_2\text{O}}} \right] \ .$$

Problem 9 (10 points)

A uniform disk of mass M_1 and radius R is pivoted on a frictionless horizontal axle through its center.

a) A small mass M_2 is attached to the disk at radius $R/2$, at the same height as the axle. If this system is released from rest:

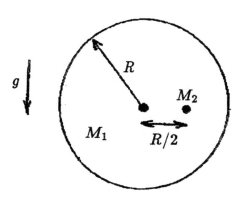

   i) What is the angular acceleration of the disk immediately after it is released?

   ii) What will be the magnitude of the maximum angular velocity that the disk will reach?

b) Now consider the situation if the mass M_2 is a disk of radius $R/2$ located with its center at the same place where M_2 is located in part (a). For this case, find the angular acceleration immediately after the system is released from rest. (You may assume that the two disks are fused together to make one rigid body.)

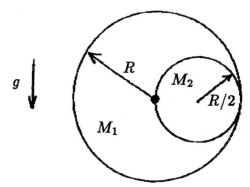

Solution:

a) i) *Since the axle goes through the center of mass of the disk of mass M_1, the gravitational force on this disk does not result in any torque about the axle. But there is a torque caused by the gravitational force on M_2, given by*

$$\tau = -R_\perp F = -\frac{1}{2}M_2 g R .$$

The moment of inertia of the combined system about the axle is that of the disk M_1 plus the mass M_2, so

$$I = \frac{1}{2}M_1 R^2 + M_2 \left(\frac{R}{2}\right)^2 = \frac{1}{4}(2M_1 + M_2)R^2 ,$$

where the moment of inertia of the disk is taken directly from the table in the formula sheets. The angular acceleration immediately after release is therefore

$$\alpha = \frac{\tau}{I} = -\frac{2M_2 g}{(2M_1 + M_2)R} \ .$$

ii) The maximum angular velocity will be attained when M_2 is at the bottom of its motion. The value of the angular velocity can be determined by using the conservation of energy. The potential energy of the disk M_1 does not change, since its center of mass does not move, so the only potential energy that needs to be considered is that of M_2. This potential energy can be written $U = M_2 g y$, where y is the vertical coordinate, measured from an arbitrary origin. I will take that origin as the height of the axle. Thus $U_{\text{initial}} = 0$, and U_{final} (at the bottom of the motion) is $-M_2 g R/2$. Then

$$E_{\text{initial}} = 0$$

$$E_{\text{final}} = \frac{1}{2} I \omega_f^2 - \frac{1}{2} M_2 g R$$

$$E_{\text{final}} = E_{\text{initial}} \implies \boxed{\omega_f = \sqrt{\frac{M_2 g R}{I}} = \sqrt{\frac{4 M_2 g}{(2M_1 + M_2)R}} \ .}$$

b) The only difference between this case and the previous one is the moment of inertia of the disk of mass M_2. According to the table, the moment of inertia of this disk about its own center is $\frac{1}{2} M_2 (R/2)^2$. But we need the moment of inertia about the center of the larger disk, for which we have to use the parallel axis theorem:

$$I_{\parallel} = I_{\text{cm}} + M d^2 = \frac{1}{2} M_2 \left(\frac{R}{2}\right)^2 + M_2 \left(\frac{R}{2}\right)^2 = \frac{3}{8} M_2 R^2 \ .$$

So,

$$I = \frac{1}{2} M_1 R^2 + \frac{3}{8} M_2 R^2 = \frac{1}{8}(8M_1 + 3M_2)R^2 \ .$$

The torque is the same as in part (a)(i), since the torque due to the gravitational force on M_2 can be calculated as if the entire force acted on the center of mass. Thus,

$$\alpha = \frac{\tau}{I} = -\frac{4M_2 g}{(8M_1 + 3M_2)R} \ .$$

516

Problem 10 (10 points)

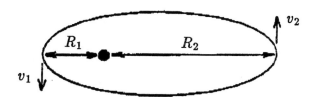

A satellite follows an elliptical orbit. Its closest approach to the earth is R_1, at which point it has speed v_1, and the furthest point is R_2, at which point it has speed v_2. Both distances are measured from the center of the earth. At the surface of the earth the acceleration due to gravity is g and the earth's radius is R.

What is the magnitude of v_1 in terms of **only** R_1, R_2, R and g?

Solution: *By conservation of angular momentum about the center of the earth,*

$$|\vec{\mathbf{r}} \times \vec{\mathbf{p}}|_1 = |\vec{\mathbf{r}} \times \vec{\mathbf{p}}|_2 \ ,$$

or

$$m v_1 R_1 = m v_2 R_2 \ ,$$

where m is the mass of the satellite. Similarly, conservation of energy implies that

$$\frac{1}{2} m v_1^2 - \frac{GMm}{R_1} = \frac{1}{2} m v_2^2 - \frac{GMm}{R_2} \ ,$$

where M is the mass of the earth. These two equations can be solved for v_1, giving

$$v_1 = \sqrt{\frac{2GM R_2}{R_1(R_1 + R_2)}} \ .$$

We are not given G or M, so this is not the final answer. However, we are allowed to use g in our answer, where g is the acceleration caused by gravity at the surface of the earth. Considering the gravitational force on an object of mass $\tilde{m}$ at the surface of the earth, we can write

$$\tilde{m} g = \frac{GM\tilde{m}}{R^2} \ ,$$

where R is the radius of the earth. So

$$GM = R^2 g \ ,$$

and

$$\boxed{v_1 = \sqrt{\frac{2R^2 R_2 g}{R_1(R_1 + R_2)}} \ .}$$

517

ESSENTIALS OF INTRODUCTORY CLASSICAL MECHANICS

GENERAL INDEX

(O) = Overview   (S) = Summary   (P) = Problems   (C) = Complete Solutions   (N) = Supplementary Notes

(O) = Overview   (S) = Summary   (P) = Problems   (C) = Complete Solutions   (N) = Supplementary Notes

(O) = Overview   (S) = Summary   (P) = Problems   (C) = Complete Solutions   (N) = Supplementary Notes

(O) = Overview   (S) = Summary   (P) = Problems   (C) = Complete Solutions   (N) = Supplementary Notes

(O) = Overview   (S) = Summary   (P) = Problems   (C) = Complete Solutions   (N) = Supplementary Notes

(O) = Overview   (S) = Summary   (P) = Problems   (C) = Complete Solutions   (N) = Supplementary Notes

(O) = Overview   (S) = Summary   (P) = Problems   (C) = Complete Solutions   (N) = Supplementary Notes

(O) = Overview   (S) = Summary   (P) = Problems   (C) = Complete Solutions   (N) = Supplementary Notes

(O) = Overview   (S) = Summary   (P) = Problems   (C) = Complete Solutions   (N) = Supplementary Notes

neglect of small quantities, 134(C)

problems involving forces and accelerations, 105(C)

simplicity of conservation law approach, 144(C), 457(Problem Answers)

small angle approximations, 80(C), 227(C)

use of approximate calculations, 38(C)

use of vector algebra, 190–191(C)

Problem-solving strategy, 3(O)

Product rule, 399(C)

Projectile, 16, 125(S)

Pump

suction, 419(P)

Pythagorean theorem

and Euclidean geometry, 52(N)

Quadratic equation

choosing appropriate root of, 28(C), 37(C)

solution of, 28(C), 98(C)

Quantum mechanics, 11, 398(C)

and specific heat ratio, 398(C)

Quarks, 63

Radian, rad, 66

Radiation pressure, 390–393(C)

Radioactivity, 155(N)

beta decay, 155(N)

Reduced mass (of two-body system), 290(C)

Reference frame, 16, 19(S)

center of mass, 169

change of, 275

Earth's surface, 207

inertial, 60–61, 67(S)

non-inertial, 62, 206–208

rotating, 207

Reines, Frederick, 155(N)

Relativity

general, 11, 51(N), 53(N), 62, 208

special, 11

Rigid body, 266–267

definition of, 266

kinetic energy of, 268–269, 276

motion of, 267, 273, 313–317, 319–320, 321–322(S)

Rocket

velocity of, 255–256(C)

Rolling without slipping, 275

Rotation, 266, 319

about fixed axis, 266–272

about moving axis of fixed orientation, 273–276

axis of, 266, 274

Scalar, 13, 19(S)

Scalar product, *See Dot product*

Scientific method, 10, 50–51(N), 441–442(O)

controlled experiment, 50(N)

experiment and theory, 51(N)

in the observational sciences, 51(N)

Second, s, 10

SI, *See Système International*

Significant figures

choosing appropriate number of, 27(C)

(O) = Overview   (S) = Summary   (P) = Problems   (C) = Complete Solutions   (N) = Supplementary Notes

(O) = Overview   (S) = Summary   (P) = Problems   (C) = Complete Solutions   (N) = Supplementary Notes

(O) = Overview   (S) = Summary   (P) = Problems   (C) = Complete Solutions   (N) = Supplementary Notes

(O) = Overview   (S) = Summary   (P) = Problems   (C) = Complete Solutions   (N) = Supplementary Notes

ESSENTIALS OF INTRODUCTORY CLASSICAL MECHANICS

PROBLEM INDEX

534

535

The International System of Units (SI)

Quantity   **Unit**   **Symbol**   **Definition**

SI Base Units:

Length   meter   m   "The meter is the length of path travelled by light in vacuum during a time interval of 1/299 792 458 of a second."

Time   second   s   "The second is the duration of 9 192 631 770 periods of the radiation corresponding to the transition between the two hyperfine levels of the ground state of the cesium-133 atom."

Mass   kilogram   kg   "The kilogram is the unit of mass, it is equal to the mass of the international prototype of the kilogram." (The international prototype is a platinum-iridium cylinder kept at the BIPM in Sèvres (Paris), France).

Electric current   ampere   A   "The ampere is that constant current which, if maintained in two straight parallel conductors of infinite length, of negligible circular cross section, and placed 1 meter apart in vacuum, would produce between these conductors a force equal to 2×10^{-7} newton per meter of length."

Temperature   kelvin   K   "The kelvin, unit of thermodynamic temperature, is the fraction 1/273.16 of the thermodynamic temperature of the triple point of water."

Amount of substance   mole   mol   "The mole is the amount of substance of a system which contains as many elementary entities as there are atoms in 0.012 kg of carbon-12."

Luminous intensity   candela   cd   "The candela is the luminous intensity, in a given direction, of a source that emits monochromatic radiation of frequency 540×10^{12} hertz and that has a radiant intensity in that direction of (1/683) watt per steradian."

SI Supplementary Units:

Plane angle   radian   rad   "The radian is the plane angle between two radii of a circle that cut off on the circumference an arc equal in length to the radius."

Solid angle   steradian   sr   "The steradian is the solid angle that, having its vertex in the center of a sphere, cuts off an area of the surface of the sphere equal to that of a square with sides of length equal to the radius of the sphere."

Some Derived Units

Quantity	Unit	Symbol	Base Units
Force	newton	N	$kg \cdot m/s^2$
Energy	joule	J	$kg \cdot m^2/s^2$
Power	watt	W	$kg \cdot m^2/s^3$
Pressure	pascal	Pa	$kg/(m \cdot s^2)$
Electric Charge	coulomb	C	$A \cdot s$
Frequency	hertz	Hz	s^{-1}

Metric (SI) Multipliers

Prefix	Symb	Value	Prefix	Symb	Value
exa	E	10^{18}	deci	d	10^{-1}
peta	P	10^{15}	centi	c	10^{-2}
tera	T	10^{12}	milli	m	10^{-3}
giga	G	10^{9}	micro	μ	10^{-6}
mega	M	10^{6}	nano	n	10^{-9}
kilo	k	10^{3}	pico	p	10^{-12}
hecto	h	10^{2}	femto	f	10^{-15}
deka	da	10^{1}	atto	a	10^{-18}

Conversion Factors

Length	1 fermi = 1 fm = 10^{-15} m
	1 angstrom (Å) = 10^{-10} m
	1 inch = 2.54 cm = 0.0254 m
	1 mile = 1609 m
	1 light-year (ly) = 9.46×10^{15} m
	1 parsec = 3.26 ly = 3.09×10^{16} m
Mass	1 atomic mass unit (u) = 1.6605×10^{-27} kg
	1 pound (lb avoirdupois) = 0.4536 kg
Time	1 year = 3.156×10^{7} s
Volume	1 liter (L) = 10^{-3} m^3
Angle	1 degree (°) = $\pi/180$ rad = 0.01745 rad
Pressure	1 atmosphere (atm) = 1.013×10^{5} Pa
Temperature	Zero degree Celsius (0° C) = 273.15 K
	$T\,(°F) = (9/5)T\,(°C) + 32°$
Energy	1 electron volt (eV) = 1.602×10^{-19} J